Readings in Health, Medicine, and Society

FIRST EDITION

Readings in Health, Medicine, and Society

EDITED BY Katherine A. Lineberger, PhD

Florida International University

SAN DIEGO

Bassim Hamadeh, CEO and Publisher
Amy Smith, Senior Project Editor
Susana Christie, Senior Developmental Editor
Celeste Paed, Associate Production Editor
Jess Estrella, Senior Graphic Designer
Natalie Piccotti, Director of Marketing
Kassie Graves, Senior Vice President of Editorial
Jamie Giganti, Director of Academic Publishing

Cover image copyright © 2013 Depositphotos/Bioraven.
Copyright © 2013 Depositphotos/Jezper.

Printed in the United States of America.

cognella® | ACADEMIC PUBLISHING
3970 Sorrento Valley Blvd., Ste. 500, San Diego, CA 92121

CONTENTS

PREFACE

....

For many years, I have struggled to expose my students to content in medical sociology outside of my own and other texts. I am also aware, pedagogically speaking, of the ways in which the use of peer-reviewed articles and other field-related literature facilitate higher-order thinking skills in students. I have tried to find a good reader but the ones I define as *good* are always very costly, sometimes running to several hundred dollars. Since I work in a public institution with students whose socioeconomic status ranges from homeless to middle class, I cannot ethically require such a text. I have tried, as well, to cobble together readings from the university library but the workings and ways of library systems leave at least some readings mysteriously unavailable at times. So when Cognella Academic Publishing suggested I edit a medical sociology reader, I was ready to put together something of quality that would both expose students to the broader literature of medical sociology and be more reliable and affordable than other options.

The resulting reader is divided into eight units. *Unit I: Introduction to Medical Sociology* provides an overview of the field and examines some field-specific concepts and theoretical perspectives. *Unit II: Culture in Health and Medicine* illustrates the ways culture impacts health and healthcare systems. *Unit III: Social Stratification, Health, Illness, and Healthcare* examines inequalities at the individual and societal level, those that exist both in health outcomes and within healthcare systems. *Unit IV: Social Structures Affecting Health* investigates how political and corporate structures impact people's health choices and behaviors. *Unit V: The Practice of Medicine* investigates key variables involved in the socialization of Western doctors, reviews the ways folk medicines differ from the Western paradigm, and illustrates an example of healing practices outside Western medicine. *Unit VI: Medical Technology* provides a review of emerging medical technologies as they relate to sociology, covering a variety of key concepts and identifying where the field of medicine is moving. Additionally, this unit offers an in-depth, critical analysis of pharmaceutical technology. *Unit VII: US and Global Healthcare* lays out an important perspective in US medicine with a critical examination of the history of power building by US doctors. This unit also compares and contrasts the French and US systems, with proposals for improving access to care in the United States. Also in this unit, there is a frank illustration and discussion of the detrimental effects of the imposition of austerity on healthcare systems in poor nations. Finally, *Unit VIII: Bioethics* offers a brief overview of the history of bioethics through a discussion of the Nuremberg Code, followed by a discussion of the important issues of patient autonomy and informed consent in the framework of patient vulnerability and doctor trustworthiness. This unit also illustrates a bioethical problem for students to investigate.

The book is generally, though not entirely, composed within a critical framework, with an overall focus on the nature of power and its impact on health, illness, and healthcare. An effort has been made to clearly define and illustrate the unique perspective of sociology, with special focus on the field's strengths in analyzing culture and social groups, structures, and organization. While the sheer scope of such a work makes it impossible to include readings from every subfield within medical sociology, many key areas of research are included to provide students both a deep and broad review of the field.

INTRODUCTION

*R*eadings in Health, Medicine, and Society *is an anthology for students being introduced to medical sociology or social science in medicine. The book has several objectives:*

- **First, students will be exposed to a variety of authors working in the field.** Traditional textbooks give students a thorough understanding of the entire field as seen by one person, while a professor provides the same perspective. At the same time, students have multiple perspectives and research interests. This book includes samples from more than nineteen different authors in the field, each with their own research interest and questions, methods, and analyses.
- **Second, students will be exposed to a variety of the most common areas of study within the field.**
- **Third, students will regularly encounter perspectives and research originating outside the mainstream American purview.** This enables readers to compare aspects of health and healthcare in the United States to aspects of these things in other countries, as well as learn from Indigenous perspectives. Eight of the twenty-one readings included in this book prompt these perspectives.

These three overarching objectives provide introductory students with a broad and well-rooted knowledge of both global and US medical sociology.

The book is organized into eight units, each with two to three readings that unpack specific aspects of major areas of study in medical sociology. In general, the readings work their way from broad to specific topics in order to provide students with a range of macro-, mezzo-, and micro-level perspectives. Some concepts, such as medicalization, are threaded throughout the book, which illustrates the explanatory strength of these concepts.

Unit I: Introduction to Medical Sociology includes a thorough introductory reading by Lonnie Hannon, then moves onto a reading that examines the definitions of health in relation to individual, social, and environmental variables. The unit ends with a theoretical piece by Kristen K. Barker, who does a beautiful job of introducing social constructionism by examining notions of medicalization and contested illness. *Unit II: Culture in Health and Medicine* begins with a reading by Donald A. Barr that compares and contrasts the histories of the Canadian and US healthcare systems to demonstrate the ways in which culture and underlying values shape the development of these systems. In "The Medicalized Society," Carl Boggs examines inequalities in healthcare through the lens of the pharmaceutical industry, while in "The Wrong Side of the River," Ronald L. Barret provides an excellent ethnography of life and culture in an East Indian leper colony. In *Unit III: Social Stratification, Health, Illness, and Healthcare*, Debra L. DeLaet and David E. DeLaet review literature related to economic, ethnic, and gender inequalities in global health. Susan Mercado et al. discuss the reasons why urban poverty is an urgent public health issue. Finally, a selection by Donald A. Barr provides an excellent and thorough review of race, ethnicity, and health. In *Unit IV: Social Structures Affecting Health*, the general aim is to turn students' attention away from individual troubles, in which mainstream explanations of health and illness are rooted, and strengthen their understanding of institutional troubles, which have strong explanatory value in studies of health and illness. Marion Nestle and Malden Nesheim examine the history and role of the food industry in today's "eat more" environment. Next, Dennis Wiedman discusses his concept of *chronicities of modernity* by examining the history and contemporary realities of Indigenous Americans' health as it relates to colonization and modernization. *Unit V: The Practice of Medicine* begins with an article by Julia E. Szymczak and Charles L. Bosk on the socialization of resident doctors, taught and determined to be efficient in increasingly overworked and chaotic environments. "Understanding Folk Medicine," by Bonnie B. O'Connor and David J. Hufford, is an excellent review of literature related to folk medicine, discussing its key concepts and comparing and contrasting folk and mainstream medical perspectives when necessary. The unit ends with another article by Dennis Wiedman, who establishes Big and Little Moon Peyotism as health care systems. *Unit VI: Medical Technology* begins with a review of literature in medical sociology and technology by Monica J. Casper and Daniel R. Morrison. The following article by John Abraham highlights and discusses the sociological aspects of the pharmaceutical industry and medications. In *Unit VII: US and Global Healthcare,* Donald W. Light introduces readers to a critical history of medical industry, with particular attention to the role of doctors and the strategies they have used to monopolize healthcare over time. Next, Victor G. Rodwin compares and contrasts the French and American healthcare systems and proposes that the US might learn from the French experience in moving toward universal care. Finally, James Pfeiffer thoroughly examines the ways in which *audit culture* has limited the strengthening of poor nations' public health systems. *Unit VIII: Bioethics* introduces the bioethical problem of doctors' involvement in executions involving lethal injection. Then, in "Vulnerability and Trustworthiness: Polestars in Professionalism in Healthcare," David Barnard examines important bioethical problems, such as informed consent and patient autonomy, in the context of the ineluctable vulnerability of patients and imperative trustworthiness of doctors.

Each unit begins with an introduction to the area of study, summary of the articles to be read, and additional, related thoughts from the author. The introductions are designed to prepare students for what they will read by highlighting some of the major ideas and conclusions within each reading. Each reading contains bolded key terms, which are defined in sidebars in the page margins. These terms familiarize students with the sociological perspective in general and medical sociology in particular. Sociology has a unique perspective, encompassing communities, groups, institutions, and organizations. Sociologists look through these lenses as explanatory variables of health, illness, and healthcare. Since US culture and US health care tend to focus on individual-level explanatory variables, such as biology or psychology, the key terms help to solidify students' growing sense of the sociological gaze. At the end of each unit, some critical thinking questions are offered to students to encourage them to delve more deeply into the readings. These questions aim to increase students' working knowledge of the topics and field.

Medical sociology is an exciting and thought-provoking field. You may find yourself intrigued, surprised, angered, validated, and everything else imaginable in the kaleidoscope of human emotion. Most importantly, studying medical sociology helps you to think more critically about health, illness, and healthcare. In 1959, C. Wright Mills[1] invited students to develop their *sociological imaginations*, or their imaginative ability to envision the relationships between the individual (personal troubles) and society (public issues). This book is designed to offer knowledge and skill-building activities toward this end. Those who closely engage with the book will come away with a strong sense of the depth and breadth of medical sociology, enhance their analytical abilities related to health and medicine, and may better prepare themselves for a career in health care.

---

1   C. Wright Mills, *The Sociological Imagination* (New York: Oxford University Press, 1959).

Introduction to Medical Sociology

Editor's Introduction

The purpose of unit I is to provide a brief overview of the history, theory, of medical sociology and to introduce some important concepts. *Medical sociology* is the systematic study of how humans manage issues of health and illness, disease and disorders, healthcare for the sick and healthy, and systems of healthcare. As it is a field within sociology, special attention is placed on the *social* aspects of health, illness, and health systems. This is very different from the medical model of disease, which focuses almost solely on the biological basis of health and illness. As these readings demonstrate, social variables are very important determinants in our definitions of health and illness, as well as in how we develop systems to address them.

As Lonnie Hannon points out in "Medical Sociology," humans increasingly encountered disease as we shifted from hunter-gatherer societies to agrarian societies. If you think about it, an agrarian society requires that larger groups of people settle together to plant, maintain, organize, and prepare the food supply. Direct interaction between humans and animals increased and these changes in human behavior had serious consequences for human health and illness. Imagine the time of the Industrial Revolution, when men, women, and children moved from rural areas to cities for work outside the home. The crowded conditions of cities, coupled with a lack of infrastructure such as plumbing, electricity, and waste disposal, and the dearth of policies to address issues such as building safety and work hours led to a phenomenal number of illnesses and deaths due to contagious diseases and accidents. These are the conditions out of which the concept of public health arose, and medical sociology grew out of this milieu as humans organized themselves in ever-more complex patterns throughout the twentieth century.

Among other things, Hannon does a great job of briefly summarizing important concepts, introducing us to functional theory and Talcott Parsons' sick role model, a most influential, early

sick role: a social role that excuses people from normal obligations because they are sick or injured.

epidemiological transition: a condition of developed societies whereby people die more from chronic conditions than infectious diseases.

social demography: the study of human populations, with special attention to factors such as race, gender, age, and socioeconomic status.

operationalization: to express or define a variable in terms that are measurable and workable.

perspective in medical sociology. A **sick role** is a social role that excuses people from normal obligations because they are sick or injured. Hannon also touches on the **epidemiological transition** throughout the twentieth century, whereby humans, particularly those in developed countries, came to die more from chronic conditions, like heart disease and cancer, than infectious diseases. Hannon also discusses the importance of **social demography** to medical sociology. Studies of human populations focusing on such things as gender, age, race, and socioeconomic status have illuminated differences in medical treatment and health outcomes based upon these statuses, highlighting the important role of structural and systemic inequality that permeates medical industry.

In "Defining Health by Addressing Individual, Social, and Environmental Determinants: New Opportunities for Health Care and Public Health," Johannes Bircher and Shyama Kuruvilla contribute to the **operationalization** of health as a social variable. Biomedical definitions of *illness* focus on the presence of observable symptoms and define *health* as lack of observable symptoms. As Bircher and Kuruvilla illustrate, definitions of health can vary depending upon the perspective of the person(s) defining it, and their article moves this discussion forward a great deal by identifying social and environmental variables that can be included with the individual and biological. Reducing definitions of health and illness to biological, symptoms-based dichotomies limits what can be diagnosed and treated. The classic nature versus nurture argument is most useful for people to position themselves within the kaleidoscope of variables that define and impact health.

Bircher and Kuruvilla's work on the Meikirch model of health defines health as a state of wellbeing based upon interactions between people's potentials, life's demands, and social and environmental variables. If you think about it, we all have unique potential; life always has demands; we are never outside a sociocultural milieu; and we are always in some sort of environment. All of these variables are always in dynamic interaction with one another, contributing to our sense of well-being. Bircher and Kuruvilla then fine-tune the concepts of *potential* and *demand*, which make the Meikirch model useful for individual, social, and policy applications at local and global levels.

In "The Social Construction of Illness: Medicalization and Contested Illness," Kristin K. Barker advocates the usefulness of the social constructionist approach to medical sociology. In short, *social constructionism* is the theory that reality and meaning are subjective and created through active interactions with other individuals and groups. Barker takes time to unfold this debated theory and to position it within sociology, demonstrating its fit within science and especially in medical sociology.

My favorite examples of social constructionism lie within gender studies, where examples abound. The moment a person is born, someone puts blue or pink booties on them and announces, "It's a boy/girl!" and everyone begins to act accordingly. Blue or pink cigars may be smoked; "little sluggers" or "pretty angels" will be remarked upon. As a parent, I have watched my toddler jump, run, climb, twirl, and roll on the playground. As a sociologist, I was interested to overhear other parents' remarks about the children. Such statements as "She'll be a great dancer" are often said in response to girls' actions and "Kid's gonna be a bruiser on the field someday" in response to boys' actions, even though the children are engaging in the very same behaviors. The social construction of gender is a critical field within medical sociology because this socialization has consequences for all people's health and wellbeing.

Medicalization is the process through which a condition or behavior becomes defined as a medical problem requiring a medical solution. Barker does a terrific job demonstrating how medicalization is the social construction of illness. One or more groups must have a vested interest in the condition and sufficient power to be heard. Groups can have a variety of reasons to medicalize. A good example is groups who believe that medicalizing drug addiction is a more humane way to deal with the problem than criminalizing it. Another example involves those who suffer from fibromyalgia and who want validation from the medical community for their condition and to stimulate treatments for it. The pharmaceutical industry has a profit motive to medicalize everything possible.

Many times, medicalization is a positive process that leads to awareness of the problem, increasing sympathy for people suffering from the condition, and stimulation in development of helpful treatments. Sometimes, medicalization can have one or more unintended consequences, however. For example, once a condition becomes medicalized, doctors are the only ones able to diagnose and treat it, which leads to a loss of input from patients and other affected parties. Some members of Mothers Against Drunk Drivers (MADD) might have an objection to the medicalization of alcoholism. Also, when something is medicalized, a biomedical response may become the only option for treating the problem. Some people who are deaf, for instance, reject the idea that they should be treated with cochlear implants to "cure" their deafness because the real problem lies with a society that undervalues variations in people's abilities. Finally, when something is medicalized, those in power tend to dismiss it as a medical problem and ignore the social facets of the condition. A classic example of this is the medicalization of homosexuality until 1973. When homosexuality was defined as a medical problem, there was no reason for the culture to assess its own prejudice and discrimination against homosexuals. Barker's discussions of both medicalization and contested illness make clear and strong arguments for the use of a social constructivist perspective in medical sociology.

Together, these articles by Hannon, Bircher and Kuruvilla, and Barker will provide you with a strong taste of the history, theory, and conceptual depth in the study of medical sociology.

Medical Sociology

By Lonnie Hannon

[...] The Fundamentals of Medical Sociology

Medical sociology examines the social factors surrounding life quality, disease, and healthcare. Unlike traditional medicine, it is less concerned with the biological and clinical attributes associated with these factors. Medical sociology borrows from several different fields within sociology and other social sciences, such as demography, economics sociology, geography, urban sociology, and rural sociology. The practice of modern medical sociology is founded upon principles developed by Talcott Parsons and later by William Cockerham.

As a **functionalist**, Parsons believed that individuals in society were all parts of a larger, complex system. In other words, everyone has a role in helping the system function. When people get sick and assume the **sick role**, then they can longer fulfill their duties to the group. As we learned in Chapter 2, **roles** are defined by the shared expectations associated with a particular **status**. My role is associated with my status. Therefore, my role comes with expectations that are understood by me as well as others in society. Furthermore, my role tends to be linked to the roles of others. The interconnectedness of roles suggests that when someone fails to complete her role, then a break in the system occurs. Functionalists use the term "**anomie**" to describe severe breaks in large systems. Therefore, the individual who cannot fulfill her role in society threatens the social order. As a result, illness is conceptualized as **deviant.**

The deviant person is therefore expected to do what she can to get well, even though society understands that it is not her fault she became ill. This perspective examines disease and illness relative to

EDITOR'S NOTES

medical sociology: the systematic study of how humans manage issues of health and illness; disease and disorders; healthcare for the sick and healthy; and systems of health care.

EDITOR'S NOTES

functionalism: a theory that views society as an orderly and stable system with interconnected parts that contribute to the smooth functioning of the whole.

EDITOR'S NOTES

sick role: the patterns of behavior expected of individuals who are sick and those who take care of them.

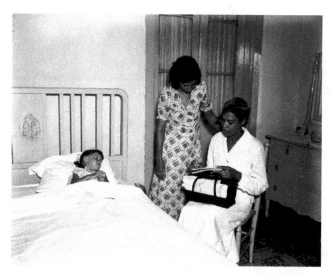

FIGURE 1.1.1 Copyright in the Public Domain.

the **structural norms** placed upon the individual, an approach further explained by sociological theorist Michel Foucault in *Birth of the Clinic* (1973). Thus, the individual is investigated as one who is structured by social norms. In order to continue operating harmoniously, society directs the action of individuals when they encounter illness. In this sense, the world is viewed as a system that is greater than the sum of its unique parts (individuals). Thus, the individual as a unique being is not as important as the role society needs her to fulfill.

Let us examine, for example, a popular quarterback for one of America's favorite NFL teams in north Texas. Millions of people watch every Sunday and follow throughout the week to mark the progress of the team. The team is doing well, but the season is nearing an end and it needs to pick up a few victories to make the playoffs. Sunday arrives and the teams meet in competition. During the third quarter, the star quarterback is sacked. He is driven to the ground by a 270-pound defensive end. The quarterback gets up slowly, but he is clearly hurt. He jogs to the sideline with bruised ribs.

It is clearly not the quarterback's fault that he is hurt; however, in his injured state he can no longer fulfill his role. The inability of the quarterback to fulfill his role interferes with the roles of his teammates. The team (society) therefore cannot function properly without his leadership. The backup quarterback has played very little all season and he is not used to high-pressure situations. The offense cannot advance the ball; in fact, the backup quarterback throws two interceptions. The center does not understand the new snap counts. The receivers run the wrong routes. The running back drops the handoff because he is not familiar with the new quarterback's style of delivery. The coaches try to compensate, but the quarterback cannot execute the plays they call. The new quarterback has a hard time running the offense, which leads to much confusion, ultimately causing the team to lose the game (anomie).

No one is really mad at the starting quarterback and everyone understands why he could not finish the game. Nonetheless, everyone is expecting him to take every measure to return to the field as soon as possible. As a result, he sees a doctor immediately after the game. He obediently follows the doctor's orders throughout the visit. The doctor is relatively unknown, but in this situation, he has all the power, even when advising the million-dollar star football player. The doctor's role is to get the star player back on the field as soon as possible. The quarterback knows this, so he submits to the authority of doctor (another system component) who can help him resume his role. The quarterback works extremely hard to recover from his injury after seeing the doctor. In fact, he works harder during rehabilitation than he does at practice when he is well. He is aware of his role. The expectations from his team serve as a primary driving force for his return.

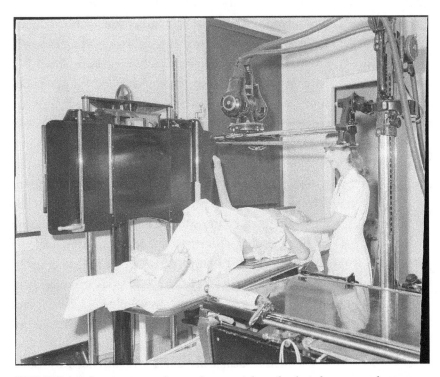

FIGURE 1.1.2 We expect those who are sick to do their best to get better so that they may continue fulfilling their roles. Copyright in the Public Domain.

Parsons' functionalist approach to disease and wellness serves as a foundation for the sociological study of medicine and healthcare. Sociology takes a unique position in this study. Biologists and medical professionals study medicine, independent of social influences. They are concerned with the science of organisms and the impact of chemical reactions in the body. However, the delivery of healthcare and medicine itself involves social interaction between the patient and the doctor. As Parsons and others like Foucault explicated, this very relationship involves a set of understood norms and a high degree of stratified interaction, with the doctor holding all the power. Illness and wellbeing involve the individual seeking help. The interaction between the individual seeking help and the healthcare deliverer is determined by social norms and values.

This view examines the individual *after* he has gotten sick, but contemporary medical sociology is more concerned with the factors that compromise wellness in the first place. William Cockerham is a renowned medical sociologist who conceptualized the "social demography of health." The **social demography of health** examines illness and wellness within the context of social factors unique to an individual or group. That allows important questions to be explored. Why do Asians have the highest life expectancy of all races? Why do poor people with strong network ties exhibit better health outcomes? Are there rural-urban differences in health access? As you can see, using the social demography of health model opens up medical sociology to a wide array of study.

One of the weaknesses of the sick role functionalist model is that it does a poor job explaining the impact of **chronic disease**. Chronic diseases are those that persist over time. The sick role is based more on infectious diseases, those that are caused by an organism in the body causing a response from the immune system. Most untreated infectious diseases tend to be relatively short-lived. You either get better or you die. You catch a cold for a few days. Malaria can be deadly, but if treated, the symptoms eventually go away. Influenza also can be deadly, but it usually goes away after a few days of rest. AIDS can be neutralized through antiviral drugs.

Humans first came in contact with infectious diseases after domesticating farm animals. From that time until the 20th century, infectious diseases were the leading cause of death across the world. Outbreaks of yellow fever, malaria, influenza, typhoid, small pox, and bubonic plague killed billions of people over time. The bubonic plague alone killed a third of Europe's population in the 14th century (Fernandez-Armesto, 2007). During the time that infectious diseases were responsible for most deaths, life expectancy past infancy was relatively low and infant mortality was high.

The Enlightenment brought a new interest in using scientific principles to guide medical discoveries. Medical doctors were no longer part-time alchemist and part-time priest as they were in the years before the Enlightenment. Medical doctors were now a professional class of biomedical scientists who studied disease using the scientific method. Innovations such as the microscope helped identify pathogens. Scientists such as Louis Pasteur were able to develop germ theories that facilitated the development of vaccines. By the 20th century, these changes in the delivery of healthcare helped eradicate or neutralize many of the worst infectious diseases.

Today the biggest threat to human life is chronic diseases. This is especially true in developed countries. People are living much longer today than in the past. Although infectious diseases have declined, the fact that people are living longer puts them at higher risk for chronic diseases. Chronic diseases include heart disease, diabetes, Alzheimer's, and hypertension. Most chronic diseases involve the diminished capacity of an organ or system to function properly. Chronic diseases often do not lead to quick death, but they involve years of maintenance and care. Importantly, chronic diseases are often developed through lifestyle practices and environmental hazards, two elements that are fundamental to sociology.

Social Factors Affecting Health

In today's world, the way we live our life has a significant impact on our health. While genes and biology are still extremely important in determining health outcomes, much more attention has been given to lifestyle with the prominence of chronic diseases. Medical sociologists and medical doctors can develop associations between lifestyle, environment, and disease. For example, a person who smokes a pack of cigarettes a day, eats fatty foods, stresses over work, and rarely exercises is at high risk for heart disease and diabetes. A person who lives near a processing plant with low standards of emissions is at risk for developing certain cancers. A person who exercises three times a week, eats healthfully, and maintains a positive frame of mind is not necessarily

FIGURE 1.1.3 Physical fitness is an important lifestyle behavior that promotes well-being. Copyright in the Public Domain.

immune from disease because genes are still important, but they have a lower probability of experiencing certain maladies, such as heart disease and hypertension.

Sociologists understand the association between lifestyle and disease. We want to dig deeper and understand how the elements of our society affect us in terms of health. This is where the social demography of health is relevant. Several demographic factors have primacy in influencing health outcomes: SES, race and ethnicity, gender, and age are all important in this regard, especially in countries that have a broad range of social classes and a high degree of racial ethnic diversity such as the United States. All of these factors are strongly interrelated. Race by itself explains very little, but race intertwined with SES tells a different story. The same is true for age and SES or gender and race.

Life Expectancy

The main indicator of health for a group is **life expectancy**. Using the latest figures, life expectancy for a child born in the United States in 2010 is 76.2 years for males and 81 years for females. Life expectancy says a lot about health. Groups that live longer tend to have higher life qualities, good access to healthcare, and strong family and friend networks. They tend to be happier and less stressed. As we will discuss, SES plays a powerful role in life quality. From Table 1.1.1 we can see that the U.S. has made great strides in improving the factors that lead to life quality. This is reflected in the increase in life expectancy from 1900 until today.

Good Health as a Commodity

In the U.S. more than in any other developed country, health outcomes and healthcare have a strong relationship with economics. In a **capitalistic** society, everything has an exchange value. This is true of health. Health has been commoditized in countries like the United States because it is perhaps the most valuable element of a human's existence. Many would argue that there is too much money at stake to conceptualize it as a natural "right," free for everyone. Given the fact that health is an exchangeable commodity, it will be affected by the forces of supply and demand. Inherently, wellness is in high demand. Access to it, therefore, will be costly.

TABLE 1.1.1 U.S. Life Expectancy from Birth for All Races, White, and Black

Year	All Races			White			Black		
	Both Sexes	**Male**	**Female**	**Both Sexes**	**Male**	**Female**	**Both Sexes**	**Male**	**Female**
1900	47.3	46.3	48.3	47.6	46.6	48.7	33	32.5	33.5
1950	68.2	65.6	71.1	69.1	66.5	72.2	60.8	59.1	62.9
1960	69.7	66.6	73.1	70.6	67.4	74.1	63.6	61.1	66.3
1970	70.8	67.1	74.7	71.7	68	75.6	64.1	60	68.3
1980	73.7	70	77.4	74.4	70.7	78.1	68.1	63.8	72.5
1990	75.4	71.8	78.8	76.1	72.7	79.4	69.1	64.5	73.6
2000	76.8	74.1	79.3	77.3	74.7	79.9	71.8	68.2	75.1
2010	78.7	76.2	81	78.9	76.5	81.3	75.1	71.8	78

Source: National Center for Health Statistics. (2011). National Table18 (page 1 of 2). Life Expectancy at Birth, at 65 Years of Age, and at 75 Years of Age, by Sex, Race, and Hispanic Origin: United States, Selected Years 1900–2010.

For example, organic foods are presumed to be more healthful because they are free of preservatives, growth hormones, and pesticides. They are carefully packaged and stored in a manner that optimizes their nutritional value. Because of these standards, organic foods cannot be mass-produced in the most cost-effective way. The demand for organic foods increases based on the perception that they are more healthful due to the associated standards of their production. They will be in low supply because of the production methods required to optimize their nutritional value. Low supply and high demand equate to higher prices. As a result, gaining access to the health benefits of organic foods is expensive.

The same is true for virtually every other aspect of wellness. The elements in society that promote wellness tend to be more expensive. Elements that are detrimental to our health or have little value in terms of health promotion tend to be less expensive. As a result, the ability for individuals to consume the elements of our society that are beneficial to health depends heavily on their **socioeconomic status (SES)**. Thus, SES has a profound impact on health outcomes. Being able to afford to

EDITOR'S NOTES

socioeconomic status (SES): a measure of a person's economic and sociological standing, composed of a number of variables, including educational attainment, occupation/industry, wealth, income, and more.

eat healthful foods, live in communities that promote wellbeing, visit the doctor, exercise at the gym are all related to SES. SES therefore is a major factor in the study of the social demography of health. The following sections will explore this relationship.

The Cost of Professional Healthcare

The cost of healthcare has grown precipitously over the last few decades. Graphs 1.1.1 and 1.1.2 demonstrate this increase (CDC, 2012). In 1970, total hospital expenditure for American residents was $27.2 billion. By 2010, that number had ballooned to $815.90 billion (Table 1.1.2).

Healthcare costs have increased exponentially over the last 40 years, but household incomes have stayed relatively the same. The growing discrepancy between the costs of healthcare and the ability of people to pay is a major social problem. This especially affects those on the lower end of the socioeconomic scale.

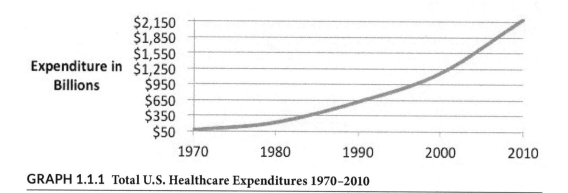

GRAPH 1.1.1 **Total U.S. Healthcare Expenditures 1970–2010**

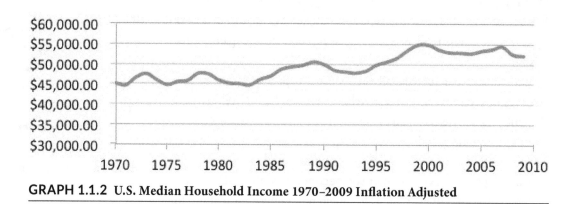

GRAPH 1.1.2 **U.S. Median Household Income 1970–2009 Inflation Adjusted**

TABLE 1.1.2 Total Costs for Selected Health Expenditures for All Americans

Type of Expenditure	Total Expenditure in Billions		Percent Increase
	1970	2010	
Hospital	27.2	815.9	2900%
Physician Care	14.3	519.10	3530%
Prescription Drugs	5.5	255.7	4549%

Source: CDC personal healthcare expenditures, by source of funds and type of expenditure: United States, selected years 1960–2011.

There are several explanations for the remarkable increase in healthcare costs. One maintains that the high cost of health technology and innovation has impacted the cost of health. The average cost of a CT scan in the U.S. is $510 compared to Canada at $122.

Another explanation suggests that as hospitals are governed under a "corporate model," there is increased pressure to turn profits. Hospitals originated as charity-based organizations seeking to provide assistance to the poor. Hospitals today are businesses *selling* healthcare. Their products include MRI, health screenings, CT scans, an overnight stay, physician consulting, and a host of expensive tests.

Administrators have titles such as CEO, CNO (Chief Nurse Officer), and CFO. These high offices come with lofty salaries. According to a recent report from Kaiser Health and ABC News (2013), it is common for hospital administrators to make over one million dollars annually (Table 1.1.3). Many of the hospitals under a corporate model regularly turn large operating profits. Using the most recent data available, the University of Pittsburgh Medical Center Presbyterian brought in $769,700,054 in operating profit, while Cleveland Clinic made $572,298,875 (Ford et al., 2013). Just like large corporations, the healthcare industry has an interest in wielding political power to maximize its profit potential. Between 1998 and 2012, the healthcare industry spent $5.36 billion lobbying politicians. In comparison, the entire defense industry spent only $1.53 billion during this period (Ford et al., 2013). The healthcare industry is one of the fastest growing in the U.S.

The corporate operating model has led to dramatic increases in the cost of healthcare. Those who are able to access the best care must demonstrate strong financial standing. Just as if you were going to buy a luxury car, before negotiating, the dealer would run a detailed check of your credit history and financial standing. This true in the hospital; before receiving care, the hospital wants to examine your insurance and determine what services are available to you. To be fair, unlike the luxury car dealer, virtually all hospitals do provide care for indigent patients, but the most powerful hospitals are able to minimize such losses.

TABLE 1.1.3 Total Annual Pay for Selected Hospital Executives Hospital

Hospital	State	CEO or President Total Pay
Kaiser Permanente	CA	$ 7,936,510.00
Providence Health & Services	WA	$ 6,379,455.00
UPMC, Pittsburgh	PA	$ 5,975,462.00
Dignity Health	CA	$ 5,136,883.00
Carolinas HealthCare System	NC	$ 4,760,026.00
Advocate Health Care	IL	$ 4,049,580.00
Memorial Hermann	TX	$ 3,826,835.00
Ochsner Health System	LA	$ 3,389,411.00
BJC HealthCare	MO	$ 3,279,956.00
Partners HealthCare	MA	$ 3,127,647.00
New York-Presbyterian	NY	$ 3,076,436.00
Cleveland Clinic	OH	$ 2,564,214.00
Intermountain Healthcare	UT	$ 2,196,481.00
Mayo Clinic	MN	$ 2,002,896.00
U. Texas MD Anderson Cancer Center	TX	$ 1,404,000.00

EDITOR'S NOTES

stratification: a system of inequality based on ranking people or groups based on power, prestige, and wealth.

Because professional healthcare has become a business, people will be **stratified** in their access to this means of fighting illness or ensuring wellness. Wealthy people will have the most access, poor people will have the least. As we will see, this structure remains true for most other factors that influence health outcomes in America. This includes the concept of "place."

Place Matters

EDITOR'S NOTES

place: (see definition in reading)

Sociologists have carefully examined the effects of place on health outcomes for years. Mark LaGory and Kevin Fitzpatrick describe the magnitude of place in their landmark study *Unhealthy Places*. They describe **place** as, a key element in our identity. Who we are is reflected in the places we occupy and the spaces we control. These places range from nation to region, state, metropolitan area, community, neighborhood, block, and residential dwelling. Each location has a profound social meaning for us, and in a literal sense defines not only who we are, but also how we live and die. (2000, p. 4)

The places that we occupy are stratified by our SES. They confer benefits and drawbacks based on SES. Places occupied by the poor are more isolated from health-enhancing resources. The neighborhood is perhaps the best-understood example of place. Many poor neighborhoods are recognized as **food deserts**, where residents have no access to grocers, farmers markets, or restaurants that supply healthful foods to the local population (Wrigley, 2002). High-quality grocers have very little reason to move to a poor neighborhood. As a business, they have to adhere to market forces. Their research helps them determine which neighborhoods will be most profitable. As a result, many low-income neighborhoods do not have the market attributes to attract pricey grocers.

Neighborhood, SES, Physical Activity

The physical composition of neighborhoods can also have health-promoting effects. This physical composition is referred to in the social sciences as the built environment. A more technical definition is provided by the CDC, which defines it as "human-formed, developed, or structured areas" (2009). To a very large degree, neighborhoods reflect the SES of residents. High-SES neighborhoods tend to have built environments conducive to physical activity. This is important because physical activity, especially among older adults, is of vital importance. Neighborhood quality tends to be correlated with the amount of physical activity that individuals receive in their community (Gordon-Larsen et al., 2006). Neighborhoods that have good lighting at night, an organized traffic structure, wide sidewalks, and open green spaces tend to promote neighborhood physical activity (Li et al., 2005). Not surprisingly, neighborhoods with these characteristics tend to be more affluent. Thus place, specifically neighborhood and its built environment, has an impact on

EDITOR'S NOTES

food deserts: parts of the country absent fresh fruit, vegetables, and other healthful whole foods. Typically found in impoverished areas, largely due to a lack of grocery stores, farmers' markets, and healthy food providers.

FIGURE 1.1.4 Place, specifically where we live and play, can have a dramatic impact on health outcomes. All images: Copyright in the Public Domain.

physical activity; whether one engages in physical activity or not has a significant impact on health outcomes, especially among older adults. In fact, Miriam Nelson and colleagues (2007) recommend that older adults incorporate moderate-intensity exercises into their daily lifestyle routine. Regular physical activity reduces the risk of cardiovascular disease, type 2 diabetes, hypertension, obesity, and colon cancer and is also associated with lower risk of anxiety and depression (Hamilton, 2007; Nelson et al., 2007). Given these health and psychosocial benefits, there is sound consensus that physical activity improves overall quality of life and that "virtually all older adults should be physically active" (Nelson et al., 2007 p. 9).

Research shows that the built environment confers benefits along racial and socioeconomic lines (Casagrande et al., 2009). Richard Cooper (2004) maintains that disease-promoting environments, not genetic factors, contribute to poor health outcomes among many African Americans. Fitzpatrick and LaGory (2000 p. 158) argue that "the characteristics of the communities that minorities live in" account for much of the difference in illness mortality between whites and African Americans. Other studies concerning racial disparities, the built environment, and physical activity focus on crime rate (Casagrande et al., 2009), obesity (Lovasi et al., 2009) and access to community exercise facilities

FIGURE 1.1.5 Greenways and wide sidewalks encourage healthy lifestyle behaviors. Copyright in the Public Domain.

(Powell et al., 2004). The general scholarship suggests that negative health outcomes are at least a partial function of socioeconomic and racial disparities in built environment composition.

Environmental Stress

Sociologists are also concerned about the influence of place on **stress**. Stress is a common feature of life for virtually all people. Stress can be the result of many different responsibilities or activities. Even activities that we generally regard as positive, such as vacations or weddings, can be stressful. For many, the requirements associated with making a living in today's economy can be stressful. As we learned earlier, workers are asked to do more at their jobs as many employers are cutting back on personnel or relying more heavily on automation. The everyday pressure of having to perform at work or school, earn enough money to be

EDITOR'S NOTES

stress: a physical, chemical, or emotional factor that causes bodily or mental tension and is a factor in disease causation.

FIGURE 1.1.6 Stress is a part of everyday life. How we manage our stress affects well-being. Copyright in the Public Domain.

comfortable, and cultivate relationships can be overwhelming. In fact, stress is a major contributor to adverse health outcomes.

Stress is a biological response to perceived danger in the environment. Most animals have stress mechanisms that help them survive in the wild. Humans do as well. When we were hunters and gatherers living in wide open expanses, our stress mechanism kicked in when we saw a lion headed our way. We get a rush of the stress hormone cortisol.

We also get a rush of adrenaline. Our heart rate and blood flow increase. Our pupils dilate. Our lungs fill with air. Importantly, most of our brain shuts down so that we can focus on three options: fight, fright, or flight (Cassim, 2013).

As you can see, our body undergoes a significant transformation when we are stressed. This same process is in motion today when we encounter day-to-day stressful situations. However, such a powerful physiological response is usually excessive in our tamed environment. In some cases, we are in real danger where such a response is necessary. If we are in the middle of a robbery or violent storm, then the rush of stress hormone is warranted. However, for most of us, these extreme situations are not everyday occurrences. Not that we do not have real worries today, but very few of us will ever be chased by a lion. The point is that our bodies are continuously being revved up due to the everyday stress that we encounter. Over time, accumulated stress can lead to negative health outcomes such as hypertension and heart disease. Stress, moreover, compromises our immune system, making us more vulnerable to infections. Stress can be mitigated through exercise and relaxing activities. We cannot avoid the complications of life, but we can learn how to deal with them in a health-promoting manner.

Stress and Place

Some places and situations are more stressful than others. Low-income people tend to reside in environments with more hazards than their middle-class or affluent counterparts encounter. Because many of these hazards are a part of life in disadvantaged neighborhoods, local residents are consistently confronted with stressful situations emanating from the environment. These neighborhoods have high rates of crime, vandalism, and vacancies. The stress of being poor and not having the means to meet financial obligations is difficult to contend with. It can become physically and mentally overwhelming when that stress is compounded by threatening activity in the environment. Catherine Ross and John Mirowsky maintain that,

> The impact of living in a disadvantaged neighborhood on physical wellbeing is mediated entirely by disorder in the neighborhood, which influences health both directly and indirectly, by way of fear. These neighborhoods present residents with observable signs that social control has broken down: the streets are dirty and dangerous; buildings are run down and abandoned; graffiti and vandalism are common; and people hang out on the streets, drinking, using drugs, and creating a sense of danger. Residents in these neighborhoods face a threatening and noxious environment characterized by crime, incivility, and harassment, all of which are stressful. The chronic stress of exposure to disorder appears to impair health. (2001)

Chronic stress occurs when an individual is continuously exposed to stressful situations. Most of the adverse health conditions associated with stress occur through this chronic exposure. James Jackson and colleagues (2010) maintain that low-income residents have fewer health-promoting resources available to help them cope with chronic stress. As a result, many of them turn to health-debilitating coping mechanisms. He talks about overindulging in the following: risky sex, which exposes one to sexually transmitted diseases; comfort foods, which encourage obesity; smoking and hard narcotics, which lead to pulmonary and cardiovascular complications. While indulging in hard narcotics is certainly not exclusive to the poor, such drugs do little to help low-income residents mitigate the problems in their environments. ...

> **EDITOR'S NOTES**
>
> **chronic stress:** stress that is persistent, or endless, in its effects.

References

Burns, Ken and Lynn Novick [Directors]. (2011). *Prohibition*. [Documentary]. United States. Florentine Films and WETA.

Casagrande, S. S., M. C. Whitt-Glover, K. J. Lancaster, A. M. Odoms-Young, and T. L. Gary, (2009). "Built Environment and Health Behaviors Among African Americans: A Systematic Review." *American Journal of Preventive Medicine*, 36(2), 174–181.

Cassim, Layla. (2013). "Optimal Health and Postgraduate Study: A Focus on Wellness, Stress Management, and Pharmaceutical Services" [PowerPoint]. 2nd National Postgrad Development Imbizo. Retrieved from: <http://www.undergraduatetoolkit.com/pdf/Dr%20Layla%20Cassim%20Health%20Presentation.pdf>.

Centers for Disease Control and Prevention. (2009). "Designing and Building Healthy Places." Atlanta: Retrieved November 27, 2009 from <http://www.cdc.gov/healthyplaces/>.

Centers for Disease Control. (2012). "Personal Health Care Expenditures, by Source of Funds and Type of Expenditure: United States, Selected Years 1960–2011." Department of Health and Human Services. Retrieved on May 16, 2014 from <http://www.cdc.gov/nchs/data/hus/2013/115.pdf>.

Cooper, R. S. (2004). "Genetic Factors in Ethnic Disparities in Health." In N.B. Anderson, R.A. Bulatao, and B. Cohen (Eds.), *Critical Perspectives on Racial and Ethnic Differences in Health Late in Life* (pp. 269–309). Washington DC: The National Academies Press.

Fernandez-Armesto, Felipe. (2007). *The World History Volume 2: The Revenge of Nature: Plague, Cold, and the Limits of Disaster in the Fourteenth Century*. Pearson, Prentice Hall: New Jersey.

Ford, Andrea, Heather Jones, Clair Manibog, and Lon Tweeten. (2013, February 20). "What Makes Health Care So Expensive?" *Time* magazine.

Foucault, Michel, (1973). *The Birth of the Clinic*. Tavistock Publications.

Gordon-Larsen, P., M. C. Nelson, P. Page, and B. M. Popkin. (2006). "Inequality in the Built Environment Underlies Key Health Disparities in Physical Activity and Obesity." *Pediatrics*, 117(2), 417–424.

Hamilton, M. T., D. G. Hamilton, and T. W. Zderic. (2007). "Role of Low Energy Expenditure and Sitting in Obesity, Metabolic Syndrome, Type 2 Diabetes, and Cardiovascular Disease." *Diabetes*, 56(11), 2655–2667.

Jackson, James S., Katherine M. Knight, and Jane A. Rafferty. (2010). "Race and Unhealthy Behaviors: Chronic Stress, the HPA Axis, and Physical Activity and Mental Health Disparities over the Life Course." *American Journal of Public Health*, 100(5):933–939.

Kaiser Health News. (2013, June 16). Chart: Hospital CEO Pay and Incentives. Retrieved on May 17, 2014 from <http://www.kaiserhealthnews.org/Stories/2013/June/06/hospital-ceo-compensation-chart.aspx>.

Li, F., K. J. Fisher, R. C. Brownson, and M. Bosworth. (2005). "Multilevel Modeling of Built Environment Characteristics Related to Neighborhood Walking Activity in Older Adults." *Journal of Epidemiology Community Health*, 59(7):558–564.

Lovasi, G. S., K. M. Neckerman, J. W. Quinn, C. C. Weiss, and A. Rundle. (2009). "Effect of Individual or Neighborhood Disadvantage on the Association Between Neighborhood Walkability and Body Mass Index." *American Journal of Public Health*, 99(2):279–284.

Martinez, Michael. (2014, January 1). "10 Things to Know About Nation's First Recreational Marijuana Shops in Colorado." *CNN*. Retrieved on May 18, 2014 from <http://www.cnn.com/2013/12/28/us/10-things-colorado-recreational-marijuana/index.html>.

McNamara, Joseph D. (2011). "The Hidden Costs of America's War on Drugs." *The Journal of Private Enterprise*, 26(2):97–115.

National Center for Health Statistics. (2011). National Table 22 (page 1 of 2). Life Expectancy at Birth, at 65 Years of Age, and at 75 Years of Age, by Sex, Race, and Hispanic Origin: United States, Selected Years 1900–2009. Health, United States, 2011: With Special Feature on Prescription Drugs. U.S. Department of Health and Human Services. Retrieved on May 18, 2014 from <http://www.cdc.gov/nchs/data/hus/hus13.pdf#018>.

National Institute on Drug Abuse (2008). Why Would Anyone Abuse Drugs? Addiction Science: From Molecules to Managed Care. National Institutes of Health. Retrieved on May 18, 2014 from <http://www.drugabuse.gov/publications/addiction-science/why-do-people-abuse-drugs/why-would-anyone-abuse-drugs>.

National Institute on Drug Abuse. (2012). National Survey of Drug Use and Health. National Institutes of Health.

Nelson, M. E., W. J. Rejeski, S. N. Blair, P. W. Duncan, J. O. Judge, A. C. King, C. A. Macera, and C. Castaneda-Sceppa. (2007). "Physical Activity and Public Health in Older Adults: Recommendation from the American College of Sports Medicine and the American Heart Association." *Med Science Sports Exercise*, 39(8):1435–1445.

Powell, L. M., S. Slater, and F. J. Chaloupka. (2004). The Relationship Between Community Physical Activity Settings and Race, Ethnicity, and Socioeconomic Status. *Evidence-Based Preventive Medicine*, 1(2):135–144.

Redonnet, Bertrand, Aude Chollet, Eric Fombonne, Lucy Bowes, and Maria Melchior. (2012). "Tobacco, Alcohol, Cannabis and Other Illegal Drug Use Among Young Adults: The Socioeconomic Context." *Drug and Alcohol Dependence*, 121(3):231–239.

Ross, Catherine E. and John Mirowsky. (2001). Neighborhood Disadvantage, Disorder, and Health. *Journal of Health and Social Behavior*, 42(3):258–276.

Wrigley, Neil. (2002). "'Food Deserts' in British Cities: Policy Context and Research Priorities." *Urban Studies*, 39(11):2029–2040.

Defining Health by Addressing Individual, Social, and Environmental Determinants

New Opportunities for Health Care and Public Health

By Johannes Bircher and Shyama Kuruvilla

Abstract: The Millennium Development Goals (MDGs) mobilized global commitments to promote health, socioeconomic, and sustainable development. Trends indicate that the health MDGs may not be achieved by 2015, in part because of insufficient coordination across related health, socioeconomic, and environmental initiatives. Explicitly acknowledging the need for such collaboration, the Meikirch Model of Health posits that: *Health is a state of wellbeing emergent from conducive interactions between individuals' potentials, life's demands, and social and environmental determinants.* Health results throughout the life course when individuals' potentials—and social and environmental determinants—suffice to respond satisfactorily to the demands of life. Life's demands can be physiological, psychosocial, or environmental, and vary across contexts, but in every case unsatisfactory responses lead to disease. This conceptualization of the integrative nature of health could contribute to ongoing efforts to strengthen cooperation across actors and sectors to improve individual and population health—leading up to 2015 and beyond. *Journal of Public Health Policy* (2014) 35, 363–386. doi:10.1057/jphp.2014.19; published online 19 June 2014.

Introduction

The **Millennium Development Goals (MDGs)** helped mobilize unprecedented global resources to promote health and socioeconomic development. Some of the MDGs, especially those related to health, may not be achieved by 2015. World leaders are now deliberating post-2015 Sustainable Development Goals—with sustainable development defined as development that meets the needs of the present without compromising the ability of future generations to meet their own needs.[1,2] They recognize that: "the MDGs fell short by not integrating

EDITOR'S NOTE

millennium development goals (MDGs): goals developed by the United Nations, which focus on such things as halving extreme poverty, halting the spread of HIV, and more.

the economic, social, and environmental aspects of sustainable development. ... People were working hard—but often separately—on interlinked problems".[2]

Promoting the health of individuals and populations is a complex endeavor—dependent upon individuals, families and communities, governments, health professionals, academics, administrators, development partners, businesses, the media, and others whose activities overlap or intertwine. A definition of health that highlights these relationships could provide a systematic way to think through required actions, and facilitate cooperation.

Our understanding of the determinants of health has broadened beyond the individual to include social determinants—by taking into account:

> the unequal distribution of power, income, goods, and services, globally and nationally, the consequent unfairness in the immediate, visible circumstances of peoples lives'—their access to health care, schools, and education, their conditions of work and leisure, their homes, communities, towns, or cities—and their chances of leading a flourishing life.[3]

Environmental determinants of health, based on the definition of environmental health, include:

> ... all the physical, chemical, and biological factors external to a person, and all the related factors impacting behaviours ... targeted towards preventing disease and creating health-supportive environments (including clean air and water, healthy workplaces, safe houses, community spaces and roads and managing climate change). This definition excludes behaviour not related to environment, as well as behaviour related to the social and cultural environment, and genetics.[4]

The far-ranging scope of social and environmental determinants of health further highlights the need for a definition of health that could link different actors and sectors.

The preamble of the World Health Organization's (WHO) constitution (1946) represents the best known definition of health—a state of "complete physical, mental and social well-being and not merely the absence of disease or infirmity".[5] The preamble also states that: "The enjoyment of the highest attainable standard of health is one of the fundamental rights of every human being"; that "Informed opinion and active cooperation on the part of the public are of the utmost importance"; and that "Governments have a responsibility for the health of their peoples which can be fulfilled only by the provision of adequate health and social measures".

The WHO definition sets out aspirational and universal goals without much guidance on how these goals could be realized. It is not clear, for example, how governments should plan the "adequate health and social measures" to improve population health, and the requirements are likely to vary with each country's context. The translation of this definition to individuals' health also poses challenges. For example, individuals with disabilities or non-communicable and chronic conditions may subjectively feel healthy, even though by this definition they might not be considered as such. *Health*, defined as a broad goal that could mean different things to different people at different times and in different places, may hamper informed and active cooperation to achieve this goal.

In 2010, an international conference of experts presented a critique of the WHO definition of health: "It contributes to medicalization of the society, it is inadequate for chronic diseases, and it is neither operational nor measurable". These experts recommended that a definition of health should include "the resilience or capacity to cope and maintain and restore one's integrity, equilibrium, and sense of wellbeing".[6] While the conference identified these useful principles, the participants stopped short of formulating a new definition of health.

Experts from a variety of disciplines have proposed alternative definitions of health, and we discuss three notable examples before explaining our own. Christopher Boorse[7] used a statistical approach to redefine health. He proposed that statistical reference values be calculated for all possible human functions. Results that lay, for example, within the 95 per cent range would represent normal health, and results outside this range would signify disease. This definition was promoted as being quantifiable and not relying on value judgments. It was rejected—largely for being unduly disconnected from the richness and uniqueness of people's experiences of health.

Lennart Nordenfelt, working independently, proposed a normative formulation: "In order to qualify as a healthy person someone must have the ability, given standard or reasonable circumstances, to reach the person's set of vital goals".[8,9] This description usefully expresses a balance between abilities and goals. Yet, when considering the needs and resources of individual patients or populations, it is difficult to establish what constitutes standard circumstances and vital goals.

In 2013, Sturmberg developed another definition concluding that health is "a personal experiential state which needs to be viewed simultaneously in terms of its somatic, psychological, social, and semiotic dimensions".[10] As a practicing physician interested in systems thinking he describes health as having four important features, but does not differentiate health from disease and does not analyze how health is constituted. (See Sturmberg commentary[10] in this special section.)

We build on our earlier publications on the nature of health[11,12] and extend these concepts in the Meikirch Model of Health (the Model), as explained in the section on methods. In the results section we describe the components of the Model and the dynamic interactions over time that determine individual and population health. We then discuss possible applications of the Meikirch Model of Health to strategies to improve individual health care and population health. We do not suggest that the Meikirch Model can, or should, replace existing mobilizing and operational frameworks for collective action to improve individual health care and population health. Instead, the Model could contribute to these efforts by providing a systematic way for different actors, from different sectors, to think through, develop shared understandings, and address the various determinants of health.

Methods: Developing the Meikirch Model of Health

The Meikirch Model of Health originated in Meikirch, Switzerland—the home village of the first author (JB). After retirement from an academic career and a medical school deanship, JB started a project at the Swiss Academy of Medical Sciences about how to orient the Swiss medical care system to the challenges of the future. When the project failed to have the desired impact, a colleague suggested to JB that more far-reaching results might have been achieved from a 'clarification of the terms' involved. Understanding the implications of this proposal, JB then started to study the term *health*. Recognizing that the many different meanings and usages of this word depended on the background and the interests of the user, he worked to tailor a new definition of health to modern needs and circumstances to facilitate cooperative action for health.

The second author (SK) approached this analysis from a global health and development perspective. Actors engaged in health and development efforts recognize that they tend to work in sectoral isolation albeit on very interlinked problems. Recognizing this challenge, the global community is currently deliberating post-2015 sustainable development goals to integrate efforts across areas of inclusive economic and social development, environmental sustainability, and peace and security.[1] The health of individuals and populations needs to be at the heart of these collective efforts.[13] As the Lancet Commission on Investing in Health demonstrates, healthier people can contribute more to countries' economies,[14] and inclusive, equitable societies and sustainable environments can enhance people's health.[1] An integrative approach is not just relevant for global development goals, but is also a fundamental principle of human rights, where rights—for example, to the highest attainable standard of health, to education, and to economic, social and cultural participation—are interdependent and indivisible.[15] To realize human rights and development goals, there needs to be a special focus on those individuals and groups most marginalized and underserved by health and social services—often the women and children in the lowest-income communities.[13] A shared understanding of the nature of health and its related determinants could contribute to ongoing collective efforts.

An earlier version of the Model (by JB) focused primarily on individual health care. Together we have worked to develop the Meikirch Model of Health to take into account population health considerations. We present a version here with the hope it will help many stakeholders and those collaborating across sectors to promote individuals' and populations' health.

To develop this expanded Meikirch Model of Health, we applied both **deductive** and **inductive analysis**, an approach that is set out in the *multi-grounded theory* method.[16] The inductive phase included reviewing and codifying literature on definitions of health and critiques of these definitions. It also involved synthesizing empirical and practical experiences in clinical practice and research, with patients' experiences with health and disease, and with population health policies and programs. The authors also used deductive considerations—theories and conceptual frameworks from evolutionary biology, clinical medicine, social, anthropological, philosophical, and systems theory—to help organize and evaluate the inductive information, and to develop the

Meikirch Model of Health further. Finally, we followed an interactive and iterative process with feedback from preliminary peer-reviewed publications[11,12] and presentations at scientific and other meetings where participants engaged in discussions of the ideas and thereby informed subsequent iterations of the Model.

Results: Explicating the Meikirch Model of Health

The Meikirch Model of Health posits that: *Health is a state of wellbeing emergent from conducive interactions between individuals' potentials, life's demands, and social and environmental determinants.* Health results throughout the life course when individuals' potentials—and social and environmental determinants—suffice to respond satisfactorily to the demands of life. Life's demands can be physiological, psychosocial, or environmental, and vary across individual and context, but in every case unsatisfactory responses lead to disease.

Figure 1.2.1 depicts the Model. It comprises three main constituents of health: (i) *Individual determinants* of health that include: (a) *Demands of life* (as outlined above); and (b) *Potentials* of individuals—biologically given or personally acquired—to meet life's demands; (ii) *Social determinants* of health; and (iii) *Environmental determinants*. These determinants interact and can modify both the demands of life and potentials to respond satisfactorily to these demands. We now define and discuss each element in the Model, beginning with Individual determinants of health, followed by the Social and Environmental determinants. We then discuss how these determinants all interact as part of a complex adaptive system of health.

Individual Determinants of Health
Demands of Life

Humans are exposed to three main types of demands of life: physiological, psychosocial, and environmental demands. In the following sections we discuss how individuals use their biologically given and personally acquired potentials to process and meet these demands, and also the social and environmental factors that may facilitate or hinder this process.

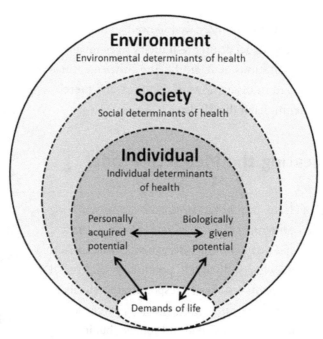

FIGURE 1.2.1 *The Meikirch Model of Health*: Health occurs when individuals use their biologically given and personally acquired potentials to manage the demands of life in a way that promotes well-being. This process continues throughout life and is embedded within related social and environmental determinants of health. Health is constituted by all three dimensions—individual, social, and environmental determinants of health.

- *Physiological demands*: For humans, physiological demands present themselves in many ways as functions related to input, output, and procreation. Procurement of oxygen, nutrients and water, excretion, fertilization, pregnancy and childbirth, and the maintenance of internal conditions within physiological limits (homeokinesis) are key examples. Some specific characteristics differentiate humans from other higher animals. Procreation is essential for the survival of the species, but only humans can make choices on whether, and when, to procreate. Humans deal with different conditions to meet physiological needs that vary with time and circumstance. For example, in low-income countries the main sources of food may be provided by traditional farming and, in high-income countries, by industrialized agriculture. Both food sources include external systems for storage and distribution, for instance, through local shops or supermarkets.
- *Psychosocial demands*: Psychosocial demands relate to individuals' personal development and social integration, including participation in social, economic, and political life. Personal development interlinks with social integration and is immediately apparent for newborns who need to attach to their care givers. This contributes to brain function and overall development.[17] Each individual is exposed to various social determinants of health throughout the life course, with roles and expectations varying around the world, for example, as related to jobs, relationships, obligations to family and society, personal aspirations, and political and economic contexts.

Thus, the way in which life's demands present and can be fulfilled depends very much on the specifics of the society in which an individual lives.

- *Environmental demands*: Health of individuals and populations can be affected substantially by factors in the environment, including extreme weather events, availability of clean drinking water, air pollution, food scarcity, radioactivity, and safe workplaces.[1,4,18] Environmental demands of life do include protection from physical, chemical, and microbiological threats, and safe disposal of waste matter (recycling). Sustainable development focuses on environmental demands. Some of these are apparent immediately, while others could be latent for many years (for example, exposure to carcinogens from tobacco smoke or pollutants). Environmental demands are not only about protection from challenges, but also about protecting the environment to reduce environmental demands to create conditions conducive to promoting both health and sustainable development.

Individuals' Potentials

The Model postulates that for health, each person must have the resources to meet the demands of life at any point in time. Figure 1.2.2 depicts possible interactions between individuals' biologically given and personally acquired potentials in relation to health across the life course. A common desire for a long life creates necessity to satisfy demands both in the present and for the long term. For this reason we chose the term *potential* to express both present and future resources. Individuals draw on two major potentials to process and meet life's demands: biologically given and personally acquired potentials.

- *Biologically given potential:* Our biologically given potential represents the biological basis of life. At the moment of birth it has a finite value resulting from genetic material and the quality of the pregnancy. The genetic component includes the genes themselves as well as their epigenetic regulation during pregnancy. After birth this potential diminishes throughout life, reaching zero at the time of death (Figure 1.2.2). Every somatic disease, injury, or defect diminishes the biologically given potential, either transiently or permanently.

- *Personally acquired potential*: This potential is the sum of all physiological, mental, and social resources a person acquires during life. It starts to develop in utero. As the brain and other organ systems mature, the personally acquired potential grows rapidly. For children, adolescents, and families schools and communities play a crucial part in supporting personal maturation and development of knowledge and skills. In adulthood, the development of potentials may slow down, but can increase throughout life provided an individual intends to and is able to actively promote her or his development, and lives in a health-enhancing social context. Emerging research on positive psychology highlights the importance of personally acquired potential for health. Individuals can enhance their well-being and longevity by building up positive emotions, engagement, relationships, meaning, and accomplishment.[19] Similarly, the **salutogenesis** *concept of Antonovsky proposes that individuals who understand their situation, can manage it, and find sense in it, can enhance their health.*[20]

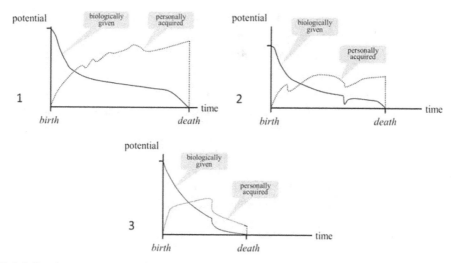

FIGURE 1.2.2 The time course of individuals' biologically given and personally acquired potentials is shown by three examples of possible time courses of the two potentials during the life of a human being. At the time of birth, biologically given potential (continuous line) has a finite value that differs from person to person, and at the time of death, it is zero. In the figure, the lines between these two points, the curves are drawn arbitrarily to illustrate these concepts. The personally acquired potential of a person (dotted lines) begins before birth, increases rapidly thereafter, and can increase throughout life, provided the individual is able to continually develop it to meet life's demands. It drops to zero at the time of death. The corresponding lines for biologically given potential in the figure are also drawn arbitrarily for illustrative purposes. Both potentials and the demands of life are strongly influenced by social and environmental determinants as depicted in the Meikirch Model. This figure focuses on the interaction of the two potentials in the context of specific individuals. In the first example the individual has succeeded in enhancing personally acquired potential. The second may have had a crisis in puberty and later a myocardial infarction—indicated by drops in the two potentials. In the third case, both curves drop at some time due, for example, to alcoholism. At each moment in life, every individual uses her or his total potential, the composite 'sum' of the two potentials, to try and effectively manage the demands of life.

Biologically given and personally acquired potentials do not split into body and mind. Although biologically given potential is reflected in an individual's somatic constitution, many aspects of personally acquired potential also reside in the body. Individuals who have been physically active while growing up develop more athletic musculoskeletal systems than those who as youths mostly read books or played with computers. In this and many other examples, dissimilarities in personally acquired potentials are expressed as anatomical and physiological differences.

Personally acquired potential can compensate appreciably for deficiencies in biologically given potential. A person with paraplegia can become functionally independent and professionally active.[21] By contrast, we cannot identify instances in which the biologically given potential has expanded to compensate for deficits in the personally acquired potential.

Highlighting the importance of the interaction between biologically given and personally acquired potentials for a person's well-being, the Model includes the possibility for people to consider themselves healthy despite having biomedical problems. A person might have rheumatoid arthritis and related physical impairments but if the disease is medically under control and the person has developed personal potentials to function well enough to lead a meaningful life, the individual might consider him—or herself as healthy despite having a chronic disease and related physical limitations. This holds true also in other situations where people experience common health problems. A 2007 Swiss survey[22] found that 87 per cent of respondents reported their health as 'good' or 'very good'. This was despite 43 per cent reporting having had backaches, 36 per cent headaches, 35 per cent sleep disturbances, and 23 per cent other significant conditions—in the prior four weeks. Biomedical symptoms can coexist with subjective perceptions of good health.

The potentials needed to meet life's demands align with the concept of *capabilities* proposed by Amartya Sen and others.[23] The **capability approach** purports that capabilities to achieve well-being are a matter of what people are able to do and to be, and thus the kind of life they are effectively able to lead. This means that promoting an individual's functional capabilities (such as the ability to participate in social, economic, and political opportunities and to make use of health care), rather than end-state utilities (health, happiness, or desire fulfillment), should be the objective of human welfare systems. It requires public or state coordination.

A difference between the capability approach and the potentials becomes evident when analyzing the fates of two people newly diagnosed with Type 1 diabetes. One living in a high-income country with adequate health care and social resources could manage the condition relatively easily—facilitated by social and environmental determinants. Another living in a low-income country—even if she or he has the same potentials as someone living in a high-income country—might not be able to afford insulin or have health care and social services required. Thus

EDITOR'S NOTES

capability approach: suggests that capabilities to achieve well-being are a matter of what people are able to do and to be, and thus the kind of life they are effectively able to lead.

the high-income country resident may have more capabilities. In discussing personally acquired potentials the Meikirch Model of Health distinguishes between personal and social resources, whereas the capability approach combines them.

The Individual determinants of health—demands of life and people's potentials to meet them—are influenced by social and environmental determinants of health, including inequalities of resources and power and insalubrious environments, as we discuss below.

Social Determinants of Health

Research shows that better social engagement, collective efficacy, and trust are associated with better health outcomes.[24] Social factors may be positive or negative for people's well-being, including by enhancing or inhibiting the development of their potentials and by influencing the demands of life and the resources available to individuals to meet these demands. Wilkinson and Pickett identified that people's health was better in countries with less inequality in incomes.[25] In many parts of the world poverty, living conditions, and work conditions limit the health people can achieve. The WHO Commission on Social Determinants of Health concluded:

> The poor health of the poor, the social gradient in health within countries, and the marked health inequities between countries are ... caused by the unequal distribution of power, income, goods, and services, globally and nationally ...[2]

Michael Marmot helped define these social gradients and importantly noted that longevity is not solely related to people's income, but strongly affected by their autonomy and social participation, which are major determinants of health.[26] He strongly emphasizes the responsibility of governments and world leaders to create circumstances that facilitate social, economic, and political participation and enable individuals and populations to improve their health.

As set out in the WHO constitution,[5] all individuals have a right to the highest attainable standard of health, and governments have the overall responsibility to improve the health of their populations by providing adequate health and social measures. The concept of *entitlements* forges an essential link between legal rights and measures required to realize these rights. Sen defines entitlements as a specification of the legal rights and the resources and opportunities that enable individuals to access these rights.[27] The 2003 health reforms in Mexico introduced a health insurance scheme known as *Seguro Popular*. Aligned with the concept of entitlements,[14] these reforms explicitly positioned health care as a social right, and not as a commodity or a privilege. The reform arrangements included legal provisions as well as specific packages of health services.

Investments in health and social services are also important to reduce inequities, both within and across countries. The Lancet Commission on Investing in Health[13] calls for a 'grand convergence' within a generation. The Commission shows how investments in health could not only promote health and reduce health inequalities, but could also provide 9 to 20 times the value of the investment in social and economic benefits—as healthier people can contribute more to their societies.

Addressing the health needs of underserved and often marginalized groups, including women, children, and older people in low-income communities, is particularly important for reducing inequities and improving health.[13] They often benefit less from health care and social services that are usually more plentiful, accessible, and of higher quality in more affluent settings. Further, in addition to communicable and noncommunicable diseases that affect the whole population, they face the additional burden of morbidity and mortality related to pregnancy, and to childhood and age-related illness.

Given the linked nature of health and social and environmental determinants, governments could also consider more integrative approaches to address health, social, and environmental requirements of their populations. The example from Belo Horizonte below illustrates how this could be done.

Environmental Determinants of Health

There is established evidence of important links between the environment, development, and health.[18] These links were highlighted in 1987 by the UN World Commission on Environment and Development's report—Our Common Future,[3] also known as the Brundtland report, that noted: "The 'environment' is where we all live; and 'development' is what we all do in attempting to improve our lot within that abode".[4]

Factors in living and work environments can directly affect health.[4,14] Solid fuels are an important environmental cause of disease as are waterborne contaminants. Early exposure to indoor air pollutants may damage healthy lung development, leading to a lifetime of morbidity. Adopting cleaner, more sustainable energy technologies and water sources could help promote both health and development. At the macro level, dwindling natural resources, population growth, and the effects of climate change are likely to impede improving global health.[4,14]

A shared understanding of the nature of health, and the links between individual, social, and environmental determinants, could help promote a dialog between leaders and citizens, between public and private sectors, and with civil society and the media on the shared responsibilities to demand, provide, and use products and services in a way that is health promoting, and to put in place an appropriate and enabling environment that protects and promotes livelihood opportunities, health, and sustainable development.

Health as a Complex Adaptive System

The Meikirch Model of Health represents health as a complex adaptive system containing ongoing interactions between individuals' potentials, the demands of life, and social and environmental determinants. This approach is in line with current thinking on complex adaptive systems.[28] It is also aligned with the work of the philosopher John Dewey (1859–1952), who highlighted the possibility, and ethical imperative, of developing a mutually beneficial relationship among individuals as constituents of a transactive system that also comprised societies and the environment.[29]

The Meikirch Model of Health views health as an 'emergent property' that results from different interactions among components of a complex, adaptive system. Together the individual determinants of health, and the system as a whole—including social and environmental determinants—can develop a high degree of adaptive capacity, resulting in resilience and the ability to address ongoing and new challenges.

To achieve and maintain health over long periods, individuals must continually readjust how they use their biologically given and personally acquired potentials to respond satisfactorily to the changing demands of life—commensurate with age, gender, personal roles, culture, environment, and other factors.

Social action also is required to create circumstances that can promote individual and population health—to improve access to public goods such as education, health care, and nutritious foods, and to mitigate harm from products that cause ill health, such as tobacco and air and water pollutants; and to address inequities. This is true for low- and high-income countries.

At any point in time individuals may be subject to many demands—some immediate and some that arise from thinking about the future. Often these demands are not clearly defined. Therefore a first step is to define or diagnose the demands of life, then to prioritize which demands to respond to, and to describe and choose a satisfactory response. Such a response to life's demands might take different forms. Dewey describes three types of changes that individuals and societies (as agents) can use to resolve problematic situations:[30,31]

- External interventions to address the agents' needs (for example, preventing diseases by building sanitation and hygiene facilities or through immunization).
- Internally oriented accommodations that agents make when circumstances cannot be changed (for example, learning to live with a chronic disease).
- Systems-wide, transformative changes in agents, environments, and the complex systems of which they are a part (for example, the evolution of species linked to changing physical environments, or deep-rooted, transformative changes in individuals and organizations in the context of socioeconomic and political reforms).

The Meikirch Model of Health postulates that if an individual's potentials and related social and environmental determinants are insufficient to respond satisfactorily to life's demands—the state is disease. When considering the balance between the potentials, determinants, and demands of life, the transition from health to disease may not be sharply demarcated. Some authors think that the two states may sometimes even overlap.[32] Yet, in most cases the Model offers a rational, systematic approach to differentiate between the two states.

At each moment the total composite of potentials is critical for health. To meet continually changing demands of life, both (i) biologically given and (ii) personally acquired potentials are always used together. Figure 1.2.2 illustrates relative contributions of each of the two potentials over time to total potential, with advancing age favoring personally acquired potential. As we get older each of us must periodically adapt to a new relationship between our biologically given and our personally acquired potentials. Older people can continue to manage their demands of life effectively and experience well-being provided they are able to cultivate their personally acquired potential.

The usefulness of the term *potential* instead of resources becomes evident when considering a 40-year-old patient with recently diagnosed arterial hypertension. Despite the disease, this person may be completely free from symptoms and feel healthy—fully able to meet the demands of life. However, the patient's future resources to meet the demands of life could be seriously jeopardized, if the high blood pressure is not treated effectively in order to avert future cerebrovascular, heart, or kidney diseases. Analogous situations would occur in considering obesity, early malignancy, Type 2 diabetes, and so on. These illuminate the need to consider potentials, not just resources at a single point in time, but through the life course.

The different determinants of health all interact and influence each other, but at different times different determinants may be the main focus of interventions. For example, general improvements in social and environmental determinants could raise living standards and promote population health overall. In individual health care, individual determinants may take precedence as a starting point for intervention. In other instances, for example in developing a public health program, all these determinants would need to be addressed.

These considerations confirm health as a state of well-being emerging from conducive exchanges among various agents as part of a complex adaptive system. Each of these components consists of many constituents, rendering their interactions even much more complex. For this reason further reductionist analytical methods to assess health may have diminishing returns, whereas complex systems approaches to understand individual and population health seem promising.[33]

Practical Applications of the Meikirch Model

Consider, for example, the application of the Meikirch Model of Health in a clinical context with a physician using the three components of health to discuss treatment with a 27-year-old patient newly diagnosed with Type 1 diabetes mellitus. Although the treatment approach is standard, the Model offers a systematic way to think through the set of factors linked with the patient's health. This could motivate the patient.

> Information for the patient: Your *demands of life* have increased because your body needs an external source of insulin throughout the day. Your *biological potential* is insufficient to meet this need. In response you must augment your *personally acquired potential* by learning the physiology of glucose and insulin and the natural history of your disease to manage it well. Management includes a special diet, physical activity, monitoring your blood glucose levels, and regularly

injecting the required amounts of insulin. *Social and environmental determinants* can support you in this process. Health care providers can help monitor your health and advise you on regulating your treatment as required. You would also benefit from a range of social and environmental services, for example health insurance to pay for clinical services, including consultations and medicines. You need access to high-quality, nutritious foods. You also need environments where you can exercise and environmentally safe means to dispose of used needles and vials. Reliable sources of information on all of these issues can also support how you treat your disease. If you can manage your condition effectively, you can lead a healthy, productive and satisfying life.

While this is an oversimplification of a more complex health-care process, it serves to illustrate that the Meikirch Model could provide a framework for all participating stakeholders involved in the care of this patient, to systematically think through, organize, and demand the required resources and services to promote the patient's health. We emphasize the importance of contextual determinants in this example. It is likely patients in higher-income settings will be better able to access the required clinical, social, and environmental services to promote their health.

Next let us consider a potential application of the Meikirch Model of Health to support ongoing efforts to promote population health and sustainable development using the Belo Horizonte Food Security Program in Brazil. This Program did not explicitly use the Meikirch Model of Health, but we discuss it to highlight how a systematic approach to think through various determinants of health potentially could support similar collective efforts.

The Belo Horizonte program exemplifies the positive impacts of a truly coordinated health and sustainable development approach. Belo Horizonte is one of the most populous cities in Brazil, with 2.5 million inhabitants. In the early 1990s, about 38 per cent of its inhabitants lived below the poverty line, close to 20 per cent of children under the age of three suffered from malnutrition, and there were high rates of child mortality.

Starting in 1993, the mayor, local government, and citizens developed the Belo Horizonte Food Security policy framework. They set up a Secretariat for Food Policy and Supply, with 20 members including citizens, workers' representatives, religious and business leaders from different sectors involved with food security. These members consulted with peers and experts and advised on the design and implementation of a new system to secure widespread access to nutritious food and to raise awareness of the need for healthy eating.[34]

By 2009, evaluations in Belo Horizonte showed that 75 per cent fewer children under 5 were hospitalized for malnutrition, 60 per cent fewer children were dying, 25 per cent fewer people lived in poverty, 40 per cent of people in Belo Horizonte reported frequent intake of fruit and vegetables compared with the national average of 32 per cent.[31] Brazil used success of the Belo Horizonte program as a model in developing its national Zero Hunger Policy. It lends credence to the value of an integrated, ethical approach to promoting health and sustainable development.

The mobilizing framework for the Belo Horizonte program was citizens' rights, and the operational framework was based on strong local governance and collective action. We are in no way suggesting that the Meikirch Model can, or should, replace existing mobilizing and operational frameworks. Instead, we propose that the Model could contribute to these ongoing efforts by offering a systematic way for different individuals and groups to think through and develop shared understandings of the determinants of health. This systematic and shared understanding could help initiate, organize, and sustain collective action.

Through the NYSASDRI Institute in India we have early feedback on better use of mother and child services and of the vaccination program, increased personal hygiene, balanced nutrition, and use of mosquito nets from explicit application of the Meikirch Model of Health in 20 tribal villages in Odisha.[35] (See Sarangadhar Samal commentary in this special section.[35])

Discussion: Some Potential Applications of the Meikirch Model of Health

The Model builds on an extensive literature of theories examining and defining the nature of health, and indeed the nature of life itself.[36] The Model is compatible with health care and public health disciplines, in that it incorporates key physiological, clinical, psychological, social, anthropological, philosophical, and systems concepts and frameworks. It specifically fulfills the postulates formulated by the group of experts reported by Huber *et al.*[6] They wanted a definition that includes resilience, the capacity to cope and maintain and restore an individual's integrity, equilibrium, and sense of well-being. The Meikirch Model of Health satisfies these requirements. With respect to its biological and anthropological foundations, the Model may be viewed as a further development of Nordenfelt's definition that postulates a balance between abilities and goals.[8,9] It also encompasses Sturmberg's idea of describing health as a personal experiential state with somatic, psychological, social, and semiotic dimensions.[10] Kuruvilla *et al.* describe how "human rights principles of the interdependence and indivisibility of rights focus attention on the linkages between health, development, and human rights goals, and help promote integration of required services".[15] The Meikirch Model is also compatible with this approach.

One important limitation of the Meikirch Model is its theoretical and conceptual nature. Being able to assess—both quantitatively and qualitatively—individuals' potentials and the demands of life in relation to the social and environmental determinants would greatly facilitate the use of the Model in practice. The International Classification of Functioning, Disability and Health (ICF), together with the currently available tools for measuring health, disability, and quality of life, may be helpful.[37,38] Yet, these tools would require further development for valid evaluation of health as a complex adaptive system. Measures usefully could be developed both for individuals in terms of health status and also for population health and social and environmental determinants. Table 1.2.1 contains an indicative checklist of aspects that could be assessed. When the Model is applied to

TABLE 1.2.1 Using the Meikirch Model of Health to Support Assessments of the Health of Individuals and Populations

CASE: (Specify and describe individual, district ...)

Determinants of health	Assessment Notes	Plans, Services, and Actors Required	Progress Measures
Individual determinants of health			
Demands of life (DL)	—	—	—
Physiological	—	—	—
Psychosocial	—	—	—
Environmental	—	—	—
Individual potentials	—	—	—
Biologically given potential (BP)	—	—	—
Personally acquired potential (PP)	—	—	—
Social determinants of health			
Social determinants of health (SD)	—	—	—
Environmental determinants of health			
Environmental determinants of health (ED)	—	—	—
Key interactions (examples)			
DL to BP and PP	—	—	—
SD to DL, BP and PP	—	—	—
ED to DL, BP and PP	—	—	—
Complex adaptive systems			
Systems responses in relation to different situations, for example, causal loop analyses	—	—	—
Health outcomes			
Based on the specific application/s for individual and population health	—	—	—

Specify the case for assessment, for example, an individual, a district, and so on. In each case the three main constituents of health and the key interactions among these components could be investigated, including at a systems level. Recognizing that more detailed, standardized assessments and tests might be required in each section, and that not all these assessments may be required in all cases, this table provides an overview of a possible checklist or worksheet to systematically think through the individual, social, and environmental determinants of health using the Meikirch Model.

a specific situation, the analysis may reveal not one, but several or many factors that contribute to suboptimal health. If feasible, all of them need to be corrected to restore long-term health for individuals, families, or populations being considered. The procedure may also be applied to evaluate political actions.

Another limitation of the Model is that it is not yet supported by strong empirical evidence on its use or impact. In the terms set out by Dewey, the application and testing of an *Ethical Postulate*[29]—that in a transactive system, shared responsibilities contribute to shared benefits—is ever more cogent and urgent; this is relevant in the context of individual health care and for collective action in public health and sustainable development efforts and to realize human rights.

A range of actors could, in principle, use the Meikirch Model of Health to support their work. The Model could be applied to enhance health literacy among all stakeholders involved in health care and public health,[39] including patients and health care providers, families, and communities. Governments could use the Model to think through how best to provide adequate health and social interventions, and the related legal rights and entitlements. There also is a need for 'systems thinking for strengthening health systems'[40] and to improve the coordination among all related actors. For this reason, health system planning and evaluation should include all relevant stakeholders, within and beyond the health sector, in the public and private sectors, in civil society, and in the media. It would be pertinent to conduct research on whether, and how, the Model could provide a systematic approach for a variety of stakeholders to think through their contributions to setting shared health and sustainable development goals, to support related multi-stakeholder planning and evaluation processes.

Conclusion

We live in an interconnected world and need collective action to successfully address the challenges we face. There are several ongoing efforts aimed at building more integrative approaches to promote health and sustainable development and to realize human rights. The Meikirch Model of Health could contribute to these ongoing efforts. The Model responds to the need to develop a definition of health better suited to the operationalization and realization of the aspirations in the WHO definition, and one that facilitates systematic examination of its varied components. This could facilitate cooperation among stakeholders willing to combine forces. Health care and public health programs generally have a special need for inter-professional and inter-sectoral coordination. Using the Model, the main components—individuals' potentials, the demands of life, and the social and environmental determinants of health including the relationships among them—can be systematically identified. Such an analysis will better support operational planning than when just the broad umbrella term *health* is used. The post-2015 sustainable development agenda aims for an integrative approach across social, economic, and environmental sectors with healthy people at the heart of these efforts.

Future practical experience and evaluation will reveal the extent to which the Meikirch Model of Health can contribute to this agenda and support ongoing collective action to promote individual and population health.

Acknowledgements

The authors are grateful for valuable discussions and feedback about the Meikirch Model of Health and this manuscript to Jörg Jeger MD, Karl-Heinz Wehkamp MD, and Andres de Francisco MD. We also thank Richard Cheeseman for help with copy editing the article.

Notes and References

1. United Nations World Commission on Environment and Development. (1987) *Our Common Future.* Oxford: Oxford University Press.

2. United Nations, High-Level Panel of Eminent Persons on the Post-2015 Development Agenda. (2013) A new global partnership: Eradicate poverty and transform economies through sustainable development, http://www.post2015hlp.org, accessed 14 January 2014.

3. Commission on Social Determinants of Health. (2008) CSDH Final Report: Closing the Gap in a Generation: Health Equity through action on the Social Determinants of Health. World Health Organization, Geneva, http://www.who.int/social_determinants/thecommission/finalreport/en/, accessed 19 February 2014.

4. World Health Organization. (2014) Health topics: Environmental health, http://www.who.int/topics/environmental_health/en/.

5. Preamble to the Constitution of the World Health Organization as adopted by the International Health Conference, New York, 19–22 June 1946; signed on 22 July 1946 by the representatives of 61 States (Official Records of the World Health Organization, no. 2, p. 100) and entered into force on 7 April 1948.

6. Huber, M. *et al.* (2011) How should we define health? *British Medical Journal* 26(343): d4163.

7. Boorse, C. (1997) A rebuttal on health. In: J.M. Humber and R.F. Almeder (eds.) *What is Disease?* Totowa, NJ: Humana Press, pp. 1–134.

8. Nordenfelt, L. (1995) *On the Nature of Health.* Dordrecht, Boston, London: Kluwer Academic Press, p. 212.

9. Nordenfelt, L. (2007) The concepts of health and illness revisited. *Medicine, Healthcare and Philosophy* 10(1): 5–10.

10. Sturmberg, J.P. (2013) Health: A personal complex adaptive state. In: J.P. Sturmberg and C.M. Martin (eds.) *Handbook of Systems and Complexity in Health*. New York, Heidelberg, Dordrecht, London: Springer Science+Business Media, pp. 231–242, doi:10.1007/978-1-4614-4998-0_15.

11. Bircher, J. (2005) Towards a dynamic definition of health and disease. *Medicine, Healthcare and Philosophy* 8(3): 335–341, doi:10.1007/s11019-005-0538-y.

12. Bircher, J. and Wehkamp, K.H. (2011) Health care needs need to be focused on health. *Health* 3(6): 378–382, doi:10.4236/health.2011.36064.

13. Presern, C. (2013) Post-2015 working group of the partnership for maternal, newborn & child health placing populations' health at the heart of the post-2015 agenda. *Bulletin of the World Health Organization* 91(7): 467–467.

14. Jamison, D. *et al.* (2013) Global health 2035: A world converging within a generation. *The Lancet* 382(9908): 1898–1955.

15. Kuruvilla, S. *et al.* (2012) The millennium development goals and human rights: Realizing shared commitments. *Human Rights Quarterly* 34(1): 141–177.

16. Goldkuhl, G. and Cronholm, S. (2010) Adding theoretical grounding to grounded theory: Toward multi-grounded theory. *International Journal of Qualitative Methods* 9(2): 187–205.

17. Sullivan, R., Sloan, A., Kleinhaus, K. and Burtchen, N. (2011) Infant bonding and attachment to the caregiver: Insights from basic and clinical science. *Clinics in Perinatology* 38(4): 643–655.

18. Haines, A., Alleyne, G., Kickbusch, I. and Dora, C. (2012) From the earth summit to Rio+20: Integration of health and sustainable development. *Lancet* 379(9832): 2189–2197.

19. Seligman, M.E.P. (2011) *Flourish: A Visionary New Understanding of Happiness and Wellbeing*. New York: Free Press, pp. 182–220.

20. Antonovsky, A. (1987) *Unravelling the Mystery of Health—How People Manage Stress and Stay Well*. San Francisco, CA: Jossey-Bass Publishers.

21. Peter, C., Müller, R., Cieza, A. and Geyh, S. (2012) Psychological resources in spinal cord injury: A systematic literature review. *Spinal Cord* 50(3): 188–201.

22. Lieberherr, R., Marquis, J.F., Storni, M. and Wiedenmayer, G. (2007) *Gesundheit und Gesundheitsverhalten in der Schweiz [Health and Health Behavior in Switzerland]*. Neuchâtel: Bundesamt für Statistik.

23. Stanford Encyclopedia of Philosophy. (2011) The capability approach, http://plato.stanford.edu/entries/capability-approach/, accessed 10 January 2014.

24. Kawachi, I. (2001) Social capital for health and human development. *Development* 44(1): 31–35.

25. Wilkinson, R. and Pickett, K. (2009) *The Spirit Level: Why Equality is Better for Everyone*. London: Penguin Books.

26. Marmot, M., Allen, J., Bell, R., Bloomer, E. and Goldblatt, P. (2012) Consortium for the European review of social determinants of health and the health divide. *Lancet* 380(9846): 1011–1129.

27. Sen, A. (1982) The right not to be hungry. In: G. Floistad (ed.) *Contemporary Philosophy, 2*. the Hague, the Netherlands: Martinus Nijhoff.

28. Allen, P., Magure, S. and McKelvey, B. (2011) *The Sage Handbook of Complexity and Management*. Sage Publications.

29. Dewey, J. (1891/1999) Outlines of a critical theory of ethics. In: J.A. Boydston and L.A. Hickman (eds.) *The Collected Works of John Dewey, 1882–1953. The Electronic Edition*. Carbondale and Edwardsville; Charlottesville: Southern Illinois University Press; InteLex 'Past Masters' series.

30. Dewey, J. (1934) *A Common Faith*. New Haven, CT: Yale University Press.

31. Joas, H. (1996) *The Creativity of Action*. Chicago, IL: The University of Chicago Press, Originally published by Suhrkamp Verlag 1992.

32. Law, I. and Widdows, H. (2008) Conceptualizing health: Insights from the capability approach. *Health Care Anal* 16(4): 303–314, doi:10.1007/s10728-007-0070-8.

33. Began, J.W., Zimmerman, B. and Dooley, K. (2003) Health Care Organization as Complex Adaptive Systems. In: S.M. Mick and M. Wyttenbach (eds.) *Advances in Health Care Organization Theory*. San Francisco, CA: Jossey-Bass, pp. 253–288.

34. World Future Council. (2009) Celebrating the Belo Horizonte food security programme, Future Policy Award 2009: Solutions for the food crisis, http://www.worldfuturecouncil.org/fileadmin/user_upload/PDF/Future_Policy_Award_brochure.pdf, accessed 21 February 2014.

35. Samal, S. and Bircher, J. (2013) What is Health? Why Do We Need to Know it? (Manual for implementing the Meikirch Model to improve health care), NYSASDRI Company, Bhubaneswar, Odisha, India, http://www.nysasdri.org/pdf/Meikirch_Model/Meikirch_Model_2nd_edition.pdf, accessed 14 January 2014.

36. Maklem, P.T. and Seely, A. (2010) Towards a definition of life. *Perspectives in Biology and Medicine* 53(3): 330–340.

37. World Health Organization. (2008) *International Classification of Functioning, Disability and Health*. Geneva, Switzerland: World Health Organization.

38. Üstün, T.B., Kostanjsek, N., Chatterji, S. and Rehm, J. (2010) Measuring health and disability Manual for WHO Disability Assessment Schedule (WHODAS 2.0). World Health Organization, Geneva, Switzerland, http://whqlibdoc.who.int/publications/2010/9789241547598_eng.pdf, accessed 19 February 2014.

39. Pleasant, A. and Kuruvilla, S. (2008) A tale of two health literacies: Public health and clinical approaches to health literacy. *Health Promotion International* 23(2): 152–159.

40. Alliance for Health Policy and Systems Research, World Health Organization. (2009) *Systems Thinking for Health Systems Strengthening.* Geneva, Switzerland: World Health Organization.

The Social Construction of Illness

Medicalization and Contested Illness

By Kristin K. Barker

··

This chapter makes a case for the usefulness of a social constructionist approach to medical sociology, emphasizing the analytic
potency of social constructionism for explaining a key cultural and
historical trend of our time: **medicalization** (Clarke et al. 2003;
Conrad 2007). It includes a detailed discussion of contested illnesses—
illnesses where patients and their advocates struggle to have their
medically unexplainable symptoms recognized in orthodox biomedical
terms—and suggests that lay practices and knowledge, and the consumer demands they engender, are increasingly crucial in advancing
medicalization in the twenty-first century.

Sociology of Knowledge and the Social Construction of Illness

Social constructionism is a diverse set of theories of knowledge
developed and used by social scientists, historians, and cultural studies
scholars. From a constructionist perspective, a social construct is an
idea that appears to refer to some obvious, inevitable, or naturally
given phenomenon, when in fact the phenomenon has been (in full or
part) created by a particular society at a particular time. Pointing to the
socially constructed character of an idea challenges its taken-for-granted
nature and the social practices premised on it. As a case in point, feminists claim that gender is a social
construction, meaning that our current ideas about gender (i.e., norms and standards concerning
femininity and masculinity) are not biologically mandated; therefore, the ideas and the social practices
they institutionalize are alterable. Social constructionism has been a centerpiece, theoretically and
substantively, of the subfield of medical sociology. Stated in brief, its chief contribution has been to
demonstrate just how complex the answers are to the seemingly straightforward questions, What is

> **EDITOR'S NOTES**
>
> **medicalization:** the pro-
> cess by which nonmedical
> problems become defined
> and treated as medical
> problems, often requiring
> medical treatment.

> **EDITOR'S NOTES**
>
> **social constructionism:**
> a theoretical perspective in
> sociology that illuminates
> the development, mainte-
> nance, and consequences
> of jointly constructed under-
> standings of the world that
> form the basis for shared
> assumptions about reality.

an illness? What is a disease? But before taking on these questions, it's useful to trace the intellectual origins that inform a sociological approach to social constructionism.

From its inception as a discipline, sociology has approached ideas as reflections of the specific historical and social environments in which they are produced. The founding sociological thinkers—Karl Marx (1818–1883), Max Weber (1864–1920), and Emile Durkheim (1858–1917)—each addressed the relationship between the ideas or beliefs of a society and the social and material conditions of that society. Published in 1936, Karl Manheim's *Ideology and Utopia* represented a significant advance in the sociology of ideas. Manheim urged sociology to study empirically how peoples' historical context and their station in life (i.e., class) condition their ideas. In the 1960s, Berger and Luckmann (1967) articulated the link between ideas, including taken-for-granted or commonsense knowledge about reality, and everyday social inter-action. In more recent decades, feminist and postmodern sociologists have demonstrated the relationship between our ideas and our social locations in race, class, and gender hierarchies of power, and have built on Foucauldian views of knowledge as a type of discourse that arbitrarily gives some groups power over others (Collins 1991; Smith 1987). Finally, sociologists contributing to the interdisciplinary field of science studies claim that scientific knowledge, like other ideas, is the outcome of concrete social practices rather than of individual discoveries of truth that "carve nature at its joints" (Knorr Cetina 1997; Latour 1987; Timmerman 2007). This long and venerable tradition—often called the "**sociology of knowledge**"—studies ideas not as true or false expressions of the world per se, but as the realized expression of particular social interests within particular social systems and contexts (Merton 1973). In other words, from a sociology of knowledge perspective, our ideas are social constructions (Berger and Luckmann 1967).

Sociologists study the social construction of many different ideas, but of interest to us here are sociologists who study ideas about illness. Although perhaps not immediately obvious, the use of social construc-tionism in medical sociology can be traced to Talcott Parsons's (1951) concept of the *sick role*. The sick role describes illness as a form of medically sanctioned deviant behavior, and specifies the rights and obligations given a sick person to ensure that an episode of sickness doesn't disrupt social order and stability. Despite Parsons's social conservatism, his theoretical claims were premised on the conceptual distinction between the biophysical nature of disease and the social experience of sickness. Over the last fifty-plus years, medical sociologists have built on this distinction to make more radical and far-reaching claims concerning the social construction of illness and disease (Brumberg 2009; Conrad and Schneider 1992; Freidson 1971; Lorber and Moore 2002).

Social constructionist scholars emphasize the relationship between ideas about illness and the expression, perception, understanding, and response to illness at the individual, institutional, and societal level. Historical and cross-cultural comparisons are effective ways to illustrate social constructionists' claims. Imagine, for example, two societies: one defines illness principally as the outcome of moral failings or spiritual transgressions (on the part of individuals or communities); the other defines illness principally as the result of organic disturbance within an individual human body. Who (or even what) is identified as "ill" in these two societies will differ dramatically, as will arrangements for how and by whom illness is to be treated. In addition, the subjective experience and meaning of being ill will be markedly dissimilar because the two societies provide very different interpretive frameworks of the illness experience. In one society, "the shamed" stand before a sacred figure who rights the wrong, cleanses the soul, or grants mercy; in the other, the individual victim of disease—"the patient"—seeks the physician's technical skills to restore or fix his or her wounded body.

Social constructionists also examine why some illnesses exist in one place and not another, or appear and then disappear in the same place. In many societies, for example, women do not suffer from premenstrual syndrome (PMS) or anorexia nervosa. Likewise, *susto* and *koro* are illnesses that exist only in certain cultures. A number of illnesses that were present in Western societies in the late nineteenth and early twentieth centuries—including fugue, hysteria, and neurasthenia—have now faded from view (Hacking 1998). These so-called culture-bound and transient illnesses effectively advance the social constructionist claim that illness and disease are something beyond fixed physical realities; they are also phenomena shaped by social experiences, shared cultural traditions, and shifting frameworks of knowledge.

From a social constructionist perspective, the task is not necessarily to determine which of the two societies has the *correct* ideas about illness, or which of the illnesses found only in certain places or certain times are *real*. Instead, the task is to determine how and why particular ideas about illness appear, change, or persist for reasons that are at least partly in dependent of their empirical adequacy vis-à-vis biomedicine. So, for example, social constructionists pay close attention to how and why particular definitions or ideas about illness became dominant in particular places and times and how they marginalize or silence alternative ideas (Conrad and Schneider 1992; Freidson 1971; Starr 1982; Tesh 1988). Additional questions follow: What factors help explain why one society defines illness in moral terms, whereas another eschews such ideas in favor of observable anatomic abnormality? What are the central consequences—for the society at large and for afflicted individuals—of one set of ideas versus another? What dynamics are at play in the appearance and disappearance of a certain illness or in the existence of an illness in one place but its absence elsewhere?

Although these are some archetypal social constructionist questions, questions about reality and truth inevitably arise: Don't some ideas about illness more accurately reflect the truth than others? Doesn't the scientific disease model better explain and treat illness than folkloric or religious approaches? Isn't death definitive proof that illness isn't simply a social construction? These questions arise because not everyone agrees what calling an illness "socially constructed" implies. This is largely because there is no single social constructionist perspective in general, or in medical sociology in particular (Brown 1995).[1] Instead there are several versions of social constructionism used by many different academic disciplines, each drawing on different intellectual assumptions about the relationship between ideas and the material world. The widespread use of several versions of social constructionism, by scholars from a host of disciplines, applied to an increasing array of phenomena (e.g., race, gender, sexuality, quarks, disability, illness) has led to a confused and mulled state of affairs with respect to what exactly is socially constructed about phenomena said to be social constructions.

In his aptly titled book *The Social Construction of What?* philosopher Ian Hacking asks the following types of questions: What does it mean to say that race, or a quark, or an illness is a social construct? Does it mean that we made these *things* and they would not exist as such if we had not made them, and/or we could have made them in a fundamentally different fashion? Or, does it mean that we made our *ideas* about these things, and we could have come up with very different ideas about these things? Does it mean that both the *things* and our *ideas* about the things are socially constructed? Are all things and all ideas social constructions? Or, if all things and all ideas are not equally socially constructed, what makes some things and some ideas social constructions and not others?

Hacking and other analytic philosophers and philosophers of science raise important questions about social constructionism (Boghossian 2001; Hacking 1999; Searle 1995; Slezak 2000). Among the principal charges they raise are that social constructionism explicitly or implicitly denies the existence of the natural world (or at least denies the possibility that we can know about it with some degree of accuracy); and, relatedly, that the approach stumbles over questions concerning whether or not some ideas are better representations of the world than are others. Hacking also alleges that social constructionism inevitably reproduces a false binary between things that are *real* (and therefore have an entirely biophysical basis) and things that are *socially constructed* (and therefore have no biophysical basis whatsoever). As a result, Hacking contends, social constructionism fails to consider the possibility that something can be *both* real *and* socially constructed (Hacking 1999, 31). However, sociologists of medicine have often supported this view, insofar as they believe that the social forces constructing the definition and treatment of illness are themselves real phenomena that can be empirically studied (Brown 1995; Freidson 1971).

What many sociologists mean when they claim that an illness is socially constructed is that the experience of illness is shaped by social and cultural context. The earlier comments concerning the variability in the experience of illness across time (history) and space (culture) are illustrative. Many sociologists have pursued this line of reasoning and in so doing have given us powerful insights into the cultural fabric of illness. Without question, the experience of cancer, epilepsy, or anxiety differs greatly historically and cross-culturally. Insofar as all illness gains meaning within the context of human society, all illness is socially constructed. Yet, if all illnesses are social constructions, then there is no point in singling out any particular illness as being a social construct. In short, the social constructionist perspective loses its expository or investigatory power when followed to its logical conclusion. Even here, however, a core conceptual contribution of social constructionism to medical sociology remains intact: the distinction between the medical model, which emphasizes biological pathology, and the social model, which emphasizes the oft-neglected social causes and character of illness and impairment.

There still is the matter of the social construction of illnesses as things. A strict constructionist position would implicitly or explicitly hold that no illness—cancer, epilepsy, or anxiety—exists outside our socially and historically bound mental constructions. These things exist at all, or exist as they are, only because we created them. Although not about illness, this position, which effectively denies the existence of the **ontological** world or the reality of what Searle (1995) calls "brute facts" (i.e., facts about the physical and natural world), was famously mocked in 1996 when the physicist Alan Sokal published a hoax article in *Social Text*, a leading journal representing the postmodern critique of science's alleged objectivity in the so-called science wars. Despite the attention given the Sokal hoax and the vocal attacks against the relativism of social constructionism, it is difficult to find scholars who make these strict types of claims. Even Hacking (1999) admits that most social constructionists avoid this pitfall.

A line of inquiry pursued by medical sociologists that thoughtfully negotiates many of these logical problems emphasizes the social construction of medical knowledge. As described by Brown (1995, 37), the social construction of illness stresses the illness experience, whereas

EDITOR'S NOTES

ontology: a branch of philosophy that investigates the concept of being. It focuses on several related questions: (1) What things exist? (2) What categories do they belong to? (3) Is there such a thing as objective reality? (4) What does the verb "to be" mean?

the social construction of medical knowledge "deals with the ways of knowing that are based on the dominant biomedical framework" and is chiefly concerned with professional beliefs and diagnoses. Of course, in our society it is impossible to fully disentangle these spheres given that people primarily make sense of and manage illness within the dominant biomedical framework (ibid.). In fact, it is difficult to overstate biomedicine's influence in shaping the prevailing ideas about illness in advanced capitalist societies. Among other things, biomedicine plays a dominant role in organizing our experiences and complaints into disease categories.

A disease does not exist, so to speak, until the social institution of medicine creates a representative diagnostic category (Brown 1995; Freidson 1971). For a disease to exist, in this limited sense, it must be identified. Disease begins with "social discovery" or the "the ways in which people, organizations, and institutions determine that there is a disease or condition" (Brown 1995, 38). This is not to suggest that there are no biological facts concerning disease, nor is the point merely one of semantics. As noted earlier, we can claim that a disease as defined in a diagnostic category is a social construction without implying that the suffering it represents has no biological basis. After all, social constructionists are primarily interested in the empirical adequacy of their own descriptions of the social forces behind medical ideas, be these forces at odds with or supplementary to the empirical adequacy of the corresponding biomedical ideas. Contrary to Hacking's allegations, medical sociologists and anthropologists clearly recognize the possibility that a condition can be both real and socially constructed (Brown 1995; Freidson 1971). For example, such a both/and stance vis-à-vis the real/social-construction dichotomy has been advanced in the case of post-traumatic stress disorder (Young 1995), mood disorders (Horwitz 2002), and anorexia nervosa (Brumberg 2009), to name but a few. Additionally, the social constructionist approach clearly addresses how diagnoses interact with the individuals who are diagnosed, again acknowledging social constructionism's both/and analytic potential (Brown 1995; Freidson 1971; Horwitz 2002).

But not all diseases, as captured in their diagnostic categories, are fundamentally or primarily social constructions. Sometimes the factors behind the creation of a new disease category and its application are straightforwardly biological. A particular type of human distress is linked to biological pathologies, and the new diagnosis represents progress in medical knowledge. In these instances it might be meaningful to talk about the social practices that resulted in the discovery of the disease and its application, but it would not be particularly meaningful to assert that the disease is a social construction simply because social activity led to its discovery. Here the deft historical accounts of the social processes leading up the discovery of tuberculosis (Tomes 1998), end-stage renal disease (Peitzman 1992), and HIV/AIDS (Epstein 1996) come to mind. Often, however, there is a level of arbitrariness concerning why a particular set of attributes comes to be organized and represented under a biomedical diagnosis. Cases characterized by apparent arbitrariness are of most interest to sociologists (Brown 1995). These cases are interesting not because they have no connection to biological facts, but because they demonstrate that "an entity that is regarded as an illness or disease is not ipso facto a medical problem; rather, it needs to become defined as one" (Conrad 2007, 5–6). Hence, the social construction of medical knowledge goes hand in hand with the process known as medicalization.

Biomedical Knowledge and Medicalization

Medicalization is the process by which an ever-wider range of human experiences comes to be defined, experienced, and treated as medical conditions.

One large sector includes the medicalization of deviance (Conrad and Schneider 1992). Calling a drunk an alcoholic or a gambler an addict are such examples. Social problems are also medicalized, as seen in the case of obesity and antisocial personality disorder (Lorber and Moore 2002). In some cases, "normal" human variation in such things as height, appearance, or temperament is defined as a medical problem and treated accordingly (Conrad 2007). In other instances, it is appropriate to speak of the medicalization of life itself. Medicine, Illich warned us, "can transform people into patients because they are unborn, newborn, menopausal, or at some other 'age of risk'" (Illich 1976, 78). The medicalization of life, therefore, includes natural physical changes ranging from the profound (e.g., senility) to the trivial (e.g., male-patterned baldness). Biotechnology promises to expand the frontier even further as genetic research medicalizes the state of being "at risk" (Skolbekken 2008). Through medicalization, natural human variation, normal experiences, routine complaints, and hypothetical scenarios become medical conditions.

Drawing on social constructionist tenets, feminist scholars have demonstrated how women's bodies and experiences have been particularly susceptible to medicalization. There are many complex reasons for this tendency, including medicine's conceptualization of male physiology as normative. Borrowing Simone de Beauvoir's (1989) central insight, men and men's bodies represent the biomedical standard and women and women's bodies are the biomedical other. It is but a short step to define normal aspects of women's embodiment as biologically aberrant. For example, women's natural reproductive functions are routinely medicalized (e.g., pregnancy, childbirth, menstruation, menopause) (Ehrenreich and English 1973; Lorber and Moore 2002, 2007; Martin 1987). That being said, women have themselves been proactive in processes of medicalization—perhaps because it represents one of a few avenues afforded them to pursue their needs and gain access to resources in a society characterized by gender inequality (Lorber and Moore 2002, 2007; Riessman 1983; Theriot 1993).

Medicalization is a complex process. Although the general historical trend has been toward ever-greater medicalization, it can be a bidirectional process, as the demedicalization of homosexuality and masturbation attest (Conrad 2007; Clarke et al. 2003). In the 1970s, at the height of the natural childbirth movement, childbirth became less medicalized (Lorber and Moore 2007). Although there is considerable evidence that this trend has reversed itself, the case of childbirth nevertheless illustrates the potential bidirectionality of medicalization. In a somewhat similar vein, there are individuals and groups who reject a medical classification of their behavior, as seen in the contemporary examples of pro-anorexia and self-injury (e.g., cutting, burning, etc.) groups (Adler and Adler 2007; Pascoe and Boero 2008). The actions of these groups have not led to demedicalization per se—the diagnoses these groups reject remain well established—but they do demonstrate pockets of resistance to the medicalization of deviant behaviors. Specifically, these groups actively produce counterconstructions of disordered eating and self-injury, affirm them as alternative lifestyles, and forge virtual subcultures, all far from the dictates of medical practitioners and the clinical gaze. Likewise, although parents and parent groups opposing childhood immunization don't undermine established medical protocol, they do show some individual and collective opposition to unlimited medicalization (Casiday 2007).

There can also be different levels or degrees of medicalization (Conrad 2007). A condition isn't necessarily medicalized or not medicalized. For instance, although a small number of individuals are treated medically for short stature (Conrad 2007), it would be an overstatement to suggest that the general public perceives shortness as an illness. Similarly, individuals who are dissatisfied with their bodily appearance can seek to have it medically altered, but so far being unattractive isn't considered an illness. In contrast to these cases of medical treatment in the absence of illness or disease, celiac disease is an illness without a medical treatment. In the case of celiac disease, the principal treatment is adherence to a gluten-free diet. Because celiac disease requires no medical intervention, it exists somewhere between a medicalized and nonmedicalized condition (Copeland and Valle 2009). Contested illnesses also illustrate different degrees of medicalization insofar as some of these conditions are further down the road toward accepted medical conditions than are others. Sociologists have referred to emergent or partial medicalization (Dumit 2006), or specified different medicalized classifications and categories (Brown 1995) to denote that certain human experiences hit a snag in the process of becoming institutionally accepted medical phenomena.

It is also clear that the principal forces behind medicalization in the present era differ from those that expanded medicine's jurisdiction up through the first three quarters of the twentieth century (Clarke et al. 2003; Conrad 2005). Dramatic changes in the organization of medicine toward the end of the twentieth century, most notably the rise of corporate managed care and the corresponding decline of physicians' professional power, underlie changing patterns of medicalization. One can briefly summarize the standard twentieth-century story of medicalization as follows: physicians carved out a professional niche for themselves by negating lay knowledge and practices and promoting the medical management of natural human experiences, social ills, and personal problems (Conrad and Schneider 1992; Freidson 1970; Illich 1976). The medicalization of childbirth and pregnancy are exemplars (Barker 1998; Wertz and Wertz 1979).

In contrast, when it comes to the forces promoting the expansion of medicine's jurisdiction in the current era, the role of physicians has declined in significance, while that of biotechnology (e.g., pharmaceuticals and genetics) and other corporate health industries (e.g., managed-care organizations), in tandem with the markets and consumers they create and serve, have increased in salience (Clarke et al. 2003; Conrad 2005). The popularity of elective cosmetic surgery and fertility treatments attests to consumer demands for medical solutions to personal problems and disappointments (Blum 2003; Conrad 2007). Direct-to-consumer pharmaceutical advertising encourages patients to ask their doctor about particular drugs to treat many previously normal or benign symptoms (e.g., toenail discoloration, heartburn) and to consider them specific medical conditions or diseases (e.g., dermatophytes, acid reflux disease) (Moynihan, Heath, and Henry 2002). The availability of a drug or other biotech treatment for a complaint significantly increases the likelihood that the compliant will be medicalized. This raises serious allegations that biotech corporations are engaging in "disease mongering" (Angell 2004; Conrad 2007; McCrea 1983).

There are important consequences of medicalization. By defining disease as a biological disruption residing with an individual human body, medicalization obscures the social forces that influence our health and well-being. Medicalization is depoliticizing: it calls for medical intervention (medication, surgery, etc.) when the best remedy for certain types of human suffering may be political, economic, or social change. Medicalization can also grant the institution of medicine undue authority over our bodies, minds, and lives, thereby limiting individual autonomy and functioning as a form of social control (Illich 1976; Zola 1972). Rarely, however, is medicalization exclusively the result of the medical profession's imperialistic claims. As patient consumers, we are increasingly active participants in the medicalization of our experiences as we earnestly seek to resolve and legitimate our suffering.

A social constructionist perspective that emphasizes the biological arbitrariness of certain diagnoses provides a powerful analytic framework for making sense of medicalization, or the process by which our complaints, disappointments, and experiences come to be defined and treated as medical conditions. In addition, such a perspective circumvents many of the critiques of social constructionism. A close examination of the social construction of contested illnesses further demonstrates these claims.

Contested Illnesses

Contested illnesses are conditions in which sufferers and their advocates struggle to have medically unexplainable symptoms recognized in

EDITOR'S NOTES

contested illnesses: (see definition in reading)

orthodox biomedical terms, despite resistance from medical researchers, practitioners, and institutions (Barker 2008; Conrad and Stults 2008; Dumit 2006). In the last several decades there has been a notable increase in the number of contested illnesses and contested illness sufferers (Barsky and Borus 1999; Henningsen, Zipfel, and Herzog 2007; Manu 2004; Mayou and Farmer 2002). Tens of millions of Americans are diagnosed with one of several syndromes characterized by a cluster of common, diffuse, and disturbing symptoms, ranging from pain and fatigue to sleep and mood disorders. Some of these illnesses include chronic fatigue syndrome/myalgic encephalomyelitis (ME), fibromyalgia syndrome, irritable bowel syndrome, urologic chronic pelvic pain syndrome, temporomandibular dysfunction (TMJ), tension head ache, multiple chemical sensitivity disorder, Gulf War syndrome, and sick building syndrome (Barsky and Borus 1999; Nimnuan et al. 2001; Wessley 2004) many sufferers and some clinician advocates suggest that these disorders—frequently called "functional somatic syndromes" in the medical literature—are unique disease entities with unique natural histories and specific characteristics. At this time, however, there is tremendous medical uncertainty concerning these conditions (Mayou and Farmer 2002).

At the very core of the uncertainty is a lack of medical consensus concerning the biological nature of these illnesses. Despite fierce claims to the contrary, none of these illnesses are associated with any specific organic abnormality. These conditions are not detectable in X-rays, blood tests, CAT scans, or any other high-tech diagnostic tool. Instead, they are diagnosed based on clinical observations and patients' subjective reports of symptoms. They are also diagnosed by exclusion, that is, after other possible explanations for the symptoms have been ruled out. Consequently, many physicians approach these "wastebasket" diagnoses, and those so diagnosed, with considerable skepticism. What is at issue is whether these syndromes are "real" (have organic biological origins) or not (are psychogenic, behavioral, or iatrogenic). With the exception of Gulf War syndrome, these disorders are highly feminized (Mayou and Farmer 2002). This unavoidable fact introduces ruminations that these diagnoses are modern-day labels for hysteria (Bohr 1995; Hadler 1997a, b; Showalter 1997).

The subjective experiences of these illnesses stand in sharp contrast to the medical uncertainty surrounding them. Individual sufferers provide persuasive accounts of their distress (Asbring and Narvanen 2003; Barker 2005; Hayden and Sacks 1998; Koziol et al. 1993; Kroll-Smith and Floyd 1997). They report significant reductions in functional abilities, health status, and quality of life, and little long-term improvement in well-being over time (Manu 2004; Nimnuan et al. 2001; Wessley, Nimnuan, and Sharpe 1999). Living with a contested illness, therefore, means managing a constellation of chronic and often debilitating symptoms, as well as coping with medical uncertainty, skepticism, and disparagement. Indeed these conditions are called "contested" illnesses precisely because of the clash between medical knowledge and patient experience (Conrad and Stults 2008; Dumit 2006; Moss and Teghtsoonian 2008).

A related line of investigation addresses contested environmental illnesses, or illnesses that involve "scientific disputes and extensive public debates over environmental causes" (Brown 2007, xiv).

A growing body of research demonstrates that when individuals claim to have an illness caused by exposure to environmental hazards, they meet with considerable resistance (Brown et al. 2004; Zavestoski et al. 2004a, b). Specifically, "corporate, government, and medical authorities" contest environmental illness claims in an effort to defend their organizational, professional, and economic interests (Cable, Mix, and Shriver 2008, 384). The principal contestation is over claims that a specific condition (e.g., breast cancer, asthma, lung cancer) is caused by exposure to a particular environmental hazard. In some cases, however, there are also disputes about the existence of the illness itself (e.g., Gulf War Syndrome, multiple chemical sensitivity disorder) said to be caused by environmental toxins (Kroll-Smith et al. 2000). These latter cases are examples of contested illness as defined in this chapter, but all contested environmental illnesses showcase conflicts between biomedical and lay ways of knowing, and hinge on the inability of medical experts to legitimate lay peoples' symptoms and suffering (ibid., 4).

According to Joseph Dumit (2006, 578), contested illnesses "are researched, discussed, and reported on, but no aspect of them is settled medically, legally, or popularly." Pamela Moss and Katherine Teghtsoonian (2008, 7) describe contested illnesses as "dismissed as illegitimate—framed as 'difficult,' psychosomatic, or even nonexistent—by researchers, health practitioners, and policy makers operating within conventional paradigms of knowledge." More than a decade ago, Brown (1995) identified two types of conflictual or contested diagnoses: conditions that are generally accepted but to which a medical definition is not routinely applied (e.g., environmental diseases); and conditions that are not generally accepted but to which a medical definition is nevertheless often applied (e.g., chronic fatigue syndrome). In both cases, for different reasons, sufferers have to convince the institution of biomedicine that their condition is medical in character. Thus, the term "contested" denotes that these illnesses exist somewhere between entirely discredited and fully legitimate diseases.

The particulars concerning the knowledge and experience of individual contested illnesses differ. For example, each condition is coupled with a body of medical research and a case definition or diagnostic criteria (Dumit 2006; Wessley, Nimnuan, and Sharpe 1999). Having been the beneficiaries of more sympathy from mainstream medical professionals, some of these classifications are more widely applied (e.g., fibromyalgia syndrome, irritable bowel syndrome) than others (e.g., sick building syndrome, multiple chemical sensitivity disorder). These illnesses can also be differentiated on the basis of subjective features and accounts: the experience and meaning of living with fibromyalgia is distinct from that of multiple chemical sensitive disorder; and individuals and groups coalesce around specific diagnoses. Nevertheless, these illnesses share a number of key similarities that account for their contested status.

Given that sufferers and their advocates want medically unexplainable symptoms to be medically recognized and legitimated, contested illnesses are examples of conditions for which individual patients and patient groups demand medicalization.[2] That is, they are evidence of a shift in the engines of medicalization: the demands of patient-consumers, rather than the professional agendas of physicians, increasingly underlie medicine's jurisdictional expansion (Conrad 2005). In addition, contested illness and medicalization are tied together conceptually via social constructionism: "Both medicalization and contested illness highlight that illness categories (usually, but not always, diagnoses) are socially constructed and not automatically ascertained from scientific and/or medical discoveries" (Conrad and Stults 2008, 332). What follows is a descriptive account of the social construction of contested illnesses.

Of specific interest to us are the shared factors and influences in the social processes by which contested illnesses were created and propagated. These include public intolerance of or anxiety about medically unexplainable but highly common symptoms; the dynamics of doctor-patient encounters and the corresponding diagnostic imperative; lay knowledge production and the emergence of illness identities and communities; and bureaucratic and institutional demands and practices (Aronowitz 1997; Barsky and Borus 1995; Brown 1995; Freidson 1971; Showalter 1997). I address each in turn.

When delineating the factors contributing to the social construction of contested illnesses, ground zero, so to speak, is the ubiquity of the symptoms they represent. Contested-illness symptoms are widespread in the general public and are particularly common among women (Fillingim 2000; Lorber and Moore 2002; Mayou and Farmer 2002). For example, pain and fatigue are the most common physical aliments reported by the general public (Barsky and Borus 1999). Fatigue is so commonly reported that the acronym TATT (tired all the time) now appears regularly in medical and popular media. The additional symptoms that make up these disorders, including mood, sleep, and bowel disturbances, are also widely prevalent (Mayou and Farmer 2002). This is not to suggest that these disorders are much ado about nothing. Whether these symptoms are common or not, their cumulative effect can be overwhelming. Aggravating this tendency is our cultural impatience with discomfort (Barsky and Borus 1995; Kleinman 1988; Kleinman and Ware 1992).

Accordingly, individuals turn to the institution of medicine for an explanation and remedy. However, even with extensive and very expensive clinical workups, many common symptoms simply can't be explained in biomedical terms (Barsky and Borus 1995; Mayou and Farmer 2002). So it is that sufferers describe a protracted and troubling road into medical uncertainty. "Nothing is wrong," they are told by one doctor after another. And yet they feel very ill indeed. In turn, sufferers must reconcile a subjective certainty of their symptoms with a lack of objective medical evidence regarding the existence of their symptoms (Asbring and Narvanen 2001). Along the way, individuals experience real or perceived accusations that they are faking their symptoms, malingering, or "just plain crazy" (Dumit 2006, 578). Their credibility is called into question. Given the gulf between their distress and the growing mound of negative medical tests, even sufferers sometimes begin to doubt their own grip on reality (Asbring and Narvanen 2003; Banks and Prior 2001). Not surprisingly, many individuals doggedly continue their search for a biological explanation in an effort to prove to medical professionals, their families, and themselves that they really are ill (Dumit 2006). In her research on chronic fatigue syndrome, Pia Bülow (2008) aptly calls this arduous search the "pilgrimage."

The dynamics of countless medical encounters that make up many such pilgrimages stand behind the creation and application of these diagnoses. There are many reasons that doctor-patient encounters favor diagnosing. For the physician, a diagnosis represents codified knowledge about a patient's experience and indicates a treatment protocol. For the patient, a diagnosis gives meaning and legitimacy to worrying symptoms and provides a framework for what he or she is facing (Balint 1957). Thus, when a doctor encounters a patient with distressing symptoms, both parties benefit from a diagnosis: it effectively legitimizes both parties and the doctor-patient relationship itself. Before contested-illness diagnoses could serve this legitimating purpose, however, they had to be created.

The creation of these diagnoses, in terms of both the specific case definitions and the actors advancing those definitions, differ in their particulars (Barsky and Borus 1999; Wessley, Nimnuan, and Sharpe 1999), but two general points can be made. First, each of these diagnoses is a descriptive category or analytic abstraction that stands for otherwise medically unexplainable symptoms (Mayou and Farmer 2002). It has been argued that many medical specialties and subspecialties have at least one functional diagnosis at their disposal to manage a large population of patients whose symptoms lack an understood biological cause; hence the creation of several different, overlapping syndromes (e.g., rheumatology has fibromyalgia, neurologists have tension headache, gastroenterologists have irritable bowel syndrome, gynecologists have chronic pelvic pain) (Barsky and Borus 1999; Nimnuan et al. 2001). Second, although none of these diagnoses would have come about without the efforts of key players who pushed for their creation—"claims-makers," as Conrad and Schneider (1992) call them—those that were advanced primarily by specialists in the medical mainstream have moved further along in the medicalization process than have those that relied more heavily on lay advocacy or were associated with marginal medical professionals. Examples of the former include fibromyalgia and irritable bowel syndrome. Examples of the latter include multiple chemical sensitivity and chronic fatigue syndrome.[3]

Although some support from sympathetic medical professionals is a necessary part in disease discovery, medical professionals also resist discovery (Brown 1995). Again, this resistance is what defines contested illnesses. Reflecting the most contested end of the continuum, an article published in the prestigious *Annals of Internal Medicine* referred to multiple chemical sensitivity as a "cult" (quoted in Kroll-Smith and Floyd 1997, 29). But even the least contested of the contested illnesses, fibromyalgia, has been resolutely attacked. The essence of the charge, captured in the following quote from a leading rheumatology journal, points to the social construction of the diagnosis: "No one can have fibromyalgia. Fibromyalgia is just a word we use to represent the situation of someone complaining about widespread chronic pain, fatigue, and sleep disturbances. ... It is not a disease, it's a description" (da Silva 2004, 828). The creation of contested illness diagnostic categories represents a decisive move toward the medicalization of common physical and mental distress, but none of these conditions is yet fully medicalized. In the absence of biomedical markers or efficacious treatments, medical professionals will continue to be skeptical of further medicalization.

Where diagnoses have been created—by whatever path and against whatever crystallized medical opposition—a number of factors have ensured their widespread application. First among these is a tendency within medicine to favor assigning illness over health. This is called the "decision rule" (Freidson 1971), but it might also be called the "diagnostic imperative." Concerned about their patients and trained to be proactive, physicians prefer to diagnose illness rather than health. Consequently, the existence of these diagnoses gives medical practitioners a new tool for managing the steady influx of patients with otherwise unexplainable symptoms. Under the weight of the decision rule, even physicians who are skeptical about contested illnesses are inclined to diagnose them.

The diagnosing behavior of physicians is only one side of the story. Once contested illnesses exist, again in the narrow sense of the creation of a diagnostic classification, individuals in distress encounter them. This makes possible perhaps the most crucial moment in the patient's pilgrimage (Bülow 2008)—the moment when her suffering is at last given a name. A diagnosis brings a coherence and order to a collection of symptoms that have heretofore been incoherent and unruly. Perhaps even more important, the diagnosis validates the sufferer and her suffering after a protracted period of disparagement (Asbring and Narvanen 2003; Barker 2005; Dumit 2006). In practical terms, a diagnosis is required to receive health care, disability compensation, and other social reparations. For all these reasons, individuals often strongly identify with their diagnosis. These are also all key factors that motivate sufferers to demand greater medicalization of their condition.

The means by which individuals encounter their diagnosis is also of interest. In some instances, the patient learns about her diagnosis only when a sympathetic (or agnostic) medical provider diagnoses her. Increasingly, however, individuals discover their diagnosis without the aid of their health-care provider. Some happen upon their diagnosis by way of a family member or friend battling the same symptoms. Others come to their diagnosis after reading a magazine or newspaper article that describes a condition that fits their symptoms to a tee. As the Internet becomes a primary source of health-related information (Fox and Fallows 2003), an ever-greater number of individuals find their diagnosis by typing their symptoms into an online search engine. In turn they connect to an extensive network of commercial and nonprofit websites that describe their symptomatic experience as evidence of a diagnosable disease about which they were previously unaware (Barker 2008; and see Conrad and Stults, this volume). Now that the FDA has approved the first drug for the treatment of fibromyalgia, some individuals find out they have this disease courtesy of a direct-to-consumer pharmaceutical advertisement. Although commonplace, self-diagnosis is insufficient; individuals need medical corroboration. Sometimes doctors are amenable, especially given the inertia of the decision rule. But many clinicians are hesitant to diagnose patients with a contested illness. Some patients go from doctor to doctor in search of a willing diagnostician. For this reason, Dumit (2006, 577) calls these "illnesses you have to fight to get." Again, issues surrounding self-validation and health/disability compensation make the fight for a diagnosis particularly salient.

Illness support communities also play an important role in the social construction of contested illnesses. Although patient advocacy, education, and mutual support are increasingly common in relation to many illnesses, contested-illness sufferers are particularly eager to affiliate with those who share their experiences. To use Bülow's (2008) metaphor again, these communities provide a welcomed shelter for the weary pilgrim. Through a variety of sources (e.g., bestselling self-help books, real and virtual support groups, and a host of advocacy organizational websites), individuals learn the biological facts—those denied by the uninformed in the medical mainstream—about their "real" disease. They also learn how to manage symptoms, deflect medical derision, and find a friendly provider who will diagnosis and treat their disease. Illness support communities produce and disseminate knowledge of sufferers' shared embodied experiences in an effort to support fellow sufferers, produce logical accounts of their distress, and challenge medical critics (Barker 2008; Dumit 2006; Kroll-Smith and Floyd 1997). At the level of experience, therefore, affiliation with a contested-illness community validates an individual's diagnosis and the diagnostic category. It would be difficult to overstate the degree to which the Internet has increased the reach and influence of these communities (Barker 2008; and see Conrad and Stults, this volume).

In this way, contested illnesses are examples of what Hacking (1999) calls "interactive kinds of things." Herein lies another important factor fueling the development of contested illnesses. In the case of interactive kinds of things, individuals react to being classified in particular ways. Unlike calling a quark a quark, which Hacking notes makes no difference to the quark, an individual reacts to being diagnosed with fibromyalgia or chronic fatigue syndrome or irritable bowel syndrome. Individuals come to see themselves as having a particular disease and reorient their symptoms and sense of self in relationship to that disease designation. This is starkly seen with respect to the self-validation that being diagnosed represents. The diagnosis launches a particular illness career, contributes to the creation of an illness identity, and makes possible affiliation with an illness community. Additionally, the creation and application of these diagnoses result in their reification: although these diagnoses are conceptual abstractions, they have come to garner status as "things." Because contested illnesses include many common symptoms and provide no exclusionary criteria, sufferers can readily see the parallels between their own illness experience and the illness experience of fellow sufferers. Not only are contested illnesses interactive kinds of things in terms of how the designation interacts with the individual so designated, but their interactive quality also creates a cultural milieu wherein even more individuals, through their brief or extensive encounters with illness support communities, come to locate themselves within these designations.

Finally, organizational imperatives and dynamics also critically influence "the type and amount of conditions discovered" (Brown 1995, 45). Patients with unexplainable symptoms can be very costly. Although managed-care organizations erect barriers to limit health-care utilization, these barriers force patients to "express their 'disease' in more urgent and exaggerated terms in order to gain access to the physician" (Barsky and Borus 1995, 1931) Additionally, health-care providers use these diagnoses to help patients gain access to health-care resources within the constraints of managed care. Curiously, a case can also be made that these diagnoses might, in the end, work to the financial advantage of managed-care organizations. When patients with medically unexplainable symptoms are diagnosed with a contested illness in its early stages, health-care costs are reduced by limiting the number of expensive diagnostic tests, referrals to specialists, and surgical procedures that otherwise characterize the contested-illness experience. Because the standard treatment protocol is often relatively inexpensive (e.g., pain, sleep, and antidepressant medications, as well as behavioral and exercise therapies), managed-care organizations may use contested-illness diagnoses as part of their agenda for cost containment.

In sum, contested illnesses reveal the conceptual union between social constructionism and medicalization. Specifically, contested illnesses are social constructions that give biomedical meaning to a broad range of distress and suffering that characterize the lives of many individuals, especially women. The contested status of these diagnoses, however, signifies only partial medicalization. Whereas advocates for contested illnesses demand greater medicalization as a route to legitimate the sufferer and secure necessary health and welfare reparations, critics hope to stem the medicalization tide to which these diagnoses contribute (Conrad and Stults 2008). There are two obvious paths toward increasing the degree to which contested illnesses are medicalized. The first includes identifying biological markers upon which the "social legitimacy and intellectual plausibility of contemporary disease categorizations often hinge" (Shostak, Conrad, and Horwitz 2008, 310). For example, recent reports of potential genetic variations associated with restless leg syndrome bode well for this condition's further medicalization (Shostak, Conrad, and Horwitz 2008). The second path includes a specific treatment option. Based on my current research, for example, sufferers and their clinician-advocates have enthusiastically embraced the recent FDA approval of the first drug specifically for the treatment of fibromyalgia syndrome, more for the drug's disease-legitimating potential than for its therapeutic efficacy.

It is worth restating what it means to call contested illnesses socially constructed. As they currently exist, these diagnoses are best understood as intellectual categories whose social etiological is more clearly understood than is their biomedical etiology. The diagnostic criteria for these illnesses are descriptive, subjectively determined, and inexactly and inconsistently applied. The creation of these diagnostic categories has more to do with the social dictates of clinical encounters, the influence of illness communities, and institutional demands than with scientific or medical discoveries. Contested illnesses are very large conceptual tents under which many dissimilar types of symptoms and distress can be located. What is more, these types of symptoms and distress are widespread in general, and particularly common among women.

Calling these syndromes socially constructed, however, does not deny the reality of their symptoms. It is clear that the suffering of those so diagnosed is real: their quality of life is significantly eroded and they would do almost anything to be well (Asbring and Narvanen 2001; Bülow 2008; Kroll-Smith and

Floyd 1997). Although the diagnostic labels are social constructions, they might, in fact, represent a number of things that have biomedical correlates that are currently unknown. The socially constructed meanings that mediate our experience of a disorder or condition can be overly simplistic, imperfect, or vague, but that does not mean that the symptoms that comprise the disorder have no biological basis or that they would cease to exist in the absence of a specific diagnosis. Instead, as Hacking has claimed, things can be *both* socially constructed *and* real; this may, in fact, prove to be the case with one or more contested illnesses.

Conclusion

All illnesses, not just those that are contested, are in some general sense socially constructed. Without exception, the meaning and experience of all illness is innately social. In this regard we can speak of the social construction of epilepsy. To be sure, the seizures are real. At the same time, however, the meaning of the seizures (possession vs. disease) and their experience (stigmatized vs. medicalized) is socially contingent. This chapter has emphasized the social construction of illness in a more limited or restricted sense, focusing on the social creation of new biomedical diagnostic categories for human experiences that do not lend themselves to such categorization, with contested illnesses as a case in point. A restricted definition of the social construction of illness gives medical sociologists a powerful expository tool for charting the concrete social forces that promote medicalization. Insofar as lay people, not the medical profession, demand the medicalization of contested illnesses, the creation of contested-illness categories is paradigmatic of the shifting engines of medicalization (Conrad 2005).

It is important to put the social construction of contested illnesses into larger perspective. Many widely accepted disorders are also characterized by uncertainties. Many uncontested conditions lack diagnostic precision or are difficult to diagnose (e.g., asthma, osteoarthritis, rheumatoid arthritis); the causal mechanisms of some illnesses are poorly understood or unknown (e.g., lupus, multiple sclerosis, scoliosis, allergies); and many conditions respond poorly or only marginally to medical therapeutics (e.g., Alzheimer's disease, pancreatic cancer). None of these disorders are discredited as biologically unreal on such grounds. Some of these conditions can hardly be in doubt, given that they dramatically and unambiguously manifest themselves in bodily disfigurement or death. But others are neither disfiguring nor deadly. In short, imperfect medical knowledge is ubiquitous to contemporary biomedicine.

One might argue that contested illnesses are but exaggerated or extreme cases of contemporary medicine's inevitable encounter with uncertainty. To a large degree, this can be attributed to the intrinsic difficulties many chronic conditions pose to conventional biomedicine, which proved far more effective in slaying our earlier infectious enemies. But biomedical uncertainty alone is an insufficient explanation. Biomedicine's lack of certitude about contemporary illnesses is also the result of its dealings with an ever-expanding range of complex human distresses. Uncertainty grows as patients and clinicians alike seek to frame multifaceted forms of human suffering within the confines of the conventional biomedical model. That is, uncertainty grows as we push for greater medicalization. Most of us live or will live with a number of long-term afflictions that are medically diffuse and elusive but that nevertheless, negatively and very tangibly, impact the quality of our lives. The creation of contested-illness diagnoses puts into sharp relief our sociocultural response to this larger dilemma, suggesting that we either come to acknowledge and address the normalization of suffering, or expect to see the creation of many new contested-illness diagnoses in the future.

Notes

1. Some of the material in this chapter appears in Barker 2002, 2005, and 2008.

2. Brown (1995, 34–35) suggests that there are three versions of social constructionism in medical sociology. The first emerges from social problems scholarship that addresses the contingent processes by which specific phenomena come to be identified as social problems. The second version draws on the Focauldian tradition and emphasizes how medical knowledge and discourse give meaning to illness. The third version, aligned with the interdisciplinary field of science studies, argues that the production of scientific facts emerges from everyday social actions and interactions in clinical settings.

3. Given the definition of contested illness, it is possible to consider post-traumatic stress disorder (PTSD) and attention deficit hyperactivity disorder (ADHD) under the rubric of contested illnesses. More generally, many mental illnesses are contested, since sufferers and advocates claim the existence of a biophysical basis for these conditions that is not currently acknowledged by medical experts. In this chapter, contested illnesses are limited to the overlapping conditions referred to as "functional" in the medical literature.

4. The campaign behind chronic fatigue syndrome originated with the claims of two physicians in Lake Tahoe concerning a link between mysterious symptoms and the Epstein-Barr virus. The subsequent path to medicalize CFS, however, was heavily lay forged (Aronowitz 1997; Showalter 1997). Along with other contested environmental illnesses, the emergence of multiple chemical sensitivity disorder also relied overwhelmingly on lay advocacy. The legitimacy of contested environmental illnesses has been further hindered (or at least not advanced) by their association with health professionals practicing in specialties that the American Medical Association does not recognize (e.g., clinical ecology and environmental medicine).

References

Adler, Patricia A., and Peter Adler. 2007. "The Demedicalization of Self-Injury: From Psychopathology to Sociological Deviance." *Journal of Contemporary Ethnography* 36:537–70.

Angell, Marcia. 2004. *The Truth about the Drug Companies.* New York: Random House.

Aronowitz, Robert. 1997. "From Myalgic Encephalitis to Yuppie Flu: A History of Chronic Fatigue Syndrome." In *Framing Disease*, ed. Charles Rosenberg and Janet Golden, 155–81. New Brunswick, N.J.: Rutgers University Press.

Asbring, Pia, and Anna-Liisa Narvanen. 2001. "Chronic Illness—A Disruption in Life: Identity-Transformation among Women with Chronic Fatigue Syndrome and Fibromyalgia." *Journal of Advanced Nursing* 34:312–19.

———. 2003. "Ideal versus Reality: Physicians' Perspectives on Patients with Chronic Fatigue Syndrome (CFS) and Fibromyalgia." *Social Science and Medicine* 57:711–20.

Balint, Michael. 1957. *The Doctor, His Patient and the Illness.* New York: International Universities Press.

Banks, Jonathan, and Lindsay Prior. 2001. "Doing Things with Illness: The Micro Politics of the CFS Clinic." *Social Science and Medicine* 52:11–23.

Barker, Kristin. 1998. "A Ship upon a Stormy Sea: The Medicalization of Pregnancy." *Social Science and Medicine* 47:1067–76.

———. 2002. "Self-Help Literature and the Making of an Illness Identity: The Case of Fibromyalgia Syndrome." *Social Problems* 49:279–300.

———. 2005. *The Fibromyalgia Story: Medical Authority and Women's Worlds of Pain.* Philadelphia: Temple University Press.

———. 2008. "Electronic Support Groups, Patient-Consumers, and Medicalization: The Case of Contested Illness." *Journal of Health and Social Behavior* 49:20–36.

Barsky, Arthur, and Jonathan Borus. 1995. "Somatization and Medicalization in the Era of Managed Care." *Journal of the American Medical Association* 274:1931–34.

———. 1999. "Functional Somatic Syndromes." *Annals of Internal Medicine* 130:910–21.

Berger, Peter, and Thomas Luckmann. 1967. *The Social Construction of Reality: A Treatise in the Sociology of Knowledge.* New York: Anchor.

Blum, Virginia. 2003. *Flesh Wounds: The Culture of Cosmetic Surgery.* Berkeley: University of California Press.

Boghossian, Paul. 2001. "What Is Social Construction?" *Times Literary Supplement*, February.

———. 2006. *Fear of Knowledge: Against Relativism and Constuctivism.* New York: Oxford University Press.

Bohr, T. W. 1995. "Fibromyalgia Syndrome and Myofascial Pain Syndrome: Do They Exist?" *Neurologic Clinics* 13:365–84.

Brown, Phil. 1995. "Naming and Framing: The Social Construction of Diagnosis and Illness." *Journal of Health and Social Behavior*, extra issue: 34–52.

———. 2007. *Toxic Exposures: Contested Illnesses and the Environmental Health Movement.* New York: Columbia University Press.

Brown, Phil, Stephen Zavestoski, Sabrina McCormick, Brian Mayer, Rachel Morello-Frosch, and Rebecca Gesior Altman. 2004. "Embodied Health Movements: New Approaches to Social Movements in Health." *Sociology of Health and Illness* 26:50–80.

Brumberg, Joan Jacobs. 2009. "Anorexia Nervosa in Context." In *The Sociology of Health and Illness: Critical Perspectives*, 8th ed., ed. Peter Conrad, 107–20. New York: Worth.

Bülow, Pia H. 2008. "Tracing Contours of Contestation in Narratives about Chronic Fatigue Syndrome." In *Contesting Illness: Processes and Practices*, ed. Pamela Moss and Katherine Teghtsoonian, 123–41. Toronto: University of Toronto Press.

Cable, Sherry, Tamara L. Mix, and Thomas E. Shriver. 2008. "Risk Society and Contested Illness: The Case of Nuclear Weapons Workers." *American Sociological Review* 73:380–401.

Casiday, Rachel Elizabeth. 2007. "Children's Health and the Social Theory of Risk: Insights from the British Measles, Mumps and Rubella (MMR) Controversy." *Social Science and Medicine* 65:1059–70.

Clarke, Adele, Laura Mamo, Jennifer R. Fishman, Janet K. Shim, and Jennifer Ruth Fosket. 2003. "Biomedicalization: Technoscientific Transformations of Health, Illness, and U.S. Biomedicine." *American Sociological Review* 68:161–94.

Collins, Patricia Hill. 1991. *Black Feminist Thought: Knowledge, Consciousness, and the Politics of Empowerment.* New York: Routledge.

Copeland, D. A. and Valle, G. 2009. "You Don't Need a Prescription to Go Gluten-Free": The Scientific Self-Diagnosis of Celiac Disease. *Social Science and Medicine* 69:623–31.

Conrad, Peter. 2007. *The Medicalization of Society: On the Transformation of Human Conditions into Treatable Disorders.* Baltimore: Johns Hopkins University Press.

———. 2005. "The Shifting Engines of Medicalization." *Journal of Health and Social Behavior* 46:3–14. Conrad, Peter, and Joseph W. Schneider. 1992. *Deviance and Medicalization: From Badness to Sickness.* Philadelphia: Temple University Press.

Conrad, Peter, and Cheryl Stults. 2008. "Contestation and Medicalization." In *Contesting Illness: Processes and Practices*, ed. Pamela Moss and Katherine Teghtsoonian, 323–35. Toronto: University of Toronto Press.

da Silva, Luiz Claudio. 2004. "Fibromyalgia: Reflections about Empirical Science and Faith." *Journal of Rheumatology* 31:827–28.

de Beauvoir, Simone. 1989 [1953]. *The Second Sex.* Translated by H. M. Parshley. New York: Knopf.

Dumit, Joseph. 2006. "Illnesses You Have to Fight to Get: Facts and Forces in Uncertain, Emergent Illnesses." *Social Science and Medicine* 62:577–90.

Ehrenreich, Barbara, and Deirdre English. 1973. *Complaints and Disorders: The Sexual Politics of Sickness.* New York: Feminist Press.

Epstein, Steven. 1996. *Impure Science: AIDS, Activism, and the Politics of Knowledge.* Berkeley: University of California Press.

Fillingim, Roger. 2000. *Sex, Gender, and Pain.* Seattle, Wash.: IASP Press.

Fox, Susannah, and Deborah Fallows. 2003. Internet Health Resources. Pew Internet and American Life Project. www.pewinternet.org. Accessed November 26, 2005.

Freidson, Eliot. 1970. *Profession of Medicine: A Study of the Sociology of Applied Knowledge.* New York: Harper and Row.

Hacking, Ian. 1998. *Mad Travelers: Reflections on the Reality of Transient Mental Illnesses*. Charlottesville: University of Virginia Press.

———. 1999. *The Social Construction of What?* Cambridge, Mass.: Harvard University Press.

Hadler, N. M. 1997a. "Fibromyalgia, Chronic Fatigue, and Other Iatrogenic Diagnostic Algorithms. Do Some Labels Escalate Illness in Vulnerable Patients?" *Postgraduate Medicine* 102:262–77.

———. 1997b. "La Maladie Est Morte, Vive le Malade." *Journal of Rheumatology* 24:1250–51.

Hayden, Lars-Christer, and Lisbeth Sacks. 1998. "Suffering, Hope and Diagnosis: On Negotiation of Chronic Fatigue Syndrome." *Health* 2:175–93.

Henningsen, P., S. Zipfel, and W. Herzog. 2007. "Management of Functional Somatic Syndromes." *Lancet* 369:946–55.

Horwitz, Allan V. 2002. *Creating Mental Illness*. Chicago: University of Chicago Press.

Illich, Ivan. 1976. *Medical Nemesis: The Expropriation of Health*. New York: Pantheon.

Kleinman, Arthur. 1988. *The Illness Narratives: Suffering, Healing and the Human Condition*. New York: Basic Books.

Kleinman, Arthur, and Norma C. Ware. 1992. "Culture and Somatic Experience: The Social Course of Illness in Neurasthenia and Chronic Fatigue Syndrome." *Psychosomatic Medicine* 54:546–60.

Knorr Cetina, Karin. 1997. "Sociality with Objects: Social Relations in Postsocial Knowledge Societies." *Theory, Culture and Society* 14:1–30.

Koziol, J. A., D. C. Clark, R. F. Gittes, and E. M. Tan. 1993. "The Natural History of Interstitial Cystitis: A Survey of 374 Patients." *Journal of Urology* 149(3): 465–69.

Kroll-Smith, Steve, Phil Brown, and Valerie J. Gunter. 2000. *Illness and the Environment: A Reader in Contested Medicine*. New York: New York University Press.

Kroll-Smith, Steve, and H. Hugh Floyd. 1997. *Bodies in Protest: Environmental Illness and the Struggle over Medical Knowledge*. New York: New York University Press.

Latour, Bruno. 1987. *Science in Action: How to Follow Scientists and Engineers through Society*. Cambridge, Mass.: Harvard University Press.

Lorber, Judith, and Lisa Jean Moore. 2002. *Gender and the Social Construction of Illness*. 2nd ed. Lanham, Md.: Rowman Altamira.

———. 2007. *Gendered Bodies: Feminist Perspectives*. Los Angeles: Roxbury Publishing.

Mannheim, Karl. 1936. *Ideology and Utopia*. New York: Harcourt, Brace.

Manu, Peter. 2004. *The Psychopathology of Functional Somatic Syndromes*. New York: Haworth Medical Press.

Martin, Emily. 1987. *The Woman in the Body: A Cultural Analysis of Reproduction*. Boston: Beacon Press.

Mayou, Richard, and Andrew Farmer. 2002. "Functional Somatic Symptoms and Syndromes." *British Medical Journal* 325:265–68.

McCrea, Frances. 1983. "The Politics of Menopause: The 'Discovery' of a Deficiency Disease." *Social Problems* 31:111–23.

Merton, Robert. 1973. *The Sociology of Science: Theory and Empirical Investigations*. Chicago: Chicago University Press.

Moss, Pamela, and Katherine Teghtsoonian. 2008. "Power and Illness: Authority, Bodies, and Context." In *Contesting Illness*, ed. Pamela Moss and Katherine Teghtsoonian, 3–27. Toronto: University of Toronto Press.

Moynihan, R., I. Heath, and D. Henry. 2002. "Selling Sickness: The Pharmaceutical Industry and Disease Mongering." *British Medical Journal* 324:886–91.

Nimnuan, Chaichana, Sophia Rabe-Hesketh, Simon Wessley, and Matthew Hotopf. 2001. "How Many Functional Somatic Syndromes." *Journal of Psychosomatic Research* 51:549–57.

Parsons, Talcott. 1951. *The Social System*. Glencoe, Ill.: Free Press.

Pascoe, C. J., and Natalie Boero. 2008. *No Wannarexics Allowed: An Analysis of Pro-Eating Disorder Online Communities*. Typescript.

Peitzman, Steven J. 1992. "From Bright's Disease to End-Stage Renal Disease." In *Framing Disease: Studies in Cultural History*, ed. Charles Rosenberg and Janet Golden, 3–19. New Brunswick, N.J.: Rutgers University Press.

Riessman, Catherine. 1983. "Women and Medicalization: A New Perspective." *Social Policy* 14:3–18.

Searle, John R. 1995. *The Construction of Social Reality*. New York: Free Press.

Shostak, Sara, Peter Conrad, and Allan Horwitz. 2008. "Sequencing and Its Consequences: Path Dependency and the Relationships between Genetics and Medicalization." *American Journal of Sociology* 114:287–316.

Showalter, Elaine. 1997. *Hystories: Hysterical Epidemics and Modern Media*. New York: Columbia University Press.

Skolbekken, John-Arne. 2008. "Unlimited Medicalization? Risk and the Pathologization of Normality." In *Health Risk and Vulnerability*, ed. Ian Wilkinson, 16–29. New York: Routledge.

Slezak, Peter. 2000. "A Critique of Radical Social Constructionism." In *Constructivism in Education: Opinions and Second Opinions on Controversial Issues*, ed. D. C. Philips, 91–126. Chicago: University of Chicago Press.

Smith, Dorothy. 1987. *The Everyday World as Problematic: A Feminist Sociology*. Boston: Northeastern University Press.

Sokal, Alan. 1996. "Transgressing the Boundaries: Towards a Transformative Hermeneutics of Quantum Gravity." *Social Text* 46/47:217–52.

Starr, Paul. 1982. *The Social Transformation of American Medicine*. New York: Basic Books.

Tesh, Sylvia Noble. 1988. *Hidden Arguments: Political Ideology and Disease Prevention Policy*. New Brunswick, N.J.: Rutgers University Press.

Theriot, Nancy. 1993. "Women's Voices in Nineteenth-Century Medical Discourse: A Step toward Deconstructing Science." *Signs* 19:1–31.

Timmerman, Stefan. 2007. *Postmortem: How Medical Examiners Explain Suspicious Deaths (Fieldwork and Discoveries)*. Chicago: University of Chicago Press.

Tomes, Nancy. 1998. *The Gospel of Germs: Men, Women, and the Microbe in American Life*. Cambridge, Mass.: Harvard University Press.

Wertz, Richard, and Dorothy Wertz. 1979. *Lying-In: A History of Childbirth in America*. New York: Schocken.

Wessley, S. 2004. "There Is Only One Functional Somatic Syndrome: For." *British Journal of Psychiatry* 185:95–96.

Wessley, S., C. Nimnuan, and M. Sharpe. 1999. "Functional Somatic Syndromes: One or Many?" *Lancet* 354:936–39.

Young, Allan. 1995. *The Harmony of Illusions: Inventing Post-Traumatic Stress Disorder.* Princeton, N.J.: Princeton University Press.

Zavestoski, Stephen, Phil Brown, Sabrina McCormick, Brian Mayer, Maryhelen D'Ottavi, and Jamie C. Lucove. 2004a. "Embodied Health Movements and Challenges to the Dominant Epidemiological Paradigm." *Research in Social Movements, Conflicts and Change* 25:253–78.

———. 2004b. "Patient Activism and the Struggle for Diagnosis: Gulf War Illnesses and Other Medically Unexplained Physical Symptoms in the U.S." *Social Science and Medicine* 58:161–75.

Zola, Irving Kenneth. 1972. "Medicine as an Institution of Social Control." *Sociological Review* 20:487–504.

CRITICAL THINKING QUESTIONS

1. Define and discuss the social constructionist perspective in medical sociology. What are the benefits and limitations of this perspective? Please provide clear examples and make sure to define pertinent terms.

2. The Meikirch model definition of health is "a state of wellbeing emergent from conducive interactions between individuals' potentials, life's demands, and social and environmental determinants." Read Burcher and Kuruvilla's article carefully and apply its concepts to your own lived experience. Identify, define, and give examples of the following:

    a. the three main constituents of health

    b. the three main types of life demands

    c. the two main potentials upon which individuals draw

    d. social determinants of health

    e. environmental determinants of health

3. Each author in unit I discusses the ways in which health is a social concept in addition to a biological or medical concept. Identify and provide examples of the social perspective(s) in each reading as they situate the meanings of the social within medical sociology. Why is it important to address the social aspects of health and illness?

UNIT 2
Culture in Health and Medicine

....

Editor's Introduction

The goal of unit 2 is to illustrate the variety of ways culture can impact people's health and even the institutions developed to address health. **Culture** is the language, beliefs, values, norms, behaviors, and material objects that are passed from one generation to the next. Culture provides a lens through which we perceive our world and which varies from place to place. Often, we are not even aware that culture is impacting our perceptions, yet it impacts virtually everything we encounter and participate in. Think about the times you have taken an elevator. You probably pushed the call button and stared at the door until the elevator arrived. Once inside, you probably pushed the button of the floor you wanted and, again, stared at the door until your floor was reached. If others were involved, they and you probably did everything possible to minimize interaction with one another. At the time, you may not have been aware you were engaging in what I term "American elevator culture," which is so strongly felt that interactions with others in the same space might feel awkward or uncomfortable. This awkwardness or discomfort illustrate an aspect of culture we often do not think about—namely, the consequences one experiences for not following cultural etiquette. In fact, you can gauge the strength of a cultural norm according to the sanctions received for violating it. These sanctions can vary from mild discomfort to the death penalty for being convicted of a serious crime.

In "Health Care as a Reflection of Underlying Cultural Values and Institutions," Donald A. Barr proposes that, to understand a healthcare delivery system, we must investigate the norms and values from which that system arises. The author uncovers cultural values that contributed to the development of the American and Canadian healthcare systems.

culture: the language, beliefs, values, norms, behaviors, and material objects that are passed from one generation to the next.

While the United States holds primary the rights of individuals, Canada holds primary that which is for the common good. These values have resulted in quite different healthcare systems in the two countries. The article details how these systems were developed. Then, Barr goes on to demonstrate how the different values of the United States and Canada, expressed through healthcare systems, result in different outcomes for doctors and patients and even different healthcare costs. Comparing and contrasting is a critical method that helps researchers to, among other things, unveil the values and beliefs underlying large social structures.

In "The Medicalized Society," Carl Boggs utilizes the conflict perspective to analyze inequalities in the US healthcare system and illustrates their consequences with a strong discussion of the dynamics of the pharmaceutical industry in healthcare. The conflict perspective is born of the work of Karl Marx, who focused on the conflicts between the *bourgeoise*, or those who own the means of production, and the *proletariat*, or those who are a key part of the means of production. In the conflict perspective, society is comprised of groups competing for scarce resources—in this case, the means to live a healthy and meaningful life. **Power**, or the ability to realize one's will despite resistance, is a key concept in critical sociology. Boggs proposes that people experience *alienation* because of the largely meaningless, consumerist, globalizing, and fragmented lives marketed to us by mammoth multinational corporations, which promise "quick fixes" for everything, medicalizing the health problems that arise from these very living conditions. These quick fixes do little to address the underlying problems causing disease and increasingly result in *iatrogenesis*, or medical harm to patients.

Boggs also utilizes the perspective and tools of *symbolic interactionism* to question the meaning of the language we use related to health and illness. For symbolic interactionists, definitions of health and illness are culturally influenced, not biologically fixed. Symbolic interactionism views symbols, things to which we attach meaning, as the basis of social life. Using symbols, people can define relationships to others and coordinate actions with others, thereby making social life possible. People also use symbols to develop a sense of who and what they are. When we define certain things as *illness*, *disease*, or *drug addiction*, the meanings we attach to these terms have consequences for the people wearing the labels. Boggs does a beautiful job of positioning these types of terms in

power: the ability to exercise one's will despite resistance.

their cultural milieu so that we come away asking, "What are we *really* talking about when we use these words?" Use of such meaning-laden language puts Boggs's earlier discussion of the alienation people experience in the face of modernity into stark perspective.

In "The Wrong Side of the River," Ronald L. Barrett investigates the stigma experienced by those with leprosy, or Hansen's disease, in India where the condition is highly stigmatized—so much so that the stigma is a significant barrier to treatment and cure for many with the disease. Barrett's investigations take him to Kusht Seva Ashram, where there is a clinic for treating Hansen's disease using modified Ayurvedic medicines. The aim of his study is to illuminate the ways stigma interacts with the occurrence of Hansen's disease throughout its progression. To do this, Boggs interviews people with Hansen's disease at the ashram and observes their treatment and interactions over the course of time. The concept of *stigma* was highly developed by Irving Goffman, a sociologist in the symbolic interactionist tradition, and Boggs does an excellent job of unpacking the many ways that the stigma of Hansen's disease in India is so severe that its effects are lifelong and impact not only those infected but also those who are close to them.

Together, these articles illustrate a variety of cultural variables that impact health and the systems developed to address health. They show that cultural institutions in their political, religious, labor, and economic forms significantly impact not only the formation of healthcare systems but also have real consequences for people experiencing health and illness.

Health Care as a Reflection of Underlying Cultural Values and Institutions

By Donald A. Barr

The Cultural Basis of Health Care: Comparing the United States and Canada

In 1932, Walton H. Hamilton wrote that "the organization of medicine is not a thing apart which can be subjected to study in isolation. It is an aspect of culture, whose arrangements are inseparable from the general organization of society" (Hamilton 1932, p. 190). Hamilton was responding to the Report of the Committee on the Costs of Medical Care. [...] This statement, made more than eighty years ago, still rings true in our examination of health care in the United States in the twenty-first century. To understand a nation's health care system, we must first understand the social and cultural norms and values around which that nation is organized.

To appreciate fully how the health care system in the United States reflects our unique American value system, we will first look to our neighbors to the north. Using Canada and its health care system as a mirror, we will see how differences in the organization of health care in our two countries reflect differences in the basic institutions around which our systems are organized.

It is important to recall that the American Revolution involved fourteen colonies, not just the thirteen that eventually became the United States. In some of the earliest fighting of the war, revolutionary armies captured Montreal and laid siege to Quebec. This revolutionary activity was short-lived, however, and what is now Canada remained under British rule. For many in the "fourteenth" colony of Canada, life after the Revolution seemed more attractive south of the border in the newly independent colonies. Many of those in Canada who supported the Revolution migrated south. Similarly, loyalists living in the successful, now-independent thirteen colonies thought life would be better either north of the border in Canada or back in England. Thus, in the aftermath of the American Revolution, there was a cultural migration, with those supporting the British Crown moving north and those in Canada supporting "life, liberty, and the pursuit of happiness" moving south.

Donald A. Barr, "Health Care as a Reflection of Underlying Cultural Values and Institutions," *Introduction to US Health Policy: The Organization, Financing, and Delivery of Health Care in America*, pp. 42–80, 399–426. Copyright © 2016 by Johns Hopkins University Press. Reprinted with permission.

Lipset (1990) summarized the fundamental similarities and differences between US and Canadian societies. Speaking of the cultural differences that arose from the time of the American Revolution, he reminds us that "the very organizing principles that frame these nations, the central cores around which institutions and events were to accommodate, were different. One was Whig and classically liberal or libertarian—doctrines that emphasize distrust of the state, egalitarianism, and populism. ... The other was Tory and conservative in the British and European sense—accepting of the need for a strong state, for respect for authority, for deference" (p. 2).

In the United States, schoolchildren study the Declaration of Independence and learn that our society continues to be organized around the principles of "life, liberty, and the pursuit of happiness." Canadian children also learn about the founding principles of their country. In the British North America Act, the act that created the Dominion of Canada, they find that the role of the Canadian government is to assure "peace, order, and good government." Lipset (1990) described the fundamental differences between these two founding documents: "The Canadian Charter of Rights and Freedoms is not the American Bill of Rights. It preserves the principle of parliamentary supremacy and places less emphasis on individual, as distinct from group, rights than does the American document" (p. 3).

Since the American Revolution, the United States has been a country that puts primacy on the rights of individuals. Social justice is most often defined in terms of the individual. In the United States, conflicts between individual needs and group needs tend to be resolved in favor of the individual. Canada, on the other hand, has a strong social democratic tradition, a tradition of redistribution so as to maximize the common good. Canadians have come to accept and expect social policies that embody this individual-group relationship. In Canada, conflicts between individual rights and group rights tend to be resolved in favor of the common good. Table 2.1.1 summarizes these differences between US and Canadian societies. To see how these cultural differences are reflected in our health care systems, we first examine the history of Canadian health care, followed by a parallel examination of the history of US health care.

TABLE 2.1.1 Cultural Differences between the United States and Canada

United States	Canada
Distrust of central government	Accept the need for strong central government
"Life, liberty, and the pursuit of happiness"	"Peace, order, and good government"
Justice often defined in terms of what is good for the individual	Justice often defined to maximize the common good

The History of Medical Care in Canada

The British North America Act of 1867 created the Dominion of Canada. In it, responsibility for managing the delivery of health care was explicitly vested in the provinces rather than the central government. This separation of powers for health care issues remains in place today.

Canada took a serious look at establishing a national system of health care following World War I. At that time, several provinces granted statutory authority for municipalities to become directly involved in the provision of medical care. During the period of the Depression, these **"municipal doctor" plans**, in which local governments hired physicians to provide care to area residents, became an increasingly important source of medical care. This was especially true in the rural, agricultural provinces (Meilicke and Storch 1980).

In 1943, the report of a governmental Economic Advisory Committee recommended that a national program of medical insurance be established. It was to have been part of a larger social insurance program also covering unemployment insurance and old age security. Despite the support of both the Canadian Medical Association and the Canadian Hospital Council, the program did not become law, the result principally of the failure to achieve a financing mechanism that adequately preserved perceptions of provincial autonomy.

As a largely rural province with a widely scattered population especially hard hit by the Depression, Saskatchewan faced a particularly pressing need for governmental support of medical care. In 1944, Saskatchewan elected a populist government by giving a large legislative majority to the Cooperative Commonwealth Federation (CCF). In the face of the earlier defeat of the proposed national health care program, one of the first priorities for the CCF in Saskatchewan was to bring provincial government support to the financing of hospital care. **The Saskatchewan Hospital Services Plan** was passed in 1946, establishing a universal, compulsory hospital care insurance system. The program did not cover physicians' fees.

Despite increased rates of hospital use and costs in excess of initial estimates, the Saskatchewan plan maintained popular support. By 1950, three other provinces had established similar hospital insurance programs. It was only a matter of time before the others would follow. In 1957, the federal government of Canada adopted the **Hospital Insurance**

EDITOR'S NOTES

municipal doctor plans: a system developed in Canada during the Great Depression in which local governments hired physicians to provide care to local residents.

EDITOR'S NOTES

The Saskatchewan Hospital Services Plan: a compulsory hospital care insurance program passed by the Cooperative Commonwealth Federation (CCF) in Saskatchewan Canada, passed in 1946.

in consideration of
the popularity and adaptation of the Saskatchewan
Hospital Services Act, the
federal government of Canada established this national
program of universal, compulsory hospital insurance
in 1957.

---

concept 2.1.1

A **monopsony** is an economic
system that has a single payer for
a set of goods or services. The
Canadian health care system is
an example of a government monopsony in health care, sometimes
called a "single-payer" system.

---

monopsony: an economic
system that has a single
payer for a set of goods or
services. The Canadian
healthcare system is an
example of a government
monopsony in health care,
sometimes called a "single-
payer" system.

---

and Diagnostic Services Act, establishing a national program of universal, compulsory hospital insurance, based on the Saskatchewan model.
The program established three important principles:

1. Shared financing between the federal and the provincial governments that partially compensated for economic inequities between
   provinces

2. Provincial administration of the plan

3. Federally established minimum standards of participation

Saskatchewan, having previously financed hospital care solely from
provincial funds, again took action that was to have national impact.
The sudden addition of federal hospital funds enabled the CCF
government to extend their medical insurance program to include
physician care. In 1962, the province established the Saskatchewan
Medical Care Insurance Plan, creating a universal, compulsory medical
care system, with the provincial government maintaining a monopsony
over the purchase of all medical care. (While a monopoly is an economic system with only one provider of a good, a monopsony is a
system with a single payer for a good.) The plan was financed by a
compulsory enrollment premium for all provincial residents. It
maintained the fee-for-service method of paying physicians but
established the principle that physicians must accept payment from
the plan as payment in full (i.e., the physician was not allowed to bill
the patient for any additional amount).

The concept of government monopsony was stridently opposed by
the Canadian Medical Association, its Saskatchewan division, and the
American Medical Association (AMA) south of the border. (The role
of the AMA in actively opposing national health insurance in Canada
is seldom fully appreciated.) Nonetheless, the Saskatchewan plan was
enacted despite the objections of the medical profession.

On July 1, 1962, physicians in the Saskatchewan Medical Association went on strike, refusing to participate in the plan. Leaders of the
association contended that "the preservation of the basic freedoms and
democratic rights of the individual is necessary to insure medical services
to the people of Saskatchewan" (Taylor 1987, p. 278). Saskatchewan
physicians were seen as the shock troops of the medical profession,

fighting the battle against governmentally imposed medical insurance on behalf of the entire Canadian medical profession. They received strong support from the AMA in the United States, which was adamantly opposed to the plan. The AMA attempted to convey a sense of crisis to the physicians and public in Saskatchewan.

While there was some support for the strike within Saskatchewan, it received little backing from the rest of Canada. To many people, the striking physicians were seen not as altruistic professionals but as lawbreakers. By July 23, a little more than three weeks after the strike had begun, the medical profession and the government reached a compromise, and the strike was called off. The Saskatchewan Agreement created a role for private insurance companies as fiscal intermediaries, allowing physicians to bill an insurance company for their services with the insurance company being reimbursed by the government. In return, physicians agreed to accept plan payment as payment in full. In addition, the Saskatchewan government promised not to establish a salaried government medical service.

In 1964, the Royal Commission on Health Services, established by the federal government to study the issue of national health insurance, recommended that Canada set up a national program of medical care similar to Saskatchewan's. The commission's goal was to make care "available to all our residents without hindrance of any kind" (Royal Commission on Health Services 1964, p. 10). It proposed federal financial assistance for provincially administered programs. Initial response to the report was mixed. Several provinces opposed further extension of government authority over health care, supporting instead a market-based program of insurance subsidies for low-income individuals and families, as had been proposed by the Canadian Medical Association.

The Liberal Party in Canada had first made a commitment to a program of national health insurance as early as 1919. In 1965, the Liberals came to power on a widely supported platform that included establishing a national system of medical care. Under the leadership of Lester Pearson, the party pushed for such a program. In contrast to the legislative system in the United States, in a parliamentary government such as Canada's the prime minister is able to exert considerable influence over the legislative process. Pearson pursued and, despite the opposition of several provinces, in December 1966 achieved passage of the national Medicare program. Provincial participation was to be voluntary; participation, if adopted by the provinces, would result in federal payment of approximately one-half of the cost of the program. For a provincial program to qualify, it had to be comprehensive, universal, publicly administered, and portable across provinces. (A fifth principle of accessibility was added later.)

The Canadian Medicare program went into effect in 1968. The lure of a 50 percent federal cost subsidy proved to be powerful. By 1971, all ten provinces had qualifying programs, creating on a national scale the same government monopsony over the purchase of medical care that had been established in Saskatchewan. Over a period of three years, and with widespread popular support, the private market for medical insurance in Canada was effectively eliminated.

The Canadian Medicare program did not adopt a specific model for the organization or delivery of care. It was solely a financing mechanism, leaving the delivery of care to physicians and the provinces. The federal government simply agreed to reimburse 50 percent of the cost of care to any province that created a plan meeting the guiding principles. In this regard, despite some who characterize the system incorrectly, Canada does not have a system of socialized medicine. Socialized medicine involves direct government involvement in the actual provision of care through policies such as the ownership of hospitals or the employment of physicians. Hospitals in Canada are mostly privately owned. Most physicians in Canada are private, independent practitioners.

When Canadian Medicare was passed by Parliament, physicians in the province of Quebec went on strike in opposition to the plan. In Quebec, there were two separate provincial medical associations: one for general practitioners and one for specialists. The association of specialists wanted their members to be able to opt out of the plan on a case-by-case basis, billing patients directly and allowing patients to seek reimbursement from Medicare. (Those familiar with the Medicare program in the United States, [...] will note that the payment mechanism sought by the specialists in Quebec was precisely the mechanism adopted by the US program only a few years earlier. The influence of the AMA on Canadian physicians' opposition to Canadian Medicare is clear.)

The specialists in Quebec voted to strike rather than participate in Medicare. In early October 1970, they held a large rally in opposition to the plan. The leaders of the specialists spoke at that rally and criticized Medicare as a "threat to liberty, freedom, and quality of care" (Taylor 1987, p. 404). The executive vice president of the AMA traveled north to speak at this rally. He supported the strike and assured any specialists who chose to do so that they could move south and establish their practices in the United States. (One should note that the cultural values espoused by the physician leaders of the Quebec strike—"liberty, freedom, and quality of care"—are more consistent with the organizing principles of US society than with the organizing principles of Canadian society. See Lipset's aforementioned comments.)

René Lévesque, at that time leader of Le Parti Québécois and later premier of Quebec, publicly criticized the physicians' strike. In doing so, he stated the following principle of Canadian society: "Organized medicine derives its power from the state, and the fact that the state has granted it a monopoly on such an indispensable service involves the responsibility to make that service available" (quoted in Taylor 1987, p. 404).

Despite government opposition, the specialists did go on strike on October 8. They refused to provide any care except for emergency cases. The Canadian press voiced a common criticism of the striking physicians, characterizing them as "operating in a social vacuum" (Taylor 1987, p. 408). Pierre Trudeau, then the prime minister of Canada, was explicit in his condemnation: "Those who would defy the law and ignore the opportunities available to them to right their wrongs, and satisfy their claims, will receive no hearing from this government. We shall ensure that the laws are respected" (quoted in Taylor 1987, p. 409).

On October 10, in an act unrelated to the Medicare controversy, Quebec's minister of labour was kidnapped and later murdered by radical separatists. Amid concerns of potential civil insurrection, the specialists called off their strike without gaining any of their demands. On November 1, Quebec Medicare began without incident, with full participation of the specialists.

Following an initial leveling of medical care costs in the period immediately following enactment of Medicare, rapid increases in the mid-1970s led to a growing concern that the costs of the program were unacceptably high, and rising. The share of Canadian gross domestic product (GDP) going to health care began to rise in ways similar to the rise seen in the United States. The federal government of Canada recognized that it needed to make future medical care costs more predictable, while the provinces wanted more direct control of financing. Accordingly, in 1977, a new arrangement was negotiated. In exchange for transferring a portion of its taxing authority to the provinces, the federal government's share of program costs was reduced from 50 percent to approximately 25 percent. In addition, future increases in the federal contribution would be limited to actual increases in GDP. Under the new formula, 100 percent of new costs exceeding the corresponding population/GDP increase would be borne by the provinces. The provinces went from being responsible for only fifty cents of every dollar spent on health care to facing responsibility for one hundred cents on the dollar for any increases in the cost of care that exceeded the growth in GDP. This limitation had a powerful effect, leading to more stringent efforts at cost control throughout Canada. For the following several years, medical care costs as a percentage of GDP were stable. As shown in figure 2.1.1, it was largely in this period that the gap developed between Canada and the United States in percentage of GDP going to health care.

FIGURE 2.1.1 Changes in the percentage of GDP going to health care in Canada and the United States, 1960–2000. *Source:* Data from OECD.

An important modification to the original Medicare program was passed in 1984. Even though Medicare created a government monopsony on the purchase of medical care, many physicians continued the practice of "balance billing," charging patients a fee over and above the established Medicare payment. In the eyes of the Canadian government, balance billing was contrary to the principles of universality and accessibility. Led by the Ontario Medical Association, many physicians clung tenaciously to this last vestige of individual entrepreneurship. In response, the government passed the Canada Health Act in 1984. While not outlawing balance billing, it mandated that for every dollar of balance billing that occurred in a province the federal allocation to that province would correspondingly be reduced by a dollar.

The Ontario Medical Association, adamantly opposed to the act, organized a physicians' strike to protest the new restrictions. Its president contended that "today's physicians believe we have a solemn duty to preserve the professional freedom that has been handed down from generation to generation for 5000 years. It is unthinkable to us that our profession's traditions, honored through the ages without the benefit of legislation, could be struck down in a modern society that has enacted a Charter of Rights and Freedoms" (quoted in Taylor 1987, p. 460).

Representatives of the Ontario government responded, "When the state grants a monopoly to an exclusive group to render an indispensable service it automatically becomes involved in whether those services are available and on what terms and conditions" (quoted in Taylor 1987, p. 460). With little support in the media, the strike was called off after twenty-eight days. As was the case in Saskatchewan twenty-two years earlier and Quebec fourteen years earlier, the Ontario physicians' strike achieved neither widespread public support nor its stated goals.

By now it should be clear that in Canada, the power of physicians and their professional associations is substantially limited, both by law and in the eyes of the public. Consistently, when physicians went on strike to protest the implementation of new health care initiatives, they were seen as violating their obligations to Canadian society. Those obligations resulted from the authority the government had granted them over the clinical practice of medicine.

The Organizing Principles of the Canadian Health Care System

From this examination of the Canadian health care system, it is possible to identify four principles around which it is organized:

1. *Health care is a basic right of all Canadians.*

Canada has made a social commitment to the concept that health care is a right of all citizens. Based on this right, the payment for health care is through taxes, with no direct connection between receiving care and paying for care.

2. ***The power of the medical profession is limited by its social obligation.***

The medical profession derives its monopoly authority over the practice of medicine from the state and has a responsibility, in return, to participate in and cooperate with programs established by the government.

3. ***The government retains monopsony power over the payment for health care (i.e., Canada's is a "single-payer" system).***

The success of the program depends on the monopsony power of the state. No other purchasers of health care (i.e., private insurance companies) are allowed.

4. ***There is one standard of health care for all Canadians.***

All people in Canada, regardless of income or social position, receive essentially the same level of care. (There is an important exception to this principle, discussed in the following section.)

Based on these principles, Canada maintained its level of national expenditure for health care at between 9 and 10 percent of GDP for more than two decades. During this same time, US spending grew from less than 12 percent of GDP to more than 16 percent. How is it that Canada has been able to keep its expenditures so low relative to those in the United States? Most of the provinces have instituted a series of fiscal policies that ensure that rises in health care expenditures parallel rises in GDP. These policies include

- a yearly, global budget for physician fees, with fee levels negotiated between the government and physicians so as to stay within the budget;
- fixed annual budgets for all hospitals; and
- government requirements that all capital expenditures for new hospital facilities and new technology (e.g., MRI machines) be separately approved and financed.

While these fiscal policies have been successful in holding down the cost of the system, they have had an important consequence for Canadians seeking care: queuing. **Queuing** refers to the need for many patients to go on a waiting list before receiving certain types of tests

> **concept 2.1.2**
>
> The Canadian health care system is based on the following principles of social policy:
> - Health care is a basic right of all Canadians.
> - The power of the medical profession is limited by its social obligation.
> - The government retains monopsony power over the payment for health care (i.e., Canada has a "single-payer" system).
> - There is one standard of health care for all Canadians.

EDITOR'S NOTES

queuing: the process by which many patients go on a waiting list before receiving certain types of tests or treatments in the Canadian healthcare system.

or treatments. Once referred by their physician, people often have to wait many months before obtaining an MRI or other types of tests that rely on expensive technology. The policy of holding down expenditures for these technologies has resulted in their short supply relative to demand. Similarly, patients referred for surgical procedures such as heart bypass, cataract removal, or hip replacement (all elective procedures that do not carry a major risk if delayed) may be scheduled for surgery months in the future. Generally, careful attention is paid to assure that patients in urgent need of these procedures are put in the front of the line, although budgetary problems that developed in the 1990s opened this principle to question.

Despite the spending controls that were part of their system, the cost of medical care in Canada continued to escalate throughout the 1980s. Faced with mounting economic problems at both the federal and provincial levels, many of the provincial plans began to experience severe shortages of both personnel and facilities in the mid-1990s. Newspaper and television reports documented increasing waits for services—often needed ones such as emergency room care or biopsies of possibly cancerous breast lumps. Public support for the health care system declined substantially; whereas 61 percent of the population rated the system as excellent in 1991, only 24 percent rated it as excellent in 1999 (Iglehart 2000).

The principle behind queuing for care in Canada is that in allocating scarce health care resources, those resources will go first to those in the greatest need, measured in terms of the risk to their life or health. Those with lesser need must simply wait their turn. Here is where the Canadian system of providing one level of care for all people breaks down somewhat. Nearly 90 percent of all Canadians live within one hundred miles of the US border. For those waiting in the queue for an elective test or procedure, the option is always there of simply traveling to the United States (where health care is available as a market commodity) and paying cash to obtain the test or procedure. Given the expense involved, this option is realistically available to only the wealthiest Canadians. Thus, to a certain extent, Canada operates a two-tiered system. One tier is available to every Canadian, although it frequently results in queuing for expensive tests and procedures. The second tier is available without queuing to those few who can afford to travel to the United States and pay out of pocket. A study of the extent to which wealthy Canadians seek medical care in the United States, however, determined that "the numbers found are so small as to be barely detectible" (Katz et al. 2002, p. 20).

The rising level of concern over queuing, shortages of facilities, and inadequate care led the Canadian government to undertake an exhaustive review of their system of health care. In 2001, the federal government established the **Commission on the Future of Health Care in Canada**. It gave the commission the charge "to recommend policies and measures ... to ensure over the long term the sustainability of a universally accessible, publicly funded health system, that offers quality services to Canadians and strikes an appropriate balance between investments in prevention and health maintenance and those directed to care and treatment" (Romanow 2002, p. iii). While the commission was asked to make serious recommendations about reforming the Canadian system of care, it was clear from the outset that Canada intended to maintain a "universally accessible, publicly funded" system, and that the central principle of the system was to remain a balancing of the costs and benefits of care.

Led by Commissioner Roy Romanow, the commission held extensive meetings with health policy experts, medical care providers, and ordinary Canadians. In November 2002, it published its report, which included a series of recommendations that fell into two general categories.

1. The Canadian system was underfunded, leading to shortages and waits that were not consistent with the level of quality Canadians deserve in their health care. To remedy the situation, the federal government should work with the provincial governments to invest additional public resources in health care, and to monitor over time that the health care system is adequately funded.

2. Canadians did not want to change the core structure or values of their system of health care. In the words of Commissioner Romanow, "Canadians have been clear that they still strongly support the core values on which our health care system is premised—equity, fairness and solidarity. These values are tied to their understanding of citizenship. Canadians consider equal and timely access to medically necessary health care services on the basis of need as a right of citizenship, not a privilege of status or wealth" (Romanow 2002, p. xvi).

Thus, while Canadians want the assurance that funds will be adequate to pay for needed care in a timely manner, they want to maintain the concept of equal care for all within fiscal limits established through open and public discussion.

While the Romanow Report, as it has come to be called, addressed most criticisms of the Canadian system, some Canadians remain opposed to certain aspects of that system. One of the issues that remain contentious is the relatively low level of payment for physician services. Recall that, as part of the financing mechanism in most of the provincial systems in Canada, a yearly budget is adopted to cover all physician services. Based on that budget, a provincial fee schedule is established by which physicians are paid for the services they provide. (Recall that all payment comes from the Provincial Health Plan.)

EDITOR'S NOTES

Commission on the Future of Health Care in Canada: established to undertake an exhaustive review of the Canadian healthcare system to ensure its long-term sustainability and quality.

As has also been the case historically in the United States, a fee-for-service system of paying physicians tends to make constraining aggregate costs for physician care difficult. Under a fee-for-service system, in which the physician is able to charge separately for each service provided, there is a clear economic incentive for the physician to provide more care. When one aggregates this incentive across all physicians, it makes it difficult to stay within a global budget intended to cover all physician services. The solution established by most provinces in Canada has been to establish a global budget for all physician services within the province, and then to monitor the extent to which physicians in aggregate stay within that budget.

For several years, provinces found that the aggregate charges of their physicians exceeded the budget established for physician care. The policy response was to reduce the fee schedule for the following year, so as to stay within the established budget. The problem with this model is in what one might consider a natural response to reductions in the payment for a given service. If a physician does not want to sustain a reduction of income, she or he will need to increase the number of services provided—either seeing more patients or providing more extensive services to each patient. While, at the level of the individual physician, this response to reduced fees might seem reasonable, if one aggregates this change in practice across all physicians, there is again a problem at the provincial level. Despite the reduction in fees enacted to account for the budget excess in the previous year, the increased level of services will again cause the province to go over budget for physicians' care.

This response of the medical profession as a whole—to react to reduced fees by providing more care—has come to be called "**churning**." For several years running, a reduction in physicians' fees was followed by churning among physicians, leading inevitably to further reductions in fees. As we will see later in this chapter, patients in Canada have about 40 percent more visits to the doctor per year than patients in the United States, while doctors in the United States charge more than twice as much for the care they provide. The result is that physicians' incomes in Canada tend to be substantially lower than those in the United States. In 2005, physicians in the United States earned at least one-third more than physicians in Canada (Duffin 2011).

EDITOR'S NOTES

churning: a reaction of the medical profession to increased care when provisional fees have been reduced.

While Canada has been dealing with the issue of physician churning in response to reduced fees, only in the past several years have physicians in the United States faced the issue of a global budget for their fees—with precisely the same response as their Canadian colleagues. [...]

Growing Pressure for a Two-Tier System in Canada

With the passage of the **Canada Health Act** in 1984, the Canadian federal government added a fifth core principle to their national system of health care: accessibility. As described by the act, "the intent of the accessibility criterion is to ensure that insured persons in a province or territory have reasonable access to insured hospital, medical and surgical-dental services on uniform terms and conditions, unprecluded or unimpeded, either directly or indirectly, by charges (user charges or extra-billing) or other means (e.g., **discrimination** on the basis of age, health status or financial circumstances)" (Health Canada 2009, p. 4).

The issue of "extra-billing" or "balance billing" had been largely settled by the failure of the 1984 physician strike in Ontario, discussed previously. A growing number of physicians, however, began to develop private clinics for services such as outpatient surgery or radiology. While the physicians in these clinics would accept payment from the provincial health plan as payment in full for their services, they would also charge the patient a "facility fee"—an extra charge for the use of the clinic facilities. A 1995 ruling by Canada's minister of health stated: "The facility fees charged by private clinics for medically necessary services are a major problem which must be dealt with firmly. ... Such fees constitute user charges and, as such, contravene the principle of accessibility set out in the *Canada Health Act*" (Marleau 1995).

Canada's federal government left it to each province to regulate private clinics and to report to the federal government any extra charges to patients levied by private clinics for "medically necessary services" that should have been provided without charge under the provincial health plan. The federal government would then deduct that amount as a penalty from the federal reimbursement to the province under the national health plan. While some provinces simply prohibited any private clinics, others permitted private clinics under certain circumstances.

EDITOR'S NOTES

Canada Health Act: passed in 1984, the act established an ethic of accessibility in healthcare for all Canadians.

EDITOR'S NOTES

discrimination: unequal treatment of an individual or group on the basis of their status (e.g., age, beliefs, ethnicity, sex) by limiting access to social resources (e.g., education, housing, jobs, legal rights, loans, or political power).

For example, British Columbia, Alberta, and Ontario elected to permit private facilities under certain circumstances.

With the numbers of these private clinics expanding, the provincial governments were sometimes lax in monitoring them for compliance with the federal prohibition of extra charges to patients (Lett 2008). The federal Health Ministry's 2009 report on compliance with the Canada Health Act found that "in 2008–9, the most prominent concerns with respect to compliance under the *Canada Health Act* remained patient charges and queue jumping for medically necessary health services at private clinics" (Health Canada 2009, p. 1).

Reports in the Canadian press provided examples of both the success of these private clinics in attracting affluent patients and the consternation of the Canadian public with these clinics. A June 18, 2007, *Montreal Gazette* news story ("Munro M. Layton Accused of Hypocrisy for Visiting Private Clinic") criticized Jack Layton, leader of the New Democratic Party, for "jumping the queue" and undergoing hernia surgery at a private clinic. The same story reported that the president of the Canadian Autoworkers union had jumped the queue to get an MRI of his leg. During the H1N1 flu epidemic of 2009, public health agencies in Toronto and Vancouver were reported to have given several thousand doses of the H1N1 vaccine to private clinics that only treated patients who had paid an "annual membership fee," thus allowing those affluent patients to jump the queue to obtain their vaccines (Howlett et al. 2009).

A 2005 ruling by the Canadian Supreme Court added to Canada's ongoing national debate about the future role of private clinics in the Canadian health care system. In the face of ongoing shortages of facilities and queues for important services, a number of physicians have argued that they should be permitted to provide these services on a private basis. Allowing such practices would, of course, create a two-tier health care system: one tier for those willing to pay for private services and one tier for those unable or unwilling to pay privately and thus relying on those physicians and hospitals who participate in the provincial plan.

The province of Quebec had enacted a law prohibiting private clinics from operating. A family physician in Montreal filed a lawsuit against the provincial government, claiming that, by creating long waits for care and prohibiting people from buying care privately, the health care system in Quebec was violating both his and his patients' constitutional protections of "liberty, safety and security" (Krauss 2005). After losing in two lower courts, the physician appealed to the Supreme Court of Canada, and in 2005 the court ruled by a 4–3 margin in the physician's favor. In the province of Quebec (the court ruling applied only to Quebec), physicians are permitted to set up a private medical care system in parallel to the publicly financed provincial system—the beginnings of a two-tier system.

Reaction throughout Canada to the court ruling was vocal. One newspaper commentator wrote, "The sacred trust—or sacred cow—of public-only medicine is finished. ... Canada will have more private health-care delivery. The only questions are when, where, and how much" (Simpson 2005). Roy Romanow, author of the Romanow Report, responded to the court decision by stating: "The evidence is overwhelming and clear: The two-tiering of health care represents a march backward in time, to when good health care depended on the size of one's wallet" (Romanow 2005). The debate over shifting the Canadian system to a two-tiered system is likely to go on for a number of years.

Most Canadians want to maintain their current system but invest more resources in that system to make care more generally available. The Canadian Medical Association commissioned a national poll of public opinion regarding the issue and found that only 15 percent of Canadians were in favor of allowing the development of private-sector alternatives to Medicare (Picard 2006). Most Canadians want to maintain Canada's single-payer system that assures the same level of care for all Canadians. They want a system that provides better access to care and enhanced quality of care, however. Canada continues to struggle with providing full access to the "medically necessary services" required under its Medicare law while also constraining the cost of its national system. It remains to be seen whether a two-tier system of care will evolve as a response to these conflicting priorities.

The History of Medical Care in the United States

While the health care system in Canada has evolved over the period of nearly one hundred years to its current form, the system in the United States was undergoing a parallel evolution, with a very different outcome. Looking back to the period surrounding World War I, we see progressive groups in the United States proposing a system of government-financed health care. While the AMA considered the issue, its affiliated state medical associations were clear and determined in their opposition to a publicly administered system. Enjoying the new legal protections that followed the publication of the Flexner Report in 1910, the medical profession was intent on consolidating its authority over medical care. By the 1930s, that authority had been firmly established. While towns and provinces in Canada were reacting to the Great Depression through a system of municipal physicians and hospitals, the medical profession in the United States was taking steps to make the private employment of physicians illegal. Even systems of paying for physician care through lump-sum payments, rather than fee-for-service payments, was deemed unethical by the AMA. (See chapter 5 for further discussion of the implications of fee-for-service versus prepayment systems of paying for care.)

The power of the medical profession, both through the AMA and through affiliated state medical associations, was substantial. ... [I]t was clear to Franklin Roosevelt that any attempt to include medical care as part of Social Security would arouse such opposition from the medical profession that it would make passage of Social Security unlikely. Harry Truman also faced the power of the medical profession to derail his attempts at reform. Despite the fact that his proposals left largely intact the private delivery system, Truman's plan was branded as "socialized medicine" by physicians and their political allies, and it was decisively defeated.

By 1960, the power of the US medical profession had reached its peak, and the system of private, market-based, fee-for-service medicine had been firmly established. While private health insurance was becoming more widespread, the medical profession maintained substantial authority over how those private plans were structured. The principle had been firmly established that there was little role for federal or state governments in the health care system. That role was largely limited to providing care for poor patients in local city or county hospitals. Only in 1965, when Lyndon Johnson was recently elected as president with large Democrat majorities in both houses of Congress, was the federal government able to take its first steps into the medical care system through the enactment of the Medicare and Medicaid systems. [...]

The Organizing Principles of the US Health Care System

The principles around which the US health care system has come to be organized stand in sharp contrast to those of the Canadian system. They reflect our society's view of the importance of the rights of the individual and of our general distrust of government programs.

1. *Health care is a market commodity to be distributed according to ability to pay. Other than basic emergency services, there is no acknowledged right to health care for those under 65 years of age.*

[...] It reflects a decision made during the early part of the twentieth century and continues to guide the distribution of access to care.

2. *For much of the twentieth century, power over the organization and delivery of health care was concentrated in the medical profession.*

Both state and federal governments relied on the medical profession to establish standards of education and licensure, guide medical ethics, define financing mechanisms
for care, and control the ways in which hospitals are used.

3. *Government has historically had relatively little role in guiding our system of health care.*

Although government's role has increased in recent years due to its growing role in paying for care, throughout most of the twentieth century there was little in the way of government policy or programs intended to establish a national system of either providing care or paying for care.

4. *There is no uniform standard of care. The quality of care received often reflects the ability to pay.*

Ours has evolved into a multitiered health care system, with differing levels of quality at different tiers. Differences in quality reflect both differences in the training and skills of the physician and differences in access to care.

It should by now be clear that the system of care in the United States is quite different from that in Canada, reflecting fundamental cultural and historical differences between our two countries. This conclusion reinforces one of the principal messages of this text: to understand our health care system, it is necessary to understand the institutional forces unique to the United States that shape that system.

The Cultural Institutions that Drive Health Care in the United States

The concept of an "**institution**" refers to the rules a society adopts that create its social, political, and economic structure. To appreciate more fully the way culturally derived institutions shape our lives, consider the following examples.

- When meeting someone in this country for the first time, one typically offers a handshake. There are no written rules that say we must; nevertheless, failure to do so might be considered rude.
- When eating in a restaurant while traveling away from home, we typically leave a tip. Even though we may never be at that restaurant again and may never again encounter our server (thus not having to worry about how good the service will be the next time we are here), we still feel obliged to leave a tip. To not do so would be insensitive to the server.
- People often discuss "the institution of marriage," its pros and cons, and the way it has changed. Here they are talking about both the formal laws that govern marriage and the social roles people fill when married.
- In most circles, Stanford University is seen as a well-respected academic institution. In both the written rules that govern the education it offers and the unwritten rules that govern relationships among individuals and groups, the very character of the university is created.

What links all these US institutions? What do they all have in common? To understand the answer to this question is to understand one of the key driving forces behind the problems we face in health care today.

---

concept 2.1.3

The US health care system is based on the following principles of social policy:

- Health care is a market commodity to be distributed according to ability to pay.
- Power over the organization and delivery of health care has historically been concentrated in the medical profession.
- Government has historically had a relatively minimal role in guiding our system of health care.
- There is no uniform standard of care. The quality of care received often reflects the ability to pay.

EDITOR'S NOTES

institution: a large-scale social system that is stable and predictable, created and maintained to serve the needs of society.

Each aforementioned example represents rules of social interaction that most people understand and take largely for granted. Douglass North, a Nobel Prize–winning economist, described how institutions shape our social as well as our economic lives: "[Institutions] are a guide to human interaction, so that when we wish to greet friends on the street, drive an automobile, buy oranges, borrow money, form a business, bury our dead, or whatever, we know (or can learn easily) how to perform those tasks. ... Institutions may be created, as was the United States Constitution; or they may simply evolve over time, as does the common law" (North 1986, pp. 3–4).

Institutions can be formal, as in written laws, codes of ethics, and prescribed procedures, or they can be informal, such as common courtesy and the strength of family ties. Many institutions have both formal and informal aspects. Consider, for example, the medical profession. As discussed previously, in this country the medical profession is commonly viewed as exercising authority over the use of specialized knowledge in ways that contribute to the social good. This perception arose informally over time. The widely held view of the medical profession led to the creation of laws that formalized this role, granting the profession autonomous authority over medical education, licensure, and practice.

Institutions have four defining characteristics (Scott 1987):

1. They are rules that guide behavior in certain situations.
2. The rules can be formal or informal.
3. Over time, those rules come to be taken largely for granted.
4. Disobeying the rules will invoke some sort of sanction, either formal or informal.

In one way, institutions tend to be socially efficient. They allow us to enter into situations without having to figure out from scratch what to do every time. Not all institutions turn out to be quite so efficient, however. Again quoting Douglas North: "Institutions are not necessarily or even usually created to be socially efficient; rather they, or at least the formal rules, are created to serve the interests of those with the bargaining power to devise new rules" (North 1986, p. 16).

Where do institutions come from? The process through which institutions are created has been characterized as "profoundly political and reflect[ing] the relative power of organized interests and the actors who mobilize around them" (DiMaggio 1988, p. 13). Economists, political scientists, and sociologists seem to agree that institutions often reflect—at least initially—the needs of powerful, organized interests. While institutions may reflect organized economic and political interests at their outset, however, they do not change easily or quickly, even in the face of a changing economic or political context. Once established, institutions limit the opportunity for further changes in social policy over the course of a nation's history. Institutions "may assume a life of their own, a life independent of the basic causal factors that led to their creation in the first place" (Krasner 1983, p. 357). This is not to say that institutions do not change; rather, they change gradually, reflecting only changes in economic forces and social perceptions that persist over time.

In comparing health care in the United States and Canada, we find fundamental differences in policy. I identified two key policies that differentiate health care in the United States from that of Canada and other developed countries: (1) approaching medical care as a market commodity and (2) granting sovereignty to the medical profession over the organization and financing of care. In addition, I discussed how health care in Canada is organized around improving the common good, while health care in the United States is organized around the rights of the individual. These three differences in policy represent institutional differences that have developed out of the social and political differences between the United States and Canada. In the United States, these institutions tend to push up the costs of health care, while other institutional forces (e.g., the American aversion to paying taxes) hold down the funds available to pay for health care. As a result, at the time ACA was enacted, one person in six had no health insurance coverage.

Protein Deprivation, Prime Rib, and Declining Marginal Returns

To understand more fully how institutional forces affect the cost of care, let us consider a basic principle of economics: the **law of declining marginal returns**. To illustrate this law, I offer the following story from personal experience.

One summer I was on a backpacking trip with my son in the Wind River wilderness in Wyoming. After seven days of hiking at high altitude, during which we survived mostly on freeze-dried food, nuts, and raisins, we came out of the wilderness and went in search of a real meal. I usually don't eat much red meat, but when we walked into the restaurant in the small town near the trailhead, the aroma of prime rib of beef hit us. Having been protein deprived during our trip, my digestive system cried out for a plate of prime rib. I gave in. Never have I enjoyed a meal quite so much as I enjoyed that prime rib. I would gladly have paid $50.00 for it. Fortunately for me, at that time it cost only $11.95.

Now, while I actually stopped at one plate, for the sake of discussion let us assume a clever waiter. Seeing how much I enjoyed the first plate, he might then have encouraged me to order a second. "After all, you enjoyed the first one so much, think how much you'll enjoy the second." So, I give in and order a second plate. I find that I derive substantially

EDITOR'S NOTES

law of declining (diminishing) marginal returns: a basic principle of economics stating that, at some point, adding an additional factor of production results in smaller increases in output.

less enjoyment from the second than the first. While I would have paid $50.00 for the first plate, I wouldn't pay a penny more than $11.95 for the second.

The waiter then encourages me to order a third plate. Again I give in. While I did derive some benefit from eating the third plate, it was only a small benefit—say, $1.00 worth of benefit. The waiter starts to get very pushy and brings me a fourth plate. Not wanting to hurt his feelings, I begin to eat it, but partway through I get up, go into the rest room, and throw up everything.

This story seems on the surface a bit silly. What rational person would pay $11.95 for a plate of prime rib from which he derived only $1.00 worth of benefit? Even more, who would ever willingly pay for food that he knows will probably make him sick? And besides, what does this have to do with health care? To understand, let us create a graph describing my folly in ordering prime rib, as shown in figure 2.1.2.

It should be clear that, consistent with the law of declining marginal returns, for each successive meal I order, I derive less benefit than from the previous meal (measured here in enjoyment and willingness to pay). It should also be easy to see that a person who is acting rationally would never order more than two meals. He or she would stop at the point where the marginal benefit equals the marginal return—often referred to as the point of indifference. Because the marginal cost and the marginal benefit are

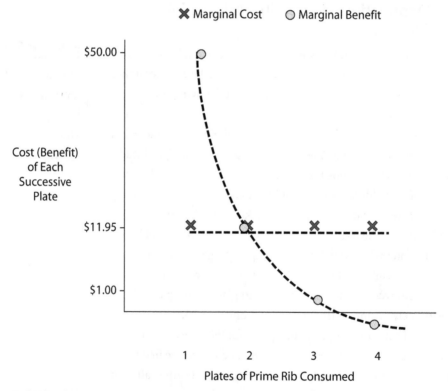

FIGURE 2.1.2 Relationship between marginal cost and marginal benefit when eating plates of prime rib.

exactly the same, a rational person could choose either to accept or not to accept one more meal. This point—the intersection of the line of marginal costs and that of marginal benefits—is one definition of economic efficiency.

Let us stay with the law of declining marginal returns but move back to health care. While the issues are quite different, the principle is the same. Figure 2.1.3 illustrates the effect of declining marginal returns in health care. The graph can be used to represent decisions at the level of the individual patient or at the level of the health care system overall. For the individual patient, consider the example of a college student who falls down and twists her knee while playing recreational soccer. Her knee becomes somewhat sore and swollen. Her first decision is whether to go to the doctor for an exam, or simply wait to see what happens if she rests the knee and gives it a chance to heal. If she does go to the doctor, the first decision the doctor may face after performing an examination is whether to X-ray the knee to see if it is broken. (While it is unlikely an injury of this type will break a bone, it is possible.) Assuming the physical examination performed by the doctor shows no clear evidence of a torn ligament or torn cartilage and the X-ray is negative, should the doctor obtain an MRI just

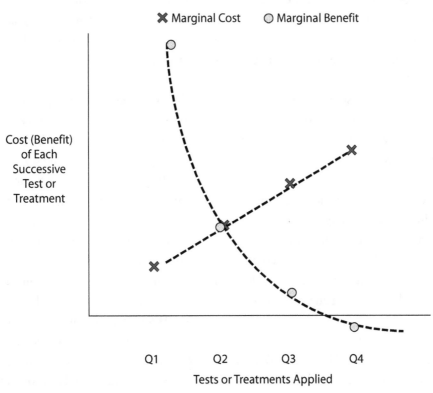

FIGURE 2.1.3 Relationship between marginal cost and marginal benefit in health care.

to be sure he is not missing anything? In the face of a negative MRI, should the doctor perform exploratory arthroscopic surgery, just to be absolutely sure nothing is wrong?

Here the physical exam represents Q1 on the graph, the X-ray represents Q2, the MRI is Q3, and arthroscopic surgery is Q4. The marginal benefit is measured as the increase in the probability the student's knee will be completely healed in six months. The one difference in this graph is that the cost of each successive test, rather than being constant, is increasing. How many tests should the patient obtain? In this example, the benefit derived from the physician's exam is more than the cost of the exam. The added benefit from the X-ray is approximately equal to its added cost. The chances of an MRI helping (given a negative exam and negative X-ray), while real and measurable, however, are less than its cost. Similarly, exploratory arthroscopic surgery not only may not help but also carries with it the chance of making the patient worse from a postoperative joint infection.

Where should a rational patient stop in obtaining tests or treatments? Where should a rational physician stop in ordering these procedures? These questions are answered differently in the United States and Canada, based on the different approaches to the trade-off between the benefit to the individual and the benefit to society. In Canada, technology such as MRI is applied sparingly, because it is felt that the added benefit to society overall does not justify the added cost of making it more widely available. In the United States, we typically expect technology to be available to us, despite its position on the marginal cost/marginal benefit curves. It is not fair to the individual, we believe, to deprive her or him of the possible benefits of the test, even though they are small compared to the cost.

As in the case of consuming prime rib, the point of intersection of the marginal cost/marginal benefit curves provides a measure of efficiency in the allocation of health care resources. In Canada, tests and procedures more closely approximate Q2 on the graph, where costs and benefits are about equal. In the United States, they typically are available all the way to Q3. (Some would say we sometimes reach Q4, providing some tests and procedures that are to the patient's detriment.) Our belief in the importance of making tests and procedures available to individuals even though the marginal costs substantially exceed the marginal benefits is uniquely American.

To illustrate, let me relate the story of a patient I took care of in my clinical practice. He was in his forties, a successful local attorney. He had twisted his knee playing sports and wanted my evaluation. After a thorough examination, I was able to determine that, in all likelihood, he had sprained a ligament in his knee without causing any permanent damage. I saw no evidence of a torn ligament or torn cartilage. Because he had simply twisted the knee and not fallen on it, the chance of a broken bone was remote. I chose not to get an X-ray, and I reassured him that he should soon have a full recovery.

"How can you be sure?" he asked. "Don't we need an MRI? Last time this happened, my doctor got the MRI right away, and even though it was negative, he went ahead and did arthroscopic surgery, *just to be sure* he hadn't missed anything. It was a good thing he did, too—during surgery he found a micro-tear in my cartilage and fixed it!"

Here was a well-educated, professional patient (an attorney, no less) whose previous doctor, in the face of a negative exam, negative X-ray, and negative MRI, had gone ahead and performed arthroscopic surgery. In doing so, he had subjected the patient to the risk of a serious joint infection with no reasonable benefit expected. I am convinced that the "micro-tear" the surgeon reported was simply a justification for having performed the surgery. I had not previously heard of "micro-tears" of the knee joint as a problem justifying surgery, but I was acutely aware that recent research reports had documented hundreds of thousands of unnecessary knee surgeries in the United States each year. Nevertheless, the patient considered my care—stopping at the exam to see if the knee healed—to be low-quality care and the care his previous surgeon had recommended to be high-quality care. To this patient, questions of marginal cost/marginal benefit had no relevance.

In Canada, it is unlikely this patient ever would have seen an MRI machine.

> **concept 2.1.4**
>
> In the United States, the value we as a society place on technology and technological advances encourages the development and use of high-tech medical treatments, even when the added benefit of these treatments is small compared to their cost.

The "Technological Imperative" and Its Effect on Health Care

Why is the lure of an MRI or of high-tech surgery so powerful, for both the physician and the patient? As a society, we have come to put substantial faith in new technology, and we often measure the benefit of a test or treatment not only in its actual benefit (often measured in the cost of saving an additional year of life) but also in its perceived benefit. A large part of our resistance to reducing the use of expensive, new technologies is due to what Victor Fuchs (1983, p. 60) described as "**the 'technological imperative'**—namely, the desire of the physician to do everything that he has been trained to do, regardless of the benefit-cost ratio." The technological imperative shapes what we define as "best medical practice." This perception, based to a large extent on the extensive use of technology so pervasive in academic medical centers, is "imprinted" on physicians during their medical school and residency training. Physicians learn to do all they feasibly can and tend to follow this institutional imperative throughout their career. Patients, in turn, tend to adopt the physician's perspective as the norm.

During the past several decades, most advances in medicine have been due to the technology we have been able to develop. New types of

EDITOR'S NOTES

the technological imperative: defined by Victor Fuchs as the desire of the physician to do everything that they have been trained to, regardless of the cost-benefit ratio.

imaging devices such as MRI scanners, the use of fiber optics for both diagnosis and surgery, the use of lasers, and bioengineered medications all have had substantial impact on our ability to treat specific patients and specific illnesses. They have been so successful that we have come to equate technology with quality. We have a commonly held belief that the more technological a treatment is, the better it is. We also have come to believe that as patients we have not received complete treatment unless we receive the most advanced technology. Thus, physicians in the United States have a tendency to do everything that is possible, regardless of the cost/benefit ratio.

I would add to Fuchs's description a corollary institution that I refer to as the "**technological benefit of the doubt.**" In comparing a new, high-tech approach to a problem with an older, low-tech alternative, we tend to expect the newer approach to be superior based on its use of advanced technology, even in the absence of empirical evidence to that effect. Take, for example, the prostate specific antigen (PSA) blood test, first introduced in 1987 as a screening test for prostate cancer. It was substantially more high-tech than the traditional method of screening for prostate cancer by digitally examining the prostate gland as part of a rectal examination. The PSA test was relatively expensive and was shown early on to have a high risk of false-positive results. Early data suggested that widespread use of the test "may result in poorer health outcomes and will increase costs dramatically" (Krahn et al. 1994, p. 773). Nonetheless, the test became widely accepted and used before it was approved by the US Food and Drug Administration and before data about its effectiveness became available. A poll reported in 1993 (Kolata 1993) found that 92 percent of physicians in one state used the test routinely on men over 50. By 2009, the PSA test had become a routine part of men's health care, with most men over the age of 50 getting the test despite a continuing lack of evidence that the test actually reduced prostate cancer death rates (Barry 2008).

In 2008, two large studies were published on the effect of PSA screening on death rates. One found no difference in death rates after 7 to 10 years of follow-up in men chosen randomly to be screened on a regular basis compared to men receiving their usual care (Andriole et al. 2009). Another found that after 9 years of follow-up, men screened with the PSA test had a reduction in the death rate of 0.71 deaths per 1,000 men screened (Schröder et al. 2009).

Both studies found that PSA screening identified the presence of prostate cancer more often than avoiding screening, typically leading to surgical removal of the prostate gland, a procedure that can have substantial side effects such as sexual impotence and urinary incontinence. By identifying and treating tumors in many men that would otherwise not have caused illness or death, the screening process led to substantially higher rates of these adverse outcomes, with resulting reduction in quality of life for the men affected. In the words of one commentator responding to the results of the studies, "I think that there is convincing evidence of harm. ... The two studies together show marginal to no benefit across several years of follow-up at the cost to so many men of overdiagnosis and overtreatment" (McNaughton-Collins 2009, p. 4).

Based on the available research results, in 2012 the US Preventive Services Task Force issued a new recommendation regarding the use of PSA as a screening test for prostate cancer: "The U.S. Preventive Services Task Force recommends against prostate-specific antigen (PSA)-based screening for prostate cancer." For more than twenty years, physicians in the United States routinely used a newer, more high-tech screening test on the faith it would reduce prostate cancer deaths, absent evidence that it actually did so. When the evidence finally came in, it showed little if any benefit of the test.

Physicians and patients seem to be willing to adopt newer, more expensive technologies on the faith that they will, in the future, prove to be superior to existing alternatives. Once they have been adopted, it is extremely difficult to go back and change established patterns of behavior that prove to have little scientific or economic justification.

As another example of the technologic benefit of the doubt, let us look at the way high blood pressure has been treated in the United States over the years. For a number of years, physicians had relatively few choices for the treatment of high blood pressure. The standard treatment was to give the patient a diuretic to reduce the salt and fluid balance in the body, thereby lowering blood pressure. In clinical trials involving comparisons to patients who received only dummy placebo pills, diuretics had been proven to be effective.

Calcium-channel blockers were a category of drug that became widely used in the 1980s. They too were shown to be effective in treating high blood pressure, when compared to treatment with a placebo. Then, in the 1990s, an even newer category of drug came into use—angiotensin-converting enzyme inhibitors, commonly referred to as ACE inhibitors. As with calcium-channel blockers, these were also proven to be effective, compared to treatment with a placebo.

Which medicine should a physician prescribe for the treatment of high blood pressure? When calcium-channel blockers became widely available, they largely supplanted diuretics as a first-line treatment. After all, they were newer, so they must be better. When ACE inhibitors became available, many physicians switched to using these. Again, as an entirely new class of drug, they were considered to be better than the older alternatives. The problem, of course, is that each successive new drug category is more expensive than the older alternatives. This is especially true when the newer drug is available only in its brand-name form. [...] While treatment today with a diuretic pill might cost $10 to $15 per month, treatment with the newer ACE inhibitors or calcium-channel blockers can easily cost five to ten times as much.

For more than two decades, physicians relied on the newer medicines to treat high blood pressure, without clinical evidence that they were better than the older diuretics. Each category had been proven effective when compared to treatment with a placebo, but no test had compared the efficacy of the three in a head-to-head trial. Then, in 2002, a large national team of researchers reported on just such a study. In what is called a "double-blind" trial—neither the patient nor the treating physician was told what was in the pill received—they studied patients with high blood pressure who were at high risk of complications. They compared the effectiveness of the three types of drugs in a number of ways. The main outcome of the study—whether the patient had a heart attack—was no different for any of the three medicines. In other measures of outcome, however, the diuretic proved to be most effective, leading the researchers to conclude that "diuretics are superior in preventing one or more major forms of [cardiovascular disease] and are less expensive. They should be preferred for first-step antihypertensive therapy" (ALLHAT Collaborative Research Group 2002, p. 2981).

In this case, physicians for years gave the technologic benefit of the doubt to the newer drugs. Only after a well-designed scientific study finally became available, directly comparing the clinical effectiveness of the available alternatives, did they learn that giving the newer alternatives the technologic benefit of the doubt had no added benefit in clinical outcomes but led to substantial increases in cost. Despite this evidence from the 2002 study, however, by 2008, only 40 percent of patients with hypertension were receiving a diuretic medication, compared to 30 to 35 percent of patients before the study was published (Pollack 2008). Once physicians give newer, high-tech treatments the technologic benefit of the doubt, it becomes extremely difficult to change their behavior.

Differing Cultural Institutions Affect the Cost of Health Care

We have seen that Canada spends about 10 percent of GDP on its health care system, while the United States spends more than 17 percent. It is not simply in limiting the availability of expensive care through long waiting lists, however, that Canada spends less than the United States. There are fundamental differences in the way physicians in the two countries practice medicine, with resulting differences in costs.

Victor Fuchs has done a number of studies comparing the patterns of care in comparable populations of patients in the United States and Canada (Fuchs 1993d). The results of these comparisons have a great deal to say about why health care costs so much more in this country than it does in Canada. Table 2.1.2 shows the pattern of care Fuchs found for physician services and hospital services. It shows the ratio of the United States to Canada in three areas: (1) expenditures on care, (2) prices of resources used in care, and (3) quantity of resources used.

TABLE 2.1.2 Comparison of the Use of Health Care Resources between the United States and Canada

Services	Ratio of US to Canadian
Physician services	
Health expenditures per capita	1.72
Physicians' fees	2.39
Prices of resources used in providing service	1.30
Number of services provided per capita	0.72
Quantity of resources used per service	1.84
Hospital services	
Hospital expenses per capita	1.26
Expenses per admission	1.39
Prices of resources	1.04
Hospital admissions per capita	0.91
Quantity of resources used per admission	1.24

Source: Data from Fuchs 1993d.

Several patterns can be seen from these data. While people in the United States go to the doctor less often (28 percent less often than people in Canada) and are admitted to the hospital less often (9 percent less often than Canadians), we nonetheless spend a great deal more per patient per year (72 percent more for physicians' services and 26 percent more for hospital care). How is it that we use health care less frequently but spend a great deal more for the care? Part of the answer is the price of resources. Resources such as laboratory tests, medications, and supplies used in providing care in physicians' offices cost 30 percent more in the United States than comparable resources in Canada. The prices physicians charge for their services are nearly two-and-one-half times more than what Canadian physicians charge. Similarly, the resources used in providing hospital care cost somewhat more in the United States (4 percent more).

In addition to higher prices for resources in the United States, we find a clear pattern of using more resources per service in the United States, for both physician care (84 percent more) and hospital care (24 percent more). This means that every time we go to the doctor or the hospital, we have more tests, X-rays, medications, and treatments than Canadians with similar conditions do.

Differing Approaches to the Treatment of Heart Disease in the United States and Canada

For people with heart disease, especially those with clogged blood vessels due to coronary artery disease, there is always the risk that something will cause the normal heart rhythm to malfunction. When this happens, the result is often sudden death. Anyone who has watched a television show about hospitals or emergency rooms will know that the treatment is to try to shock the person back to life using a defibrillator. Unfortunately, if a person is not in the immediate vicinity of a defibrillator and someone who knows how to use it, little can be done to prevent death due to a cardiac arrhythmia.

In the 1990s, physicians began using a new device to treat patients who might be at risk of sudden death from a cardiac arrhythmia. The device combined a small computer that can monitor the heart rhythm and determine if a life-threatening abnormality has begun and a stored electrical charge that, on command from the computer, will automatically deliver an electric shock to the heart. With advances in computer technology, these devices became small enough to implant surgically under the skin of a patient's chest.

The next question to be answered was whether these implantable cardiac defibrillators (ICDs) would be effective in saving patients' lives. In 2005, a major study appeared showing that, for patients with severe heart failure, having an ICD reduced the death rate after about four years from 29 percent of patients to 22 percent (Bardy et al. 2005). The results of this and other studies also carried with them some cautions. Some patients were found to have a difficult time with inappropriate, painful shocks being delivered by the devices, leading to a decrease in the quality of their lives. In addition, the cost of the devices was quite high—it might typically cost $50,000 to have one implanted.

Because many of the patients who might be helped by ICDs are 65 years old or older, the federal Medicare program is one of the principal payers for these devices. As we will see in chapter 6, Medicare is facing rapidly increasing costs and concerns about the long-term fiscal viability of the program. To what extent should Medicare pay for the use of ICDs? Given that fewer than one in ten patients will actually be helped by them, should Medicare pay for ICDs only for the sickest patients, leaving some low-risk patients to suffer sudden cardiac death that might have been prevented by an implantable defibrillator? Alternatively, should ICDs be made more widely available to patients with heart disease, placing the lives of patients above economic concerns about the financial impact on the Medicare program?

These were the questions the health policy experts at the federal Centers for Medicare and Medicaid Services grappled with. In early 2005, they came down on the side of preventing as many deaths as possible, substantially widening the range of patients eligible for the devices (McClellan and Tunis 2005). As a result, the aggregate cost of using ICDs was expected to rise substantially. Based on earlier research results, while a relatively small number of patients are likely to be helped by them, for most patients the use of ICDs will make no difference in the course of their disease.

Despite recent research studies, it simply is not possible to say with certainty which patients will be helped and which will not. To cover the few who will be helped, many who will not be helped will need to be treated, leading to substantially higher costs. This is the approach typically taken in the United States when a new device or treatment becomes available. It is the approach most compatible with our historic emphasis in the United States on the needs of the individual rather than on the needs of the social group.

How has Canada dealt with ICDs? In 1999, Canada convened a national Working Group on Cardiac Pacing to study the issue. This group issued a preliminary report in 2000. After the publication of further studies on the efficacy of ICDs, a national consortium of heart specialists published more detailed guidelines on the use of ICDs that recognized the usefulness of the devices and recommended a plan to make them more available to Canadians with heart disease. Recognizing that it is not possible to provide all care to all people in a health care system that must function under a fixed yearly budget, they outlined a careful approach based on the best available clinical evidence. Patients who were found by their primary care physician to be potential candidates for an ICD will be seen by two consulting specialists before a decision is made to use an ICD. They acknowledged that patient queues would develop in this process and recommended a careful monitoring program to assure that those queues do not become excessive. In addition, as is typically the case in Canada, they emphasized that the ordering of patients in the queues would be based on need—the sickest patients would always be in the front of the queue.

As a result of the more cautious approach Canada has taken compared to that of the United States, Canadian patients with heart disease receive far fewer ICDs than those in the United States. In 2003, 84 ICDs were used per 1 million people in Canada, while about 470 ICDs were used per 1 million people in the United States (*Canadian Journal of Cardiology* 2005).

A closely related issue is how doctors in the United States and Canada differ in the way they diagnose and treat patients with clogged coronary arteries that have resulted in a heart attack. Pilote et al. (2003) were able to obtain the treatment records of all patients age 65 or older who were treated for a heart attack in either the United States or the Canadian province of Quebec. For these two patient populations, they compared the increase in the use of newer, high-tech treatments for heart attacks and the death rate from heart attacks. They compared the percentage of patients with a heart attack who had a revascularization procedure (a procedure to open up the clogged blood vessels to the heart that had caused the heart attack) and the percentage of patients who died within one year of their heart attack. These data are shown in figure 2.1.4. It can be seen that between 1988 and 1994:

- the rate of revascularization approximately doubled in both countries,
- revascularization was used approximately three times more often in the United States than in Canada at both points in time,
- the death rate decreased for both countries by approximately the same amount, and
- the death rate was lower in Quebec than in the United States at both points in time.

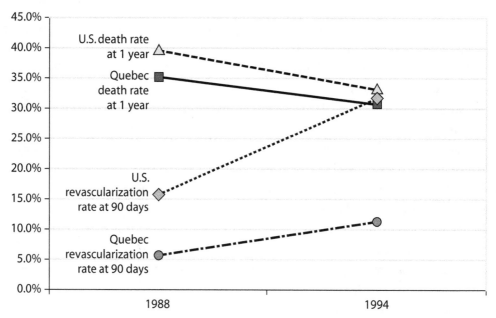

FIGURE 2.1.4 Comparing treatment rates and death rates in the United States and Quebec for elderly people with heart attacks, 1988 and 1994. *Source:* Data from Pilote et al. 2003.

It appears that, while the substantially higher rates of revascularization in the United States undoubtedly helped some of the patients treated, the marginal benefit of the extra procedures was not large enough to show up in the overall death rate from heart attacks.

Despite these data showing little long-term benefit of revascularization procedures as measured by death rates, the frequency of diagnostic tests that often lead to revascularization has been growing in the United States. One reason is that these tests are being used increasingly in patients with a low likelihood of having clogged blood vessels in the heart (Patel et al. 2010). In response to this study, Brenner suggested that "it is appropriate to ask whether current coronary imaging techniques are being used optimally" (Brenner 2010, p. 943).

This is precisely the question Ko et al. (2010) explored. They used data from the state of New York (NYS) and the Province of Ontario to compare the rates at which revascularization procedures were done there. They did their analysis for two different forms of revascularization: coronary artery bypass graft (CABG), a major surgical procedure used principally in patients with multiple clogged arteries, and percutaneous coronary intervention (PCI), a less invasive and less risky procedure used principally with patients with lower expected risk of coronary artery disease (CAD). Both procedures require that cardiac catheterization, a diagnostic test typically performed by cardiologists, first be done. Ko and colleagues found that in 2006, physicians in New York and Ontario performed CABG at approximately the same rate, while physicians in New York performed both cardiac catheterization and PCI at twice the rate as physicians in Ontario. They also noted that in 2006, there were 2.9 times more interventional cardiologists in New York as compared to Ontario (on a population-adjusted basis), 1.8 times more cardiac surgeons, and 2.6 times more hospitals equipped with facilities to perform PCI.

Commenting on these findings, Ko et al. (2010) suggested that "a market-oriented approach to financing cardiac procedures provides incentives for providers to maximize the volume of procedures performed and incentives for hospitals to set up cardiac invasive facilities because cardiac procedures are profitable for hospitals. ... It has been shown that the use of cardiac invasive procedures is highly dependent on the availability of resources, thus explaining why substantially greater numbers of additional cardiac catheterizations and subsequent PCI procedures are being performed among patients without [a heart attack] in NYS" (p. 2638).

Ko and colleagues also raised a second point of broader relevance, considering the growing focus on constraining health care costs in the United States. "One might also question whether patients in NYS with stable coronary artery disease were undergoing more unnecessary PCI procedures compared with Ontario" (2010, p. 2639). They subsequently took further steps to answer this question directly by examining data on all patients who underwent cardiac catheterization in New York and Ontario between October 2008 and September 2011 (Ko et al. 2013). They asked two fundamental questions.

1. Based on known risk factors for CAD, what was the predicted probability a patient undergoing cardiac catheterization would be found to have CAD?

2. What percentage of patients were found to have CAD, based on the outcomes of the cardiac catheterization?

Their results provided clear answers to both these questions. Of patients undergoing catheterization in New York, 19.3 percent had a greater than 50 percent probability of having CAD, while 41 percent of patients in Ontario had greater than 50 percent probability of having CAD. Consistent with these probabilities, 44.8 percent of patients in Ontario were actually found to have CAD, while 30.4 percent of patients in New York were found to have the disease. These results led the authors to conclude that "increased use of cardiac catheterization in New York relative to Ontario was primarily the result of selecting more patients at low predicted probability of obstructive CAD. ... These findings demonstrated that a more restrictive approach in selecting patients for cardiac catheterization did not lead to substantial underdetection of patients with surgical coronary anatomy on a per capita basis" (Ko et al. 2013, pp. 167–68).

The editors of the journal *Health Affairs* suggested that there has been an "imaging boom" in US health care, with the use of CT scanners, MRI scanners, PET scanners, cardiac catheterization facilities, and other similar devices proliferating over the past several years (*Health Affairs* 2008). Hillman and Goldsmith have argued that "an unknown but substantial fraction of imaging examinations are unnecessary and do not positively contribute to patient care. ... The evidence basis for using imaging is incomplete; much imaging practice is driven by habit or anecdote" (Hillman and Goldsmith 2010, p. 1).

In a commentary published in *JAMA*, Leff and Finucane (2008) referred to this explosion of high-tech imaging and other devices as "gizmo idolatry." They explain this concept as follows: "gizmo is used to refer to a mechanical device or procedure for which the clinical benefit in a specific clinical context is not clearly established, and gizmo idolatry refers to the general implicit conviction that a more technological approach is intrinsically better than one that is less technological unless, or perhaps even if, there is strong evidence to the contrary" (p. 1830). The explosion in the use of high-tech tests and treatments represents three common beliefs that are at the core of the US health care system: (1) that high-tech is better than low-tech, (2) that newer is better than older, and (3) that patients deserve the most advanced treatment available regardless of considerations of marginal cost/marginal benefit.

The Institutional Basis of Medical Malpractice

A final example of an institution with powerful effects on health care and its costs is our current malpractice system. Errors in medical care are dealt with under the broad category of personal injury law, often referred to as tort law. If a health care provider provides negligent care, and if a patient is injured as a result, that patient has a right to sue the provider and, if successful, to obtain economic compensation for the injury. The compensation is typically of two types:

1. compensation for the actual costs that result from the injury for things such as required medical care and lost income, referred to as "economic damages," and

2. payment to compensate the patient for the added pain and suffering that result from the injury during the patient's lifetime, referred to as "noneconomic damages."

To be protected from the possibility of having to pay these costs, nearly all physicians and hospitals purchase an insurance policy—malpractice insurance—that protects them should they be named in a malpractice suit. Malpractice suits are governed by state, rather than federal, law.

For several years after the turn of the twenty-first century, a "malpractice crisis" was seen as sweeping our country. Responding to increasing jury awards and decreasing financial returns, companies that provide physicians with malpractice insurance had been raising the rates charged for coverage by substantial amounts. Newspapers regularly reported on physicians who had chosen to leave practice rather than pay the increased cost of malpractice insurance and on the communities that found themselves without enough physicians as a result. A review of the changing world of medical malpractice in the United States concluded that "physicians revile malpractice claims as random events that visit unwarranted expense and emotional pain on competent, hardworking practitioners. ... Within the health care industry, there is a nearly universal belief that malpractice litigation has long since surpassed sensible levels and that major tort reform is overdue" (Studdert et al. 2004b, p. 283).

As a society, we have often adopted the implicit assumption that a poor outcome from medical care implies negligence on the part of the physician. Responding to the perception that malpractice awards are based on irrational responses of lay jurors, physicians have added billions of dollars to our health care budget by ordering extra tests and procedures that add little to care but present a stronger defense in the case of a malpractice suit. This practice of "defensive medicine" offers little added benefit to patients.

Negligence in medical care occurs when a physician provides care that is not consistent with the "community standard of care"—that is, with what an expert or panel of experts would expect a reasonably competent physician to do under similar circumstances. Thus, malpractice is derived from other physicians' assessments of the quality of the care provided.

As part of a large research project, a panel of expert physicians looked at more than 30,000 hospital records in 51 different hospitals. Based on their independent review of these records, they found that hospitalized patients experienced some sort of adverse outcome from their care about 4 percent of the time. They then looked to see how many of the patients who experienced a bad outcome did so because the physician or the hospital had provided substandard care (the legal basis for a finding of negligence). They found that 28 percent of bad outcomes could be traced to negligence (Brennan et al. 1991).

The researchers then asked, of those patients who had a bad outcome and who experienced substandard care, how many filed a malpractice lawsuit? Among the patients who received negligent care, only a tiny fraction (between 1 and 2%) filed a malpractice suit in response to their care.

The panel looked at the same data in a different way. They asked, of those patients who filed malpractice suits, how many had experienced negligent care? According to this expert panel, less than 20 percent of the malpractice suits represented instances of negligent care. Thus, when negligent care occurs, the patient usually does not sue, and when a patient does sue, it more often than not does not involve negligent care. As the researchers concluded, "the civil justice system only infrequently compensates injured patients and rarely holds healthcare providers accountable for substandard care" (Localio et al. 1991, p. 250).

The panel went on to look at the eventual judgment against the physician or hospital (if any) from the malpractice suits that were filed. They found no association between the amount of money received by the patient and whether the patient had received negligent care. The only factor that was associated with the level of judgment was the level of disability of the patient. The more disabled the patient as a result of treatment, the larger was the malpractice award, independent of negligence occurring (Brennan et al. 1996).

Another series of studies looked at a small group of obstetricians who had a record of repeated malpractice suits against them. A panel of experts compared the quality of the care provided by these physicians to the quality of care provided by comparable physicians who had not been sued in the past. The panel found no difference in the quality of the care between the two groups (Entman et al. 1994).

The panel again looked at the obstetricians who had been sued and those who had not. This time they evaluated patients' satisfaction with the quality of their interpersonal interaction with these doctors. The doctors who had been sued were rated much lower on this scale of quality. From the perspective of their patients, these doctors did not communicate well, and the patients' interactions with the doctors felt more awkward (Hickson et al. 1994). It appears that the reason these obstetricians were being sued and their colleagues were not was not because the quality of their care was lower; it was because they had a weaker interpersonal relationship with their patients. An editorial that accompanied this research concluded, "The same communication skills that reduce malpractice risk lead to patient satisfaction and improved quality of care. Caring, concerned physicians who communicate well with their patients are likely to provide the best quality of care" (Levinson 1994, p. 1620).

How does malpractice in Canada differ from that in the United States? As with health care more generally, the answer lies in the differing historical and cultural traditions of the two countries. Canada's legal system is based on the British tort system. The standards by which suits are judged differ, and the rate at which lawsuits are filed is substantially lower than in the United States. Canadian physicians still have to be concerned about malpractice, but not nearly as much as their colleagues in the United States. This is because

- patients in the United States file three-and-one-half times as many malpractice suits as patients in Canada (measured as suits per one thousand population),
- plaintiffs are successful in obtaining either a judgment or a settlement at approximately the same rate in the two countries, and
- even though the average malpractice judgment or settlement is slightly higher in Canada than in the United States, the overall per capita costs of the malpractice system are approximately four times higher in the United States than in Canada (Anderson et al. 2005).

The Affordable Care Act did not include malpractice reform, other than to encourage individual states to try new approaches to addressing the issue (Bovbjerg 2010). Mello et al. (2014) summarized the principal directions state-based malpractice reform efforts are taking. A common method to reduce malpractice costs is for states to enact laws that place a cap on the "noneconomic damages" that can be awarded to a plaintiff. A study of the impact of limiting these damages to $250,000 found that, as a result, average jury awards were reduced from an average of $293,645 to $234,314—a decrease of 20 percent (Seabury et al. 2014).

A second approach many have recommended is to create what are often referred to as "safe harbors" for physicians who follow established professional guidelines for care. An example is provided by the discussion of the use of PSA tests for the possible presence of prostate cancer. What happens if a physician, adhering to the guidelines published by the US Preventive Health Services Task Force, does not order a PSA on a patient, and the patient is later found to have metastatic prostate cancer? From the patient's perspective, failure to order the test might constitute negligence on the part of the physician, subjecting him or her to a potentially large liability judgment. Under "safe harbor" policies, this physician would be immune to a finding of negligence based on his or her adherence to the national guidelines. Bovbjerg and Berenson (2012) referred to safe harbor protections as "rare trifecta—better medical quality, more cost restraint through limits on liability's influence over medicine, and a potential avenue for political compromise on malpractice reform. A win-win-win" (p. 1).

The third approach identified by Mello et al. (2014) is what they refer to as "communication and resolution" programs. If an unexpected adverse outcome were to occur, the physician and/or health care facility providing the care, with the collaboration and support of their malpractice insurance carrier, would immediately "conduct an expedited investigation, provide the patient and family with an explanation of why the harm occurred, and offer an apology and acceptance of responsibility appropriate to the circumstances" (p. 2149). Even if the investigation finds no evidence of negligence, the provider would still issue an explicit and sincere apology to the patient and family. About two-thirds of states have passed laws, often referred to as "I'm sorry" laws, encouraging these expressions of regret, and when appropriate admissions of negligence, while preventing these expressions from being admitted as evidence should a lawsuit ensue. Given that, as described earlier, poor communication between physician and patient in the context of an adverse outcome is a principal driver of malpractice suits, these innovative approaches to improving physician/patient communication in these contexts hold substantial promise for reforming the medical malpractice process. Is his editorial response to the article by Mello et al., Sage (2014) suggested that "the core commitments of a communication-and-resolution program are to explain to patients what occurred, try to put things right, improve safety for the future, and empower and support caregivers. This is simply good medicine" (p. 2104).

Summary

In the United States, our fascination with technology, our orientation to the needs of the individual, our expectation that we will have expensive tests and procedures even if the added benefit is relatively small, and our propensity to sue physicians for malpractice all add up to care that is much more resource intensive and thus much more expensive than that in Canada. The marginal benefit of this extra care, measured in overall mortality rates, appears to be relatively small. The cost differences between the two countries take on even more significance, however, when we recall that, whereas all Canadians have health insurance as a right of residency, at the time ACA was enacted, more than 50 million people in the United States had no health insurance.

What about shifting the United States to a "single-payer" system of care? Some have been calling for this option for nearly three decades (Himmelstein and Wool handler 1989). Both California and Vermont considered statewide single-payer plans in the early 1990s, only to have the Vermont legislature and California voters turn down the option. In 1994, Californians voted against a single-payer ballot initiative by a 73 percent to 23 percent margin, "largely the result of voters' attitudes against 'big government' and higher taxes" (Danelski et al. 1995, p. 1).

In May 2010, two months after passage of ACA, Vermont tried again to adopt a statewide single-payer plan. The Vermont legislature passed Act 128, committing the state to enact a new state health system based either on a single-payer approach or an alternative approach developed by a state Health Care Reform Commission. In May 2011, the legislature passed Act 48, which called for phasing out private insurance plans and, by 2017, shifting to a publicly financed, universal coverage system referred to as Green Mountain Care (Fox and Blanchet 2015). This turned out not to be feasible. Analysts determined that such a plan would require new payroll taxes of 11.5 percent for employers and up to 9.9 percent for individuals. In December 2014, Vermont's governor dropped the plan. In response, a former Massachusetts state legislator and self-avowed single-payer advocate wrote: "After years of failure, I reluctantly concluded that single payer is too heavy a political lift for a state. Though the economic case is compelling, our body politic cares about more than just economics" (McDonough 2015, p. 1585).

The US health care system has developed over time in response to our dominant cultural and political institutions. While political and cultural institutions can change over time, any new system of care will have to be consistent with those institutions.

concept 2.1.6

Cultural and political institutions unique to the United States have helped create a health care system that is the most expensive in the world while also excluding more people from care than any other developed country. Any attempt to reform the system to address these problems must consider the institutions that led to the problems in the first place.

Provisions in the Affordable Care Act to Address the Appropriate Use of Medical Technology and Other High-Cost Medical Care

In comparing the treatment of heart disease in the United States and Canada, we find that US physicians use expensive, high-tech tests and treatments at a substantially higher rate than Canadian physicians, often with little evidence of added benefit to patients. Lee (2012) posed the question that is central to addressing the issue of potentially inappropriate use of care. "Health care costs are the pounding headache to which all of us in medicine will awaken each day for the rest of our lives. ... How do we resolve the tension between the imperative to do all we can to help patients and the needs of societies with constrained resources?" (p. 466).

Echoing this sentiment, Rosenbaum and Lamas (2012) described the dilemma many physicians face in the context of growing efforts to constrain costs: "Many who have been in practice for decades argue that at no point, no matter the economic environment, should cost factor into physicians' decisions. ... Yet some physicians now believe that considering cost serves not only the equitable distribution of finite services, but also the real interests of individual patients" (p. 100).

By 2015, the Affordable Care Act (ACA) had extended health insurance coverage to more than 20 million people who previously were uninsured. ACA aims to continue to expand coverage without adding to the already high cost of our health care system. With the realization that one of the principal drivers of rising health care costs is the way we have come to use newer and high-tech approaches to diagnosis and treatment, ACA creates a mechanism intended to constrain the inappropriate use of these expensive care modalities. It does so by establishing a national program of **comparative effectiveness research (CER)**.

From our earlier discussion of the evolution of treatment alternatives for high blood pressure, we saw how, as newer medications became available, they were tested only against dummy placebo pills to measure their clinical effectiveness. For a period of several decades, medications were never tested against each other to compare their relative effectiveness. When this research was finally done, it was determined that, compared to the newer alternatives, the older diuretic medication provided the

> **EDITOR'S NOTES**
>
> **comparative effectiveness research (CER):** the conduct and synthesis of research comparing the benefits and harms of various interventions and strategies for preventing, diagnosing, treating, and monitoring health conditions in real-world settings.

optimal clinical effectiveness. Distinct from research that asks the question "Does this treatment work?," CER asks the question "Which of these alternative treatments works best?" Patrick Conway and Carolyn Clancy, both senior officials in the US Department of Health and Human Services, explained the purpose of CER: "We defined CER as the conduct and synthesis of research comparing the benefits and harms of various interventions and strategies for preventing, diagnosing, treating, and monitoring health conditions in real-world settings. The purpose of this research is to improve health outcomes by developing and disseminating evidence-based information to patients, clinicians, and other decision makers about which interventions are most effective for which patients under specific circumstances" (Conway and Clancy 2009, p. 328). The Institute of Medicine of the National Academies of Science reports that "the purpose of CER is to assist consumers, clinicians, purchasers, and policy makers to make informed decisions that will improve health care at both the individual and population levels" (Sox and Greenfield 2009, p. 203).

In order to expand the reach and impact of CER, ACA established a national Patient-Centered Outcomes Research Institute (PCORI). PCORI is structured as an independent, nonprofit organization. It has a nationally representative Board of Governors, a series of national advisory panels, and a staff of experienced researchers. With funding provided by ACA, PCORI has initiated a series of research studies that compare existing alternatives for diagnosis or treatment. The Institute of Medicine of the National Academy of Sciences has recommended a list of one hundred topics that should receive priority in being addressed by PCORI-sponsored research (Iglehart 2009c). Perhaps the most important topic on this list is a study comparing alternative models for the organization of health care delivery so as to optimize health care access and quality. Second on the list is the broad topic of identifying optimal approaches to diagnosing and treating cardiovascular diseases.

ACA is explicit in requiring that CER provide recommendations for the optimal approach to care but not create mandates as to how specific conditions should be approached. Similarly, CER results are not to be used to determine insurance coverage or payment for differing approaches to care. Thus, CER, at least as carried out under ACA, is not intended to be cost-effectiveness research, in that it will not make recommendations as to which of the available alternatives provides the optimal balancing of costs and benefits.

In our aforementioned comparisons of the Canadian and the US approach to balancing costs and benefits, we saw that Canada, under the constraint of a fixed, global budget for care, explicitly attempts to balance the cost of care and the effectiveness of care at the margins (i.e., in deciding what treatments to provide and in prioritizing patients for access to resource-intensive care). The United States, on the other hand, has stridently resisted marginal cost/marginal effectiveness considerations, seeing such an approach to care as unwarranted rationing. Weinstein and Skinner (2010) suggested that, in order to constrain the historical rise in health care costs, "at some point ... we will have to confront the problem of cost-effectiveness at the level of the patient. The limitless pipeline of effective clinical strategies ... offers improved outcomes, but the costs of development and production are often very high" (p. 463).

ACA leaves unanswered the question of when, if ever, it is appropriate to deny a patient care that has some small yet well-documented marginal benefit but an extremely high marginal cost. It also leaves unanswered the question of how the medical profession, for decades invested in the belief that more care is better care, will shift its institutional belief system to one that accepts health care resources as scarce, and not only supports but expects physicians and other providers to balance costs and effectiveness when making clinical recommendations for individual patients. As described by Alexander and Stafford (2009), "Despite the allure, no amount of comparative effectiveness data alone, regardless of how rigorously assembled, will suffice to fundamentally transform clinical practice. … The primary problem is not the absence of knowledge regarding comparative effectiveness, but the absence of the necessary mechanisms to put this knowledge to work" (p. 2490).

References

Alexander GC, and Stafford RS. 2009. Does comparative effectiveness have a comparative edge? *JAMA* 301:2488–90.

ALLHAT Collaborative Research Group. 2002. Major outcomes in high-risk hypertensive patients randomized to angiotensin-converting enzyme inhibitor or calcium channel blocker vs diuretic. *JAMA* 288:2981–97.

Anderson GF, Hussey PS, Frogner BK, and Waters HR. 2005. Health spending in the United States and the rest of the industrialized world. *Health Affairs* 24(4):903–14.

Andriole GL, Crawford ED, Grubb RL, et al. 2009. Mortality results from a randomized prostate-cancer screening trial. *New England Journal of Medicine* 60:1310–19.

Bardy GH, Lee KL, Mark DB, et al. 2005. Amiodarone on an implantable cardioverter-defibrillator for congestive heart failure. *New England Journal of Medicine* 352:225–37.

Barry MJ. 2008. Screening for prostate cancer—the controversy that refused to die. *New England Journal of Medicine* 360:1351–54.

Bovbjerg RR. 2010. Will the Patient Protection and Affordable Care Act address the problems associated with medical malpractice? Urban Institute, http://www.rwjf.org/en/library/research/2010/08/will-the-patient-protection-and-affordable—care-act-address-the-.html.

Bovbjerg RR, and Berenson RA. 2012. The value of clinical practice guidelines as malpractice "safe harbors." Urban Institute, http://www.rwjf.org/en/library/research/2012/04/the-value-of-clinical-practice-guidelines-as-malpractice--safe-h.html.

Brennan TA, Leape LL, Laird NM, et al. 1991. Incidence of adverse events and negligence in hospitalized patients: Results of the Harvard Medical Practice Study I. *New England Journal of Medicine* 324:370–76.

Brennan TA, Sox CM, and Burstin HR. 1996. Relation between negligent adverse events and the outcomes of medical-malpractice litigation. *New England Journal of Medicine* 335: 1963–67.

Brenner DJ. 2010. Medical imaging in the 21st century—getting the best bang for the rad. *New England Journal of Medicine* 362:943–45.

Canadian Journal of Cardiology. 2005. Vol. 21: Supplement A contains a series of papers reporting on the guidelines for the use of ICDs and the policy considerations surrounding their use.

Conway PH, and Clancy C. 2009. Comparative-effectiveness research—Implications of the Federal Coordinating Council's report. *New England Journal of Medicine* 361:328–30.

Danelski AE, Altman DE, Eldred J, et al. 1995. The California single-payer debate: The defeat of Proposition 186. Kaiser Family Foundation, http://kff.org/health-costs/report/the-california-single-payer-debate-the-defeat/.

DiMaggio PJ. 1988. Interest and agency in institutional theory. Pp. 3–21 in Zucker L., ed., *Institutional Patterns and Organizations.* Cambridge, Mass.: Ballinger.

Duffin J. 2011. The impact of single-payer health care on physician income in Canada, 1850–2005. *American Journal of Public Health* 101(7):1198–1208.

Entman SS, Glass CA, Hickson GB, et al. 1994. The relation between malpractice claims history and subsequent obstetrical quality. *JAMA* 272:1588–91.

Flexner A. 1910. *Medical education in the United States and Canada.* New York: Carnegie Foundation for the Advancement of Teaching.

Fox AM, and Blanchet NJ. 2015. The little state that couldn't could? The politics of "single-payer" health coverage in Vermont. *Journal of Health Politics, Policy, and Law* 40(3): 447–85.

Fuchs VR. 1983. *Who Shall Live?* New York: Basic Books.

Fuchs VR. 1993d. *The Future of Health Policy.* Cambridge, Mass.: Harvard University Press.

Hamilton WH. 1932. Statement. Pp. 189–200 in *Medical Care for the American People: The Final Report of the Committee on the Cost of Medical Care, Adopted October 31, 1932.* Chicago: University of Chicago Press.

Health Affairs. 2008. The imaging boom. *Health Affairs* 27(6):1466.

Health Canada. 2009. Canada Health Act annual report 2008–2009, www.hcsc.gc.ca/hcs-sss/pubs/cha-lcs/2009-cha-lcs-ar-ra/index-eng.php#intro.

Hickson GB, Clayton EW, Entman SS, et al. 1994. Obstetricians' prior malpractice experience and patients' satisfaction with care. *JAMA* 272:1583–87.

Hillman BJ, and Goldsmith JC. 2010. The uncritical use of high-tech medical imaging. *New England Journal of Medicine,* June 23, www.nejm.org.

Himmelstein DU, and Woolhandler S. 1989. A national health program for the United States: A physicians' proposal. *New England Journal of Medicine* 320:102–8.

Howlett K, Paperny AM, and Walton D. 2009. Private-clinic patients jump the line for flu shot. *The Globe and Mail,* November 2.

Iglehart JK. 2000. Revisiting the Canadian health care system. *New England Journal of Medicine* 342:2007–12.

Iglehart JK. 2009c. Prioritizing comparative effectiveness research—IOM recommendations. *New England Journal of Medicine* 361:325–28.

Katz SJ, Cardiff K, Pascali M, Barer ML, and Evans RG. 2002. Phantoms in the snow: Canadians' use of health care services in the United States. *Health Affairs* 21(3):20–31.

Ko DT, Tu JV, Samadashvili Z, et al. 2010. Temporal trends in the use of percutaneous coronary intervention and coronary artery bypass surgery in New York State and Ontario. *Circulation* 121:2635–44.

Ko DT, Tu JV, Austin PC, et al. 2013. Prevalence and extent of obstructive coronary artery disease among patients undergoing elective coronary catheterization in New York State and Ontario. *JAMA* 310(2):163–69.

Kolata G. 1993. How demand surged for unapproved prostate test. *New York Times,* September 29.

Krahn MD, Mahoney JE, Eckman MH, et al. 1994. Screening for prostate cancer: A decision analytic view. *JAMA* 272:773–80.

Krasner SD. 1983. *International Regimes.* Ithaca, N.Y.: Cornell University Press.

Krauss C. 2005. Canadian court chips away at national health care. *New York Times,* June 9.

Lee TH. 2012. Care redesign—A path forward for providers. *New England Journal of Medicine* 367:466–72.

Leff B, and Finucane TE. 2008. Gizmo idolatry. *JAMA* 299:1830–32.

Lett D. 2008. Private health clinics remain unregulated in most of Canada. *Canadian Medical Association Journal* 178:986–87.

Levinson W. 1994. Physician-patient communication, a key to malpractice prevention. *JAMA* 272:1619–20.

Lipset SM. 1990. *Continental Divide.* New York: Routledge, Chapman, and Hall.

Localio AR, Lawthers AG, Brennan TA, et al. 1991. Relation between malpractice claims and adverse events due to negligence. Results of the Harvard Medical Practice Study III. *New England Journal of Medicine* 325:245–51.

Marleau D. 1995. Letter RE: Canada Health Act, January 6, 1995, in Health Canada (2009), p. 229.

McClellan MB, and Tunis SR. 2005. Medicare coverage of ICDs. *New England Journal of Medicine* 352:222–24.

McDonough JE. 2015. The demise of Vermont's single-payer plan. *New England Journal of Medicine* 372(17):1584–85.

McNaughton-Collins M. 2009. Perspective roundtable: Screening for prostate cancer. *New England Journal of Medicine* 360:e18, http://content.nejm.org/cgi/reprint/360/13/e18.pdf.

Meilicke CA, and Storch JL, eds. 1980. *Perspectives on Canadian Health Services Policy: History and Emerging Trends.* Ann Arbor, Mich.: Health Administration Press.

Mello MM, Studdert DM, and Kachalia A. 2014. The medical liability climate and prospects for reform. *JAMA* 312(20):2146–55.

North DC. 1986. *Institutions, Institutional Change and Economic Performance.* New York: Cambridge University Press.

Patel MR, Peterson ED, Dai D, et al. 2010. Low diagnostic yield of coronary angiography. *New England Journal of Medicine* 362:886–95.

Picard A. 2006. Public wants Medicare changed, poll finds. *The Globe and Mail,* June 8.

Pilote L, Saynina O, Lavoie F, and McClellan M. 2003. Cardiac procedure use and outcomes in elderly patients with acute myocardial infarction in the United States and Quebec, Canada, 1988 to 1994. *Med Care* 41(7):813–22.

Pollack A. 2008. The minimal impact of a big hypertensive study. *New York Times,* November 28.

Romanow RJ. 2002. Building on values: The future of health care in Canada. Final Report of the Commission on the Future of Health Care in Canada. www.hc-sc.gc.ca/english/care/romanow/index1.html.

Romanow RJ. 2005. Now's the time to stand up for Medicare. *The Globe and Mail*, June 10.

Rosenbaum L, and Lamas DL. 2012. Cents and sensitivity—Teaching physicians to think about costs. *New England Journal of Medicine* 367:99–101.

Royal Commission on Health Services. 1964. *Report*. Ottawa: Queen's Printers.

Sage WM. 2014. Medical malpractice reform—When is it about money? Why is it about time? *JAMA* 312(20):2103–105.

Schröder FH, Hugosson J. Roobol MJ, et al. 2009. Screening and prostate-cancer mortality in a randomized European study. *New England Journal of Medicine* 360:1320–28.

Scott WR. 1987. The adolescence of institutional theory. *Administrative Science Quarterly* 32: 493–511.

Seabury SA, Helland E, and Jena AB. 2014. Medical malpractice reform: Noneconomic damages caps reduced payments 15 percent, with varied effects by specialty. *Health Affairs* 33(11):2048–56.

Simpson J. 2005. The new face of medicare. *The Globe and Mail*, June 10.

Sox HC, and Greenfield S. 2009. Comparative effectiveness research: A report from the Institute of Medicine. *Annals of Internal Medicine* 151(3):203–205.

Studdert DM, Mello MM, and Brennan TA. 2004b. Medical malpractice. *New England Journal of Medicine* 350:283–92.

Taylor MG. 1987. *Health insurance and Canadian public policy*, 2nd ed. Montreal: McGill-Queens University Press.

US Preventive Services Task Force. 2012. Final recommendation statement—prostate cancer: Screening, May 2012, http://www.uspreventiveservicestaskforce.org/Page/Document/RecommendationStatementFinal/prostate-cancer-screening.

Weinstein MC, and Skinner JA. 2010. Comparative effectiveness and health care spending—implications for reform. *New England Journal of Medicine* 364:460–65.

The Medicalized Society

By Carl Boggs

Capitalist modernity today is shaped increasingly by evolving forms of technological rationality—a dimension of ideological **hegemony** that, in the United States, is especially powerful in the realm of medicine, which has become intertwined with the general economy, health care, food production and consumption, the environment, science, and culture. In this context, capitalist rationalization develops alongside of—and coincides with—what might be called the **medicalization** of American society. At the center of a historical process giving rise to technological rationality, anticipated many decades ago by such theorists as Max Weber, Antonio Gramsci, the Frankfurt School, and Herbert Marcuse, is an expanding medical-pharmaceutical behemoth—commodified, bureaucratic, dysfunctional, iatrogenic—that pushes the matrix of ideological domination to new levels.[1]

The War on Drugs and the steadily expanding role of Big Pharma in American society are twin expressions of a progressively hypermedicalized system in which social progress is hitched to the corporate-technocratic growth model that has driven postwar US economic development. A moralistic crusade against "drugs" coexists with the lucrative production and marketing of drugs favored by the medical establishment. What might be viewed as an addictive culture is located squarely on both sides of this trajectory—legal and illegal, medicinal and recreational, synthetic and natural. Today health care is increasingly colonized by private interests, corporate agendas, and treatment programs composed of expensive therapies, high-tech interventions, surgery, and, of course, drugs, drugs, and more drugs. While drugs of every conceivable type (and for every conceivable purpose) have long saturated American society, in recent decades the political warriors have become obsessed with outlawing *selected* categories of drugs, on the basis of rather arbitrary and inconsistent criteria. For the contemporary gatekeepers of public morality, "good" drugs are those prescribed by licensed doctors, "experts" in health, medicine, and treatment. Other chemical substances are framed as illicit, addictive, even sinful—yet another source of moral panic.

In this context, Andrew Weil, Ronald K. Siegel, and kindred critics have called for urgent and thorough reassessment of the entire drug phenomenon, hoping to challenge the ideological narrowing of American medical discourse.[2] In purely economic terms, capitalist modernity advances a project of material growth through the benefits of science and technology—a project that has given rise to expanded corporate, state, and bureaucratic power. Such power is tied to an ethos of instrumental rationality and new forms of expertise, hierarchy, and professionalism that coexist with heightened mass **alienation** and disempowerment—beneath a façade of democratic politics. In the United States, where corporate dominion has reached its pinnacle and material abundance has delivered questionable benefits for society as a whole, the medical system—supposedly a beacon of modernity—is beset with mounting dysfunctions, reliance on illusory quick fixes, and spreading **iatrogenesis** (that is, causing more harm than good). Rising drug (and other) addictions—and hypermedicalized strategies of treatment—represent opposite sides of the same intensifying social crisis. Modern governance, built on a confluence of corporate, governmental, and (for the United States) military power, contains a deep authoritarian logic in which a formal liberal-democratic order is sustained alongside oligarchical and bureaucratic structures. The medical behemoth, still influenced by its Rockefeller corporate origins and close linkages to Wall Street, fits this matrix of modern domination perfectly.[3]

Here the thesis presented by Theodor Adorno and Max Horkheimer in their classic *Dialectic of Enlightenment*—where modernity is understood as a "new kind of barbarism"—might be more fully appreciated today. As Enlightenment rationality underpins expanding modes of production and consumption, systemic capacity for institutional controls and ideological hegemony deepens, allowing for the transformation of people into consumer-driven, alienated, largely impotent objects. For Adorno and Horkheimer, modernity was likened to a "totalitarian" order by its very rationalizing logic, creating a world in which "life and death, heaven and hell hang together."[4] Further, "the paradoxical nature of faith [in progress] ultimately degenerates into a swindle, and becomes the myth of the twentieth century; and its irrationality turns it into an instrument of rational administration by the wholly enlightened as they steer society toward barbarism."[5] Here domination and alienation, as twin historical modalities, represent two sides of the same trajectory: people, ideas, and goods are ritually converted into objectified entities. Viewed thusly, the present-day drug disaster—extremely high levels of consumption, nightmarish abuses and addictions, medicalized "treatment" schemes, the fears and myths that are generated—takes on special ideological meaning.

As state-corporate capitalism expands, the health of the planet deteriorates just as the health of human populations faces increasing threats—the result of heightened economic growth, widespread use of toxic chemicals, accelerated depletion of natural resources, wasteful animal-based food production, and Mc Donaldization of dietary patterns.[6] With US health care the most commodified and resource-depleting in the world, consuming nearly 20 percent of domestic output, the consistently high rate of deaths from cancer and other chronic diseases (perhaps one million yearly)—connected to remarkably high levels of obesity—speaks volumes about the dysfunctional, poorly accessible, and iatrogenic features of American medicine. While Big Pharma alone accounts for vast healthcare expenditures, it is easy to see how chemicalized treatment programs (to counter the deadly effects of an already toxic world) are likely to only worsen iatrogenic tendencies. The idea that healthcare outcomes can be significantly altered with more of the same—that is, more spending, more expertise, more technology, more pills—amounts to one of the grand illusions of the current period.

The corporate medical system requires, even celebrates, the power of its technical apparatus, consistent with the spread of technological rationality, often with deadly consequences.[7] While trumpeting individualism (mainly as *consumerism*), the ideology thinly conceals a technocratic instrumentalism bereft of human subjectivity and agency. In a society where personal alienation and social misery are the norm, who can be astonished to find an endless (and mounting) list of "disorders" requiring (physical or mental) treatment by chemical miracles, including "narcotic" properties found in mind-altering (or mind-numbing) drugs? Alienation ultimately gives rise to a variety of psychological coping mechanisms, including addictive behaviors in the form of shopping, food, sex, gambling, sports, the Internet, alcohol, tobacco, pharmaceuticals, and illegal drugs. Within capitalist modernity, the perpetual search for escape, for superficial and temporary meaning, produces a multitude of addictions fueled by anxiety, stress, depression, and physical disorders. Here "medicalization" and "addiction" become twin expressions of the same modern, rationalized, administered social order.[8]

Corporate Medicine Today

The practice of medicine in the United States since World War II cannot be understood without discussing the rapid growth of a labyrinthine corporate network—hospitals, clinics, institutes, universities—combined with an even larger ensemble of business interests: Big Pharma, insurance companies, finance, energy, food, agriculture, and the chemical industry. This corporate empire amounts to the most costly, bureaucratic, and commodified medical system ever created—a system in which failure and iatrogenesis are built into its very modus operandi.[9] At the time of this writing (fall 2014), in the midst of heated debates over Obamacare reforms, the American demand for medical services across the board—insurance, hospitals and clinics, drugs and other medications—has skyrocketed. Drug consumption alone in the United States expanded by 3.2 percent during 2013. Chronic health problems (heart disease, diabetes, cancer, infectious diseases) have been dramatically on the rise, imposing new burdens on the healthcare system. By 2020 Americans are expected to spend nearly $5 trillion on "health care"—the total of the next ten highest-spending nations combined—at a time when chronic illnesses have reached peak levels, obesity extends to nearly 40 percent of the population, pill taking has become the norm, and ineffective or harmful medical procedures now outweigh the beneficial ones.[10]

The burdensome costs of corporate medicine have become a source of economic misery and psychological despair for tens of millions of people—especially for those suffering from chronic ailments. An exhaustive *Time* magazine report on the state of American health care, assembled by Steve Brill, points out that cancer treatment, as one example, can bring costs totaling a half million dollars (only partially covered by insurance), to one individual or family—a common source of financial and personal ruin that worsens the medical traumas.[11] A single hospital visit can cost several thousand dollars, not including expensive tests and procedures. The United States is now a nation of sick people who can expect problematic treatment at exorbitant prices, for hospital or clinic visits, doctors' fees, lab tests, drug therapies, CT scans, high-tech procedures, and surgeries.

While people suffering from chronic illnesses can spend tens of thousands of dollars for drugs and hundreds of thousands more for hospital stays of a few weeks, CEOs and hospital executives, Big Pharma, and insurance firms make huge profits and salaries: incomes of beyond $1 million yearly are common. Brill reports that fourteen high-level administrators at the Sloan Kettering Institute, a major center of cancer research and treatment, receive incomes of more than $500,000 annually, while CEO compensation at health facilities such as Cleveland Clinic and New York Presbyterian Hospital can reach $5 million, augmented by generous benefits.[12] The CEO of the Sutter Health chain received $5.2 million in 2011, just as a ninety-year-old woman was charged $121,000 for treatment of a broken bone.[13] Hospitals, doctors, drug companies, laboratories, equipment providers, and many others within the medical establishment amass private fortunes from human misfortune and suffering. To help secure this privilege, the pharmaceutical industry spent $2.9 billion on lobbying the US Congress during 1998–2014.[14] In 2012 annual per capita healthcare spending in the United States had reached $8,000 yearly, more than double that of any other nation—a predicament the hotly debated Obama reforms were not likely to significantly alleviate. Patients with severe health problems can spend tens of thousands of dollars in a single day, especially if costly drug therapy is prescribed. Overcharges and huge markups are routine. Insurance coverage is spotty and limited by huge copays, deductibles, exemptions, and loopholes. Anyone with chronic health problems can expect a steady flow of inflated charges, what Brill calls "reams of bills to people."[15] Within corporate medicine the incentives for doctors to order drugs, testing, and procedures appear difficult to resist. With trillions of dollars spent by a public inundated with advertising, fearful of alternatives, and anxious to find ready fixes, life expectancy in the United States ranks fiftieth among nations—and overall health indicators are no more flattering, placing it near the bottom of industrialized countries.

The Many Faces of Addiction

No discussion of the medicalization of American society is possible without addressing the pervasive reality of **addiction**, a term that—like most linguistic constructions—has long been subject to multiple definitions and perspectives. I refer here to established, habitual patterns of behavior that can apply to most human objects and activities, from drugs to food, sex to gambling, technology to shopping. Addictive behavior varies according to duration, intensity, nature, and focus. Unfortunately, the familiar understanding of "addiction" in media, government, and medical discourse revolves around nightmarish tropes of the sort popularized on TV and in Hollywood movies, where the problem typically refers to "drugs" (illegal drugs), with occasional diversions into alcoholism—an outlook that continues to drive the War on Drugs.

Hoary stereotypes about drugs and addiction have brought untold harm to American society, yet they remain central to social policy, law enforcement, and personal treatment approaches. Few contemporary public discourses have become more ideologically hardened or politically self-defeating. A broader, more critical perspective on addictive behavior, today more urgently needed than ever, might start with the following generalizations:

- Habitual behavior patterns unfold through a dialectical interaction between personal and social life, within a complex totality involving subject, object or objects, and a range of intervening or mediating factors such as family life, work, health conditions, and culture. This helps explain why the vast majority of people who consume particular substances or engage in specific behaviors do not automatically end up habituated or dependent—or, if so, manage by means of their own resources to control potentially dysfunctional consequences. It is not the concrete *object* as such, seen in isolation, but rather *multiple* factors shaping the social context that crucially shape behavior leading (or not leading) to addiction.

EDITOR'S NOTES

addiction: according to Boggs, established, habitual patterns of behavior that can apply to most human objects and activities and which can vary in duration, intensity, nature, and focus.

- Addictions follow a continuum, with dependency spanning many possibilities, from virtually harmless to extremely destructive, most cases falling between. Many common types of habituation—daily coffee intake, regular TV watching, weekend football gambling, wine with dinner, repeated trips to McDonald's, nonstop texting—might be rather harmless even where defined as addictive. Indeed what we all-too-glibly label addictive behavior is not typically—much less innately—destructive.

- Even where addictions turn problematic or destructive, as with excessive daily consumption of drugs or alcohol, people can endure the behavior and carry on more or less "normally" with their work, careers, family, and everyday life. In regions of South America people chew coca leaves regularly; in Mediterranean countries red wine is consumed abundantly with dinner; in many American homes men drink a six-pack of beer or more daily; in modern society untold numbers of people are fixated on electronic devices; and millions of people around the world smoke pot routinely. In few of these cases is there much thought, if any, of harmful addictions requiring medical treatment. Even regular users of "hard" drugs, such as coke, heroin, and methamphetamines, can lead satisfying and productive lives, with harmful effects often controlled or minimized through human will power.

- Even in cases of severe, disabling addictions, people frequently manage to outgrow them, moving through well-known processes of adaptation to changing life situations. Youth inclined toward indulgent, outrageous behavior in their late teens and early twenties—college years when extreme use of alcohol and drugs is common—usually "mature out" of such behavior when faced with new pressures from job, career, family, health, and finances. Historical evidence suggests as much: fewer than 10 percent of long-term hospital patients dependent on painkillers remained addicted once the general *setting* had dramatically changed. The same applies to Vietnam veterans once strung out on opiates. The presumption of fixed, immutable forms of addiction—whatever the substance or behavior in question—can be dismissed as yet another myth of the drug enforcers' ideological arsenal.[16]

From the foregoing generalizations it follows that harm from addictive behavior cannot be taken for granted; worst-case scenarios are hardly inevitable, but must be determined through empirical investigation. What are the measurable consequences of daily pot consumption—or of wine, beer, cocaine, sugar, and fast foods—within a given social totality? Damaging consequences can be identified and measured according to how, and to what degree, habituation negatively influences a person's job, career, health, and finances. Scientific focus on tentative hypotheses and factual evidence appears all too forgotten when it comes to dealing with addiction or, more emphatically, "drug addiction."

As Stanton Peele and other critics argue, conventional "disease" theory, central to most medical strategies and basic to mainstream understanding of both addiction and treatment, has shaky empirical foundations, grounded as it is on oversimplified assumptions about human behavior. Habituation is better framed as a *condition* shaped by and mediated through contextual factors like those mentioned previously.[17] Proof of addiction as disease would have to depend on a range of biological variables, which have never been established through actual research that, in any event, generally ignores social, nutritional, lifestyle, and other contextual influences on patterns of human behavior.

Harmful and costly addictive behaviors actually occur at the highest rates for such legal substances as fast foods, sugar, alcohol, tobacco, and many pharmaceuticals. Those sources of habituation are so common and so thoroughly part of the culture as to be routinely overlooked as addictions—abuses and excesses perhaps, but rarely (aside from alcohol) understood as especially addictive. The potentially destructive impact of food, alcohol, cigarettes, and legal drugs should nowadays be scarcely questionable, as the evidence mounts. Matters worsen, it should be added, when individuals consume potent substances in various (and untested) combinations, such as mixing alcohol with prescribed medications or taking two or more drugs simultaneously in the form of "cocktails." Drug problems, it is often forgotten, follow multiple possible outcomes—among them adverse reactions, overdoses, drug-related accidents, and lethal episodes.

The grand myths of prevailing addiction discourse, which shape both the medical model and the War on Drugs, have in recent decades achieved something of a life of their own. Official definitions of sickness, disorder, abuse, and treatment, interwoven with the reigning medical ideology, serve to legitimate norms of technocratic intervention and quick fixes. Fixated on the discrete *objects* of behavior, such addiction theory detaches the problem from the complex totality of social life, thus diminishing the role of human agency.[18] "Addiction" results from the innate properties of substances (or activities), devaluing the immense variations in human experience, perspective, context, and volition. If certain substances or behaviors are intrinsically addictive, how is it possible—as is clearly the case—for the overwhelming majority of users to suffer few if any of the harmful outcomes so glibly imputed to those choices?

Alternatives to the dominant medical paradigm are routinely dismissed within the official discourse, riveted as it is by narratives of "disease" and "disorders" said to inhere in the *object* of individual choice. Leading sectors of the medical establishment, along with familiar twelve-step recovery programs, remain wedded to the disease model, understood as more enlightened than earlier views of addiction that focused on moral depravity and sinful behavior. The National Institute on Drug Abuse (NIDA) upholds the premise that drug abuse and addiction fit the disease model, situated within a biological framework. A recent NIDA proclamation concludes, "As a result of scientific research, we know that addiction is a disease that affects both brain and behavior." More specifically, "addiction is defined as a chronic, relapsing brain disease that is characterized by compulsive drug seeking and use, despite harmful consequences. It is considered a brain disease because drugs change the brain."[19] Generalizations about addiction refer to such determinants as the "biological makeup of the individual." Genetic variables, it is claimed, account for between 40 and 50 percent of those who experience some type of addiction.[20]

More widely circulated statements about drug addiction can be found in the *Diagnostic and Statistical Manual of Mental Disorders* (DSM-IV), which focuses more on "disorders" than on "disease"—something of an advance over NIDA—but that still imbues particular chemical substances with innately (often irresistible) addictive properties. The DSM identifies eleven classes of such disorders, among them psychotic, mood, anxiety, sleep, and sexual conditions linked to drug abuse or dependency.[21] Some disorders are associated with use of intoxicating drugs; "hallucinogenic disorders" (including maladaptive behavior), for example, are associated with consumption of LSD, mescaline, and psilocybin. Addiction means dependency, including extreme tolerance, withdrawal, persistent desire, and compulsive overindulgence, often leading to "recurrent and significant adverse consequences related to repeated use of substances," including possible social, legal, or personal difficulties.[22] The DSM emphasis on "disorders," more helpful than the NIDA model, is broad enough to apply far beyond those specific drug habituations analyzed in the manual. As for harmful consequences, the criteria for distinguishing intoxicants like cannabis and cocaine from many pharmaceuticals, as well as ordinary products like fast foods and sugar, remain vague and arbitrary.

A deeper problem is that preoccupation with "disorders" tends to stigmatize forms of behavior that, upon serious reflection, turn out to be rather common, even "normal." Conditions such as depression, anger, anxiety, shyness, and self-absorption, where not so extreme as to cause breakdown or dysfunction, can hardly be classified as distinctly medical problems—much less as something requiring expensive drug treatment. Viewed thusly, "diagnosis" emanating from the DSM and kindred psychiatric sources relies on labels best understood as moral rather than scientific. The proliferation of such "disorders," however, does ensure a steady flow of patients for the medical system and revenues for Big Pharma.[23]

By avoiding the "disease" trap, DSM manages to take into account contextual factors that contribute to addiction, though it does so as a largely peripheral concern. Referring to "substance intoxication," the manual states, "The maladaptive nature of a substance-induced change in behavior depends on the social and environmental context."[24] At other points the text refers to "cultural traditions" and "social settings" that can influence patterns of alcohol consumption.[25] While such generalizations are essentially truisms, the DSM still formulates the bulk of its addiction discourse as a more or less singular fixation on specific *objects* of abuse and dependency. Its conceptual advance beyond the disease model, therefore, remains more limited and one-dimensional than might be hoped.

The NIDA and important sectors of the medical-treatment apparatus still follow the unsupported notion that drugs (though only some categories of drugs) are immediately and inescapably addictive, transforming the user into a hopeless slave of desire and habit, powerless to change under any circumstances—at least until the experts appear on the scene. The War on Drugs is based entirely on such official fallacies. Where "disease" is the label, addiction becomes all-consuming, with a steady descent into hell being one likely outcome—a fate obviously more probable for some drugs than for others. Yet even where addictions occur at a high rate, as in stressful environments like prisons, military combat, impoverished street life, and family strife, the level and incidence of habituation usually decline, often dramatically, once the main contextual factors change.[26]

Peele refers to the disease theory of addiction as "useless folklore," a view consistent with that adopted here.[27] According to such "folklore," drug habituation is produced by an irresistible biological or medical logic—a permanent state of being created by powerful external forces. Opposition to the disease model is cavalierly dismissed as an elaborate psychological ruse, or "denial"—that is, an irrational refusal to submit to expert opinion and medical intervention. Even moderate or episodic use of (illicit) drugs is said to possibly overwhelm, even transform, the victimized user.

A crucial flaw in disease theory is that no distinct, generally agreed-upon biological or genetic mechanisms for addictive behavior have been identified—nor are they likely to be, given the complex, ever-shifting elements of individual psychology that cannot be understood apart from social factors, health and nutritional patterns, fortuitous circumstances, cultural differences, and, above all, dynamics of personal *choice*. For research on drugs to fully account for *all* such variables related to addiction—in the absence of which no biological determinants can be proven—is virtually impossible or, in any case, far too cumbersome, time-consuming, and expensive for any investigator or group of investigators to pursue. Moreover, the varieties of addictive behavior that *do not* include consumption of drugs or food, such as gambling, sex, and shopping, clearly possess no biological markers, as these are undeniably a function of social-psychological dynamics. By framing a multifaceted problem like addiction as biological and externally imposed, disease theory removes human psychology from the complexities of everyday life.

Even casual familiarity with addiction reveals a *continuum* of behavior—no different from other human problems. A common addiction is excessive fast-food consumption, typical of the McDonaldized culture. While physical and mental harm from a steady diet of fast foods is well documented, levels of dependency naturally vary, with few people consuming the amounts depicted in the film *Super Size Me*, where monthlong gorging on almost exclusively fast foods led to a near-lethal outcome. Millions of habitual fast-food patrons suffer from problems of heart disease, diabetes, cancer, and osteoporosis, but even these conditions differ widely in terms of severity. Long-term consumers of beer, wine, liquor, and cigarettes, of course, can expect above-normal serious health challenges; risks are well known, but vary according to amount and regularity of consumption, among other factors. Patterns related to food and nutrition are just as valid for products like alcohol, tobacco, and other drugs, independent of legal status. Those who abuse alcohol inevitably do so in terms of degree, with a small percentage considered extreme addicts. A person who drinks two or more glasses of wine daily with meals might be labeled an "alcoholic," yet this routine—normal for many European countries—might be perfectly functional, serving ordinary psychological needs or desires. The labeling tendency within established medicine comes easy and often, nowhere more so than for antidrug crusaders obsessed with banned substances. As for drugs, the rate of addiction among those using pot, coke, hallucinogens, and most pharmaceuticals is typically below 10 percent—among alcohol drinkers slightly higher, and among meth users still higher but not much over 15 percent.[28] Data concerning habitual gamblers and shoppers, on the other hand, are murkier as the criteria for addiction seem less well established, more vague and arbitrary.

Cocaine is one substance that the NIDA and similar official sources claim to be inherently addictive, but the reality speaks differently: just *1 percent* of coke users wind up with a daily habit, and fewer yet risk jobs, careers, health, and families to satisfy cravings. As noted, millions of people have routinely chewed coca leaves in the Andes for centuries, with few if any known problems of abuse or addiction. No evidence suggests that coke habituation, even with the more concentrated form of the drug, is more difficult to quit than, say, Valium or Vicodin dependency. Peele writes, "With cocaine as with every other illicit drug that has ever been used by large numbers of people, the majority of those who take it do not become regular users, the majority of regular users do not become addicted, and the majority of those who become addicted cease their addiction on their own without treatment."[29] Contrary to official antidrug discourse, people usually possess enough inner resources to break with dependency. The example of Vietnam veterans has been mentioned: 90 percent of returning troops hooked on cannabis or heroin soon outgrew their addictions once the social context had profoundly changed. Viewed *contextually*, therefore, hard drugs provided an escape from the stresses and horrors of combat but no longer served that function in more "normalized," less stressful civilian settings. A break with addictive behavior usually occurs with advancing age and maturity, extreme dependency becoming rare past age fifty-five. No doubt treatment can be successful, especially where it allows for self-directed change. Evidence shows that therapy for alcoholism and drug addiction is best when it focuses on self-help manuals; family and/or community reinforcement; and elevation of social, job, and communication skills—a modality far removed from a disease model that strips people of human agency.[30]

In the dominant medical ideology, the term "addict" refers to a fixed, monolithic, unchangeable state of being: once an addict, perpetually an addict. This fiction not only degrades human capacity for adaptation and change, but ignores the very *complexity* of human experience. For one individual chemical substances might serve as a medium of escape, while for others it may be a source of pain relief, a remedy for depression, a vehicle of psychological exploration, or a simple means of intoxication. The degree to which drugs can be "mind-altering" varies immensely, depending on many factors. The drug experience taps into a great variety of personal behaviors, contradicting simple notions of automatic habituation and dependency. What the drug user brings to the experience—history, age, health, nutrition, personal outlook, etc.—decisively shapes outcomes.[31]

Lost in the familiar obsession with (illegal) drug "horrors" is a far more urgent problem facing American society today—widespread and severe harm from habitual consumption of fast foods, sugar, and similar legal products that have contributed to an obesity rate in the United States of nearly 40 percent.[32] The McDonaldized diet, research shows, is largely responsible for heart disease, cancer, and diabetes—conditions leading to far more deaths than all illegal drugs combined. The fast-food culture is so deeply embedded in American life, so normalized as to be virtually invisible, yet is fully implicated in the continuing obesity "epidemic," thanks to high intakes of saturated fats and sugar. Highly popular Coca-Cola, originally laden with caffeine, cocaine, and sugar, nowadays contains up to thirty-two teaspoons of sugar per eight ounces of liquid, composed largely of high-fructose corn syrup. As tens of millions of Americans continue long-ingrained dietary patterns in the face of potentially severe harm, such habituation might well be considered addictive, at least according to the DSM criteria: dependency, loss of control, and refusal to change.

The problem here is less one of biology—"genetics" or "disease"—than of socialization processes, influence of advertising and peer communication, societal changes in food consumption, and (lest we forget) personal *choice* when faced with serious risks. With the national incidence of obesity—and associated health problems—escalating in recent decades, the idea that genetic markers (requiring *centuries* to alter even slightly) are behind this sea change is too preposterous to take seriously. That a steady increase in postwar drug consumption—and addictive behavior—could be explained in strictly biological terms makes just as little sense. What might be a problematic habit in one setting—a target of cultural taboos and legal prohibitions—can be normal, perhaps salutary, in other settings. Teenagers drinking red wine with dinner in Italy and Spain is a practice that raises few alarms, not too different from the daily chewing of coca leaves in regions of South America or regular use of cannabis in some cultures (for example, many communities and groups influenced by sixties counterculture in the United States). While marijuana is indeed liberally consumed around the world, it has long been demonized in the United States as among the most harmful of drugs. Less than a century ago in American society, liquor was savaged by moral enforcers as the devil's potion, yet today it qualifies as big business, is vigorously advertised, and is considered essential to many celebrations. Given Americans' regular intake of hundreds of potentially abused drugs, what is striking is the rather *low* rate of addiction to illegal drugs (generally less than 10 percent, as noted previously). Severe addictions to banned products, while surely too frequent, impact a relatively small percentage of drug users. Other addictions, as mentioned—to fast foods, sugar, alcohol, tobacco, and pharmaceuticals—are in fact more shockingly common today. Cigarette smoking, perhaps the most familiar of modern addictions, harms every bodily organ, contributing to many forms of cancer as well as heart disease, bronchitis, and emphysema. Tobacco is particularly harmful to reproductive health, being associated with reduced fertility, high rates of miscarriage, premature births, and even infant deaths. More than 4,000 chemicals can be found in tobacco and its smoke, including sixty substances (among them ammonia, tar, and carbon monoxide) that produce high risks of cancer. Peele, among others, has described smoking as the "toughest habit to lick."[33]

One striking reason for addictions of all sorts is that capitalist modernity is so riddled with manifestations of human misery and alienation: workplace oppression, joblessness, poverty, family crises, crime and violence, environmental problems, social disempowerment. Addictions can offer ready-made escapes from the debilitating stress, anxiety, and conflict of urban life, with its congestion, noise, pollution, economic pressures, and loss of identity that accompany steady erosion of family, work, and community. The system is virtually designed to create broken people. When this reality is combined with the aggressive marketing (and easy availability) of potent legal substances, including a cornucopia of psychotropic drugs, the spread of addictive behaviors should come as no surprise. According to some sources, no fewer than eighty-five million Americans are today impacted in some way by addictive behavior.[34]

One of the newest, reportedly widespread "diseases" manufactured by the drug industry in partnership with psychiatrists is Internet addiction, which is said to take hold once a person spends more than thirty-eight hours a week at their computer.[35] (Precisely how ordinary work activity is distinguished from compulsive behavior is never made clear.) This illness, according to the experts, can be treated by such medications as Ritalin, Valium, and Prozac, helpful in countering the (imputed) depression and "mood swings" resulting from excessive technological access. No doubt the Internet, like other parts of the technological landscape (social media, email, cell phones, texting, etc.), can be addictive, cutting off users from normal social life and generating extreme dependency. While people typically approach the Internet and kindred venues as sources of information, entertainment, research, and writing, some develop a use pattern where technology winds up all-consuming, larger than life. Reports indicate that American teenagers send and receive an average of 3,700 text messages monthly—some in dangerous situations like driving a car. Many constantly access the Internet for random, anonymous chat rooms, gaming, pornography, and sex cameras, no doubt exceeding the thirty-eight-hour threshold set by the psychiatrists. Whether such addiction frequently leads to aggressive, antisocial behavior, as is often claimed, has yet to be proven. Whatever the case, to imagine that large amounts of psychotropic drugs might remedy this problem is to partake of the most fanciful medical illusions.

Internet addiction is just the latest in a rapidly expanding list of diseases that Big Pharma and the medical profession have created to sell more pills. A strategy of medicalization is premised on the belief that millions (actually *tens* of millions) of physically sick or mentally disordered Americans will guarantee heightened drug sales—indifferent to the prospect that these drugs will give rise to new cycles of addiction, not to mention adverse reactions. For the pharmaceutical giant Roche, "social phobia" (being shy or withdrawn) is a serious illness best treated by the potent drug Manerix. At Pfizer, this same condition is rendered as "social-anxiety disorder," requiring daily use of Zoloft or other psychotropic substances. At GlaxoSmithKline, the perfect medication for individuals "allergic to other people"—a condition said to afflict millions of Americans, including children—is Seroxat, developed in 1999. Meanwhile, sexual disorders have supposedly become rampant in the United States among both men and women, generally treatable by Cialis, Viagra, and other widely advertised drugs.[36]

The medical establishment is nowadays trapped in an iron cage of hypermodernity: as health disorders multiply, pills are generously prescribed by doctors and psychiatrists as "remedies" for hundreds of problems, real or contrived.[37] Patients are expected to submit to professional authority, follow medical orders, and embrace drug therapies that often bring more harm than good. While presumably more enlightened than earlier theories emphasizing "moral" defects, the contemporary disease model, like the general medical paradigm, reinforces alienation and disempowerment while legitimating existing high levels of drug consumption the War on Drugs claims to oppose. [...]

Modernity, Disease, Iatrogenesis

The medicalized society evolves within an ultracommodified system of production and consumption marked by the continuous growth of state-corporate power. Peter and Carole Ann Kennedy note, "With the advent of industrial capitalism and the rise to dominance of modern science, medicine became central to developing the medical model or discourse of mental illness."[63] Put differently, medicine—as both ideology and practice—colonizes broader areas of daily life, the economy, culture, and politics. Despite appearances of social and technological progress, the system turns increasingly iatrogenic at a time when sophisticated treatment methods are available to record numbers of consumers, or "patients." Gary Null characterizes this phenomenon as "death by medicine"—an advanced iatrogenic state of affairs in which the medical behemoth—including the profession, hospitals, technical devices, and drug therapies—is now a leading cause of death in the United States, with adverse reactions to legal medications near the top of the list.[64] With drugs prescribed in copious amounts, to children as well as adults, Americans now consume more than half the world total of legal drugs. By 2012, US doctors were writing some three billion prescriptions yearly for drugs that, as we have seen, often bring life-altering risk and harm. The large number of unreported adverse reactions to drugs will, of course, never be known given the difficulty of establishing clear linkages and the visceral impulse to cover up drug-related episodes owing to legal and professional fears.[65]

According to the Nutrition Institute of America, conventional medicine ranks at the top of causes of death in the United States, accounting for an estimated 700,000 fatal episodes yearly—the largest number resulting from drug problems: abuse, overuse, overdoses, accidents, severe adverse reactions, and addiction-related episodes. Antidepressants such as Halcion, Prozac, and Effexor have been known to give rise to violent impulses and outbursts, including suicide and murder. In 2013 antidepressants remained the most widely prescribed of all medications.[66] Opioids such as codeine, morphine, fentanyl, and oxycodone, prescribed for pain relief, possess enormously high abuse potential, including severe addiction, lowered blood pressure, dizziness, and comas. Popular amphetamines (Dexedrine, Adderall, Ritalin, etc.) commonly produce elevated blood pressure, heart attacks, seizures, and strokes. A frequently used muscle relaxant like Soma brings extreme risks, including vision problems, disorientation, dizziness, and strong bouts of drowsiness. Although this drug has been widely prescribed in the United States since 1959, it is located squarely on the "do not use" list by Wolfe and associates, who add that carisoprodol (Soma) is little more effective than aspirin.[67]

A mounting iatrogenic problem, in the United States and globally, concerns the precipitous overuse of antibiotics, which have now lost their capacity—first unleashed during World War II—to treat bacterial and other infections. As pathogens are increasingly widespread around the world, we are headed to a time when common bacterial afflictions resulting from ordinary injuries will become more severe, even fatal. As new classes of antibiotics have exhausted their potential over the past few decades, the overuse of antibiotics for both humans and animals has brought us into a post-antibiotic era when bacterial forms have erected massive resistance to even the most potent medications. This public-health menace, international in its dimensions, is the predictable outcome of an irrational antibiotics regimen spanning perhaps fifty years—with no strictly domestic solution in sight.[68]

Modernity, as noted, has bequeathed a flourishing medical tradition made possible by the historical triumph of science and technology, positioning an ever-growing stratum of experts—doctors, researchers, technicians, pharmacists, therapists, etc.—at the center of human problem solving. In the United States, under the aegis of Rockefeller and kindred corporate interests, this system took hold in the early twentieth century, when technocratic medicine first took its place within modern capitalism.[69] The system gained power and legitimacy through advances in biomedical science: quantitative research, biological work, genetics, varieties of germ theory, the disease model, a panoply of technical innovations. As Barbara Ehrenreich and Deirdre English show, scientific medicine took on a quasi-religious outlook that, in the United States above all, would profoundly shape healthcare structures, practices, and norms.[70] Ehrenreich and English observe that in the earliest days of technocratic medicine the experts set out to identify and label all manner of psychological conditions—most said to afflict women—as diseases that would ultimately require treatment by those same (male) experts. Even then, sickness (disorder) had become a way of life, referred to as a "medical strategy of disease by decree."[71] For women, of course, there was the familiar problem of "hysteria," along with such ailments as "nervous prostration" and "dyspepsia,"[72] and of course the list of diseases (for both males and females) would greatly multiply over the years. In this ideological milieu the (exclusively male) experts had scientific authority at their disposal while tending to the frailty, dependency, and vulnerability of growing numbers of their (mostly female) patients. An imputed biological fact, "disease" was widely understood to be a more or less fixed state, though possibly ameliorated or managed by means of expert intervention. Later the public would be warned about fearsome contagions, diseases, and epidemics requiring expensive forms of medical treatment.

Treatment programs are today a major growth industry in themselves, aligned with the medical system, corporate interests, and government programs. The recovery-treatment industry, long dominated by Alcoholics Anonymous (AA) and allied support groups, relies heavily on the disease model for addiction therapy promoted within academia, medicine, therapeutic circles, the media, and government agencies as the final word in psychological solutions. For these experts, addicts are condemned to impotence, told to submit to expert opinion and respect the mystique of "a higher power." As Jack Trimpey observes in his critique of such therapy, a great appeal of AA is that on the surface of its authoritarian structure can be found a progressive, democratic façade that celebrates virtues of personal growth, individual freedom, and human spirituality.[73]

For main currents of the American recovery business, alcoholism—arguably the most widespread of all addictions—is a permanent, incurable disease best "treated" through personal surrender to a higher force (experts, therapists, God). Lifetime abstinence is imperative. The notion that addictive behavior might be understood as a human *condition* shaped or mediated by social factors, subject to individual choice, and open to perpetual adaptation and change is rejected outright. Here Trimpey argues, with only slight exaggeration, that "our addiction treatment industry has become an American gulag that runs parallel to the former Soviet Union's past misuse of psychiatry to enforce the will of the government on its citizens."[74]

As far back as the early nineteenth century, Benjamin Rush defined "intemperance"—along with such crimes as murder—as a manifestation of "disease," a condition in which individuals had lost all will power. Rush's ideas, a mixture of religion, folklore, and pseudoscience, would strongly influence the later temperance movement, Protestant revivalism, and groups like the Anti-Saloon League that drove the prohibitionist upsurge. Today, the view of addiction caused by a brain disease involving "altered brain structure and function" has long been held by the AMA (beginning in 1956) and influential sectors of the scientific and medical communities. Disease theory has ritually invoked family patterns, where addictive tendencies are supposedly passed on from parents to children—as a set of shared illness-producing genes. Yet such "family patterns" could just as easily—more easily, even—involve long-shared eating habits and lifestyles transmitted across generations. The disease model, however, favors a medicalized strategy heavily reliant on drug therapy, which, as mentioned, brings harmful outcomes consistent with mounting iatrogenesis.

There can be little doubt: problems of substance abuse and addiction are indeed pervasive in American society, perhaps more so today than at any other time in history. The key problem is how to explain, contextualize, and treat (or, better, prevent) addictive behavior without reducing humans to passive, objectified, impotent victims—that is, without destroying their agency—as occurs within the medicalized society. As Peele writes, "The real cure for addiction lies in a social change which reorients our major institutions and the types of experience people have within them."[75] Today we are given addiction theories and recovery programs built on slogans, rituals, sound bites, and oversimplified formulas marketed as "therapy." Such programs, like so much of the medicalized society, have turned out to be widely iatrogenic. More crucially yet, they lack anything resembling a model of individual or collective empowerment. As Wendy Kaminer notes, the mainstream recovery industry upholds the virtues of individualism and self-activity but is ultimately conformist and authoritarian in its norms and practices.[76] She asks, "What are the political implications of a mass movement that counsels surrender of will and submission to a higher power describing almost everyone as hapless victims … ?"[77] Those implications are surely destined to carry us a great distance from the venerated legacies of personal freedom and democratic politics.

Notes

1. On the motif of technological rationality as a form of ideological hegemony, see Antonio Gramsci, "Americanism and Fordism," in *Selections from the Prison Notebooks*, ed. Quintin Hoare and Geoffrey Nowell Smith (New York: International Publishers, 1971), pp. 271–318; Max Horkheimer and Theodor W. Adorno, *Dialectic of Enlightenment* (New York: Continuum, 1995), pp. 3–42; and Herbert Marcuse, *One-Dimensional Man* (Boston: Beacon Press, 1964), pp. 1–120.

2. See Ronald K. Siegel, *Intoxication: The Universal Drive for Mind-Altering Substances* (Rochester, VT: Park Street Press, 2005), and Andrew Weil, *Chocolate to Morphine: Everything You Need to Know about Mind-Altering Drugs* (Boston: Houghton Mifflin, 2004) and *The Natural Mind: A Revolutionary Approach to the Drug Problem* (Boston: Houghton Mifflin, 2004) for more in-depth, complex, and balanced treatments of the drug phenomenon than is usually available from mainstream sources.

3. On the Rockefeller-corporate origins of American medicine, see E. Richard Brown, *Rockefeller Medicine Men: Medicine and Capitalism in America* (Berkeley: University of California Press, 1979), ch. 3.

4. Horkheimer and Adorno, *Dialectic of Enlightenment,* p. 14.

5. Ibid., p. 20.

6. See George Ritzer, *The McDonaldization of Society* (Thousand Oaks, CA: Pine Forge Press, 2000). See also Eric Schlosser, *Fast Food Nation: The Dark Side of the All-American Meal* (Boston: Houghton Mifflin, 2001).

7. See Harriet A. Washington, *Deadly Monopolies: The Shocking Corporate Takeover of Life Itself—And the Consequences for Your Health and Our Medical Future* (New York: Doubleday, 2011), especially the introduction.

8. On the connection between the medicalization of society and approaches to addiction, see Stanton Peele, *The Diseasing of America: How We Allowed Recovery Zealots and the Treatment Industry to Convince Us We Are Out of Control* (Lexington, MA: Lexington Books, 1989), chs. 3 and 5.

9. On the phenomenon of iatrogenesis in American medicine, see Ivan Illich, *Medical Nemesis: The Expropriation of Health* (New York: Pantheon, 1976), and Otis Webb Brawley, *How We Do Harm: A Doctor Breaks Ranks about Being Sick in America* (New York: St. Martin's, 2011).

10. Gary Null, Martin Feldman, Debora Rasio, and Carolyn Dean, *Death by Medicine* (Mt. Jackson, VA: Praktikos Books, 2011), chs. 1–3.

11. See Steven Brill, "The High Cost of American Medicine," *Time* magazine (March 4, 2013), p. 20.

12. Ibid., p. 20.

13. Ibid., p. 49.

14. See www.opensecrets.org/orgs/list.php.

15. Ibid., p. 50.

16. Peele, *The Diseasing of America*, ch. 4.

17. Stanton Peele, *The Truth about Addiction and Recovery* (New York: Fireside, 1991), part 1. See also Jack Trimpey, *Rational Recovery: The New Cure for Substance Addiction* (New York: Pocket Books, 1996).

18. On the authoritarian implications of prevailing addiction theory, see Peele, *The Diseasing of America*, ch. 9, and Wendy Kaminer, *I'm Dysfunctional, You're Dysfunctional: The Recovery Movement and Other Self-Help Fashions* (New York: Vintage, 1993), conclusion.

19. For the NIDA statement on drug abuse and addiction, see www.drugabuse.gov/publications/drugfacts/ understanding-drug-abuse-addiction.

20. See, for example, statements made by AddictionsAndRecovery.org, at www.addictionandrecovery.org/ is-addiction-a-disease.htm.

21. *Diagnostic and Statistical Manual of Mental Disorders* (DSM-IV) (published by the American Psychiatric Association, 2000), pp. 210–114.

22. Ibid., p. 198.

23. For a penchant critique of the DSM approach, see Eugenia Tsao, "Inside the DSM: The Drug Barons' Campaign to Make Us All Crazy," *CounterPunch* (June 16–30, 2009). www.counterpunch.org/2009/08/20/ the-drug-barons-campaign-to-make-us-all-crazy/.

24. DSM-IV, p. 200.

25. Ibid., p. 219.

26. On the capacity of humans to control and escape addiction, see Peele, *The Diseasing of America*, ch. 7.

27. Peele, *The Truth about Addiction*, p. 21.

28. According to the US Department of Health and Human Services, fewer than 10 percent of users of any drug wind up with severe addictions; see www.enterhealth.com/docs/FactSheet-AlcoholandDrugAddiction (2012). See also Stanton Peele, "The Deluded Mantras of Addiction," *Huffington Post* (October 11, 2012).

29. Peele, *The Truth about Addiction*, p. 76.

30. This point is thoroughly developed, with practical implications, in Trimpey, *Rational Recovery*, chs. 20 and 21.

31. On the dialectics of addictions and recovery, see Peele, *The Truth about Addiction*, part III.

32. For data on obesity rates in the United States, see reports of the Centers for Disease Control and Prevention, which have found that (in 2013) 35 percent of adults over age twenty in the United States are obese while 69 percent are classified as overweight. See www.cdc.gov/obesity/data/facts.html.

33. See Peele, *The Truth about Addiction*, p. 95.

34. *Los Angeles Times* (September 28, 2013).

35. On the dynamics of "Internet Addiction" disorder, described as an "impulse-control disorder," see information from the Illinois Institute for Addiction Recovery, at www.addictionrecov.org/internet.htm.

36. According to some research, no fewer than 43 percent of women and 31 percent of men report some type of sexual dysfunction. See https://my.clevelandclinic.org/health/diseases_conditions/hic_An_Overview_of_Sexual_Dysfunction.

37. On the iatrogenic dysfunctions of modern medicine, see Null et al., *Death by Medicine*, chs. 1–3.

38. On the evolution of obesity-inducing dietary patterns within the context of the food industry, see Schlosser, *Fast Food Nation*, chs. 5 and 9.

39. On the sordid history of beef production and consumption, see Jeremy Rifkin, *Beyond Beef: The Rise and Fall of the Cattle Culture* (New York: Penguin, 1992).

40. George Ritzer, *The McDonaldization of Society* (Thousand Oaks, CA: Pine Forge Press, 2000), ch. 9.

41. Barry Popkin, *The World Is Fat: The Fads, Trends, Policies, and Products That Are Fattening the Human Race* (New York: Penguin, 2010), p. 90.

42. T. Colin Campbell, *The China Study* (Dallas: BenBella Books, 2006), pp. 99–101. This work, the most scientifically comprehensive of its kind, explores nutritional patterns far beyond China itself.

43. Ibid., p. 110.

44. Wolfe et al., *Worst Pills, Best Pills*, p. 434.

45. Ibid., p. 431.

46. Ibid., p. 430.

47. Advertisement in *Star* magazine (September 2, 2013).

48. Ibid.

49. See the overview on drug sales by Megan Brooks, "Top 100 Selling Drugs of 2013," *Medscape* (January 30, 2014).

50. *Los Angeles Times* (November 19, 2013).

51. See John Abramson, *Overdosed America* (New York: HarperCollins, 2004), pp. 235–237.

52. Ibid., p. 222.

53. *Los Angeles Times* (February 21, 2013).

54. Campbell, *The China Study*, p. 124.

55. *Los Angeles Times* (June 19, 2013).

56. Cited in Peele, *The Diseasing of America*, p. 118.

57. Popkin, *The World Is Fat*, p. 162.

58. Gina Kolata, *Rethinking Thin: The New Science of Weight Loss* (New York: Farrar, Strauss, and Giroux, 2007).

59. On the "low-carb" approach to weight loss, see Robert Atkins, *Dr. Atkins' New Diet Revolution* (New York: Avon Books, 2002), and John Mansfield, *The Six Secrets of Successful Weight Loss* (London: Hammersmith Heath Books, 2012).

60. Campbell, *The China Study*, p. 95.

61. For a critique of the Atkins diet and kindred programs, see ibid., pp. 95–102.

62. See David H. Freedman, "How Junk Food Can End Obesity," *Atlantic* (July/August, 2013). www.theatlantic.com/magazine/archive/2013/07/how-junk-food-can-end-obesity/309396/.

63. Peter Kennedy and Carole Ann Kennedy, *Health, Medicine, and Society* (Portland, OR: Policy Press, 2010), p. 110.

64. Null et al., *Death by Medicine*, p. 59.

65. According to Wolfe and associates, the yearly toll of adverse reactions to drugs is horrific: it includes 61,000 people with drug-induced parkinsonism, 16,000 with injuries from car crashes, 32,000 with hip fractures, and 41,000 hospitalizations resulting from anti-inflammatory drugs. See Wolfe et al., *Worst Pills, Best Pills*, p. xxii.

66. According to the National Center for Health Statistics, the rate of prescriptions for antidepressants in the United States skyrocketed by 400 percent from 1988 to 2008. See Peter Wehrwein, "Astounding Increase in Antidepressant Use by Americans," *Harvard Health Publication* (October 20, 2011).

67. Wolfe et al., *Worst Pills, Best Pills*, p. 484.

68. See *Guardian* (May 9, 2014).

69. Brown, *Rockefeller Medicine Men*, chs. 2 and 3.

70. Barbara Ehrenreich and Deirdre English, *For Her Own Good: Two Centuries of the Experts' Advice to Women* (New York: Anchor Books, 1979), pp. 71–73.

71. Ibid., p. 134.

72. Ibid., p. 102.

73. Trimpey, *Rational Recovery*, p. 308.

74. Ibid., p. 58.

75. Peele, *The Diseasing of America*, p. 223.

76. See Kaminer, *I'm Dysfunctional, You're Dysfunctional*, p. 6.

77. Ibid., p. 152.

The Wrong Side of the River

By Ronald L. Barrett

....

Y ou can make an ass of yourself, quite literally, by dying on the wrong side of the Ganga. The Kashi Kanda guarantees that those who die immediately across the river from Banaras will be reborn as donkeys, just as it promises spiritual liberation for all who die within the sacred interior of the city.[1] So while pilgrims and priests scramble for a few square feet along the ghats, not a single *sadhu* is willing to take up residence along the wide open spaces on the far shore of Mother Ganga. None, that is, except an Aghori.

On the "wrong side" of the river is where Awadhut Bhagwan Ram established an ashram and clinic to treat people with leprosy and other skin diseases using modified Ayurvedic medicines. Built in 1961, Kusht Seva Ashram (KSA) lies beside the Grand Trunk (GT) Road in the town of Parao, directly across the river from Banaras's northernmost bathing ghat. GT Road is a centuries-old trade route that has since become a perpetual traffic jam of honking trucks, cars, and autorickshaws moving between eastern Uttar Pradesh and the nearby state of Bihar. Parao is a noisy, sooty truck stop where mechanics, transport workers, and roadside vendors long ago displaced most of its local farming and fishing communities.

Parao would seem to be the worst possible location for a clinic or hospital. Yet Kusht Seva Ashram has become host to one of the most popular leprosy-treatment centers in the world. Indeed, the KSA clinic recently entered the *Guinness Book of World Records* for claiming to have treated over two hundred thousand people with leprosy since its founding (see www.guinnessworldrecords. com). While the *Guinness* book is certainly no substitute for census statistics, it is nevertheless a gold standard in the popular Indian imagination.

If the patients at Parao are anything like those at Krim Kund, then they must have practical reasons for pursuing this medicine, at least for *kushṭh* conditions. But these advantages are not immediately apparent. People do not choose the ashram medicines as a matter of convenience, for the average KSA treatment regimen is four times longer than the biomedical standard,[2] and many patients complain about the dietary restrictions that go along with KSA medicines. Nor is Aghor medicine more accessible or cheaper than biomedicine. Although the ashram is close to a major highway, it is also only two miles away from a major biomedical clinic that provides treatment free of cost. In contrast, a month's supply of KSA medicines represents several days of work for the tenant farmers and unskilled laborers who comprise most of the patient population.[3]

One must understand the social **stigma** of leprosy to understand the popularity of Aghor medicine in these circumstances. Many Indians consider leprosy (Hansen's disease, or HD) to be the most untouchable of human conditions. Thus, people travel great distances to avoid public discovery and the resulting social ostracism. The intense stigma also leads to the segregation of biomedical services for leprosy. Both these challenges impede effective communication between physicians and patients, which in turn impedes long-term adherence to treatment regimens. This lack of communication is especially problematic given the need to monitor and manage the more common side effects of biomedical treatment (Barrett 2005).

Blame is also a serious issue. Although biomedical models of etiology do not explicitly blame the patient, neither do they explain why one person and not another is afflicted with leprosy—a central feature of explanatory models in most medical systems (Kleinman 1988; 1978). Aghor medicine provides this kind of explanation using the metaphysics of traditional healing, but without the blame that comes from traditional notions of pollution and purity. Finally, the issue of **efficacy** is important in Aghor medicine. Simply put, people believe that the Aghori are powerful and that their medicine works. Yet this belief too is related to the stigma of leprosy insofar as the power of Aghor, like that of the Ganga, largely relies on its ability to assimilate the pollution of others.

A large mural on the wall beside the front gate of Kusht Seva Ashram depicts the boar-headed Varaha, one of the nine avatars of Vishnu. The common myth is that Varaha rescued the world by plunging into the ocean and raising it up with his tusks. But the Aghori residents of KSA tell a slightly different version in which Varaha plunged into the filth of humanity to rescue the world from itself. This latter story has special significance for the practice of Aghor medicine at Parao, for it was here that Awadhut Bhagwan Ram reformed the Aghor tradition. The cremation ground became a leprosy-treatment center, and the Aghori began to engage the world in social service to save people from themselves, disciples included. This was the reason I came to Banaras in the first place: to study the dynamics of stigma and healing for the most ritually polluting of human conditions, as well as those willing to embrace that pollution on the wrong side of the purest river in the world.

Stigma and Socialization

I interviewed the resident patients of Kusht Seva Ashram in the late winter of 1999. At the time, thirty-one leprosy-diagnosed adults resided within the ashram, a typical census, according to the clinic physicians. All but one of these people identified with a Hindu religious tradition, and half were from twice-born castes. This number was a large proportion even for Banaras, which touted an unusually high number of Brahmins (20 percent) in its population (Freitag 1989). Most Banarsi Brahmins are poor, however, illustrating that caste is but one of several axes of social inequality in India. Upper caste notwithstanding, the resident patients of KSA were mostly tenant farmers, unskilled laborers, and housewives from poor and landless families in rural Uttar Pradesh and Bihar. Their economic situation reinforced the longtime association of leprosy and poverty in India (Buckingham 2002). One-third of the patients claimed some kind of formal education, but only five of them had reached the tenth grade or higher. None had a college education, and no woman claimed to have any education at all. The ratio of men to women among the resident patients was especially problematic. With twenty-six men and only five women, the five-to-one gender ratio at KSA was much greater than the two-to-one ratio of registered cases and the four-to-one ratio for permanent disabilities nationwide (Kumar et al. 2001; Noordeen 1994). These discrepancies were part of an unresolved puzzle that may well be explained by the diminished autonomy of women to make medical decisions and gain access to essential health resources (Bloom, Wypij, and das Gupta 2001; Beals 1976) as well as possible gender differences in manual labor practices (Barrett 1997).[4] However, the even lower representation of women at KSA was closely linked to issues of child care, for the ashram did not allow children to live on its grounds. I was therefore not surprised that the five female residents at KSA either had grown children or had none.

Given the centrality of family life in Indian society, I cannot imagine a more difficult challenge for these people than to live apart from their kin for extended periods. At most, the residents made two or three family visits each year, and only then, for a few days at a time. These visits usually tapered off over time, and several of the long-term residents had stopped visiting altogether. In addition, the resident patients were segregated within the ashram itself, hidden behind walls in a separate

EDITOR'S NOTES

socialization: the lifelong process of an individual or group learning the expected norms and customs of a group or society through social interaction.

living area. They rarely made contact with the nonpatient visitors to the ashram, nor did they participate in regular ashram religious activities. Despite this isolation, people stayed at the ashram for years at a time. Indeed, the average length of stay for KSA residents was 5.2 years, well beyond the 3-year treatment period.

Whatever efficacy people attributed to the medicines of Kusht Seva Ashram, the inpatients clearly had a different reason for being there. The KSA inpatient facility was essentially a religiously sanctioned leprosy colony. As I soon learned, this religious element was very important, for it provided a well-known script of austerity for a tragic set of circumstances. Aside from labor migrations and village exogamy, family separations usually bore the mark of suspicion and blame for all involved. In contrast, living in an ashram was seen as an important religious duty, an auspicious act that might even raise the status of a family that would otherwise have difficulty concealing its relative's extremely inauspicious disease.

Here, the Ganga metaphor is highly appropriate, for leprosy is among the five major reasons for throwing the dead directly into the river.[5] Banarsis often speak of death as the great (social) equalizer, but they consider a person with leprosy to be so ritually polluted that his or her body is not a fitting sacrifice for the cremation fire. Thus, the pollution of leprosy mandates transportive purification, with the body still attached to the problem. Similarly, KSA patients' families dump both their afflictions and their afflicted upon the Aghori. Like Mother Ganga, the Aghori are even less discriminating than the funeral pyre. Yet as we shall soon see, much can be gained from this radical level of nondiscrimination.

The Social and Physical Stigma of Leprosy

The social stigma of leprosy is far worse than the disease itself. Contrary to many popular beliefs, Hansen's disease is a mildly contagious condition that usually responds readily to treatment with antibiotics (Bryceson and Pfalzgraff 1990). In the minority of more prolonged and difficult cases, simple precautions and careful observation can prevent the onset of permanent disabilities (Srinivasan 1994). In contrast to these clinical realities, however, Indians often ascribe people with HD to the most untouchable categories of humanity (Frist 2000). Moreover, this untouchability often persists long after people have been "cured" of the disease, creating lifelong prospects of divorce, eviction, loss of employment, and ostracism from family and social networks (Kopparty, Karup, and Sivarum 1995).

The extreme discrepancies between the clinical and social realities of HD in India underscore a common distinction in medical anthropology between the pathophysiology of disease and the human experience of illness as suffering (Kleinman 1988).[6] As such, it is tempting to segregate the bacteria of Hansen's *disease* from the social burden of leprosy. Yet although this distinction may be useful for initial criticism, further examination reveals that, as with many other discredited medical conditions, the physical and social stigmata of HD are too interconnected to disentangle in a useful way. Thus, leprosy is best approached as an illness of discrimination inclusive of its physical condition.

One can see both a sharp contrast and an intimate connection between the clinical and social realities of leprosy in India. *Myco-bacterium leprae* is among the least contagious of human pathogens. Researchers estimate that the bacterium produces symptoms in less than 10 percent of the human population, and only then after prolonged exposure and a five-year incubation period (Bryceson and Pfalzgraff 1990). Although some evidence suggests a hereditary component to this susceptibility, most spouses and children of those infected never contract the disease (Mira et al. 2004; Seghal 1994). *M. leprae* fares even worse outside of its human hosts. Indeed, it grows so poorly under most conditions, natural or artificial, that researchers have yet to prove its exact mode of transmission (Sasaki et al. 2001).[7]

In contrast to the bacterium, the social mark of leprosy in India is highly contagious. Consistent with Goffman's so-called **courtesy stigma** (1963), friends and relatives of people with HD risk severe social and economic losses for their affiliations. Consequently, many Indian families would rather banish their diagnosed relatives to a distant town or city than risk discrimination against the entire household (Kopparty, Karup, and Sivarum 1995). With very poor chances of employment, and little if any support from home, these exiles have few options for survival. Typically, they must find subsidized living in an isolated colony, or else live on the streets and beg in areas frequented by tourists and pilgrims. Both of these subsistence modes contribute, in turn, to the stereotypes from which their discrimination originated.

Among those susceptible to *M. leprae* infection, the disease is usually treatable with a combination of three antibiotics, commonly referred to as multi-drug therapy (MDT). This regimen can render most patients noninfectious in thirty days and noninfected in six to nine months (Ponnighaus 1995).[8] Yet for many people, the social stigma of leprosy can last a lifetime, regardless of whether they have been biomedically cured of the disease.

Some of the most prevalent myths about HD focus on its associated deformities and disabilities. Contrary to many popular beliefs, HD does not cause limbs to "rot off." Though a small percentage of patients can undergo internal loss of cartilage and bone at the face and digits, the vast majority of physical deformities result from accumulated trauma. Typically, the selective infection of peripheral nerves results in limb anesthesia,

EDITOR'S NOTES

courtesy stigma:
stigma that is extended to those who are close to a stigmatized person.

diminishing people's ability to rely upon touch and pain to prevent injuries to their hands and feet and to make the constant microadjustments necessary to prevent pressure ulcers. The resultant injuries and ulcers accumulate, and along with secondary infections, lead to progressive amputations not unlike those for people with diabetes (Brand and Yancey 1997; Bryceson and Pfalzgraff 1990; Jopling 1988).

Even in cases of permanent neuropathy, physical deformities and disabilities are preventable through basic measures like custom footwear and training in injury prevention. But that which is basic is not always easy. Because of the ever-present threat of injury to anesthetic limbs, people with HD neuropathies must be hyperaware of their bodies' relationship to their surrounding environments (Brand and Yancey 1997). Without the patient's constant visual inspection of an insensate hand, a cigarette or hot stove can result in a third-degree burn in less than a minute. More insidiously, without regular attention to footwear, or scheduled readjustments while sleeping, a pressure ulcer can work its way to the bone in a manner of weeks. Although the necessary preventive measures are straightforward, they are challenging to maintain under the best of conditions. They become formidable under the conditions of extreme poverty and demoralization that is common among people who are publicly branded as "lepers" in India.[9] The social and physical disabilities of HD are not only mutually engendering, but each actually impedes efforts to prevent the other.

The Disembodiment of Leprosy

At Kusht Seva Ashram, I investigated whether the dynamics between the social and physical marks of leprosy discrimination could be interrupted within this more tolerant environment, and in a system informed by an ethos of radical nondiscrimination. I did not expect the Aghori to change the attitudes of Indian society as a whole, but I was keen to find out if Aghori healers had better rapport with their patients than did other health providers and if the explanatory models of Aghor medicine helped improve the self-concept of patients with leprosy. This avenue of inquiry actually produced mixed results, which are well illustrated in the following two cases.

Disavowal and Undertreatment

Sita was an energetic and outspoken woman in her early forties who belonged to a community of goldsmiths in a small town about seventy kilometers from Banaras. She was illiterate beyond the ability to sign her own name and cynically laughed at the slim chance that she or any other woman from her community could have a formal education. She had been living at Kusht Seva Ashram for many years and repeatedly spoke about the loneliness she felt from the years of separation from her natal family.

Sita was fourteen when she first noticed a gray patch on her upper arm. This spot caused great concern in her family, because any skin blemishes or spots would adversely affect her chances for marriage. Although she could still conceal the patch beneath her sari, no one knew whether the condition would spread. The senior males of Sita's family decided to send her to a doctor of "English medicine," who diagnosed the HD and prescribed a course of dapsone.[10] She was then sequestered at home while the family hastily arranged her marriage. With her condition kept secret, Sita was married within a month, after which she ceased taking her medication lest it be discovered.

Sita's condition remained unchanged until the birth of her first child, a daughter, four years later. She then began having numbness along her left arm and leg and contractions in her toes. With her condition no longer concealable, she feigned surprise when she was diagnosed a second time. To avoid being recognized at a regional leprosy clinic, she, along with her affines, went on long trips for treatment in the adjacent state of Bihar. Sita's daughter died of undisclosed causes at six months of age, and her husband died the following year. With no male children and no one to advocate for her within the family, Sita saw her already-marginal status decline further. With strong pressure from her mother-in-law, Sita took up residence at KSA. Years later, her natal and affinal families kept up the story that she was living the pious life of a widow in an ashram somewhere in Banaras.

Sita's story illustrates the tragic consequences of denial and concealment in the progression and spread of a discredited disease. Given the social consequences, it is understandable that people go to great lengths to conceal their condition. Unfortunately, such strategies usually result in delays between initial symptoms and diagnosis and foster nonadherence to medication regimens (Kopparty, Karum, and Sivarum 1995; Mull et al. 1989). Compounding this problem is the segregation of HD-treatment services in India (Arole et al. 2002).[11] Under these conditions, the most public sign of early-stage HD is someone's appearance near a leprosy-treatment worker or clinic. To prevent such associations, people often travel great distances to nonlocal clinics or avoid treatment altogether (Arole et al. 2002; Dharmshaktu 1992).

In my interviews with KSA patients, the majority (60 percent) reported delays between initial symptoms and their first visit to a licensed professional healer. Most interviewees described these delays in the context of concealment strategies, as in Sita's history, or some form of denial ("I did not want to know"). Others reported that not only were they ignorant of early signs of HD, but their health providers were as well. The latter issue reflects discrimination of another sort: the **segregation** of leprosy-treatment services also results in a segregation of clinical knowledge.

Goffman (1963), in his reformulation of **deviance** as stigma, includes a taxonomy of strategies for disavowing the social mark: (1) sheltering—segregation within protective social environments; (2) passing—concealing or camouflaging the mark; and (3) covering—minimizing tensions during social interactions. Yet these disavowal strategies provide only limited benefits to the discredited and can even reinforce the stigma of a condition over time (Goffman 1963; Jones, Scott, and Markus 1984). This situation is even worse when the stigmatized condition is an infectious disease, and the disavowal results in delayed testing or incomplete adherence to treatment (Alonzo and Reynolds 1995; Rubel and Garro 1992).[12]

Such dynamics forge a direct link between social stigma and the **epidemiology** of Hansen's disease in India. Unfortunately, however, this link has yet to be adequately measured. In accordance with World Bank guidelines, India's National Leprosy Elimination Program (NLEP) bases statistics solely on the passive detection of registered cases in WHO-approved treatment centers (Ponnighaus 1995). Among such centers that I observed in the Varanasi district, staff members assumed that registered patients who fail to return after six months have sought treatment elsewhere, and they drop these patients from the books. Significantly, 74 percent of the KSA inpatients had initially sought biomedical treatment for their condition elsewhere.[13] Yet because all these patients had now shifted to an unrecognized mode of treatment, they were not represented in national or WHO statistics. It was not just patients and families who were concealing the problem of leprosy.

Dissociation and Self-Neglect

Sadness and resignation were pervasive emotions among the KSA residents. Laxman was no exception in this regard. In his mid-twenties, he had a ninth-grade education and an acre of land, which would have made him an attractive marriage prospect in many parts of rural Bihar were it not for contracted fingers and wounds on his toes and feet. Ten years before I spoke with him, he had begun having difficulties holding on to farm implements and repeatedly injured himself while working in the fields. Initially misdiagnosed, his condition worsened until he started MDT six months later. Unlike Sita, however, Laxman was never able to conceal his condition. Soon after his diagnosis, his neighbors spotted a local leprosy-treatment worker visiting his home. In no time, word spread among prospective in-laws, and Laxman's family gave up trying to arrange his marriage after two aborted attempts. Laxman related these latter events as if they marked the end of his life.

Laxman continued MDT on a sporadic basis, and I suspected he was eventually cured. Although he was tolerated in his family and village, no one spoke with him and he kept to himself. In accordance with ritual pollution **taboos**, he ate his meals from separate pots and *thalis* (rimmed plates) and sat alone during village celebrations. Laxman stated, "In our society, people hate anyone with this disease." Yet he insisted that the problem did not lie with his village but with himself.

I was struck not only by the content of Laxman's story but also by the manner in which he related it. Laxman kept his hands to his sides throughout most of the interview. He related his loss of manual dexterity and subsequent injuries without making a single gesture. This gesture-free narrative was repeated by nearly all the KSA residents with whom I spoke. They kept their affected limbs beneath garments whenever possible and assumed positions and postures that minimized any remaining exposure. Even within the isolated confines of the ashram, the mimetic disavowal of leprosy seemed to persist as a deeply ingrained habit.

The KSA residents also expressed linguistic dispossession from their affected limbs. In their illness narratives, they dropped the possessive pronoun when narrating the succession of injuries to, and problems with, their hands and feet. Thus, in accounts of a cut or burn in regional Bhojpuri, *hamāre hāth* (my hand) simply became *hāth* ([the] hand). In Standard Hindi, someone would say, "Doctor pair ka ilāj kya" (The doctor treated [the] foot) instead of *mera pair* (my foot). A few even went so far as to say *yah angulī* (that finger) without looking or gesturing toward the digit. It was as if the appendages that remained had already been amputated, and those that were amputated had left no signs of previous attachment.

These habits of word and gesture were particularly disconcerting given that many KSA residents continued to suffer from limb anesthesia, necessitating constant visual inspection and a hyperawareness of affected limbs to prevent further injuries. Though the residents of KSA may have been all too aware of their situation on the whole, these data indicate that

EDITOR'S NOTES

taboo: a forbidden act considered so offensive to norms, particularly mores (moral norms), as to be reviled and unthinkable.

they were actively dissociating themselves from their physical disabilities on a moment-by-moment basis. If so, this dissociation would have significant consequences for the further progression of their physical condition, even in the absence of infection.

With this background, it is interesting to note that leprologists from the U.S. Hansen's Disease Center in Carville, Louisiana, relate anecdotal observations of some patients' disdain for and neglect of affected limbs (Yoder 1998). Although situated in very different cultural contexts, many Carville patients describe themes of isolation and shame very similar to those of the KSA residents (Gussow 1989). When I conducted life-history interviews in Carville in 1997, two patients presented their narratives without making gestures or using personal pronouns for disabled limbs.

Murphy (1990) described a similar process of dissociation during the progression of his paralysis and cancer. He examined the "silencing" of his body, beginning with a loss of proprioception and ending with emotional detachment. In his book, he refers to his limbs as "the arm" or "the leg," his body as a "faulty life support system," and his remaining self as "Donovan's Brain." Murphy and others examined issues of stigmatization among people with paralysis, characterizing them in terms of liminality arising from lost social roles associated with sexuality and physical independence (1988). Within the same time frame, Murphy ignored parts of his own body to the point that he became nearly septic from bone-deep pressure ulcers (1990).

For stigmatized neurological conditions with anesthesia, the combined loss of physical sensation and social identity creates a strong potential for bodily neglect, thereby perpetuating feedback between physical pathology and the social pathology of its discrimination. Moreover, the internalization of stigma is likely to be deeper in people who acquire such conditions in adulthood, given that disability **prejudices** are often learned early through socially ascribed prototypes of health and beauty (Ablon 1995; Jones, Scott, and Markus 1984). Thus, when confronting the physical parts by which they once identified themselves, parts that had since become misshapen and senseless, it is not surprising that some of these people would dissociate themselves from that which they have long known to be alien, and that which marks their alienation from the world around them—a process constituting a disembodiment of leprosy.

EDITOR'S NOTES

prejudice: a favorable or unfavorable preconceived feeling or opinion formed without knowledge, reason, or thought that prevents objective consideration of an idea, individual, group, or object.

From Pollution to Healing

I was disappointed to find that Aghor medicine had done little to change the attitudes of the KSA resident patients. On the contrary, the prolonged isolation from family, as well as segregation from the social and religious activities of the broader ashram community, seemed only to reinforce the already-diminished self-concept of these people.

Granted, the Aghori provided their residents with medicines that were both free of cost and free of blame. They also created a protected living environment with a veneer of social legitimacy. Nevertheless, by sheltering the stigma of leprosy behind ashram walls on the wrong side of the river, the Aghori ultimately reinforced the social attitudes that brought disability to an otherwise treatable condition. These attitudes, in turn, were further internalized by KSA inpatients to the point that they exacerbated the progress of the disease. Waxler (1981) discusses how people "learn to become lepers" by being socialized into the discriminatory models around them. In the case of Sita and Laxman, these models were not only deeply internalized, they were ultimately inscribed onto flesh per the original definition of stigma: a permanent mark, cut or burned upon the skin of people to publicly brand them as members of a socially discredited group.

In contrast to their resident patients, the Kina Ram Aghori appeared to benefit a great deal from having a major program for leprosy treatment. In chapter 3, we saw how leprosy treatment became a central prototype for the reformation of Aghor. Before this development, the Aghori were part of a socially marginalized sect whose members and practices were largely isolated within the cremation grounds. Twenty years after establishing the Kusht Seva Ashram and clinic, they had accumulated 150 ashrams and service centers, receiving thousands of members from the middle-class Indian society, as well as millionaires, politicians, and even an Indian prime minister.[14] Apparently, leprosy did much more to destigmatize Aghor than the other way around.

Yet these dynamics were only part of the picture. I had been volunteering as a part-time nurse in a street clinic for leprosy patients in the city, where I gained an appreciation of the range of people with this condition. I came to know the street-dwelling beggars on the main bathing ghats at Dashashwamedha, the Bengali squatter community near the Sankat Mochan Temple, and the colony residents in the nearby town of Asapur. I noted their different backgrounds and how these differences resulted in radically different life trajectories after they were diagnosed with the disease. I saw even greater contrasts among the outpatient visitors at Banaras Hindu University and the Seva Sadan hospital, the two major biomedical treatment centers in the city. Though all patients faced the threat of social ostracism, and all shared a willingness to try anything and everything to fix the problem, some were clearly better able to seek medical help and to do so while concealing the disease. Not surprisingly, these hospital outpatients seemed most able to manage the physical and social stigma of leprosy. I expected the same to be true of the many outpatient visitors to Kusht Seva Ashram.

Unfortunately, collecting outpatient data at the KSA clinic proved very difficult. Most outpatient visitors were still actively concealing their condition, and were therefore reticent to share personal information with anyone, least of all with a foreign researcher. I had little if any opportunity to establish rapport and therefore had to rely on the physicians and staff to vouch for me. This strategy was helpful in approaching return visitors, but many more were visiting the clinic for the first time. Subsequently, my efforts resulted in only twelve outpatient interviews, and a lot of time watching clinical dynamics. These latter observations, however, proved especially helpful.

In South Asia's highly pluralistic medical cultures, Nichter and Nordstrom (1989) identified the Sri Lankan concept of "**medicine answering**," a term used to describe healers who effectively communicate with their patients and are able to meet their broader needs for overall well-being, regardless of the treatment modality. Although not articulated as such, this concept could be readily applied to the more highly regarded medical providers in Banaras. Moreover, I would argue that the KSA clinic appeared to approach this ideal of medicine answering more closely than did most other providers I observed in this region.

The physical layout of the KSA clinic reminded me of the better-managed clinics in rural South India. Patients entered the ashram from an entrance near the main gate, just beside the mural of Varaha. A hundred meters down a tree-lined path, and right next to the inpatient compound, visitors approached a large cottage building with two sets of open and closed porches. The latter served as a waiting room, flanked on either side by a pharmacy and (unusually) a records department. Unlike most Indian outpatient providers, the KSA clinic kept detailed records on its patients. Beyond the waiting area was a spacious room with abundant natural lighting and a few outer rooms for (rare) private consultations. Most doctor-patient interactions took place in the center of the main room around a large square table: doctors sat on either side of the table, and an assistant stood nearby when not running errands.

The table in the center of the room is a ubiquitous feature of Indian clinics, regardless of the type of medicine practiced. People huddle around it, waiting for an opportunity to talk with the physician, and pass the time listening in on other people's problems. In most clinics, the patient sits orthogonal to the physician, who gives a cursory pulse reading or auscultation with a stethoscope while barely pretending to listen to the clinical history. The physician then writes a long shopping list of medications and vitamin supplements, and hands the patient

EDITOR'S NOTES

medicine answering: a Sri Lankan concept used to describe healers who effectively communicate with their patients and are able to meet their broader needs for overall wellness, regardless of treatment modality.

the prescription with a highly authoritative and terse set of instructions. Under these conditions, the patient is too intimidated to ask questions, nor is he or she encouraged to do so. I have observed these interactions again and again: in clinics both private and public, in northern and southern India, and with different kinds of healing systems—allopathic (biomedical), homeopathic, and Ayurvedic. These interactions were the baseline dynamics of professional healing in India. They reinforced a long-held assertion among those who study medical pluralism in India that the quality of provider-patient relations is usually independent of the kind of medicine practiced (Nichter and Nordstrom 1989; Kakar 1982; Minocha 1980).

The patient-healer dynamics at the KSA clinic were exceptional in this regard. Although I would not characterize its physicians as especially warm and friendly, they appeared to have good rapport with their patients. The doctors actually faced their patients and looked them in the eye while talking. The patients spoke more freely than I had seen in other clinics, and the physicians encouraged them by giving frequent cues that they were listening. At the conclusion of the consultation, the KSA doctors usually asked their patients if they had questions. I had seen such inquiries only twice in the two dozen or so clinics that I had visited during my fieldwork.

Granted, these people were aware of my presence. But their interactions were more practiced and natural than they would have been if they had been performed for my benefit. Moreover, I could see the comfort with which returning patients initiated questions and conversations with their doctors. Finally, the fact that the doctors could effectively vouch for me spoke to the trust that the patients had in their healers. These physicians, Aghor disciples themselves, appeared to have learned the practice of medicine answering. Thus, it is not surprising that they would have so many patients.

In addition to having a good "tableside" manner, the physician-disciples of KSA strongly adhered to an etiological model of leprosy that displaced the blame, both implicit and explicit, of previous sins. The classic text of Ayurvedic medicine, the Caraka Saṃhitā, gives many reasons for the affliction of leprosy. For example, the condition may stem from the sins of previous lives, such as killing a Brahmin or cow, or from sex with a menstruating woman or prostitute (CS II.7: 1). Yet the text also points to dietary incompatibilities, such as the consumption of fish with milk, as the cause of a *kushṭh* condition such as leprosy. The chief medical officer of the KSA clinic, Dr. K.P. Singh (also known as Dr. Sahib), was adamant about this point. A middle-aged man with a friendly manner and a white coat, Dr. Sahib contrasted the Aghor approach to that of traditional Ayurveda. He affirmed the Ayurvedic emphasis on bodily constitution over that of pathogens but did not subscribe to the "old ideas" that leprosy was caused by "bad deeds." "Fooding and eating is the main cause for these things," he said.

The KSA emphasis on dietary etiology contrasted with the models of blame that other physicians in Banaras, regardless of medical persuasion, promoted in explaining leprosy. In addition to physicians who cited past misdeeds to explain differential susceptibility, several promoted more implicit models of self-neglect or evoked random chance to explain leprosy. On the surface, chance would seem to absolve the patient of personal responsibility, but it instead left open a metaphysical niche that physicians inevitably filled with a more common answer: *bhāgya* (fate) and its associated models of karma.

In exploring the role of karma in popular explanations of suffering, Sharma (1973) observes that although karma is never the first explanation given for a misfortune, it is also the last explanation to be abandoned. This phenomenon makes sense in light of two important themes. The first is psychological indeterminacy about the actions of previous lives. The second is the tendency to shift in and out of karmic frames of reference so as to maximize agency and minimize personal responsibility (Daniel 1983). When people combine karmic explanations with other explanatory traditions, they almost always give the former as the ultimate cause and the latter as the proximate cause of misfortune. Only when people cannot find a proximate cause for a misfortune, or when nothing can be done about it, do they explicitly evoke karma (Babb 1983; Keyes 1983). So even when people with leprosy are not explicitly blamed for their condition, the blame is implicit in the absence of an explanation for why the disease occurred, especially when the blame impedes the treatment.

Most residents and inpatients with whom I spoke cited the dietary explanation, even if it was not their first or primary model. Raju, a young tailor with leukoderma who lived with his wife and daughter in Banaras, once believed that his condition was caused by Brahminicide. "Actually ... it is a custom here that [leukoderma] is *Brahm rog* [a Brahmin disease]. It [is] the blame you get for killing a Brahmin." He quickly disclaimed this idea as an old belief. In the modern world, according to Raju, leukoderma is "all from eating and drinking [dietary habits], meaning from eating and drinking it starts in the liver."

Raju was more explicit about causes than most patients were, however. As with other explanatory models, people commonly cited their beliefs using the third person—"the doctors say" or "Baba says"—as if to defer responsibility until the final therapeutic outcome was certain. This stance is typical of Indian religious-healing traditions: people place their faith in the ideology and prescriptions of the guru or deity for a while, with the understanding that they need not maintain their commitment if the problem is resolved within a reasonable period (Kakar 1982; Obeyesekere 1981). Thus, although everyone acknowledged the Aghori model of dietary incompatibility, their commitment to the model also appeared to be tied to the outcome of the treatment. They were optimistic for the time being, opting to place their problems in the hands of the Aghori, and doing their best to follow the treatment regimen, should the treatment eventually work.

As with the bathers at Krim Kund, the power of the Aghori was the most common theme among the resident and outpatients of the Kusht Seva Ashram. This power was typically validated with the performance of miracles. Raju, for instance, spoke of how Sarkar Baba brought a young boy back to life during his travels in Switzerland. "This [ashram] is therefore a sacred place," he said. "Concerning only me, I have seen only this Guruji. I mean Baba [Sambav] Ram [the current baba in residence at KSA]. The landlord of this place at the present time is considered to be a big blessing." As with the saints and sacred geography of Banaras, the healing miracles of the Aghori were closely tied to Kusht Seva Ashram: one was a proxy for the other.

Once again, people cited the metonymic relationship between the Aghori, the Ganga, and the *shmashān* when speaking of their healing powers. Rohit, a Banarsi metalworker in his thirties, spoke hopefully about the power of the Aghori to cure his skin condition: "The synonym of the word *Ganga* is Aghor. So that which is Aghor ... that [is how] God happens. There are Ishwars [lords]. They are one Aghoreshwar. He is one in the world. A human has worshipped him, I mean, in all forms. ... Therefore, we can get everything by doing the *tapasyam*[austerities] of only one. I mean, Aghor means guru *tapasyā*; guru *sadhāna*."

Shivani made a more explicit connection between the Ganga and the *shmashān*. A student in her early twenties, she was worried about the consequences of early-stage leukoderma for her marriage but had great faith in the curative powers of the Aghori, which she explained as follows: "Actually Baba and these [other people] are Aghoris. They sit only at the *shmashān*. Their [relationship is] just there. Because ... Baba had done *sadhāna* only sitting at Ganga. And Kina Ram, he used to sit only at the Ganga. He used to call the Ganga. Sitting at the *shmashān*, visiting with Kaluram Baba ... was those people's [routine], and eating fried fish. It was their daily routine. [Baba Kina Ram] was the avatar of Shiva."

Notably, Shivani referred to Lord Shiva in the feminine, an obvious reference to the Divine Mother, especially given the Mother's manifestation as both Ganga Ma and Svaha of the cremation fire. Patients, even those who knew little about the Aghori, commonly cited the maternal source of Aghor healing. Srikant, an elderly farmer with visible leprosy deformities, had traveled from central Bihar to see the Ganga and Kusht Seva Ashram, referring to the latter as a kind of *shmashān* on the sacred river and describing how both could purify a person of anything, just like "one's mother."

The eating of fish also has an important connection to Aghor medicine. Having been raised near the Kina Ram Ashram, Shivani knew that the Aghori made a point of eating fish as the *prasād* of the river. Informing this practice is the belief that Mother Ganga embraces the excreta of humanity, including the corpses rejected for cremation. Fish eat everything within the Ganga, and the Aghori eat the fish with the conscious intention of assimilating—physically as well as symbolically—everything and anything rejected by society.

Although most patients did not have the benefit of Shivani's background, nearly everyone from Banaras understood there to be some connection between the healing powers of the Aghori, the Ganga, and (sometimes) the *shmashān* and their common ability to transcend limitations. Newcomers who came from outside Banaras learned this from more experienced patients or from the people who referred them to the clinic. It could therefore be argued that the nondiscriminatory nature of Aghor was ultimately responsible for Kusht Seva Ashram's becoming home to one of the most popular leprosy-treatment centers in India. First, the popularity of Kusht Seva Ashram resulted from a common perception that the Aghori were powerful healers. Second, this power was closely linked to the Aghori's transcendence over pollution and purity taboos. Third, one could find evidence for this transcendence in the Aghori's voluntary and public embrace of the feared and discarded. And finally, because the *shmashān* was once the ultimate site of human aversions, the place where the Aghori tested their mettle, the leprosy clinic became the new cremation ground.

The ritual pollution of leprosy and other diseases is extremely disempowering for the afflicted as well as for their kin and close associates. Yet this pollution can be as intensely empowering for those who voluntarily embrace it. The former situation is a product of misfortune, of *bhāgya,* with all the karmic baggage that it entails. The latter situation, however, is an austerity: Aghor *tapasyā,* Aghor *sadhanā.* Devotees and nondevotees alike see this voluntary embrace of pollution as the driving force of Aghor medicine. The Aghori gain much more status for their healing of leprosy than the resident patients can ever hope to achieve, but they channel that power into medicines that they distribute to thousands of people each year. They also channel their power into schools, public works projects, and the social education of those who seek the Aghori for spiritual guidance—people who are usually former patients of Aghor medicine. [...]

Notes

1. A few noteworthy people have defied this warning. The famous poet Kabir, who railed against the hypocrisy of all major religions, insisted on dying across the river from Kashi, making the point that his salvation would depend solely on divine grace and the fruit of his actions.

2. The KSA clinic staff claimed that they could cure most forms of leprosy in three years.

3. The typical monthly prescription for KSA medicines costs between Rs 180 and Rs 220. Although difficult to measure in cash, farm labor in this region is typically about Rs 80 to Rs 100 per day.

4. Although statistics show that Indian women have worse access to health-care resources than men do, one would expect a higher proportion of physical deformities among those women who eventually obtained treatment than among a similar population of men. However, among people who receive treatment, four times as many men have deformities as women. I hypothesize that men's greater participation in certain forms of manual labor subjects them to higher rates of physical trauma, and therefore to a greater frequency of high-titer infections. This phenomenon needs further research.

5. Snakebite and smallpox are the other two afflictions for which cremation is prohibited in most Hindu religious traditions. Babies are not cremated because they have not yet achieved the full status of personhood. Renunciates are buried, for reasons I describe in chapter 3.

6. Kleinman's (1988) case studies illustrate that, though illness and disease are distinguishable from each other, they need not be exclusive categories.

7. The highest bacterial titers are found in nasal secretions, and researchers have hypothesized a number of transmission modes, including respiratory paths (Naafs et al. 2001), water transmission (Matsuoka et al. 1999), and an anaerobic soil intermediary (Chakrabarty and Dastidar 2001). However, the model cannot be validated until scientists can grow the organism under laboratory conditions. To date, the

only naturally infected nonhuman host for leprosy is the armadillo, an animal that does not reproduce easily under captive conditions (Bruce et al. 2000).

8. A minority of people who are infected are particularly susceptible to the mycobacteria. Known as lepromatous, or LL cases, these people often require a longer and more involved course of treatment over three to five years (Bryceson and Pfalzgraff 1990).

9. Understandably, activists in the international HD community consider the term *leper* to be highly derogatory (Gussow and Tracy 1977).

10. Dapsone was the leading treatment for *M. leprae* infection until the early 1980s. Unfortunately, the organism began showing resistance to this sulfa drug within a decade of its introduction in 1943. Today, dapsone is considered to be merely bacteriostatic against *M. leprae*.

11. The solution of reintegrating leprosy treatment into primary care services can also be problematic. For a critical perspective, see Justice 1986.

12. See Nichter (2002) for a counterexample in which health providers relabel tuberculosis within a less stigmatizing ethnomedical category in order to improve health seeking and adherence to treatment.

13. Twenty-three out of thirty-one inpatients had previously sought treatment elsewhere: three first sought a homeopathic physician, two sought an Ayurvedic physician, and one was unreported.

14. Chandra Shekhar, who was prime minister from November 1990 to June 1991, was in frequent contact with Sarkar Baba and several senior disciples during his time in office.

References

Ablon, J. 1995. The "Elephant Man" as "Self" and "Other": The Psychosocial Costs of a Misdiagnosis. *Social Science & Medicine* 40 (11): 1481–89.

Alonzo, A. A., and N. R. Reynolds. 1995. Stigma, HIV and AIDS: An Exploration and Elaboration of a Stigma Trajectory. *Social Science & Medicine* 41 (3): 303–15.

Arole, S., R. Premkumar, R. Arole, M. Maury, and P. Saunderson. 2002. Social Stigma: A Comparative Qualitative Study of Integrated and Vertical Care Approaches to Leprosy. *Leprosy Review* 73 (2): 186–96.

Babb, L. 1983. Destiny and Responsibility: Karma in Popular Hinduism. In *Karma: An Anthropological Inquiry,* ed. C. F. Keyes and E. V. Daniel, 163–81. Berkeley: University of California Press.

Barrett, R. 1997. Male Health and Leprosy in Northern India: A Biocultural Perspective. Paper presented at the 96th Meeting of the American Anthropological Association, Washington, DC.

———. 2005. Self-Mortification and the Stigma of Leprosy in Northern India. *Medical Anthropology Quarterly* 19 (2): 216–30.

Beals, A. R. 1976. Strategies of Resort to Curers in South India. In *Asian Medical Systems: A Comparative Study,* ed. C. Leslie, 184–200. Berkeley: University of California Press.

Bloom, S. S., D. Wypij, and M. das Gupta. 2001. Dimensions of Women's Autonomy and Influence in Maternal Health Care Utilization in a North Indian City. *Demography* 38 (1): 67–78.

Brand, P., and P. Yancey. 1997. *The Gift of Pain.* Grand Rapids, MI: Zondervan.

Bruce, S., T. L. Schroeder, K. Ellner, M. Rubin, T. Williams, and J. E. Wolf. 2000. Armadillo Exposure and Hansen's Disease: An Epidemiologic Survey in Southern Texas. *Journal of the American Academy of Dermatology* 43 (2 Pt. 1): 223–28.

Bryceson, A., and R. Pfalzgraff. 1990. *Leprosy.* London: Churchill Livingstone.

Buckingham, J. 2002. *Leprosy in Colonial South India: Medicine and Confinement.* New York: Palgrave.

Chakrabarty, A. N., and S. G. Dastidar. 2001. Is Soil an Alternative Source of Leprosy Infection? *Acta Leprologica* 12 (2): 79–84.

Daniel, E. V. 1983. Karma Divined in a Ritual Capsule. In *Karma: An Anthropological Inquiry,* ed. C. F. Keyes and E. V. Daniel, 83–117. Berkeley: University of California Press.

Dharmshaktu, N. S. 1992. A Project Model for Attempting Integration of Leprosy Services with General Health Care Services after the Prevalence of the Disease Is Reduced in the Endemic Districts on Multidrug Therapy for over Five Years. *Indian Journal of Leprosy* 64 (3): 349–57.

Freitag, S. B. 1989. Introduction: The History and Political Economy of Banaras. In *Culture and Power in Banaras: Community, Performance, and Environment, 1800–1980,* ed. S.B. Freitag, 1–23. Berkeley: University of California Press.

Frist, T. F. 2000. Stigma and Societal Response to Leprosy: Experience of the Last Half Century. *Indian Journal of Leprosy* 72 (1): 1–3.

Goffman, E. 1963. *Stigma: Notes on the Management of Spoiled Identity.* Englewood Cliffs, NJ: Prentice Hall.

Gussow, Z. 1989. *Leprosy, Racism, and Public Health: Social Policy in Chronic Disease Control.* Boulder, CO: Westview Press.

Gussow, Z., and G. S. Tracy. 1977. Status, Ideology, and Adaptation to Stigmatized Illness: A Study of Leprosy. In *Culture, Disease, and Healing: Studies in Medical Anthropology,* 394–402. New York: Macmillan.

Jones, E. E., R. A. Scott, and H. Markus. 1984. *Social Stigma: The Psychology of Marked Relationships.* New York: W. H. Freeman and Co.

Jopling, W. 1988. *Handbook of Leprosy.* London: William Heinemann.

Justice, J. 1986. *Policies, Plans, and People: Culture and Health Development in Nepal.* Berkeley: University of California Press.

Kakar, S. 1982. *Shamans, Mystics, and Doctors: A Psychological Inquiry into India and Its Healing Traditions.* New York: Alfred A. Knopf.

Keyes, C. F. 1983. Introduction: The Study of Popular Ideas of Karma. In *Karma: An Anthropological Inquiry,* ed. C. F. Keyes and E. V. Daniel, 1–24. Berkeley: University of California Press.

Kleinman, A. 1978. Concepts and a Model for the Comparison of Medical Systems as Cultural Systems. *Social Science & Medicine* 12: 85–93.

———. 1988. *The Illness Narratives: Suffering, Healing, and the Human Condition.* New York: Basic Books.

Kopparty, S. N. M., A. P. Karup, and M. Sivarum. 1995. Problems and Coping Strategies of Families Having Patients with and without Deformities. *Indian Journal of Leprosy* 67 (2): 133–51.

Kumar, A., A. Girdhar, V. S. Yadav, and B. K. Girdhar. 2001. Some Epidemiological Observations on Leprosy in India. *International Journal of Leprosy & Other Mycobacterial Diseases* 69 (3): 234–40.

Matsuoka, M., S. Izumi, T. Budiawan, N. Nakata, and K. Saeki. 1999. *Myco-bacterium Leprae* DNA in Daily Using [*sic*] Water as a Possible Source of Leprosy Infection. *Indian Journal of Leprosy* 71 (1): 61–67.

Minocha, A. A. 1980. Medical Pluralism and Health Services in India. *Social Science & Medicine* 14B: 217–23.

Mira, M. T., A. Alcais, VT Nguyen, M. O. Moraes, C. Di Flumeri, H. T. Vu, C. P. Mai, T. H. Nguyen, et al. 2004. Susceptibility to Leprosy Is Associated with PARK2 and PACRG. *Nature* 427 (6975): 636–40.

Mull, J. D., C. S. Wood, L. P. Gans, and D. S. Mull. 1989. Culture and Compliance among Leprosy Patients in Pakistan. *Social Science & Medicine* 29 (7): 799–811.

Murphy, R. F. 1990. *The Body Silent.* New York: W. W. Norton.

Murphy, R. F., J. Scheer, J. Murphy, and R. Mack. 1988. Physical Disability and Social Liminality: A Study in the Rituals of Adversity. *Social Science & Medicine* 26 (2): 235–42.

Naafs, B., E. Silva, F. Vilani-Moreno, E. C. Marcos, M. E. Nogueira, and D. V. Opromolla. 2001. Factors Influencing the Development of Leprosy: An Overview. *International Journal of Leprosy & Other Mycobacterial Diseases* 69 (1): 26–33.

Nichter, M. 2002. The Social Relations of Therapy Management. In *New Horizons in Medical Anthropology,* ed. M. Nichter and M. Lock, 81–110. New York: Routledge.

Nichter, M., and C. Nordstrom. 1989. A Question of Medicine Answering: Health Commodification and the Social Relations of Healing in Sri Lanka. *Culture, Medicine, and Psychiatry* 13: 367–90.

Noordeen, S. K. 1995. Elimination of Leprosy as a Public Health Problem: Progress and Prospects. *Bulletin of the World Health Organization* 73 (1): 1–6.

Obeyesekere, G. 1981. *Medusa's Hair: An Essay on Personal Symbols and Religious Experience.* Chicago: University of Chicago.

Ponnighaus, J. M. 1995. Leprosy: The Beginning of an End to a Public Health Problem? *Dermatological Clinics* 13 (3): 525–36.

Rubel, A. J., and L. C. Garro. 1992. Social and Cultural Factors in the Successful Control of Tuberculosis. *Public Health Reports* 107 (6): 626–35.

Sasaki, S., F. Takeshita, K. Okuda, and N. Ishii. 2001. *Mycobacterium Leprae* and Leprosy: A Compendium. *Microbiology & Immunology* 45 (11): 729–36.

Seghal, V.N. 1994. Leprosy. *Contemporary Tropical Dermatology* 12 (4): 629–44.

Sharma, U. 1973. Theodicy and the Doctrine of Karma. *Man* 8: 347–64.

Srinivasan, H. 1994. Disability, Deformity, and Rehabilitation. In *Leprosy,* ed. R. C. Hasting, 411–47. Edinburgh: Churchill Livingstone.

Waxler, N. 1981. Learning to Be a Leper: A Case Study in the Social Construction of Illness. In *Social Contexts of Health, Illness, and Patient Care,* ed. E. G. Mishler, 169–94. Cambridge: Cambridge University Press.

Yoder, L. J. 1998. Personal communication.

CRITICAL THINKING QUESTIONS

1. Identify and discuss at least one of the cultural differences between the United States and Canada. Compare and contrast the organizing principles and values underlying the healthcare systems in the two countries. Please be specific, provide examples, and define pertinent concepts.

2. According to Boggs, is the War on Drugs necessary and successful? Why or why not? What is the pharmaceutical industry's role in the US healthcare system? Identify, define, and discuss the roles of *capitalist modernity* and of *alienation* in both systems.

3. Define *stigma*, then identify and discuss three examples of how stigma plays out in the lives of people with Hansen's disease in the Kusht Seva Ashram, as discussed by Barrett.

UNIT 3
Social Stratification, Health, Illness, and Healthcare

Editor's Introduction

The purpose of Unit III is to explore the variety of ways that social stratification impacts health, illness, and healthcare, both globally and within nations. *Stratification* is the unequal distribution of power, status, and wealth between people and between nations. Stratification between nations is largely, yet not entirely, due to economic inequalities, while stratification between people is closely related to issues such as racism, sexism, ageism, and more. Stratification is often experienced **intersectionally** because it is impossible to parse out what parts of inequality are due to any one variable. For example, it is most likely that the **life chances** of a white, middle-class American male are quite different from those of an African American, working-class female. It is impossible to exactly attribute how much these differences are due to race alone, class alone, or gender alone, but we do know that race, class, and gender work together, resulting in highly predictable inequalities.

Socioeconomic status (SES) is the strongest, most consistent predictor of health status globally. The Department of Health and Human Services in Australia notes that "the single strongest predictor of our health and wellbeing is our position on the social gradient (or the 'social ladder')" in its informational pages on health risks.[1] Educational level is also a very strong predictor of health status because education imbues us with the skills to find and maintain jobs, housing, insurance, health information, and so much more. According to UNICEF,[2] on any given day, over 1

intersectionality: the complex and cumulative ways that the effects of multiple forms of discrimination (such as racism, caste prejudice, sexism, and classism) combine and overlap in the lives of marginalized groups and persons.

life chances: a term used by Max Weber to describe opportunities to increase one's *social location*, effected by such things as caste, geographic origin, class, race, gender, and more.

---

1   "Determinants of Health," Department of Health and Human Services, Tasmanian Government, http://www.dhhs.tas.gov.au/wihpw/principles/determinants_of_health.
2   "Education: Every Child Has the Right to Learn," UNICEF, https://www.unicef.org/education.

billion children are in school, while one in five children receive no schooling, and over 600 million children are unable to reach minimum educational proficiencies whether they are in school or not. In talking about global health issues, it is important to note that colonialization and its vestiges also play a significant role in health outcomes for billions of people across the world.

In "Economic, Ethnic, and Gender Inequities in Global Health," Debra L. DeLaet and David E. DeLaet discuss global health inequalities in different parts of the world, as well as within nations. In the first part of their article, the focus is on territorial and regional health disparities. However, they make the very astute observation that research on global health inequities neglects the inequalities that occur within countries. The second part of the article is devoted to samples of research about health disparities due to inequalities within nations. DeLaet and DeLaet make a convincing argument that using gross domestic product (GDP), as is most common in global health research, to predict the health statuses of nations is quite inadequate. For example, how would studies using GDP capture the rich data gathered by Ronald Barrett about persons with Hansen's Disease in India, which we read about in unit II? DeLaet and Delaet do a wonderful job of addressing their topic through the lenses of race and gender in healthcare. Addressing health issues calls for both large-scale economic measurements as well as deep knowledge of within-country inequalities.

In "Urban Poverty: An Urgent Public Health Issue," Susan Mercado, Kirsten Havemann, Mojgan Sami, and Hiroshi Ueda continue this theme, indicating that "Rapid, uncontrolled urbanization results from the interaction between global and local forces." The urban environment is increasingly the grounds of major pollution, infectious diseases, and disasters, among other things, and the poor are most vulnerable in relation to these. *Without reliable housing, food, or healthcare access, impoverished people are at the highest risk of health crises in a geography at the highest risk of health crises.* The authors utilize case studies to illustrate the ways in which health can surprisingly unite people and organizations from a variety of disparate venues to address problems. When these disparate groups have common goals and work together, they are engaging in *integrated interventions.* Mercado et al. stress that stakeholders from all levels of urban areas, from poor inhabitants to bankers, must work together to solve health issues for the most successful outcomes. This article is reminiscent of previous research on homeless persons engaged in survival sex work.[3] There was a need in homeless communities to address a number of health issues, including exposure to violence and to communicable diseases (e.g., tuberculosis and HIV). Representatives from the Department of Health and from nongovernmental organizations (NGOs) were joined by people from the affected groups to develop strategies and programs that improved health outcomes for this population. As Mercado et al. demonstrate through their case studies, health inequalities can successfully be addressed by the participation of all involved.

---

3   Katherine Lineberger, "STARS Program Evaluations," 2003–2008. The Women's Empowerment Program, in cooperation with the Substance Abuse and Mental Health Administration; Katherine Lineberger. "Unfortunate Choices: Risk in the Lives of Street-Level Sex Workers and Non-Sex Working Streetwise Women" (PhD diss., University of Colorado Boulder, 2009).

In "Race, Ethnicity, and Health," Donald A. Barr begins with the importance of defining the terms *race* and *ethnicity*. Race and ethnicity are very important variables in US studies of health and much research that is done underplays and even misinterprets their importance. An understanding of both concepts is critical to understanding demographic inequalities in health, illness, and healthcare in the United States. Barr compares the United States to Canada, which uses no "race" or "ethnicity" categories, leading to questions about the fit of these categories for use in health studies. Barr follows this discussion with illustrative examples of data related to low birth weight, heart disease, and high blood pressure, and we are left with a deeper understanding of the importance of knowing how race and ethnicity are defined in American studies of health, illness, and healthcare.

Social tratification is largely invisible to us because of socialization. Each nation is stratified and this is simply treated as "the way things are." In the United States, for example, we tend to think that racial inequalities are due to racist individuals. The articles presented in this unit do a creditable job of showing that racism and other forms of stratification are deeply structural as well. These problems are global and local, social and individual, and must be addressed as such in any holistic healthcare research.

Economic, Ethnic, and Gender Inequities in Global Health

By Debra L. DeLaet and David E. DeLaet

Introduction

Different levels of economic development and inequitable distribution of economic resources fundamentally shape health outcomes for individuals, communities, and populations across the globe. Additionally, inequities in individual and population health stem from a variety of cultural, political, and social variables. Gender norms also contribute to inequities in global health. Accordingly, this chapter explores inequities in global health at multiple levels: territorially based inequities among different regions and countries of the world, poverty-based inequities that cut across territorial borders, racial and ethnic inequities within countries, and gender inequities in the health status of men and women.

Economic Development and Territorially Based Inequities in Global Health

National Economic Development and Population Health

The achievement of higher levels of national **economic development** tracks closely with significant improvements in population health. The growth of the modern state in the 20th century was accompanied by unprecedented improvements in human health. As Richard Skolnik notes, "It is an astonishing fact that half of all the increase in human life expectancy over recorded time occurred in the 20th century."[1] It is not a coincidence that this century involved the buildup of public infrastructure that either directly or indirectly contributed to improved living conditions and health outcomes among populations living in areas that attained high levels of economic and social development. Millions of lives have been saved due to large-scale public health interventions, including the creation of public water systems and public sewers.[2] In fact, the relationship between economic development and population health is mutually reinforcing. Investments in public infrastructure help fuel economic development that, in turn, contributes to improvements in public

Debra L. DeLaet and David E. DeLaet, "Economic, Ethnic, and Gender Inequities in Global Health," *Global Health in the 21st Century: The Globalization of Disease and Wellness*, pp. 87–113, 231–237. Copyright © 2012 by Taylor & Francis Group. Reprinted with permission.

health. A healthier, longer-living population sustains high levels of economic development, which enables a country to make long-term investments in population health.

Many reasons help explain the strength of the positive relationship between national wealth and population health. Economic development increases the amount of financial resources available to national governments to direct toward investments in public health. Such investments might include

---

Box 3.1.1 Key Terms in the International Political Economy of Global Health

Economic Development: growth in income and improvements in standard of living in a country, region, or community.

Gross Domestic Product (GDP): the market value of all final goods and services produced within a country during a specified period.

Human Development: a concept of development that takes not only national income but life expectancy, literacy rates, poverty rates, and other indicators of quality-of-life of individuals in particular countries into account.

North-South Gap: a term used to describe the significant economic, political, and social divisions between developed countries (largely concentrated in the northern hemisphere) and developing countries (largely concentrated in the southern hemisphere).

Per Capita Gross Domestic Product (GDP): the market value per person of all final goods and services produced within a country during a specified period.

Political Liberalization: a process of political change involving the adoption of democratic reforms, increased governmental transparency, the protection of the rule of law, and the expansion of individual political freedoms as means for reducing poverty in the developing world.

Poverty Trap: a self-perpetuating condition that keeps individuals, households, or populations in poverty.

State Capacity: the ability of a state to govern itself effectively and to implement important public policy objectives, such as social and economic development.

Structural Adjustment Policies: policy changes involving privatization and deregulation required by the World Bank and the International Monetary Fund as a condition for receiving low-interest development loans.

World Bank: an international financial institution that provides low-interest loans to developing countries for the purpose of reducing poverty.

Box 3.1.2 Under the Microscope

The Inequitable Effects of Natural Disasters

When natural disasters strike, people living in poverty are more likely to suffer negative consequences. The inequitable effects of natural disasters are felt at country, community, and neighborhood levels. The negative effects of natural disasters are often amplified in developing countries. At the community level, low-income populations living in areas of concentrated poverty often suffer catastrophic injury at higher rates than people living in wealthier neighborhoods.

Developing countries and low-income populations are more vulnerable to the negative effects of so-called natural disasters for many reasons. Developing countries often have weak state capacity to respond to calamitous events. Moreover, they typically do not have adequate public infrastructure to meet basic needs in the face of serious natural disasters or to respond to major public emergencies. The lack of effective regulations on safety standards in public buildings or housing contributes to the negative consequences when natural disasters strike. In low-income communities, the housing of people in poverty is more likely to be made from substandard materials that are vulnerable to collapse and destruction in the face of hurricanes, earthquakes, flooding, and other natural disasters. People living in poverty also do not have the income or other resources to seek necessary medical care, emergency housing, or transportation out of a disaster zone.

The comparative mortality outcomes from the 2010 earthquakes in Haiti and Chile serve as a stark example of this problem. The 8.8-magnitude earthquake in Chile resulted in a death toll numbering in the hundreds, whereas the 7-magnitude earthquake in Haiti led to an estimated 220,000 deaths.[1] While some of this disparity can be attributed to geological differences between the two regions as well as energy differences between the two earthquakes, socioeconomic factors also played a role. Chile's national income is significantly higher than Haiti's. In 2010, the per capita GDP in Chile was $14,780 compared to $1,040 in Haiti.[2] Differences in state capacity and public infrastructure, including emergency response planning and building code regulations, also contributed to these disparate outcomes.[3]

---

1   Stephen Kurczy, Leigh Montgomery, and Elizabeth Ryan, "Chile Earthquake Facts: Chile vs. Haiti, in Numbers," *Christian Science Monitor,* March 2, 2010.

2   United Nations Development Programme, *International Human Development Indicators.* Available online at: http://hdr.undp.org/en/statistics/data/.

3   Tim Padgett, "Why Chile Is Better than Haiti at Handling Earthquakes," *Time,* March 1, 2010.

funding or subsidization of health care for individuals, the use of financial resources to implement and enforce regulations that contribute to improvements in population health (for example, regulations governing workplace, food, or drug safety or environmental regulations), or public investments in infrastructure (like safe roads and public water systems) that improve public health. Higher levels of national wealth also make it more likely that individuals and families will have access to employer-funded health care. More simply, a healthy national economy creates socioeconomic benefits in the form of higher levels of education and income for individuals and families, which contribute to better health outcomes. [...]

If national wealth and population health are positively correlated, the reverse, unfortunately, is also true. Major health problems within a country can lead to **poverty traps** that hinder national economic development. In turn, low levels of economic development make it difficult for countries to promote public health and, in fact, can exacerbate pre-existing health challenges, leading to a vicious cycle of poverty and disease. A strong negative relationship exists between health indicators and **state capacity**, a state's ability to govern itself effectively and to implement basic public policy objectives.[3] According to Andrew T. Price-Smith, disease serves as a stressor on state capacity and increases deprivation in a population, thereby leading to more demands on the state to meet basic needs and provide public services and, ultimately, it may undermine or reverse development gains.[4]

In countries with a high incidence of communicable disease, there are considerable negative implications for economic growth. For example, between 1965 and 1990, countries with high rates of malaria experienced an average growth in per capita GDP of 0.4 percent per year, whereas average growth in other countries was 2.3 percent per year.[5] Although it does not fully explain the disparity in economic growth, the negative effects that high rates of malaria have on trade, tourism, and foreign domestic investments are likely a significant factor. Decreased demand for agricultural imports from regions with high rates of communicable illness also contributes to this problem.[6]

Not surprisingly, a strong **correlation** between national wealth and health status exists. Data from the United Nations Development Programme (UNDP) illustrate the strength of this correlation. According

EDITOR'S NOTES

correlation: statistically, a term representing how change in one variable is related to change in another. A positive correlation (+1) occurs when an increase in one variable results in the increase of another variable. A negative correlation (–1) occurs when an increase in one variable results in the decrease of another variable, and vice-versa.

to 2010 data, the ten countries with the highest **per capita gross domestic product** (GDP in U.S. dollars), the market value per person of all final goods and services produced within a country during a specified period, included Liechtenstein ($94,569), Qatar ($77,178), Luxembourg ($76,448), Norway ($58,278), United Arab Emirates ($56,485), Kuwait ($50,284), Singapore ($50,266), Brunei Darussalam ($49,915), the United States ($46,653), and Hong Kong ($45,049). Each of these countries achieved high rankings on measures of life expectancy, ranging from 76 years in Qatar to 82.5 in Hong Kong.[7]

In contrast, the ten countries with the lowest per capita GDP were Zimbabwe ($187), the Democratic Republic of the Congo ($326), Liberia ($400), Burundi ($403), Guinea-Bissau ($554), Eritrea ($648), Niger ($677), the Central African Republic ($766), Sierra-Leone ($825), and Togo ($846). Four of these countries were among the countries that ranked lowest globally on measures of life expectancy—Zimbabwe (47 years), the Central African Republic (47.7 years), the Democratic Republic of the Congo (48 years), and Sierra Leone (48.2 years). The other countries with the lowest per capita GDP also had relatively low average life expectancy: Togo achieved the highest ranking on this measure, with life expectancy of 63.3 years, a figure still significantly below measures for more developed countries.[8]

As these data suggest, a strong correlation between national wealth and population health exists. However, the relationship between wealth and health does not tell the entire story. UNDP data on wealth and health also contain interesting gaps that indicate other factors are at play in shaping population health outcomes. Japan, with a per capita GDP of only $33,649, achieved the highest ranking on measures of life expectancy, at 83.2 years. Numerous additional countries, including Switzerland, Iceland, Australia, France, Italy, Sweden, Spain, and Israel, had higher life expectancy than the countries that were ranked in the top ten based on per capita GDP; only Hong Kong was ranked in the top ten on both measures.[9]

At the other end of the spectrum, several low-income countries that had higher per capita GDP when compared with other low-income countries performed the worst on measures of life expectancy. Afghanistan, with a per capita GDP of $1,419, ranked the lowest worldwide on life expectancy, at 44 years. The ongoing war in Afghanistan certainly plays a role in this outcome. Next to Afghanistan, Lesotho and Swaziland had the lowest life expectancy, at 45.9 and 47 years, respectively, despite having higher per capita GDPs ($1,608 for Lesotho and $5,058 for Swaziland) than many other developing countries. High prevalence of HIV/AIDS in these countries likely plays a role in these outcomes. Notably, these countries are still quite poor in comparison to high-income countries, but they have significantly higher GDPs than the very poorest countries. Yet, their relatively higher levels of national wealth did not contribute to higher life expectancies for their populations. Such gaps make clear that national wealth alone is not sufficient for measuring or promoting population health.

Human Development and Population Health

Critics argue that measures of national wealth are an imperfect indication of the quality of life or well-being of individuals within a country. In response, the United Nations Development Programme came up with the concept of **human development**. Rather than assuming that national income is the best measure for human well-being within countries, the concept of human development suggests that other indicators, including life expectancy, literacy rates, and levels of poverty, need to be taken into account when trying to assess the well-being of individuals in particular countries.

Although the human development index incorporates a variety of indicators in addition to national wealth, country rankings on the human development index do not vary dramatically from measures of national wealth as a general rule. There is considerable overlap among the countries that rank highest on both indicators. Countries categorized as high-income tend to rank high on the human development index. Conversely, countries categorized as low-income tend to be located toward the bottom of the scale on the human development index.

For example, in the Human Development Report 2009, Norway had the highest ranking on the UNDP's human development scale, and Niger had the lowest ranking. Norway's per capita GDP was US$58,278 in comparison to per capita GDP of only $294 in Niger. In both cases, the countries were at the extremes of the scale in terms of relative national wealth. The discrepancy between life expectancy in each country was equally stark: 80.5 years in Norway compared to just 50.8 years in Niger. Government expenditures on health also dramatically differed, with the Norwegian government spending $3,780 per capita in comparison to only $14 by the government in Niger. These figures suggest a very strong correlation between national wealth and health status.[10] This correlation is especially strong at the extreme ends of the spectrum, with the wealthiest countries tending to have high rankings on leading health indicators and the poorest countries having the worst outcomes.

Although there is a strong relationship between national wealth and population health, these correlations are not perfect. A comparison of the 2009 data from the Human Development Report for four countries—the United States, Cyprus, China, and Mexico—effectively demonstrates the imperfect correlation between relative wealth and population health. Among these countries, the United States had the highest per capita GDP at $45,592 and a life expectancy of 79.1 years. The U.S. government spent $3,074 per capita on health. In Cyprus, the per capita GDP was $24,895, yet life expectancy was slightly higher, at 79.6 years. That year, Cyprus spent $759 per capita on health. During this time period, Mexico had a per capita GDP of only $9,715, a life expectancy of 76 years, and government health expenditures of just $327 per capita. Despite much lower national income and government spending on health, the life expectancy in Mexico was not dramatically lower than in the United States. Similarly, China had a per capita GDP of just $2,432, a life expectancy of 72.9 years, and government health expenditures of just $144.[11]

These figures indicate that the correlation between national income and health outcomes is not perfect and that other factors are in play in determining the health status and well-being of populations across the globe.

As these figures suggest, a human development lens applied to global health provides some interesting insights and leads to a number of important questions.[12] On the one hand, measures of national wealth and human development indicators tend to follow the same trajectory. As a general rule, wealthy countries score high on measures of human development, whereas poor countries produce low levels of human development. On the other hand, important gaps between national wealth and human development exist. These gaps can signify the existence of inequities within societies that are not captured by measures of a country's income alone.

What, then, explains the fact that health outcomes may not be significantly worse in countries with much lower national incomes and government health expenditures than in wealthier countries? Health policy is one variable that may help explain that national income and health outcomes do not correlate perfectly. Some countries with relatively low national income may, despite their relative poverty, spend health care dollars in a more efficient, effective, and equitable manner than wealthier countries. [...]

Moreover, national income does not account for inequities within societies, and, thus, it is not a perfect predictor of health outcomes. A high per capita GDP might mask vast inequities between the wealthiest and the poorest members of a society. Similarly, bad health outcomes within disadvantaged groups in particular societies will bring down measures of average life expectancy even if such inequities are not captured by aggregate measures. Subsequent sections of this chapter explore the inequities *across* and *within* societies that are not captured by measures of national wealth.

Poverty and Economic Inequities Across and Within States

Poverty and health are linked in fundamental and complicated ways. Strong connections between wealth and health status exist at the global, regional, state, and individual levels. The previous section focused on national-level indicators of health, which illustrate the strong, if imperfect, correlation between wealth and health. Although the relationship between national wealth and health is powerful, we need to move away from a country-based analysis in order to gain a fuller understanding of the ways in which wealth shapes health outcomes. As we will see, a state-centric lens does not provide a complete picture of the nature of economic inequities in global health.

A North-South Gap in Global Health

Structural features of the global economy and international political system create dynamics that produce and reinforce inequities between developed and developing countries, contributing to systemic inequities in global health that transcend the territorial borders of specific countries. As shown in

EDITOR'S NOTES

colonialism: the practice by which powerful countries establish and maintain control over less powerful countries in order to maintain economic dominance.

EDITOR'S NOTES

globalization: the process through which economic interests and culture(s) become international.

EDITOR'S NOTES

North–South gap: key social and economic divisions between countries that, grouped geographically, highlight the development of northern countries and the underdevelopment of southern countries.

the previous section, measures of population health vary dramatically among states. Much of this variation can be attributed to different levels of national economic development. However, it is not enough to look at the state as a unit of analysis in order to understand the ways in which economic inequities shape population health outcomes. Rather, these economic inequities are rooted in broader economic and social forces, including the legacy of **colonialism** and **globalization** processes, which transcend the borders that divide states. Variations among states matter, to be sure. But a more general divide between developed and developing countries is also significant.

This division between developed and developing countries is often referred to as a **North-South gap** and is characterized by significant differences in levels of social and economic development as well as varying degrees of political influence and power on the global stage. The North-South gap describes real and important divisions between developed and developing countries that break down largely along geographical lines. The vast majority of developed countries are geographically located in the northern hemisphere. Conversely, most developing countries are located in the southern hemisphere. Hence, scholars often describe the divisions between developed and developing countries as a North-South gap.

Despite the geographic distribution of this gap, the most notable feature of the north-south division of the international system is inequitable access to global economic resources. Five and a half billion of the world's approximately 6.7 billion people—82 percent—live in developing countries.[13] Almost 1.4 billion people live on less than $1.25 per day, the figure that the **World Bank** uses to define the poverty line. Most of the people surviving on less than $1.25 per day live in developing countries. Poverty rates are significantly higher in some regions. For instance, whereas 20 percent of the population in East Asia lives on less than $1.25 per day, over 50 percent of the population in sub-Saharan Africa lives below the poverty line.[14] The inequitable distribution of global economic resources is also reflected in the high concentration of wealth in developed countries. For instance, the UNDP has estimated that populations in high-income countries have over eighty times as much income as people in low-income countries.[15]

Although poverty levels remain high throughout the developing world, it is important to note significant reductions in global poverty. According to the World Bank, the number of people living below the poverty line has fallen from 1.9 billion in 1981 to 1.4 billion in 2005. This decline represents a significant reduction in the percentage of the world's population living below the poverty line—from 52 to 26 percent[16]—and is particularly notable given that the world's population has been increasing during this time period. Despite the reduction in the number and percentage of people living in abject poverty, the number of people living in moderate poverty—on less than $2 per day—increased during the same time period from 2.5 billion people to 2.6 billion people. Because the world's population has been growing, this increase in the absolute number of people living in moderate poverty still represents a reduction in the proportion of the world's population living in moderate poverty, from 70 to 48 percent.[17] Declining rates of global poverty are a welcome development. Nevertheless, both the absolute number and the proportion of the world's population living in either abject or moderate poverty remain incredibly high.

Not surprisingly, the economic inequities between developed and developing countries contribute to significant gaps in global health. On the whole, developing countries have worse outcomes across the board on most health indicators. They have lower life expectancy; higher rates of maternal, infant, and child mortality; higher rates of malnutrition; and higher prevalence of communicable illnesses. The high concentration of poverty-related disease in the developing world is especially notable. For example, diarrhea is the second major cause of death among children globally, and most of these deaths—over 99 percent—occur in the developing world.[18] The fact that preventable childhood deaths from diarrhea occur almost exclusively in the developing world is a striking figure. It indicates clear evidence of a pattern throughout the developing world, suggesting that the causes of poverty-related illness cannot be located only in specific countries. Rather, scholars, practitioners, and policy makers must be attentive to the systemic roots of poverty and poverty-related health challenges.

The necessity of paying attention to the systemic roots of the North-South gap raises the question of what causes the fundamental divide between developed and developing countries. The history of colonialism in the developing world certainly has played a significant role. The negative legacy of colonialism is far reaching. Colonial powers created administrative structures and political borders in colonized territories that did not correspond to the ethnic, social, or cultural composition of these areas. As a result, new states that were created during the process of decolonization were based on arbitrary boundaries that have contributed to ongoing civil conflict and power struggles in these countries decades later. Colonial administrative practices also disrupted traditional modes of governance while excluding the majority of indigenous populations from colonial governing institutions. Thus, when colonial rule ended, much of the indigenous population had not had access to the education and administrative experience essential for effective governance of large modern states. Moreover, colonial governance was antidemocratic and antithetical to the rule of law. Therefore, it should not be surprising that the departure of colonial powers left in place political structures and systems that were not grounded in democracy or the rule of law. Obviously, the structure of colonialism also created lasting economic dependencies—in which former colonial powers continue to exert control over natural resources, markets, and financial resources in former colonies—that reinforce inequities between developed and developing countries.

Although virtually all scholars acknowledge the historical role of colonialism in creating and perpetuating inequities between developed and developing countries, consensus does not exist among scholars, practitioners, and policy makers regarding the ways in which global economic structures and processes affect this gap today or on the question of how the international community should respond. Marxist scholars argue that neocolonialism or imperialism is to blame. In this view, the political and economic relationships between developing and developed countries are characterized by ongoing subordination, exploitation, and domination.

In a similar vein, many scholars and practitioners (Marxist and otherwise) point to globalization as the driving force underlying many inequities between developed and developing countries. Critics of globalization argue that the increasing interconnectedness of the global economy puts pressure on all countries to reduce wages, to eliminate or forgo environmental and workplace safety regulations, to limit human rights protections, and to implement cutbacks in the provision of basic social services, including health services, in an effort to attract or keep corporate investment. These pressures can have particularly strong effects in developing countries, which already have lower levels of economic development, relatively weak state capacity, and limited public infrastructure. **Structural adjustment policies** required by the World Bank as a condition for low-cost development loans also contribute to such pressures.[19]

Other scholars believe that economic liberalization [...] is precisely what is needed to foster social and economic development. According to this perspective, economic liberalization generates higher national wealth, which, in the aggregate, increases the resources available to national governments, communities, families, and individuals. These resources can strengthen state capacity, thereby enabling states in the long run to build up public infrastructure and to govern more effectively. Additionally, proponents argue that the wealth generated by economic liberalization expands the resources available to families and individuals for spending on goods and services, like health and education, that confer important socioeconomic improvements. In a similar vein, other scholars believe that **political liberalization** is essential for reducing the gap between developed and developing countries. In this view, inefficient, corrupt, and illiberal governments share a significant portion of the blame for poverty in developing countries. Proponents of this view advocate political reforms involving the adoption of democratic reforms, increased governmental transparency, the protection of the rule of law, and the expansion of individual political freedoms as means for reducing poverty in the developing world.[20]

Despite the lack of scholarly consensus on how to respond, the concept of a North-South gap helpfully draws attention to systemic inequities in global health. Nevertheless, this approach is also problematic. Grouping the world into two single categories obscures important differences across, between, and within countries. For one thing, a North-South gap suggests a strictly geographic dividing line between developed and developing countries that is not accurate. For example, Australia and New Zealand are developed countries geographically located in the global south. In a similar vein, reducing the world to two categories of development is overly simplistic. For instance, many countries from the former Soviet bloc, including Belarus, Georgia, Armenia, Kazakhstan, Azerbaijan, Uzbekistan, and Kyrgyzastan, score lower on measures of human development than some countries in the global south. Russia itself is ranked lower on the scale of human development than many southern hemisphere countries. Thus, despite the fact that a North-South gap suggests a geographic division between developed and developing countries, it does not, strictly speaking, indicate that this division is rooted in territorially based inequities. Rather, it involves poverty-based inequities rooted in the global economic system.[21] For these reasons, we must look *inside* states as well as *beyond* them in order to understand the nature of poverty-based inequities in global health.

Poverty and Economic Inequities Within Societies

Economic inequities *within* states are just as powerful a determinant of health outcomes as inequities between developed and developing countries. Low-income populations in developed countries face many of the same economic constraints that negatively impact their health that low-income populations in developing countries face. Likewise, high-income populations in developing countries share many of the same socioeconomic advantages as their counterparts in developed countries and achieve similar health outcomes.

Regardless of overall levels of national development or a country's position in the global economy, individuals living in poverty tend to have worse health outcomes in every country and region of the world. A variety of reasons help explain the strong relationship between poverty and relatively poor health. Individuals living in abject poverty often do not have access to adequate food and suffer the effects of malnutrition. If they do not have access to clean water, low-income populations are more likely to contract waterborne illnesses. Individuals living in poverty may live in substandard housing, which can lead to a variety of health problems, including chronic respiratory illness due to indoor cooking without adequate ventilation (an illness with particularly high prevalence among women in poor communities) or communicable illnesses resulting from a lack of access to basic sanitation infrastructure.

The ways in which poverty contributes to and exacerbates the global burden of communicable diseases are illustrative. People living in poverty are more likely to reside in crowded conditions, putting them at increased risk for exposure to infectious agents, such as tuberculosis, that are transmitted via the respiratory route. Lack of access to clean drinking water and poor sanitation and hygiene increase the risk for the spread of waterborne agents that lead to diarrheal illnesses. In regions of high malaria risk, poor people have less access to insecticide-treated bed nets that serve to decrease the spread of disease by mosquitoes. Individuals living in poverty, particularly women, are less likely to use condoms to prevent the spread of HIV due to limited access to condoms, a lack of education about the efficacy of such practices, and cultural obstacles to condom use.[22] Once exposed to infectious agents, individuals living in poverty are more likely to develop disease, often with more severe clinical manifestations. The most notable reason for this increased susceptibility is that people who are poor are often malnourished, a condition that adversely impacts an individual's immune system and skin integrity, two of the most important barriers to infection. Notably, malnutrition is more prevalent in developing countries. More than four out of five children who are underweight for their age live in developing regions in Africa or South Asia.[23] This fact helps explain why communicable illnesses make up such a large proportion of the burden of disease in developing countries.

Box 3.1.3 Under the Microscope

Reflections on Global Health Aid to Developing Countries

I lived in Botswana for six months in 2009. Prior to my arrival, most of what I knew about public health in southern Africa involved the HIV/AIDS crisis. Because this crisis has had such devastating consequences throughout the region, discussion of HIV and AIDS dominates much of the news on southern Africa. Similarly, international aid efforts to the region have been largely directed to HIV/AIDS projects. My first weeks in Botswana confirmed the importance of HIV/AIDS—you could not travel a block in the capital city, Gaborone, without seeing an AIDS-related billboard or an HIV clinic, and the city is full of American medical students doing short rotations at Princess Marina Hospital, the primary public medical facility in the city.

Yet, it did not take me long to realize that the public health situation in Botswana is more complicated than the media, dominated by coverage of the AIDS crisis, suggest. Despite the fact that Botswana is a middle-income country, it is a highly inequitable society with enormous gaps between the wealthy and the poor in terms of income and health care access. AIDS has hit the poorest and most vulnerable people in the society especially hard, and international programs focused on dealing with the AIDS crisis address this reality. Although these contributions have obvious importance to individuals suffering from HIV/AIDS, the international community has paid less attention to the poverty-related health challenges faced by the poor on a daily basis—lack of access to adequate nutrition, high rates of child and maternal mortality, and substandard housing and working conditions.

On a drive from Gaborone to the Khutse Game Reserve, we passed through the town of Molepolole. At the edge of town, we saw a state-of-the-art medical facility, one I presumed had been partially funded through global health aid. It was located in proximity to low-income neighborhoods with substandard housing. It was a stark visual reminder of the gap between the extremes of wealth and poverty in the developing world. My observations led me to question whether the international community has been providing the type of public health aid most needed by the populations it purports to serve. Certainly, the government of Botswana welcomes global health aid, and international programs have helped to bring the HIV/AIDS crisis under control. However, general poverty-related public health challenges have not been adequately addressed by HIV/AIDS funding. Notably, international organizations and major aid donors (public and private) have dominated the process by which public health priorities have been determined in Botswana and elsewhere in the developing world.

A related criticism is that local health care workers and other individuals with skills to contribute to improving public health infrastructure get drawn into working for international programs directed toward the AIDS crisis rather than working on public health more generally. According to Laurie Garrett, this dynamic represents a sort of internal brain drain where well-intentioned international actors place a high demand on local financial and human resources in ways that may not be the best for long-term, sustainable solutions to public health problems in the developing world.[1] In short, Garrett's criticisms suggest that there may be a fundamental gap between the international community's assessment of public health priorities in the developing world and actual public health needs in these countries.

The global emphasis on the HIV/AIDS crisis has developed despite the fact that HIV/AIDS is not the leading cause of death in the developing world. Rather, a number of other risk factors, including high blood pressure, smoking, high cholesterol, and childhood underweight, cause a greater number of deaths throughout the developing world. Thus, a preliminary evidence-based assessment of the causes of death in the developing world lends some support to the argument that the overarching emphasis on HIV/AIDS in global health funding initiatives might be misplaced.

My own observations of daily life in Botswana certainly made me wonder whether the international community should be devoting more resources to sustainable development and general poverty alleviation measures rather than disease-specific funding.

—Debra L. DeLaet

---

1   Laurie Garrett, *The Coming Plague: Newly Emerging Diseases in a World out of Balance* (New York: Penguin Books, 1994): 456.

Additionally, individuals living in poverty are less likely to have access to adequate health care services. As a result, they are less likely than individuals in higher-income brackets to receive preventive care or appropriate treatment in the case of illness. For example, many children living in poverty do not receive appropriate oral rehydration therapy for diarrheal illness—a simple, inexpensive treatment shown to decrease morbidity and mortality due to diarrheal illnesses. In fact, in developing countries, less than 40 percent of children receive such therapy, with those in the lowest percentiles of household income being particularly vulnerable.[24] Many children living in poverty fail to receive care for other communicable diseases as well. One survey in rural Tanzania found that children from low-income families with malaria were less likely than their counterparts from higher-income families to be evaluated by a health care professional and less likely to receive antimalarial drugs even when being evaluated by a clinician.[25] Low-income populations often do not receive expensive, long-term treatments for chronic illnesses, such as diabetes, because the treatments are unaffordable and because these individuals do not have regular access to health care facilities. As a result, people living in poverty are more likely to suffer greater morbidity and mortality from both communicable and noncommunicable illnesses.

Several factors contribute to this disparity in the receipt of appropriate medical treatment. Due to limited education, individuals living in poverty often fail to recognize the clinical severity of an illness, making it less likely that they will seek medical evaluation and treatment. For example, one survey in western Nepal demonstrated that poor education was associated with a greater likelihood of parental failure to recognize the severity of respiratory illness in their children and to seek medical care.[26] Across the globe, the working poor also may not have adequate health insurance and may not be able to take off work in order to get the care they need.

People living in poverty often forgo accessing medical care due to the considerable distance they must travel to receive such care. Individuals and families living in poverty often do not have means of transportation to hospitals, doctors' offices, or other medical facilities. This problem is especially acute for more serious health issues that require care at medical facilities offering advanced care. For instance, hospital-based clinics are typically located in urban centers at some distance from rural populations living in poverty. Thus, the rural poor have difficulty accessing treatments that are available only in hospital-based settings.

Moreover, care is often perceived to be of higher quality in hospital-based facilities in urban centers.[27] One example of the lower quality of care offered by rural primary facilities is that they are less likely than urban hospital-based centers to stock vital medications, such as antibiotics.[28] Where available in rural areas, antimicrobials are often of lesser quality due to poor governmental regulation of handling and manufacturing of these products. Preventive services such as vaccinations are also less likely to be available to low-income populations. In many countries, this disparity in quality among health centers is a direct result of an allocation of national and regional budgetary resources that favors urban centers. Further, an underdeveloped private-sector health care system in these countries often results in many public-sector resources being utilized by wealthier individuals in that country, further limiting access for low-income populations who are unable to financially compete for these resources. Many families living in poverty are then left to prioritize spending for health care services, with adult males often receiving care at the expense of women and children.[29]

Health challenges may also create poverty traps for individuals and households, contributing to the likelihood that low-income populations will get stuck in poverty. Ill health undermines people's ability to be economically productive and to pursue education that would enable them to improve their economic opportunities. Also, catastrophic illness can result in the loss of employment and can bankrupt individuals who do not have adequate health care. Indeed, illnesses and injuries are among the most common reasons that individuals fall into poverty. People affected by disease are less likely to be able to work, with resultant loss of income. Additionally, they are often forced to sell assets to help pay medical expenses. Children who are sick also face negative socioeconomic consequences. For example, infectious illnesses during early childhood can have a negative impact on both physical and cognitive development. An appropriate level of iron in the blood is necessary for the cognitive development of a young child. Because certain intestinal parasites, such as hookworms, are associated with decreased iron absorption, infection with these parasites leads to cognitive delay in children.[30] In another example, infection due to malaria is a significant contributor to school absenteeism among low-income populations in many developing countries.[31] Illness also increases a person's risk for malnutrition (and vice versa), with an obvious effect on the ability to work or to attend school.

The types of inequities discussed here are not reflected in aggregate measures of national wealth and population health. In every country in the world, high-income populations have a high probability of good health outcomes because of socioeconomic advantages that give them access to preventive care, appropriate treatments in the event of illness, education, and good nutrition. Conversely, people living in poverty—in developed as well as developing countries—face numerous constraints in their efforts to stay healthy.

Racial and Ethnic Inequities in Global Health

Race refers to a classification of human beings into distinct population groups historically based on presumed biological and genetic differences. In contrast, **ethnicity** refers to a classification of human beings into distinct population groups based on the self-identification of people according to shared language, history, culture, or other social factors. Although these terms are often used interchangeably, they reflect a deep tension regarding the nature of differences among human populations. Historically, the concept of race has been used to suggest that innate physical variations among populations, most notably skin color, are at the root of social and cultural differences among groups of people. At one level, such categorization might be seen as a harmless way to describe real differences—cultural, linguistic, social—that appear to be associated with skin color. At another level, such categorization

> **Box 3.1.4** Key Definitions Pertaining to Race, Ethnicity, and Global Health
>
> **Ethnicity:** a classification of human beings into distinct population groups based on the self-identification of people according to shared language, history, culture, or other social factors.
>
> **Race:** a classification of human beings into distinct population groups historically based on presumed biological and genetic differences, usually manifested in visible physical differences such as skin color.

has had nefarious consequences. Historically, the concept of race has been used to rationalize slavery, colonialism, genocide, and a wide range of human rights abuses. Indeed, critics argue that the very idea that fundamental biological and genetic distinctions divide the human species is itself at the heart of racism. Critics of the concept of race also note that all human beings are members of the same species. As such, humans largely share the same genetic material across population groups. Indeed, some geneticists note that human beings are genetically more homogenous than other mammal species and that more genetic variation exists within specific populations than among these populations.[32] For these reasons, many social scientists prefer to use the term *ethnicity* rather than *race* when describing significant differences among human populations.

The controversy over the concept of race notwithstanding, it provides an important framework for discussing significant economic and social inequities in the world. Whether or not the concept of race itself captures real differences among human populations, racism and racial inequities are very much real phenomena. Accordingly, scholars and practitioners still rely on this category to investigate inequities faced by disadvantaged racial and ethnic groups. For our purposes, the category of race remains very important in the medical literature on disparities in health among population groups. Moreover, it should be noted that some scholars use the term *race* because they see it as interchangeable with *ethnicity*, not because they want to signify innate physical differences among populations. We will follow that convention by referring to both racial and ethnic inequities throughout this section.

Health Disparities Among Disadvantaged Racial/Ethnic Populations

Significant disparities in health have been demonstrated among disadvantaged racial and ethnic groups across the globe. Racial and ethnic populations experience inferior physical and mental health outcomes in terms of both morbidity and mortality in all geographic regions in which such comparative data are available. In most cases, such inequities are faced by racial and ethnic minorities within countries, but, in some cases, racial and ethnic populations that face health disadvantages actually constitute the majority of a population. Blacks in South Africa, where the legacy of apartheid fundamentally shapes population health outcomes, are a prominent case in point. The available data are particularly robust in developed countries, but evidence from developing regions supports similar conclusions.

While a comprehensive review of data from developed regions is beyond the scope of this section, several examples highlight these inequities. According to 2009 data, the life expectancy among whites in the United States was 76.2 years for males and 80.9 years for females, as compared to 70.9 years for males and 77.4 years for females among African-Americans.[33] The infant mortality rate was 5.32 per 1,000 live births for whites and 12.71 per 1,000 live births for African-Americans.[34] Similarly, African-Americans, Asian-Americans, Pacific Islanders, and Hispanics have a higher overall childhood mortality rate than their white counterparts.[35] Data from other developed countries, such as Canada and Brazil, also demonstrate racial and ethnic inequities in infant and childhood mortality rates.[36]

Using health-related quality-of-life measures such as healthy days, defined as "the overall number of days during the previous 30 days during which a person reported good (or better) physical and mental health," it appears that racial and ethnic minorities in the United States also experience greater morbidity.[37] Similarly, with the exception of Asian-Americans, racial and ethnic minorities are much less likely than whites to report their health status as "excellent" or "very good," as is demonstrated in Figure 3.1.1. These self-reported measures of disparities in health status are consistent with the extensive body of evidence demonstrating racial and ethnic inequities in health outcomes for specific

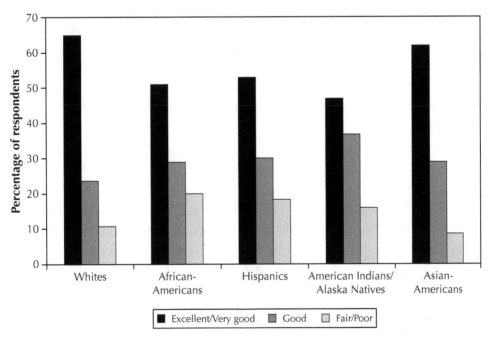

FIGURE 3.1.1 Self-reported Health Status by Race, 2005.

Source: Adapted from Holly Mead, Lara Cartwright-Smith, Karen Jones, Christal Ramos, and Bruce Siegel, "Racial and Ethnic Disparities in U.S. Health Care: A Chartbook" (The Commonwealth Fund, 2008). Available online at: http://www.commonwealthfund.org/usr_doc/mead_racialethnicdisparities_chartbook_1111.pdf.

medical conditions. To cite only a few examples, studies have shown that racial minorities in the United States experience poorer outcomes for cardiovascular disease, asthma, and cancer.[38] This is particularly true for African-Americans, who are significantly more likely than other racial and ethnic groups to suffer a chronic medical condition or disability, even after adjusting for income.[39] These findings have been replicated in other developed countries. For example, racial and ethnic minorities in the United Kingdom, Australia, South Africa, and Brazil are more likely to develop end-stage kidney disease as a result of an increased incidence of hypertension and diabetes mellitus.[40] As a final example, among both children and adults, racial and ethnic minorities have been found to experience an increased burden of mental health disease, including depression and anxiety, in countries such as the United States, Canada, and the United Kingdom, to name just a few.[41]

Though considerably sparser, data from developing countries across global regions also demonstrate similarly increased morbidity and mortality for disadvantaged racial and ethnic populations. For example, studies in sub-Saharan Africa reveal that, consistent across all countries studied, ethnic inequalities exist in the infant and under-five mortality rates. In Asia, a recent study from Vietnam found that ethnicity was the main socioeconomic determinant for neonatal mortality.[42] In lower-income countries in Central and Latin America, overall health inequities have been demonstrated among indigenous and black people in comparable geographic and social locations.[43] Just as in the case of developed countries, disease-specific differences in health outcomes have been demonstrated in developing countries. For example, the risk for lung cancer in Nepal has been shown to differ by ethnicity.[44] Data also demonstrate an increased risk for mental health disorders among racial and ethnic minorities in developing countries.[45]

The Causes of Health Disparities Among Disadvantaged Racial/Ethnic Populations

Because race and ethnicity are so intimately linked with socioeconomic status, it is difficult to fully tease out the contribution of race and ethnicity to population-level health outcomes. Nevertheless, studies have suggested that as much as one-half of mortality differences among racial and ethnic groups may be attributable to socioeconomic factors.[46] The corollary is the suggestion that a significant portion of health status is determined by factors specifically unique to race and ethnicity. This section explores the factors that may lead to disparities in health outcomes for disadvantaged racial and ethnic populations.

Research has suggested that many social variables likely contribute to racial and ethnic inequities in health. First among these includes determinants directly related to the neighborhoods in which these populations live. For example, as was discussed in Chapter 5, obesity is associated with poor access to healthful foods and neighborhood green space for people of lower socioeconomic status, an association more likely to affect minority groups due to their higher rates of poverty.[47] In the United States, African-American and Hispanic children are more likely to develop asthma in part due to their increased likelihood of living in public housing and the resultant exposure to such asthma triggers as cockroaches.[48] Disadvantaged racial and ethnic groups are also much more likely to be exposed to violence, with negative ramifications for physical and mental health.[49] Similarly, indigenous populations across the globe tend to experience higher injury and death rates due to accidents associated with cramped living conditions, unsafe housing, lack of space and facilities for safe play, and exposure to a high volume of fast-moving traffic.[50] The social environment in which disadvantaged racial and ethnic populations live and the associated self-perception of inequalities lead to an increase in risk taking and unhealthy behaviors.[51]

Social factors also likely contribute to racial and ethnic inequities in health outcomes as a result of their impact on access to care. Again, the case of the United States is instructive. As shown in Figure 3.1.2, racial and ethnic minorities in the United States have historically been less likely than whites to have health insurance coverage.

... This situation has existed due to a health care model that relies heavily on employer-based health insurance and does not provide universal coverage to all residents.

Consistent with this inequity in insurance coverage, racial and ethnic minorities are much less likely than whites to access the health care system. For example, African-Americans, Hispanics, and Asian-Americans are more likely to be without a regular doctor than are whites.[52] Additionally, racial and ethnic minorities are much less likely than whites to receive health care services, including preventive care, such as screening for colorectal cancer and prostate cancer.[53]

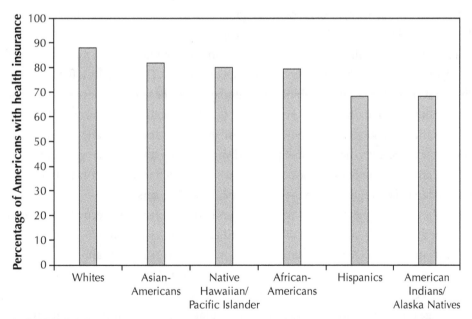

FIGURE 3.1.2 Percentage of Americans with Health Insurance Coverage, by Race and Ethnicity.

Source: Reproduced from Lesley Russell, "Fact Sheet: Health Disparities by Race and Ethnicity" (Center for American Progress, 2010). Available online at: http://www.americanprogress.org/issues/2010/12/disparities_factsheet.html.

Even in countries where universal health care coverage is provided, inequities in access to care for disadvantaged racial and ethnic populations exist. For instance, certain immigrant populations in Australia have been shown to receive lower rates of orthopedic surgery for severe osteoarthritis.[54] Racial and ethnic minorities have been shown to have similarly decreased access to therapies for end-stage renal disease in Venezuela.[55] Finally, in South Africa, a study revealed that, even after adjusting for other socioeconomic factors, black women were less likely than nonblack women to receive preventive care services during pregnancy and birth,[56] and another study revealed that 40.8 percent of blacks, as compared with 10.9 percent of whites and 6.9 percent of Asians, reported going without necessary medical care at some point in the previous year.[57]

These findings of racial and ethnic inequities in health care among countries with universal health care coverage suggest that factors other than health insurance status affect access to high-quality care. Some of these determinants are likely rooted in socioeconomic factors. For example, a 2008 study demonstrated that transportation barriers are significantly more often responsible for unmet medical care needs for children among Native Americans than for other racial groups.[58] Disparities in access to care can also result from inequities in educational attainment among racial and ethnic minorities. For example, lower levels of health literacy and educational attainment serve as a barrier to the receipt of preventive services such as screening mammography among racial and ethnic minorities in the United States.[59] Ethnic minorities in Vietnam occasionally forgo seeking care for their children because they have not been appropriately educated on recognizing the signs of illness.[60] Geographic determinants have also been associated with inequities in the quality of care delivered to disadvantaged racial and ethnic groups. In the United States, individuals living in predominantly racial and ethnic minority communities are much more likely than whites to report having little choice in where to seek medical care.[61] This inequity is further complicated by findings that show that racial and ethnic health disparities in the United States exist across hospitals rather than within individual facilities.[62] According to this study, whites and racial and ethnic minorities treated within the same hospital were shown to receive the same standard of care; minorities, however, were more likely to present to hospitals that provided lower-quality care.[63] Similar geographic disparities have been demonstrated in South Africa, where medications such as antimicrobials in rural primary facilities are often of lesser quality than in urban hospital-based centers.[64]

Because they are intimately linked with racial and ethnic status, socioeconomic determinants likely account for a significant portion of the inequities in health status and health care access seen among disadvantaged racial and ethnic populations. However, there are almost certainly factors specific to race and ethnicity that also contribute to these disparities. Biological differences in risk for developing certain conditions exist among racial and ethnic groups. For example, individuals of African heritage are much more likely to inherit the mutated gene responsible for causing sickle cell disease. Genetic factors also influence the predisposition of individuals of certain racial and ethnic groups to the development of conditions such as Type II diabetes mellitus and hypertension. Racial and ethnic minorities may also experience inferior health outcomes as a result of language barriers.

In the United States, individuals with limited English proficiency (LEP) often have limited access to care or receive a lesser quality of care. Though Title VI of the Civil Rights Act requires that any health care provider receiving federal funds, including providing Medicaid and Medicare services, must provide adequate language assistance to an LEP patient,[65] language discordance can still limit the quality of care provided. For example, in one study, Spanish-speaking Hispanics noted that communication difficulties made it more challenging to fully explain symptoms, ask questions of providers, follow through with filling of prescriptions, and fully understand physician recommendations; nearly 20 percent reported not seeking medical treatment due to language barriers.[66]

Disadvantaged racial and ethnic populations also tend to be more likely to exhibit mistrust toward health care providers. For example, Malay-Muslims in Singapore expressed concern about the potential for racial discrimination as well as the participant selection process for genetic research.[67] As a result of patient mistrust, disadvantaged racial and ethnic groups may be less likely to seek critical preventive care and treatment. For instance, patient mistrust contributes to lower prostate cancer screening among African-Americans in the United States.[68] Patient race and ethnicity can also influence physicians' perceptions of patients. Data from a 2000 study revealed that patient race was associated with physicians' assessment of patient intelligence, feelings of affiliation toward the patient, and beliefs about the patient's likelihood of risk behavior and adherence with medical advice.[69] These potential barriers of language discordance, patient mistrust of providers, and patient stereotyping by physicians likely exist in no small part due to the underrepresentation of disadvantaged racial and ethnic populations in the physician workforce. In the United States, although African-Americans, Hispanics, and Native Americans constitute more than 30 percent of the population, these groups accounted for only 8.7 percent of physicians, 6.9 percent of dentists, 9.9 percent of pharmacists, and 6.2 percent of registered nurses, according to 2007 data.[70]

Several overarching themes can be gleaned from this examination of the causes of health disparities faced by disadvantaged racial and ethnic populations. First, social determinants play a critical role in the development of racial and ethnic inequities in health. Only by addressing these disparities in the condition of daily life of disadvantaged racial and ethnic groups can greater equity in the health status of populations be achieved.[71] As concerns health care systems, measures must be taken to improve access, including expansion of health care coverage to the uninsured and underinsured members of the population. Education of patients to improve their understanding of disease processes, treatment options, and methods to most effectively access health care systems is important.[72] Additionally, it is critical to provide better education of health care professionals so that communication barriers, both cultural and linguistic, can be addressed and providers might more consistently exhibit cross-cultural competency in the care of patients. Implementing policies that will better ensure medical training for a greater diversity of health care providers would be of obvious benefit in eliminating these language and cultural barriers. Lastly, improving public awareness of the scope of the problem is likely to result in greater support and more realistic achievement of these goals.

Box 3.1.5 Under the Microscope

Reflections on Patient-Physician Language Discordance

I have worked as a primary care provider for pediatric and adult populations since 1995. During this time, I have had the opportunity to work in a variety of settings. I worked at three large academic health centers in Cincinnati and New York City that served a wide variety of patients, but I largely provided care for children and adults with public health insurance, the majority of whom were racial and ethnic minorities. I also worked at a community health center in Cincinnati, where many of the patients were uninsured minorities. Lastly, I worked briefly providing care to a population of patients who were mostly healthy, nonminority young adults with employment-based private health insurance while I was employed by a private practice in an affluent neighborhood in New York City. Prior to entering the workforce, I had the privilege as a medical student to work for a limited period of time with the Indian Health Services in Oklahoma caring for a population of Native Americans. Given this breadth of experience, I feel that I can offer a unique perspective on the challenges faced in accessing high-quality care for racial and ethnic minorities.

It has been my experience that racial and ethnic minorities are at a clear disadvantage when attempting to navigate the health care system. The challenges faced result not only from issues related to our current organization of health care in the United States but also from social and cultural factors. One important example is that of patient-physician language discordance.

Many of the patients for whom I have provided care, and continue to provide care, are individuals with limited English proficiency. I am limited in that I am fluent only in English. In our practice, we see patients who speak Spanish, French, Portuguese, Senegalese, Mandarin, Bengali, and Hindi, to name just a few. Many of my patient encounters, therefore, have language discordance as an obstacle that must be addressed to ensure the best possible delivery of care. To deal with this challenge, we have available to us, at a cost to our institution, language interpreter services. Given the volume of patients and the diversity of languages for which such services are required, on-site interpreters are impractical. Rather, we employ an off-site service accessed via telephone.

Communication in this manner is less than ideal, for both patient and provider. In a system that places a priority on seeing a high volume of patients in an efficient manner, the time intensity required to ensure mutual understanding of key elements of the patient's history and the provider's prescribed plan of care steals critical minutes from an already-limited visit. This is particularly troubling when providing care to patients with a complexity of medical problems. Additionally, a large portion of communication is subtle, in terms of both spoken word and nonverbal cues, and these subtleties are easily missed during language discordant evaluations. Given the inherent intimacy of the professional relationship between patient and physician, these missed opportunities for information gathering might negatively affect physician decision making. Lastly, even when language discordance is not, strictly speaking, an issue during a patient evaluation, ethnic and cultural differences in spoken word between provider and patient can also affect communication—if I ask for "a lift" in London, I may be surprised to be led to an elevator rather than to one's car.

Underscored in this reflection is the critical importance of effective communication between patient and physician. It is a common medical teaching, one that I have found to be confirmed in my years as a clinician, that 90 percent of arriving at a correct medical diagnosis is based on a detailed patient history of symptoms. How, then, can one provide the best possible care to his or her patients if the starting point is one of limited communication? To remedy this, it is imperative that, when necessary, clinicians be provided with language interpreter services. Also, having available culturally appropriate and language-specific reading materials for patients is critical. Providing education to expand provider language skills is helpful, though, as suggested, any one provider being able to gain fluency in the multitude of languages that may be encountered in practice is likely impractical. Thus, the ultimate goal should be to increase the diversity of trainees in the field of medicine to ensure the most appropriate care for the greatest breadth of patients seen in our health care systems.

—Debra L. DeLaet

Gender Inequities in Global Health

Health Disparities Between Men and Women in Global Health

The health status of men and women across the globe is characterized by significant differentials. Several indicators used to measure health status, including life expectancy, health-adjusted life expectancy (HALE), and disability-adjusted life years (DALYs), demonstrate the health disparities that exist between men and women.

In every region of the world and across all levels of economic development, women have a higher life expectancy than men. In 2007, the global average female life expectancy was 70 years, compared to 65 years for men. Women's higher average life expectancy is especially pronounced in the developed world, where more than twice as many women than men live past the age of 80.[73] A narrower gap between female and male life expectancy exists in low-income countries, where women can expect to live 58 years, compared to 55 years for men.[74] The female health advantage in life expectancy holds true across all regions of the world.[75] The starkest gap in life expectancy between women and men emerges in Central and Eastern Europe and the Commonwealth of Independent States, where women can expect to live roughly 74 years, compared to just 65 years for men. The gap between women and men is smallest in sub-Saharan Africa, where female life expectancy is 52.5, compared to 50.4 for men.[76] According to United Nations Development Programme (UNDP) data for 2007, male life expectancy was higher than female life expectancy in only two countries: Afghanistan (43.5 for women versus 43.6 for men) and Swaziland (44.8 for women versus 45.7 for men).[77] Taken together, World Health Organization (WHO) and UNDP data on life expectancy demonstrate a striking, if surprising, pattern of greater longevity for women that holds across the globe.

HALE estimates follow the same pattern as life expectancy indicators. Women can expect to live more years in full health in every region of the globe, and women's health advantage on this indicator holds across all levels of economic development. However, the gap between men and women is smaller in HALE estimates than in general estimates of average life expectancy. The 2007 HALE for women globally was 61 years compared to just 58 years for men. Women's advantage in HALE estimates is somewhat more pronounced in high-income countries, where females have a HALE of 72 years compared to 68 years for males. As in the case of general life expectancy, the gap between men and women on HALE indicators narrows at lower levels of economic development. In lower-middle-income countries, females have a HALE estimate of 62 years compared to 60 years for men in good health. The gap is narrowest in low-income countries, where women can expect to live 49 years in full health compared to 48 years of expected good health

EDITOR'S NOTES

HALE: health-adjusted life expectancy; an adjustment to life expectancy which considers the amount of time lived in less-than-perfect health.

for men.[78] The female advantage in HALE estimates again holds across all global regions, although the HALE gap between men and women is smaller than the gap in general life expectancy.

The most interesting discrepancies between life expectancy and HALE indicators show up in individual countries. Unlike life expectancy measures, which show a male advantage over females in only Afghanistan and Swaziland, HALE estimates are higher for males in a number of countries: Bangladesh, Botswana, the Central African Republic, Pakistan, Qatar, Tajikistan, Tonga, and Zimbabwe. In numerous other countries—Afghanistan, Bahrain, Benin, Cameroon, Chad, Kuwait, Mali, Mozambique, Nepal, Nigeria, Sudan, Swaziland, Tuvalu, United Arab Emirates, and United Republic of Tanzania—HALE estimates for men and women are identical. The male advantage in HALE is not large in the cases where it exists—typically just one or two years.[79] Nevertheless, the shift is notable and suggests that HALE estimates, which incorporate variables related to quality of life and not just longevity of life, are more likely to capture the effects of variables that have negative effects on women's health.

An examination of lost healthy life expectancy years, which is the difference between total life expectancy and HALE,[80] provides another lens for examining health differentials between men and women. In contrast to life expectancy and HALE indicators, data on lost years of full health suggest a health disadvantage for women. Globally, women lose an average of nine years of HALE compared to seven years for men. This pattern holds across all regions of the world and across all levels of economic development. In every region of the world, women lose eight or nine years of full health compared to six to eight years for men.[81] The estimated number of lost years of full health for females is highest in upper-middle-income countries, where women lose an average of eleven years of good health and males lose an average of nine years. In low-income countries, the number of lost years of good health drops to nine for females and seven for males. Despite women's health advantage in longevity and HALE, these data show that women have higher morbidity than men and will spend a higher percentage of their lives in less than a state of full health.[82]

In addition to differentials in life expectancy measures, men and women experience different burdens of disease, as measured in DALYs, which indicate the number of years of healthy life lost due to particular diseases and injuries. As DALY data show, men and women suffer disproportionately from different kinds of illnesses. Table 3.1.1 shows the leading causes of burden of disease measured in DALYs by sex. In high-income countries, the top five causes of DALY losses in women include unipolar depressive disorders, migraines, health problems associated with alcohol use, bipolar disorders, and schizophrenia. In low-income countries, the major causes of DALY losses for women are HIV/AIDs, tuberculosis, abortion complications, schizophrenia, and maternal sepsis.[83] Conditions specific to women make up a significant proportion of women's burden of disease. Globally, maternal conditions (including maternal hemorrhage, maternal sepsis, hypertensive disorders, obstructed labor, obstetric fistula, and complications from unsafe abortions) contribute to 2.8 percent of women's DALY losses.[84] Cancers, including breast and cervical cancer, contribute to 1.1 percent of DALY losses for women.[85] Women also have higher disease prevalence for certain illnesses, such as Alzheimer's, osteoporosis, and arthritis, due, in part, to their

TABLE 3.1.1 Leading Causes of Burden of Disease (DALYs) by Sex, 2004

Disease or Injury	Percentage of Total DALYs	
	Female	Male
Infectious and parasitic diseases	19.6	20.1
Neuropsychiatric disorders	13.9	12.4
Cardiovascular diseases	9.4	10.4
Unintentional injuries	7.1	10.9
Perinatal conditions	8.5	8.1
Sense organ disorders	6.2	5.3
Cancers	4.9	5.3
Maternal conditions	5.4	–
Respiratory diseases	3.6	4.2
Digestive diseases	2.5	3.1
Intentional injuries	1.8	4.6
Diabetes mellitus	1.5	1.1

Source: Adapted from the World Health Organization, *The Global Burden of Disease*: 2004 Update: 60–64. Available online at: http://www.who.int/healthinfo/global_burden_disease/GBD_report_2004update_full.pdf.

average higher life expectancy.[86] Injuries contribute disproportionately to men's burden of disease, and men are also more prone to suffer from heart disease and coronary artery disease. A significant proportion of the global male burden of disease—2.7 percent of DALY losses—results from war and violence.[87] Men also have significantly higher prevalence rates of drug and alcohol disorders.[88]

The causes of death for males and females also shed light on disparities in the health status of men and women across the globe. Figure 3.1.3 illustrates the distribution of the major causes of mortality by sex. At the global level, cardiovascular disease is the major cause of death for both men (26.8 percent) and women (31.5 percent). Globally, other major causes of male mortality are infectious and parasitic diseases (16.7 percent), cancers (13.4 percent), unintentional injuries (8.1 percent), respiratory infections (7.1 percent), and respiratory disorders (6.9 percent). After cardiovascular disease, the major causes of death for females include infectious and parasitic diseases (15.6 percent), cancers (11.8 percent), respiratory infections (7.4 percent), and respiratory disorders (6.8 percent).[89]

Men have higher adult mortality rates across all regions, which can be attributed in large part to high male mortality due to injuries. Although this pattern holds across the globe, sex-based disparities in mortality rates are apparent across regions. Differences are most pronounced in Africa, where females have significantly higher mortality due to communicable illnesses and to maternal and nutritional conditions. Overall, HIV/AIDS causes 40 percent of female deaths in Africa compared to the 14 percent of deaths resulting from maternal conditions. Communicable illnesses are also the major cause of mortality for African men, but they are less likely to die from communicable illnesses than women. Males in Africa have a somewhat higher mortality resulting from injuries than women. In Europe, cardiovascular disease and injury are major causes of male mortality. Men face much higher mortality rates than women in the Eastern Mediterranean Region due to injuries. In South-East Asia, minimal differences between men and women manifest in mortality rates due to communicable illnesses. Men have slightly higher mortality

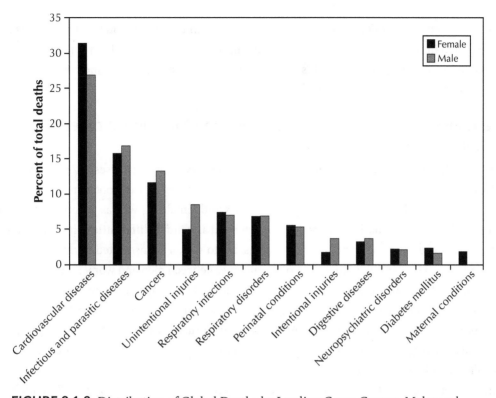

FIGURE 3.1.3 Distribution of Global Deaths by Leading Cause Groups, Males and
Females, 2004.

Source: Adapted from the World Health Organization, The Global Burden of Disease: 2004
Update: 10. Available online at: http://www.who.int/healthinfo/global_burden_disease/
GBD_report_2004update_full.pdf.

rates due to noncommunicable illnesses and injuries. In Latin America and the Caribbean, injuries
are a major cause of death for men, contributing to higher male mortality rates in this region.

A final indicator that underscores a serious global health disadvantage for women is the surplus
male population in the developing world. Approximately 50.3 percent of the world's 6.2 billion people
are male, and roughly 49.7 percent are female. Records of live births across all societies indicate a
"natural" sex ratio of 103–106 male births for every 100 female births. In China today, this ratio is
124 to 100 in favor of boys. India, South Korea, Singapore, and Taiwan have similarly distorted sex
ratios. These sex ratios indicate a surplus male population. Globally, estimates suggest that 100 million
women are "missing" from the total global population.[90] The discrepancy results from gender-biased
practices in areas of the developing world, most notably sex-selective abortion and the killing of girl
children in infancy. These practices stem from cultural preferences for boy children in many societies.
The neglect of girl children, dowry violence, and other forms of domestic violence also contribute
to surplus male population across the globe. This "gender paradox"—of longer average female life

expectancy and HALE but a lower percentage of women in the world's total population—is largely concentrated in the developing world.[91] High-income countries have a higher proportion of women than men in the total population; this relationship is reversed in low-income countries, and it is especially pronounced in the region of South Asia.

The Causes of Health Disparities Between Men and Women in Global Health

The global health disparities between men and women have varying causes. In some cases, these disparities can be described as **sex differentials**. Here, health disparities are rooted in biological causes, including basic biological differences between males and females as well as genetic and hormonal factors. Other health disparities are better characterized as **gender differentials**, in which case men and women experience different health outcomes due to socially constructed norms of masculinity and femininity. Gender differentials in health outcomes between men and women result from health behaviors, cultural practices, and governmental policies shaped by **gender norms**—the culturally prevailing constructs of presumed "normal," "appropriate," or "ideal" behavior and identities of men (masculinity) and women (femininity.) Although it is helpful to distinguish between sex and gender differentials, divergent health outcomes for men and women, in many instances, represent a complex interplay of biology and gender.

Many health disparities between men and women can be attributed to sex differentials. Take women's longer average life expectancy as an example. Women have certain biological advantages that contribute to their greater average longevity. Scientists have offered a variety of potential explanations for the female longevity advantage. For one, sex chromosomes give females a health advantage. To understand this advantage, it is necessary to review some very basic fundamentals regarding sex chromosomes. Female offspring result from two X chromosomes, whereas male offspring are the product of an X chromosome and a Y chromosome. X chromosomes carry more genes than Y chromosomes,

---

Box 3.1.6 Key Definitions Pertaining to Gender and Global Health

Gender Differentials: health disparities between men and women that are rooted in socially constructed norms of masculinity and femininity.

   Gender Norms: the culturally prevailing constructs of presumed "normal," "appropriate," or "ideal" behavior and identities of men (masculinity) and women (femininity).

   Sex Differentials: health disparities between men and women that are rooted in basic biological differences between males and females as well as genetic and hormonal factors.

and, as a result, more sex-linked traits, including illnesses, are carried on the X chromosome. Most sex-linked illnesses result from recessive genes carried on the X chromosome. Therefore, males have a 50 percent chance of getting a sex-linked illness if their mother carries one abnormal gene. Conversely, females would need to inherit a recessive gene from both the mother and the father in order to develop the condition. Hemophilia is a classic example of a sex-specific illness that is more common among males for precisely this reason. Women may have certain hormonal as well as chromosomal advantages that contribute to their longer average life expectancy. The male hormone testosterone may increase risk taking and aggressive behavior that lead to high rates of unintentional injury among men. Metabolic differences, which predispose men to higher levels of LDL ("bad cholesterol"), may also contribute to longevity disadvantages for men.[92] For instance, to the extent that metabolic differences lead to higher levels of bad cholesterol among men, they contribute to the higher rate of cardiovascular disease seen in men.

Although sex differentials produce certain health advantages for women, biological factors are responsible for a number of significant health challenges faced by women alone. For example, women's reproductive health issues are fundamentally rooted in biological differences between the sexes. Numerous examples fall under this category. Ovarian cancer, eclampsia, gestational diabetes, pregnancy and birth-related hemorrhage, obstetric fistula, and maternal death during childbirth all involve reproductive and maternal health conditions faced by women alone. Thus, these health challenges have roots in basic biology. Higher rates of depression and migraine headaches among women also can be attributed to hormonal and genetic factors fundamentally rooted in sex differentials. Additionally, autoimmune disorders, such as hypothyroidism and hyperthyroidism, as well as lupus and rheumatoid arthritis, are more common among women and can be attributed to inherent biological differences.

Men also face a number of health challenges that are primarily biologically based. Obvious examples include prostate and testicular cancer. Males also have a much higher incidence of cardiovascular morbidity and mortality in young and middle adulthood, at least in developed countries. Higher rates of cardiovascular disease among men have been attributed in large part to hormonal differences between males and females. Interestingly, these hormonal differences are essentially neutralized after women become postmenopausal, and women experience a similar incidence of cardiovascular morbidity and mortality in late adulthood.[93]

As these examples illustrate, health disparities between men and women in global health can be partially attributed to sex differentials. However, gender differentials also contribute fundamentally to various disparities in health outcomes between men and women. For example, maternal conditions are sex-specific health challenges rooted in biology. Over 500,000 women die each year due to complications from pregnancy and childbirth; most of these deaths would be preventable with simple and affordable public health interventions.[94] The extent to which these maternal conditions contribute to burden of disease depends very much on socially constructed gender norms that partially determine women's access to perinatal and postnatal care as well as the general social and economic determinants that shape women's health status across the globe. As the example of maternal health suggests, divergent health outcomes in some areas reflect gender biases that lead to underfunding of women's health priorities.

Gender biases that prioritize men's health over women's health also manifest in different ways. Men in most societies have dominated political decision making over health care policy and budgets.[95] Male biases in medical research also have played a role here. For example, a great deal of medical research on cardiovascular disease has historically been based primarily on male subjects, which limits the applicability of research findings to female patients. Due to prevailing conceptions of femininity in many societies that lead women to prioritize the health of the male members of their families and communities more highly than their own health or that of their daughters, women are often less likely than men to seek necessary health care. The uneven distribution of financial resources within households also makes many women less likely to seek professional medical care even if they would otherwise be inclined to do so.[96] Gender differentials also contribute to underreporting of certain diseases for women. For example, due to social stigmas that place high value on sexual "purity" among women, women are often reluctant to undergo testing or to seek treatment for sexually transmitted diseases.

Gender norms also contribute to health disadvantages for women in other ways. In particular, gender norms that devalue girl children and women contribute to all sorts of harmful practices that threaten the health and lives of women and girls across the globe. These harmful practices include sex-selective abortion and female infanticide, feeding practices that prioritize giving more of scarce food to boy children and men, dowry violence, sexual violence, and other forms of domestic violence. Such practices lead to a wide range of health problems for girls and women, including debilitating injury, malnutrition, and death. Unlike maternal conditions, these health problems have no biological basis and are rooted almost entirely in discriminatory gender norms. Gender norms also shape the transmission, experience, and treatment of critical illnesses for women. HIV/AIDS is a case in point. Gender inequalities embedded within societies can make women more susceptible to contracting the disease. For example, gender inequalities can limit women's ability to control their sexuality or to use birth control in sexual relationships (especially within marriage) and, thus, contribute to high HIV prevalence rates among women in many societies. Sexual violence against women also exacerbates the spread of disease. Unequal economic and power relations within families and societies at large also can limit women's ability to receive effective treatment for the disease.[97]

Additionally, women face gendered health challenges that undermine their well-being without necessarily constituting disease or disability. For instance, women in the developing world, especially in rural areas, commonly have primary responsibility for running households. Women are often responsible for child rearing, growing and cooking food for the family, obtaining water for the household (which often involves walking significant distances), caring for frequently sick children, and facing high mortality rates among their children. These burdens are especially pronounced in high-fertility countries where women are often pregnant and raising several young children at the same time. These sorts of socioeconomic burdens may negatively affect women's physical and mental health without necessarily resulting in diseases or disabilities that show up in general health indicators.[98]

Gender differentials also contribute to specific health challenges faced by men. Although women's longer average life expectancy can be attributed in part to biology, social factors also contribute to a lower average life expectancy for men. For example, fatal injuries are a major cause of male mortality in regions across the globe. Socially constructed gender norms contribute to this phenomenon. A form of masculinity that encourages aggressive, risk-seeking behavior results in a greater propensity of men to engage in behaviors (for example, fast or reckless driving) that could lead to life-threatening injuries. Prevailing forms of masculinity in most societies contribute to high mortality rates among men in other ways as well. High rates of male morbidity and mortality due to injuries result in large part from gendered social and economic norms that place many men at risk of occupational threats to their health. Occupational injuries are a major cause of morbidity and mortality for men in most societies across the globe. The fact that men are more likely than women to work in more dangerous occupations (for instance, construction, mining, or factory work involving heavy or dangerous equipment) can be attributed, at least in part, to socially constructed norms that treat such work as largely masculine endeavors.

Similarly, male burden of disease and mortality stemming from war-related violence is a highly gendered phenomenon resulting from the deep associations between prevailing forms of masculinity and military combat in most societies. For example, in countries with forced military conscription, such policies typically apply only to men. (The case of Israel, where women as well as men face compulsory military service, is a prominent exception.) As a result, men are more likely to be injured or killed as combatants even when they do not have a real choice about participating in military service. This phenomenon stems from gender norms that fundamentally tie responsibility for military service in national defense to a masculine conception of civic duty. Gender norms that presume men are potential combatants and women and children are innocent civilians also contribute to war-related morbidity and mortality for men during war.[99] Many civilian men are likely to be killed as *potential* soldiers simply because they are males of "fighting age."[100]

Many crucial questions remain about the relative effect of sex differentials versus gender differentials on health disparities between men and women. In some cases, it is clear that sex differentials are the primary cause of disparate health challenges. Maternal health conditions, experienced only by women, are a good example. In other cases, such as female infanticide and sex-selective abortion, discriminatory gender norms are obviously the primary determinant of this gender gap in health outcomes—neither practice is fundamentally rooted in biology.

However, in many cases it can be very difficult to disentangle the relative contribution of biological sex versus gender constructs in shaping health outcomes. For instance, high rates of unintentional injury among men are caused, in part, by risk-taking behavior shaped by prevailing conceptions of masculinity. At the same time, hormonal differences rooted in biology also contribute to such behavior. The same thing can be said of the higher rates of war-related injury and death for men. On the one hand, masculine norms that prioritize aggressive, self-sacrificing behavior among men shape these outcomes. On the other hand, we can ask ourselves how much of this behavior is influenced by fundamental biological differences between men and women. Some evidence exists that men are more prone to violence due to higher testosterone levels, biological propensity to greater size and strength, biologically rooted differences in cognition, and other biological or genetic factors.[101] Furthermore, there is evidence that suggests that aggressive behavior itself increases testosterone levels, indicating that the relationship between biological sex and gender works in both directions.[102]

Due to the complex interplay of biology and gender, we cannot reach definitive conclusions about what causes various gender gaps in global health. Clearly, both biology and gender play a role, and interactive effects of both biology and gender are important. Disentangling the relative influence of biological sex and gender goes well beyond the scope of this chapter. For the beginning student of global health, the important thing to remember is that both sex and gender differentials are responsible for the disparities in health outcomes between men and women.

Conclusion

This chapter provided an overview of a range of inequities in global health. These inequities are manifested across numerous borders—territorial, poverty-based, and social borders—that shape the international relations of global health. Territorial borders reveal distinct inequities between high-income countries with good aggregate population health outcomes and low-income countries with comparatively poor aggregate population health outcomes. The strength of this general correlation between levels of national wealth and population health reflects a larger North-South gap in global health that is rooted in broad systemic features and underlying structural inequities in the global economy.

Despite the importance of broad territorially based inequities between countries and between developed and developing regions in general, significant inequities within, between, and across territorial borders are also critical. Differences in population health outcomes across countries are not entirely rooted in levels of national income, and variations in national health systems (as will be discussed in Chapter 10) influence population health, as do social, political and cultural inequities within societies. In particular, poverty-based inequities are a fundamental source of disparities in population health outcomes, as are disparities rooted in socioeconomic inequities among racial and ethnic groups across and within societies. Across the globe, both women and men face important health disparities rooted in both sex and gender differentials. Notably, poverty-based, racial/ethnic, and gendered health disparities cut across national borders, suggesting transnational causes and trends, at the same time as they are manifested in unique ways in particular societies.

The economic, ethnic, and gender inequities in global health considered in this chapter do not represent isolated, discrete categories. Rather, considerable overlap exists in terms of both the disparities in health outcomes and the root causes of these disparities. Territorially based inequities have been shaped by racialized transnational processes and events, such as colonialism. Sexism on a global scale has contributed to poverty-related health challenges faced by women across the globe. The reverse is also true: Health disparities faced by disadvantaged racial and ethnic populations, as well as health disparities between men and women within particular societies, are rooted in broader, transnational economic forces and trends. As a result of the complicated intersections among poverty, race/ethnicity, and gender both within and across societies, it is difficult to disentangle the relative weight of each of these categories.

For our purposes, the critical point is to highlight the importance of all of these inequities. Students of public health need to be aware of the multiple sources and manifestations of economic, ethnic, and gender inequities in global health. The range of inequities in global health—and the complex interplay among various forms of inequities—underscores the importance of drawing on the knowledge of scholars and practitioners from many disciplines in seeking to promote global health. To mitigate inequities in global health, the insights and contributions of medical professionals, social workers, sociologists, economists, cultural anthropologists, public policy experts, and political scientists will be essential in efforts to address the underlying socioeconomic determinants of health in a comprehensive manner on a global scale.

Discussion Questions

1. Do you agree with the assertion that national wealth is directly correlated with better population health outcomes? Why or why not?

2. What factors make individuals living in poverty more susceptible to the morbidity and mortality associated with communicable diseases? What are "poverty traps," and how does a high burden of communicable disease cause poverty traps for individuals as well as populations?

3. What are the major determinants of racial and ethnic disparities in health?

4. What critical interventions might help eliminate racial and ethnic disparities in health?

5. What are some of the specific health challenges faced by women and men across the globe?

6. What factors contribute to gender gaps in global health?

7. What actions might be taken to reduce gender gaps in global health?

Notes

1. Richard Skolnik, *Essentials of Global Health* (Sudbury, MA: Jones and Bartlett Publishers, 2008): xiii.

2. Ruth Levine, *Case Studies in Global Health: Millions Saved* (Sudbury, MA: Jones and Bartlett Publishers, 2007).

3. Andrew T. Price-Smith, *The Health of Nations: Infectious Disease, Environmental Change, and Their Effects on National Security and Development* (Cambridge, MA: MIT Press, 2002): 174.

4. Price-Smith: 77–116.

5. J. Gallup and J. Sachs, "The Economic Burden of Malaria," *American Journal of Tropical Medicine and Hygiene* 64: 1,2S (2001): 85–96.

6. World Health Organization, *Health, Economic Growth, and Poverty Reduction* (2002): 40. Available online at: http://whqlibdoc.who.int/publications/9241590092.pdf.

7. United Nations Development Programme, *International Human Development Indicators*. Available online at: http://hdrstats.undp.org/en/indicators/default.html#G.

8. *Ibid.*

9. *Ibid.*

10. United Nations Development Programme, "Statistics of the Human Development Report," *Human Development Reports*. Available online at: http://hdr.undp.org/en/statistics/. The online versions of the *Human Development Reports* provide access to its statistics in a variety of forms: by country, indicator, and tables. Users can also create their own tables, incorporating specific countries and indicators that interest them. To access these features, use the link listed in this citation and click on "Getting and Using Data."

11. *Ibid.*

12. United Nations Development Programme, "The Human Development Concept," *Human Development Reports*. Available online at: http://hdr.undp.org/en/humandev/.

13. Population Reference Bureau, *2008 World Population Data Sheet*. Available online at: http://www.prb.org/Publications/Datasheets/2008/2008wpds.aspx.

14. World Bank, *Poverty and Inequality Statistics*. Available online at: http://web.worldbank.org/WBSITE/EXTERNAL/TOPICS/EXTPOVERTY/0,,contentMDK:22927860~pagePK:148956~piPK:216618~theSitePK:336992,00.html.

15. Obijiofor Aginam, "Global Village, Divided World: A South-North Gap and Global Health Challenges at Century's Dawn," *Indiana Journal of Global Legal Studies* 7: 2 (2000): 603–628.

16. World Bank, *Poverty and Inequality Analysis*. Available online at: http://web.worldbank.org/WBSITE/EXTERNAL/TOPICS/EXTPOVERTY/0,,contentMDK:22569747~pagePK:148956~piPK:216618~theSitePK:336992,00.html.

17. *Ibid.*

18. United Nations Children's Fund, *Progress for Children: A World Fit for Children Statistical Review* No. 6 (December 2007): 23. Available online at: http://www.unicef.org/publications/files/Progress_for_Children_No_6_revised.pdf.

19. Obijiofor: 608–623.

20. Amartya Sen, *Development as Freedom* (New York: Anchor Press, 1999).

21. Scholars of international relations continue to debate the criteria by which countries should be classified as developed or developing, and no consensus exists on a comprehensive scheme of categorization. The old practice of categorizing countries as belonging to the First World (advanced industrialized countries), Second World (a term traditionally used to describe the Soviet Union and the countries in its sphere of influence), or Third World (developing countries) has gone out of fashion. Economists sometimes simply refer to high-income, middle-income, and low-income countries, with additional variations acknowledged within these categories (e.g., high-middle income, low-middle income). Each approach to categorizing countries according to levels of economic and social development has its own strengths and weaknesses. A categorization based on a North-South territorial divide makes broad generalizations that do not capture important differences across, between, and within countries. Grouping countries into several income categories captures more of the differences between countries but misses a larger systemic pattern that reveals inequities rooted in the historical legacy of colonialism. For our purposes, the concept of a North-South gap captures important realities about broad, contemporary divisions between developed and developing countries that are rooted in historical social, economic, and political processes even as it obscures important differences across, between, and within countries.

22. World Health Organization, Western Pacific Regional Office, *Women, Girls, HIV, & AIDS* (2004). Available online at: http://www.wpro.who.int/NR/rdonlyres/F1F88521-518C-4EAC-AF7E-1F07A4E9FF0B/0/WAD2004_Women_Girls_HIV_AIDS.pdf.

23. United Nations Children's Fund and World Health Organization, *Diarhoea: Why Children Are Still Dying and What Can Be Done* (2009). Available online at: http://whqlibdoc.who.int/publications/2009/9789241598415_eng.pdf.

24. *Ibid.*: 23.

25. J.A. Schellenberg, C.G. Victora, A. Mushi, D. de Savigny, D. Schellenberg, H. Mshinda, and J. Bryce, "Inequities Among the Very Poor: Health Care for Children in Rural Southern Tanzania," *Lancet* 361: 9357 (2003): 561–566.

26. C.T. Sreeramareddy, R.P. Shankar, B.V. Sreekuraman, S.H. Subba, H.S. Joshi, and U. Ramachandran, "Care-seeking Behavior for Childhood Illness—A Questionnaire Survey in Western Nepal," *BMC International Health and Human Rights* 6 (2006): 7–16.

27. J. Akin and P. Hutchinson, "Health Care Facility Choice and the Phenomenon of Bypassing," *Health Policy and Planning* 14: 2 (1999): 135–151; D. Chernichovsky and O.A. Meesook, "Utilization of Health Services in Indonesia," *Social Science & Medicine* 23: 6 (1986): 611–620.

28. D. Thomas, V. Lavy, and D. Strauss, "Public Policy and Anthropometric Outcomes in the Côte d'Ivoire," *Journal of Public Economics* 61: 2 (1996): 155–192.

29. F. Castro-Leal, J. Dayton, L. Demery, and K. Mehra, "Public Social Spending in Africa: Do the Poor Benefit?" *World Bank Research Observer* 14: 1 (1999): 66–74.

30. World Health Organization, *Health, Economic Growth, and Poverty Reduction* (2002): 37. Available online at: http://whqlibdoc.who.int/publications/9241590092.pdf.

31. J. Sachs and P. Malaney, "The Economic and Social Burden of Malaria," *Nature* 415 (2002): 680–685.

32. Jeffrey Long and Rick Kittles, "Human Genetic Diversity and the Nonexistence of Biological Races," *Human Biology* 75: 4 (2003): 449–471.

33. Kenneth D. Kochanek, Jiaquan Xu, Sherry L. Murphy, Arialdi M. Miniño, and Hsiang-Ching Kung, "Deaths: Preliminary Data for 2009," *National Vital Statistics Report* 59: 4 (2011): 1–51.

34. *Ibid.*

35. Glenn Flores and the Committee on Pediatrics Research, "Racial and Ethnic Disparities in the Health and Health Care of Children," *Pediatrics* 125: 4 (2010): e979–e1020.

36. Janet Smylie, Deshayne Fell, and Arne Ohlsson, "A Review of Aboriginal Infant Mortality Rates in Canada: Striking and Persistent Aboriginal/Non-Aboriginal Inequities," *Canadian Journal of Public Health* 101: 2 (2010): 143–148; Charles H. Wood, José A. Magno de Carvalho, and Cláudia J. Guimarães Horta, "The Color of Child Mortality in Brazil, 1950–2000: Social Progress and Persistent Racial Inequality," *Latin American Research Review* 45: 2 (2010): 114–139.

37. U.S. Centers for Disease Control and Prevention, "CDC Health Disparities and Inequalities Report—United States, 2011," *Morbidity and Mortality Weekly Report* 60: Suppl. (2011): 1–114.

38. Stacey Jolly, Eric Vittinghoff, Arpita Chattopadhyay, and Kirsten Bibbens-Domingo, "Higher Cardiovascular Disease Prevalence and Mortality Among Younger Blacks Compared to Whites," *American Journal of Medicine* 123: 9 (2010): 811–818; Tanisha D. Hill, LeRoy M. Graham, and Varada Divgi, "Racial Disparities in Pediatric Asthma: A Review of the Literature," *Current Allergy & Asthma Report* 11: 1 (2011): 85–90; Ganna Chornokur, Kyle Dalton, Meghan E. Borysova, and Nagi B. Kumar, "Disparities

at Presentation, Diagnosis, Treatment, and Survival in African American Men Affected by Prostate Cancer," *Prostate* 71: 9 (2011): 985–997.

39. Holly Mead, Lara Cartwright-Smith, Karen Jones, Christal Ramos, and Bruce Siegel, "Racial and Ethnic Disparities in U.S. Health Care: A Chartbook," *The Commonwealth Fund* (2008). Available online at: http://www.commonwealthfund.org/Publications/Chartbooks/2008/Mar/Racial-and-Ethnic-Disparities-in-U-S—Health-Care—A-Chartbook.aspx.

40. Antonio A. Lopes, "End-stage Renal Disease Due to Diabetes in Racial/Ethnic Minorities and Disadvantaged Populations," *Ethnicity & Disease* 19: Suppl. 1 (2009): 47–51.

41. Morton N. Beiser and Feng Hou, "Ethnic Identity, Resentment Stress and Depressive Affect Among Southeast Asian Refugees in Canada," *Social Science & Medicine* 63: 1 (2006): 137–150; M. Kelaher, Sheila Paul, Helen Lambert, Waqar Ahmad, Yin Paradies, and George Davey Smith, "Discrimination and Health in an English Study," *Social Science & Medicine* 66: 7 (2008): 1627–1636; Margarita Alegria, Melissa Vallas, and Andres J. Pumariega, "Racial and Ethnic Disparities in Pediatric Mental Health," *Child and Adolescent Psychiatric Clinics of North America* 19: 4 (2010): 759–774.

42. Martin Brockerhoff and Paul Hewett, "Inequality of Child Mortality Among Ethnic Groups in sub-Saharan Africa," *Bulletin of the World Health Organization* 78: 1 (2000): 30–41; Mats Målqvist, Nguyen T. Nga, Leif Eriksson, Lars Wallin, Dinh P. Hoa, and Lars Å. Persson, "Ethnic Inequity in Neonatal Survival: A Case-referent Study in Northern Vietnam," *Acta Paediatrica* 100: 3 (2011): 340–346.

43. David Mayer-Foulkes and Carlos Larrea, "Racial and Ethnic Inequities: Bolivia, Brazil, Guatemala, Peru," in Antonio Giuffrida, ed., *Racial and Ethnic Disparities in Health in Latin America and the Caribbean* (Washington, DC: Inter-American Development Bank, 2007): 131–137. Available online at: http://idbdocs.iadb.org/wsdocs/getdocument.aspx?docnum=1148586.

44. M. Hashibe, B. Siwakoti, M. Wei, B.K. Thakur, C.B. Pun, B.M. Shrestha, Z. Burningham, Y.C. Lee, and A. Sapkota, "Socioeconomic Status and Lung Cancer Risk in Nepal," *Asian Pacific Journal of Cancer Prevention* 12: 4 (2011): 1083–1088.

45. Brandon A. Kohrt, Rebacca A. Speckman, Richard D. Kunz, Jennifer L. Baldwin, Nawaraj Upadhaya, Nanda R. Acharya, Vidya D. Sharma, Mahendra K. Nepal, and Carol M. Worthman, "Culture in Psychiatric Epidemiology: Using Ethnography and Multiple Mediator Models to Assess the Relationship of Caste with Depression and Anxiety in Nepal," *Annals of Human Biology* 36: 3 (2009): 261–280.

46. Robert A. Hummer, Maureen R. Benjamins, and Richard G. Rogers, "Racial and Ethnic Disparities in Health and Mortality Among the U.S. Elderly Population," in Norman B. Anderson, Rodolfo A. Bulatao, and Barney Cohen, eds., *Critical Perspectives on Racial and Ethnic Differences in Health in Late Life* (Washington, DC: The National Academies Press, 2004): 53–94; Peter Franks, Peter Muennig, Erica Lubetkin, and Haomiao Jia, "The Burden of Disease Associated with Being African-American in the United States and the Contribution of Socio-economic Status," *Social Science & Medicine* 62: 10 (2006): 2469–2478.

47. Ana V. Diez-Roux and Christina Mair, "Neighborhoods and Health," *Annals of the New York Academy of Sciences* 1186: 1 (2010): 125–145.

48. Jennifer Northridge, Olivia F. Ramirez, Jeanette A. Stingone, and Luz Claudio, "The Role of Housing Type and Housing Quality in Urban Children with Asthma," *Journal of Urban Health* 87: 2 (2010): 211–224.

49. Julie L. Crouch, Rachelle F. Hanson, Benjamin E. Saunders, Dean G. Kilpatrick, and Heidi S. Resnick, "Income, Race/Ethnicity, and Exposure to Violence in Youth: Results from the National Survey of Adolescents," *Journal of Community Psychology* 26: 6 (2000): 625–641.

50. World Health Organization, *World Report on Child Injury Prevention* (World Health Organization, 2008): 1–211. Available online at: http://whqlibdoc.who.int/publications/2008/9789241563574_eng.pdf.

51. Kathy Sanders-Phillips, Beverlyn Settles-Reaves, Doren Walker, and Janeese Brownlow, "Social Inequality and Racial Discrimination: Risk Factors for Health Disparities in Children of Color," *Pediatrics* 124: Suppl. 3 (2009): S176–S186.

52. Mead et al.: 44.

53. Natalie D. Crawford, Camara P. Jones, and Lisa C. Richardson, "Understanding Racial and Ethnic Disparities in Colorectal Cancer Screening: Behavioral Risk Factor Surveillance System, 2002 and 2004," *Ethnicity & Disease* 20: 4 (2010): 359–365; William R. Carpenter, Paul A. Godley, Jack A. Clark, James A. Talcott, Timothy Finnegan, Merle Mishel, Jeannette Bensen, Walter Rayford, L. Joseph Su, Elizabeth T. Fontham, and James L. Mohler, "Racial Differences in Trust and Regular Source of Patient Care and the Implications for Prostate Cancer Screening Use," *Cancer* 115: 21 (2009): 5048–5059.

54. Yuanyuan Wang, Julie A. Simpson, Anita E. Wluka, Donna M. Urquhart, Dallas R. English, Graham G. Giles, Stephen Graves, and Flavia M. Cicuttini, "Reduced Rates of Primary Joint Replacement for Osteoarthritis in Italian and Greek Migrants to Australia: The Melbourne Collaborative Study," *Arthritis Research & Therapy* 11: 3 (2009): R86.

55. Ezequiel Bellorin-Font, Nidia Pernalete, Josefina Meza, Carmen L. Milanes, and Raul G. Carlini, "Access to and Coverage of Renal Replacement Therapy in Minorities and Ethnic Groups in Venezuela," *Kidney International* Suppl. 97 (2005): S18–S22.

56. Sarah Burgard, "Race and Pregnancy-related Care in Brazil and South Africa," *Social Science & Medicine* 59 (2004): 1127–1146.

57. Zeida R. Kon and Nuha Lackan, "Ethnic Disparities in Access to Care in Post-apartheid South Africa," *American Journal of Public Health* 98: 12 (2008): 2272–2277.

58. Glenn Flores and Sandra C. Tomany-Korman, "Racial and Ethnic Disparities in Medical and Dental Health, Access to Care and Use of Services in US Children," *Pediatrics* 121: 2 (2008): e286–e296.

59. Ian M. Bennett, Jing Chen, Jaleh S. Soroui, and Sheida White, "The Contribution of Health Literacy to Disparities in Self-rated and Preventive Health Behaviors in Older Patients," *Annals of Family Medicine* 7: 3 (2009): 204–211.

60. Bussarawan Teerawichitchainan and James F. Phillips, "Ethnic Differentials in Parental Health Seeking for Childhood Illness in Vietnam," *Social Science & Medicine* 66: 5 (2008): 1118–1130; Målqvist et al.: 340.

61. Karen S. Collins, Allyson Hall, and Charlotte Neuhaus, "U.S. Minority Health: A Chartbook," *The Commonwealth Fund* (1999). Available online at: http://www. common wealthfund.org/Publications/Chartbooks/1999/May/U-S—Minority-Health—A-Chartbook.aspx.

62. Darrell J. Gaskin, Christine Spencer, and Patrick Richard, "Do Hospitals Provide Lower-quality Care to Minorities than to Whites?" *Health Affairs* 27: 2 (2008): 518–527.

63. *Ibid.*

64. Duncan Thomas, Victor Lavy, and John Strauss, "Public Policy and Anthropometric Outcomes in the Côte d'Ivoire," *Journal of Public Economics* 61: 2 (1996): 155–192.

65. U.S. Office for Civil Rights, *Guidance to Federal Financial Assistance Recipients Regarding Title VI and the Prohibition Against National Origin Discrimination Affecting Limited English Proficient Persons—Summary* (Washington, DC: U.S. Department of Health and Human Services, 2000). Available online at: http://www.hhs.gov/ocr/civilrights/resources/laws/summaryguidance.html.

66. Robert Wood Johnson Foundation, "Language Barriers Contribute to Health Care Disparities for Latinos in the United States of America," *Pan American Journal of Public Health* 11: 1 (2002): 56–58.

67. Mee L. Wong, Kee S. Chia, Sharon Wee, Sin E. Chia, Jeannette Lee, Woon P. Koh, Han M. Shen, Julian Thumboo, and Dickey Sofjan, "Concerns over Participation in Genetic Research Among Malay-Muslims, Chinese and Indians in Singapore: A Focus Group Study," *Community Genetics* 7: 1 (2004): 44–54.

68. Carpenter et al.: 5048.

69. Michelle van Ryn and Jane Burke, "The Effect of Patient Race and Socio-economic Status on Physicians' Perceptions of Patients," *Social Science & Medicine* 50: 6 (2000): 813–828.

70. Louis Sullivan and Ilana S. Mittman, "The State of Diversity in the Health Professions a Century After Flexner," *Academic Medicine* 85: 2 (2010): 246–253.

71. World Health Organization, *Closing the Gap in a Generation: Health Equity Through Action on the Social Determinants of Health* (2008). Available online at: http://whqlibdoc.who.int/hq/2008/WHO_IER_CSDH_08.1_eng.pdf.

72. Institute of Medicine of the National Academies, *Unequal Treatment: What Health Care System Administrators Need to Know About Racial and Ethnic Disparities in Healthcare* (Institute of Medicine of the National Academies, 2002). Available online at: http://www.nap.edu/openbook.php?record_id=10260&page=1.

73. Mayra Buvinic, André Médici, Elisa Fernández, and Ana Cristina Torres, "Gender Differentials in Health," in Dean T. Jamison, Joel G. Breman, Anthony R. Measham, George Alleyne, Maria Claeson, David P. Evans, Prabhat Jha, Anne Mills, and Phillip Musgrove, eds., *Disease Control Priorities in Developing Countries*, 2d ed. (New York: Oxford University Press; Washington, DC: The World Bank, 2006): 197.

74. World Health Organization, *World Health Statistics 2009* (2009): 44. Available online at: http://www.who.int/whosis/whostat/EN_WHS09_Full.pdf.

75. Data on life expectancy from both the UNDP and the WHO confirm women's advantage in life expectancy in all regions. World Health Organization, *World Health Statistics 2009*: 44; United Nations Development Programme, "Statistics of the Human Development Report," *Human Development Report* 2009. Available online at: http://hdr.undp.org/en/statistics/.

76. *Ibid.*

77. *Ibid.*

78. World Health Organization, *World Health Statistics 2009*: 44.

79. *Ibid.*: 36–43.

80. Colin D. Mathers, Christopher J.L. Murray, and Joshua A. Salomon, "Methods for Measuring Healthy Life Expectancy," in Christopher J.L. Murray and David B. Evans, eds., *Health Systems Performance Assessment: Debates, Methods, and Empiricism* (Geneva: World Health Organization, 2003): 439.

81. World Health Organization, *World Health Statistics 2009*: 44.

82. Morbidity simply refers to illness "or any departure, subjective or objective, from a psychological or physiological state of well-being." Skolnik: 22.

83. World Health Organization, *The Global Burden of Disease: 2004 Update*: 46.

84. Buvinic et al.: 199.

85. *Ibid.*

86. *Ibid.*: 196.

87. *Ibid.*: note 2 at 209.

88. World Health Organization, "Disease Incidence, Prevalence, and Disability," in *The Global Burden of Disease: 2004 Update* (2008): 36.

89. World Health Organization, *The Global Burden of Disease: 2004 Update*: 10.

90. "Gendercide: The Worldwide War on Baby Girls," *The Economist*, March 4, 2010. Available online at: http://www.economist.com/node/15636231/.

91. Buvinic et al.: 197.

92. "Mars vs. Venus: The Gender Gap in Health," *Harvard Men's Health Watch* (January 2010). Available online at: http://www.health.harvard.edu/newsletters/Harvard_Mens_Health_Watch/2010/January/mars-vs-venus-the-gender-gap-in-health/.

93. In fact, the role of female hormones in reducing the risk of cardiovascular disease was sufficiently well established by the 1990s that doctors recommended hormone replacement therapy (HRT) for peri/postmenopausal women not solely for relief from the symptoms of menopause but also to decrease the incidence of coronary disease. However, in the early years of the 21st century, a large randomized controlled trial (the Women's Health Initiative) demonstrated just the opposite effect—an increased risk of stroke and heart attack in the first two years of HRT. Thus, the pendulum swung, and the medical profession quit routinely using HRT for symptomatic control of hot flashes, except in cases of severe menopausal symptoms not responsive to nonhormonal treatments, out of fear of this increased cardiovascular risk. Writing Group for the Women's Health Initiative Investigators, "Risks and Benefits of Estrogen Plus Progestin in Healthy Postmenopausal Women: Principal Results from the Women's Health Initiative Randomized Control Trial," *Journal of the American Medical Association* 288 (2002): 321–333.

94. United Nations Development Programme, "Millennium Development Goals: A Compact Among Nations to End Human Poverty," *Human Development Report 2003*: 9. Available online at: http://hdr.undp.org/en/reports/global/hdr2003/.

95. Buvinic et al.: 197.

96. *Ibid.*: 198.

97. Jelke Boesten and Nana K. Poku, *Gender and HIV/AIDS: Critical Perspectives from the Developing World* (Burlington, VT: Ashgate Publishers, 2009).

98. I would like to thank Dr. John Murray, a consultant on child and maternal mortality with the World Health Organization, for discussions that contributed to this insight.

99. Charli Carpenter, "'Women and Children First': Gender Norms and Humanitarian Evacuation in the Balkans: 1991–1995," *International Organization* 57: 4 (2003): 661–694.

100. Adam Jones, "Gendercide and Genocide," *Journal of Genocide Research* 2: 2 (2000): 185–211.

101. Joshua Goldstein, *War and Gender: How Gender Shapes the War System and Vice Versa* (Cambridge, UK: Cambridge University Press, 2001): 128–182.

102. Will Courtenay, "A Global Perspective on the Field of Men's Health: An Editorial," *International Journal of Men's Health* 1: 1 (2002): 4.

Urban Poverty

An Urgent Public Health Issue

By Susan Mercado, Kirsten Havemann, Mojgan Sami, and Hiroshi Ueda

The World Health Organization (WHO) Commission on Social Determinants of Health (CSDH) has posed a provocative question for public health: "Why do we keep treating people for illnesses only to send them back to the conditions that created illness in the first place?"[1] For the WHO Centre for Health Development (WHO Kobe Centre), hub of the CSDH's Knowledge Network on Urban Settings (KNUS), this question represents a challenge to the public health sector not only to acknowledge the pervasiveness of urban poverty as a critical pathway to ill health and health inequities, but also to address the problem as an urgent public health issue affecting a billion people living in informal settlements, or "slums."[2]

People who live in informal settlements are often systematically excluded from opportunities, decent employment, security, capacity, and empowerment that would enable them to gain better control over their health and lives.[3] As noted in the interim report of the Millennium Development Goals (MDG) Task Force, which focuses on improving the lives of urban slum dwellers: "Much of urban poverty is not because of distance from infrastructure and services but from exclusion. They [slum dwellers] are excluded from the attributes of urban life that remain a monopoly of a privileged minority—political voice, secure good-quality housing, safety and the rule of law, good education, health services, decent transport, adequate incomes, access to goods and services, credit—in short, the attributes of full citizenship."[4] The issue of urban poverty is not new, but it is often narrowly viewed as an economic issue best addressed by economic policies and interventions. Urban poverty today, as driven by globalization and rapid uncontrolled urbanization, also needs to be recognized as a social, political, and cultural process that has profound impacts on public health. Exclusion of the urban poor from the benefits of urban life fosters discontent and political unrest. Within the broader context of health and human development, rapid urbanization of poverty and ill health has been characterized as a new human security threat.[5]

Rapid uncontrolled urbanization results from the interaction between global and local forces. The interconnectedness of cities through trade, business, industry, tourism, international travel, information technology, and media is reshaping social determinants of health that are manifest at the city level. On the other hand, local and national governance capacity in relation to health systems, housing, transport, property rights, migration, land use policy, working conditions, and employment may be unable to cope with the speed of change brought about by global economic restructuring. Both inequity in cities that leads to urban poverty and poor health, therefore, are also products of global and local forces in the urban setting. Public health can play an important role in ameliorating urban poverty through social processes (participation, **social capital**, social accountability, and social inclusion) that influence urban governance at multiple nodes of **power**.[6] Addressing urban poverty as an urgent public health issue opens a policy space for fairer health opportunities and healthier and more equitable cities.

Imagine the World as a Growing City

Today, for the first time in history, half of the world's population lives in cities. The United Nations estimates that the number of urban residents will increase by more than 2 billion people by 2030, whereas the rural population will decline by about 20 million.[7] Of the many risks to health that are linked to rapid urbanization, none is more compelling than the rise of urban poverty, manifested by the growth of informal settlements. Whereas rising urban poverty is evident in the developed world, this trend is more pronounced in developing countries.

UN-Habitat states that the global urban slum population is expected to double from 1 billion (estimated in 2002) to nearly 2 billion by 2030 (from 32 percent to 41 percent of the world's urban population), and to approximately 3 billion by 2050.[8] Among the 1 billion people who live in informal settlements today, one-third of households are headed by women. Hundreds of millions of children and youth live and work in deprived conditions in urban areas.[9] According to the latest *Global Report on Human Settlements,* 43 percent of the urban population in developing regions lives in slums. In the least developed countries, 78 percent are slum dwellers.[10] The scale and speed of this phenomenon pose serious and compelling risks and challenges to health—in sum, it is a crisis of unprecedented magnitude.

When disaggregated into the regions of the World Health Organization, the largest numbers of impoverished people living in poor conditions in urban settings are found in the Western Pacific Region (around 233 million), followed by the Southeast Asian Region (217 million) and the African Region (156 million).[11] Whereas the Western Pacific Region has the highest number of urban slum dwellers, they represent a relatively low one-third of the total urban population of approximately 700 million, on a par with the developing countries of the Americas Region.[12] The rapid expansion of urban areas in South and East Asia is creating megacities of unprecedented size and complexity that present new challenges to providing a decent environment for the poor: the urban slums of the South-East Asia and Eastern Mediterranean Regions account for almost half of urban populations there. Worst affected is the (largely sub-Saharan) African Region, where two-thirds of its urban inhabitants live in informal settlements. It is also experiencing the world's fastest rates of urbanization. Northern Africa is the only developing region where the quality of urban life is improving: here, the proportion of city dwellers living in slums has decreased by 0.15 percent annually (see box 1.1).[13]

The urban setting in a globalized world is increasingly exposed to unhealthy environments, disasters, climate change, violence and injuries, tobacco and other drugs, and epidemics including HIV-AIDS. Without access to adequate shelter, health care, and resources, the urban poor face the greatest threat. If current demographic trends continue, the majority of all urban inhabitants in years to come will suffer disproportionate exposure to the triple burden of ill health: injuries, communicable diseases, and noncommunicable diseases.[14]

Understanding the Role of Public Health in an Urbanizing World

Between 2005 and 2006 the Knowledge Network on Urban Settings (KNUS) worked with researchers, local communities, academia, development organizations, donors, and practitioners from local, national, regional, and global organizations to distill what was known about social determinants of health and health inequities in urban settings.[15] While KNUS research is ongoing, the following findings are of particular relevance to public health:

> The urban poor do not "wait" for governments or organizations to act on their behalf. They have the desire and resourcefulness to find ways to improve their shelters, access running water, produce food, organize child care, educate themselves and their children, and protect each other amid extreme poverty.[16]

> While poor communities are severely affected by violence, it is important to recognize the wealth of untapped social resources within informal settlements. One case study from the favelas of Brazil notes the presence of "social networks, trust, solidarity and mutual support, celebration, cultural life, local businesses, informal activities on education, recreation, sports, religion, politics, and much more."[17]

Uncontrolled, rapid urbanization and the unraveling of the traditional social fabric deepen inequity and give rise to alternative governance structures such as gangs (which target impoverished youth) and paramilitary organizations (known to recruit children for warfare).[18] People who live in informal settlements are at higher risk of exposure to crime and violence.[19]

Since 2000, the world's fastest-growing urban areas are also those where there are increasing concentrations of informal settlements. This has profound consequences for public health strategies to control communicable (HIV-AIDS, TB, H5N1 virus, dengue, and other vector-borne diseases) as well as noncommunicable diseases (obesity, diabetes, cancer, chronic heart disease, stroke, hypertension)[20] and mental health and physical conditions associated with urban life (road traffic injuries, urban violence, obesity, unsafe settlements).

Urban poverty has been narrowly framed as an economic development issue. Unless a broader development perspective is used, policies, programs, measurements, evaluations, and strategies—as well as the "actors" and "stakeholders" who are expected to take action—will fail to fully engage the social, cultural, environmental, and health dimensions of urbanization and urban poverty.

Improving local urban governance as a strategy for alleviating urban poverty (as exemplified by the work of UN-Habitat[21]) has created a new policy space for linking development to health and vice-versa, but the public health sector has not effectively used this space as a means of shaping healthier public policy in the majority of cities.

Given the high concentration of national resources in cities, it is often assumed that city dwellers have better access to services including health care, and that poor people in urban settings are therefore better off than their rural counterparts.[22] This is where the issue of equity emerges as crucial for the urban poor, who, in fact, grapple with complex and debilitating challenges: inability to pay for goods and services, lack of social support systems,[23] unhealthy and unsafe living and working conditions,[24] exposure to crime and violence,[25] limited food choices,[26] discrimination, isolation,[27] and powerlessness.[28]

Despite the obvious linkage between urban poverty and ill health and the potential impact on the rest of the population, the health sector in many countries continues to narrowly define its role as that of finding ways to improve access to services and improve the financing of health care services for the poor. Although important, this effort is far from sufficient.[29]

Public Health: A Rallying Point for Equity in Cities

The need for intersectoral action and policy to address social determinants of health is not a new concept. The challenges and difficulties of mobilizing intersectoral support for policy and resources are known. In its review of eighty case studies, KNUS discovered that "health" can unite individuals, communities, institutions, leaders, donors, and politicians from divergent sectors, even in complex and hostile contexts where structural determinants of health are deep and divisive. Some of the case studies are highlighted below.

Whether it is mobilizing the members of a local community to design a health plan for themselves (e.g., Dar es Salaam, Tanzania's Healthy City Programme[30]), enabling citizens to vote for priorities in local resource allocations for health (participatory budgeting in Porto Alegre, Brazil[31]), decreasing dengue incidence (Marikina Healthy Cities Programme, The Philippines[32]), or involving the entire community in designing shared spaces that encourage walking and cycling (Healthy by Design, Victoria, Australia[33]), public health is an effective rallying point for achieving greater health equity in the urban setting.

While debate and discourse inevitably arise over methods, terminology, resources, and priorities for achieving better health, invoking health as a social goal and the imperative for "fairer health opportunities for all" has been a powerful lever for addressing social determinants of health in urban settings. The research and analysis also point to the critical importance of social processes in achieving more equitable health outcomes. Preliminary findings from KNUS thematic papers suggest that:[34]

> Integrated interventions that support community action through participation and empowerment (such as urban primary health care,[35] healthy cities,[36] community-based initiatives,[37] sustainable cities,[38] local agenda sites,[39, 40] "cities without slums,"[41] and many other integrated approaches) have been shown to reduce health risks, improve health outcomes, and promote better quality of life.

> Where integrated interventions are further linked to better urban governance (local government accountability, local capacity building in support of decentralization, land use policy, participatory budgeting, urban planning and design, sustainable food systems), a healthier social environment is possible.

> Where "change agents," "catalysts," and "facilitators" have stepped in to mobilize communities toward public health action and ultimately to influence intersectoral policy and mobilize resources for health equity (as in national urban renewal programs, agricultural policy, national housing policy linked to urban development), bringing interventions to scale is more likely.

> Networked governance,[42] whereby urban poor communities and other organized groups (e.g., Shack/Slum Dwellers International[43]) work with local or national government agencies—such as the Community Organizations Development Institute of Thailand[44]

and the Committee of Resource Organizations of Mumbai, India[45]—and with international alliances or organizations—such as the Alliance of Healthy Cities,[46] European Healthy Cities Network,[47] Network of Healthy Municipalities,[48] Cities Alliance,[49] UN-Habitat, and WHO— demonstrates the power of harnessing social processes created by the interconnectedness of cities. Taking the principles of empowerment and participation a step further through city-to-city learning is a means of transforming global power relations and overcoming the structures that perpetuate urban poverty.[50]

Sharpening the Focus on Social Processes

Primary health care and its emphasis on community action and social process in the urban setting constitute a key strategy in achieving health equity for the urban poor.[51] Sharpening the focus on social processes throughout the entire public health arena paves the way for scaling up interventions that work.

The case studies of KNUS describe a range of actions that contribute to strengthening and supporting the role of public health:

1. Engaging in political processes (including budget hearings, elections, lobbying, and campaigns) that impact social determinants such as violence prevention, employment, child development, and gender equity

2. Strengthening "bonding" and "bridging" social capital by facilitating dialogue among stakeholders across sectors and within hierarchies

3. Using a "healthy settings approach"[52]

4. Engaging communities through participation and use of empowering processes

5. Engaging in intersectoral policy debates on non–health equity drivers (e.g., transportation, land use policy, land tenure, human rights)

6. Using existing networks to advance policy issues (local, national, regional, international)

7. Advocating social and financial accountability at all levels

8. Recognizing the links between mental health and well-being and public places, community spaces, parks, and gardens where social cohesion and the expression of diversity are simultaneously nurtured through cultural activities, art, recreation, sports and play

9. Using local data (intraurban health differentials) and local situations to forge the links between health and other sectors such as transportation, housing, and public services that impact social determinants

10. Supporting regulations that protect people, especially vulnerable or exposed groups, from threats and hazards (in workplaces, communities, schools)

Using Social Capital to Influence Urban Governance

How can we do a better job of linking disadvantaged people living in cities to the human and financial resources, policies, programs, and actions that would enable them to gain control over their health and their lives? How can we mobilize the resources to enable this process to happen at a scale that will make a difference for the world's urban poor? What is the link between social processes and urban governance?

Social capital, as part of social processes, is a critical means of changing power relations in cities. Public health can provide the glue to link, network, and bind the growing groups of poor and marginalized populations to nodes of power.

The urban setting is in itself a social determinant of health. Public health gains in disease prevention and control in our cities can easily unravel with the growth of physical and social environments of extreme deprivation. In an interconnected world, our cities can continue to be "engines of economic growth"[53] and "centres of culture."[54] The question is whether public health can use the interconnectedness of cities as a positive pathway to enhancing equity in health between and among cities and nations.

Notes

1. Marmot, M. (2006). Social determinants of health. First Meeting of the Social Determinants of Health for the Asia Network. Tokyo: Asia Network.

2. UN-Habitat Features (2003). *What are slums and why do they exist?* United Nations Human Settlements Programme.

3. Kawachi, I., & Wamala, S.P. (2006). Poverty and inequalities in a globalized world. In Kawachi I. & Wamala S.P., eds. *Globalization and Health*, 122–37. New York: Oxford University Press.

4. Garau, P., & Sclar, E.D. (2004). Interim report of the Millennium Development Goal Task Force 8 on Improving the Lives of Slum Dwellers. New York: United Nations.

5. IDEA (2006). Democracy and human security. In *Democracy, conflict and human security: Further reading.* Stockholm: International Institute for Democracy and Electorate Assistance, 22.

6. Burris, S., Hancock, T., Herzog, A., & Lin, V. (2007*). Emerging strategies for healthy urban governance. J Urban Health.* DOI 10.1007/s11524-007-9174-6.

7. United Nations Population Fund. Urbanization: A majority in cities. http://www.unfpa.org/pds/urbanization.htm. Accessed 15 February 2007.

8. UN-Habitat (2005a). Urbanization, urban population and urban slum dwellers. In *Financing urban shelter: Global Report on Human Settlements, 2005.* London: Earthscan.

9. Bartlett, S., UN Children's Fund, Hart, R., Satterthwaite, D., de la Barra, X., & Missair, A. (1999). *Cities for children: Children's rights, poverty and urban management.* London: Earthscan.

10. UN-Habitat. (2005b). *Financing urban shelter: Global Report on Human Settlements.* London: Earthscan.

11. UN-Habitat (2005a).

12. UN-Habitat Features (2003).

13. UN-Habitat (2005a).

14. UN-Habitat (2003). *The challenge of slums: Global Report on Human Settlements.* London: Earthscan.

15. Kawachi & Wamala (2006).

16. Chitekwe, B., & Mitlin, D. (2001). The urban poor under threat and in struggle: Options for urban development in Zimbabwe, 1995–2000. *Environ Urban,* 13(85):85–101.

17. Becker, D. (2006). *Network of Healthy Communities of Rio de Janeiro, Brazil.* Rio de Janeiro: Network of Healthy Communities.

18. Rodgers, D. (2005). Youth gangs and perverse livelihood strategies in Nicaragua: Challenging certain preconceptions and shifting the focus of analysis. In *New Frontiers of Social Policy: Development in a Globalized World.* Arusha, Tanzania: World Bank.

19. Pangaea. Street children—Community children: Worldwide Resource Library. http://pangaea.org/street_children/kids.htm. Accessed 15 February 2007.

20. WHO (2005). *Preventing chronic diseases: A vital investment.* Geneva: World Health Organization.

21. UN-Habitat (2002). The Global Campaign on Urban Governance. 2nd ed. Nairobi, Kenya. http://unhabitat.org/books/global-campaign-on-urbangovernance-the/. Accessed 13 February 2016.

22. Waelkens, M.P., & Greindl, I. (2001). *Urban health: Particularities, challenges, experiences and lessons learned.* A Literature Review. Eschborn, Germany: Deutsche Gesellschaft fur Technische Zusammenarbeit (GTZ).

23. Pridmore, P., Havemann, K., Sapag, J., Thomas, L., & Wood, L. (2007). Social capital and healthy urbanization in a globalized world. *J Urban Health.* DOI 10.1007/s11524-007-9172-8.

24. Kjellstrom, T., Friel, S., Dixon, J., et al. (2007). Urban environmental health hazards and health equity. *J Urban Health.* DOI 10.1007/s11524-007-9171-9.

25. Campbell, T., & Campbell, A. (2007). *Emerging disease burdens and the poor in cities of the developing world.* J Urban Health. DOI 10.1007/s11524-007-9181-7.

26. Dixon, J., Friel, S., Omwega, A., Donati, K., Burns, C., & Carlisle, R. (2007). *The health equity dimensions of urban food systems.* J Urban Health. DOI 10.1007/s11524-007-9176-4.

27. Pridmore et al. (2007).

28. Burris et al. (2007).

29. Marmot, M. (2005). *Status syndrome: How your social standing directly affects your health and life expectancy.* London: Bloomsbury.

30. Sheuya, S., Patel, S., & Howden-Chapman, P. (2007). Improving health and building human capital through an effective primary care system and healthy setting approach. *J Urban Health* 84(Suppl 1). DOI 10.1007/s11524-007-9175-5.

31. Wechtler, M. (2006). *Participatory budgeting in Porto Alegre.* Philadelphia: Temple University.

32. David, A. (2006). Marikina City, Guam.

33. Dixon, J. (2006). *Healthy by design: A planners guide to environments for active living.* Victoria, Australia: VicHealth and the Planning Institute.

34. Garau & Sclar (2004).

35. Regional Committee for the Western Pacific, WHO (1985). Urban primary health care. http://www.wpro.who.int/rcm/en/archives/rc36/wpr_rc36_r19.htm. Accessed 17 February 2007.

36. WHO. Healthy Cities and Urban Governance. http://www.euro.who.int/healthy-cities. Accessed 17 February 2007.

37. WHO. Community Based Initiatives. Available at: http://www.emro.who.int/cbi/. Accessed 17 February 2007.

38. WHO (1997). City planning for health and sustainable development. Geneva: World Health Organization.

39. Rodgers (2005).

40. United Nations (1992). *Agenda 21.* United Nations Conference on Environment and Development, Rio de Janeiro, Brazil, 3–14 June. UN Division for Sustainable Development. https://sustainabledevelopment.un.org/milestones/unced/agenda21. Accessed 23 November 2015.

41. Cities Alliance (1999). Cities without slums action plan. World Bank; UN-Habitat. http://www.citiesalliance.org/cws-action-plan. Accessed 24 November 2015.

42. Burris et al. (2007).

43. Slum/Shack Dwellers International. The challenge of engagement. http://www.sdinet.org/bulletins/b17.htm. Accessed 17 February 2007.

44. Community Organization Development Institute. http://www.codi.or.th/index.php?option=com_content&task=section&id=9&Itemid=52. Accessed 17 February 2007.

45. Palnitker, S. (1988). New culture of urban sanitation, Mumbai (CORO). Available at: http://www.archidev.org/article.php3?id_article=391. Accessed 24 November 2015.

46. AFHC. Healthy cities lead the way. Alliance for Healthy Cities. http://www.alliance-healthycities.com/. Accessed 17 February 2007.

47. Regional Committee for the Western Pacific, WHO (1985).

48. Panamerican Health Organization. BVSDE: Healthy Municipalities. http://www.bvsde.ops-oms.org/sde/ops-sde/ingles/municipios-acerca.html. Accessed 24 November 2015.

49. Cities Alliance (1999).

50. Campbell & Campbell (2007).

51. Lee, A., Kiyu, A., Molina, H., & Jimenez de la Jara, J. (2007). Improving health and building human capital through effective primary care system and healthy setting approach. *J Urban Health.*

52. WHO. Healthy Settings. World Health Organization. http://www.who.int/healthy_settings/en/. Accessed 24 November 2015.

53. Li, H. (2003). Management of coastal mega-cities—a new challenge in the 21st century. *Marine Policy* 27:333–337.

54. Rees, W.E. The conundrum of urban sustainability. http://www.earthscape.org/r3/ES14446/devuyst_introb.pdf. Accessed 17 February 2007.

Race, Ethnicity, and Health

By Donald A. Barr

....

I n reporting data for 2011 on overall birth rates and death rates for the U.S. population, the federal government's National Center for Health Statistics reported separate data for the following categories:

- White (non-Hispanic)
- Black (non-Hispanic)
- American Indian or Alaskan Native
- Asian or Pacific Islander
- Hispanic

These reports combine categories of both race and ethnicity in describing changes in the population of the United States. In studying the health disparities that exist in our society and the potential means to reduce them, it is important to understand how the categories of race and ethnicity are used, and what they mean. Accordingly, I will clarify what I mean (and what I don't mean) by the terms *race* and *ethnicity*. To illustrate, I would like to describe some of the history of my family and the family of my wife.

In Figure 3.3.1 you will see two photographs. One is of a portrait of my great-great-grandfather. The second is of the great-great-grandfather of my wife—the older man with a mustache sitting with his family.

My great-great-grandfather was born in Boston in the late 1700s and trained as a minister in the Congregational Church. (The Congregational Church is a Protestant Christian sect that is descended from the New England Puritan community.) His ancestors came to New England on the *Mayflower*. He spent his career founding and leading churches on the edges of the wilderness of the New World—first in Maine, and then in Ohio.

My wife's great-great-grandfather was born in Russia and was Jewish. Throughout much of his life he suffered from the anti-Jewish pogroms that swept through Russia and Central Europe. My wife's grandfather (the small boy on a tricycle in the picture) finally fled Europe in the early 1900s, landing at Ellis Island and subsequently settling in New York City.

It is useful to ask two questions about my wife and myself. Are we of the same ethnicity? Are we members of the same race?

Donald A. Barr, "Race, Ethnicity, and Health," *Health Disparities in the United States: Social Class, Race, Ethnicity, and Health*, pp. 89–114, 271–296. Copyright © 2014 by Johns Hopkins University Press. Reprinted with permission.

FIGURE 3.3.1 Ancestors of the author and the author's wife.

The answer to the first question is apparent. We certainly are not of the same ethnicity. A Russian Jew and a New England Protestant Christian (our respective great-great-grandfathers) are of quite different ethnicities. As descendants of these ethnic groups, my wife and I bring to our family very different ethnic traditions.

Are we members of the same race? The answer is yes. We are both white. When it comes time to check a box on a census form or a birth certificate, we each check "White." New England Protestants and Russian Jews, by both common perception and government policy, are white.

The disparate answers to these two questions raise a third question. Which category provides more information about an individual—race or ethnicity? In the case of my wife and me, our ethnicity will tell you quite a bit more about us than simply that we are white. This same question can be applied in the context of health. For a given individual, which category—race or ethnicity—will provide more information about his or her health status? As we will see in this chapter and the one that follows, it is crucially important to answer this question, and to do so using scientific data rather than tradition or popular perception.

What Are Race and Ethnicity?

The *Oxford English Dictionary* offers two definitions of the word *race* that capture the two most common ways the concept is used. Under one concept, race implies common ancestry. This definition states that race is "a group of people belonging to the same family and descended from a common ancestor." The second concept approaches race as categorizing people based on differences in physical appearance. This definition states that a race is "any of the major groupings of mankind, having in common distinct physical features or having a similar ethnic background."

It is interesting to note that the editors of the *Oxford English Dictionary* chose to qualify this second definition, informing readers that the concept of race "in early use usually applied to groups of people with obviously distinct physical characteristics such as skin colour, etc. ... Now frequently used more generally to denote groups of different cultural or ethnic origin." It appears that, from a lexicological perspective, the two historical meanings of the word now overlap.

The U.S. Census Bureau is the federal agency charged with measuring and categorizing the U.S. population. In gathering data for the decennial census conducted in 2010, it asked all respondents the following two questions.

1. Is this person Hispanic, Latino, or Spanish origin?

2. What is this person's race?

The census divided responses to the second question into the five racial groups listed and defined as follows

— "White" refers to a person having origins in any of the original peoples of Europe, the Middle East, or North Africa.
— "Black or African American" refers to a person having origins in any of the Black racial groups of Africa.
— "American Indian or Alaska Native" refers to a person having origins in any of the original peoples of North and South America (including Central America), and who maintains tribal affiliation or community attachment.
— "Asian" refers to a person having origins in any of the original peoples of the Far East, Southeast Asia, or the Indian subcontinent.
— "Native Hawaiian and Other Pacific Islander" refers to a person having origins in any of the original peoples of Hawaii, Guam, Samoa, or other Pacific Islands. (In the 1990 census, this category was included in the "Asian" category of race.)

While offering a number of Asian categories as possible choices in response to the question about race ("for example, Cambodia, China, India, Japan, Korea, Malaysia, Pakistan, the Philippine Islands, Thailand, and Vietnam"), each respondent who checks one of these boxes is categorized as Asian by race.

Contrast the approach to race used by the U.S. census with that used by the Canadian census. Canada conducts its national census every five years, the most recent being in 2011. In establishing the standards for categorizing Canadians, Statistics Canada (the analogue of the U.S. Census Bureau) defined the term race as, "based primarily upon genetically imparted physiognomical features among which skin colour is a dominant, but not the sole, attribute." However, the following statement precedes this definition. "This standard is no longer recommended for use and is not to be used."

Instead, the Canadian census gathers data on "the population group or groups to which the person belongs." It divides these population groups into two categories, listed below.

Aboriginal Peoples

Is this person an aboriginal person, that is First Nations (North American Indian), Métis or Inuit?

Non-Aboriginal People

Is this person (mark more than one if applicable):

- White
- Chinese
- South Asian
- Black
- Filipino
- Latin American
- Southeast Asian
- Arab
- West Asian
- Korean
- Japanese
- Other

While the Canadian census categorizes people into the two broad groups of Aboriginal/Non-Aboriginal, with further subdivision of the latter group, the U.S. Census Bureau divides people into the categories of Hispanic/Non-Hispanic, with further subdivision by race. The Canadian census places primary emphasis on the ancestral origins of its population, without using the concept of race.

The *Oxford English Dictionary* defines *ethnic* as "pertaining to or having common racial, cultural, religious, or linguistic characteristics." From this definition, ethnicity can be based on the use of a common language. This is the approach the U.S. Census Bureau takes regarding ethnicity. With "Hispanic" and "Non-Hispanic" as the two principal ethnic categories, it differentiates those whose ancestors came from a Spanish-speaking country from those whose ancestors did not. While Spanish-speaking countries include Spain, for practical purposes in the United States, Hispanic means having ancestors who came from the Spanish-speaking countries of Central America, South America, or the Caribbean.

Thus, the United States categorizes its population along two independent axes: race and Hispanic ethnicity. A white person can be either Hispanic or non-Hispanic. Similarly, a Hispanic person can be any race—including Asian (for example, Alberto Fujimori, former president of Peru and the child of Japanese parents who emigrated to Peru). While the list of possible ethnicities is extensive in Canada, it is limited in the United States. Anglo-Saxon Protestant and Russian Jew are not categories that are recorded by the U.S. Census Bureau. Despite the potential wealth of information regarding health risks that ethnicity often contains, it is not a category that receives much attention in either population data or health data in the United States.

The Overlap between Race and Ethnicity

Despite being approached as separate categories by the U.S. Census Bureau, a close examination of the way race and ethnicity are defined and used reveals substantial overlap between the two categories. Recall that one of the dictionary definitions of race cited above sees it as identifying people with a common ancestry. Similarly, the definition of ethnicity includes "having common racial ... characteristics." Common ancestry can be used to define either race or ethnicity.

Earlier we saw that the U.S. Census Bureau defines black as "people having origins in any of the Black racial groups of Africa" and white as "having origins in any of the original peoples of Europe, the Middle East, or North Africa." The racial categories defined by the U.S. Census Bureau are based largely on ancestry. How does the use of ancestry in defining race differ from the use of ancestry in defining ethnicity? A group of genetics researchers has reviewed the distinction between race and ethnicity. While acknowledging that both categories are derived from a person's ancestry, they "define racial groups on the basis of primary continent of origin" while they define ethnicity as "a self-defined construct that may be based on geographic, social, cultural, and religious grounds" (Risch et al. 2002, p. 3). Race uses the continent from which one's ancestors originated to define its categories; ethnicity uses the geographic region from which one's ancestors originated (for example, Anglo-Saxon or Russian) coupled with commonalities of religion or language to create its categories.

If race refers to one's continent of origin and ethnicity refers to one's narrower geographic roots coupled with religious or cultural roots, which category should we use in evaluating the health status or health risks of the U.S. population? This question receives a great deal of attention in both scientific and policy contexts. Despite decades of research, the answer remains contentious. By knowing a person's race (as defined by the U.S. Census Bureau), do we gain useful information about his or her health risks? Will we learn more by knowing that person's ethnicity? If there are certain health risks associated with a certain racial or ethnic group, what is the basis of those risks? Are they due to biologic factors, or are they due to social or cultural factors? Is there a biologic basis by which we can separate people into consistent racial or ethnic groups? These are some of the questions around which the discussion of race, ethnicity, and health revolves.

To illustrate this discussion and the different perspectives that are part of it, let us consider the results of a study of the way people respond to a particular medication for heart failure. The medicine is called angiotensin-converting enzyme inhibitor (ACE-I). It has been shown to be effective in the treatment of a condition called congestive heart failure (CHF), in which the heart muscle is weakened and unable to pump the blood effectively. By acting on the kidney to reduce the amount of fluid in the body, ACE-I can reduce the strain on the heart and reduce the symptoms caused by CHF.

To determine if ACE-I treatment is equally effective in blacks and whites, Exner and colleagues (2001) treated about 2,000 patients drawn from these two racial groups, each having CHF.

After following these patients for about three years, the researchers were able to identify two principal findings:

1. The death rate was not reduced by treatment with ACE-I in either blacks or whites.
2. The frequency with which patients were hospitalized for treatment of CHF was reduced in whites taking ACE-I, but was not reduced in blacks taking ACE-I.

From these results the authors concluded that "therapeutic recommendations may need to be tailored according to racial background" (p. 1357). The authors suggested that a person's race (as distinct from ethnicity) can be used to predict that person's response to a specific treatment such as ACE-I therapy.

Realizing that such a conclusion was controversial, the editors of the journal in which the study was published asked two different authors, representing two different perspectives, to respond. Wood responded by stating, "Racial and ethnic differences in drug responses have now been well described for a range of drugs and reflect genetic differences, environmental differences (including shared cultural and dietary habits), and fundamental differences in the pathogenesis of diseases. ... Thus, racial differences in the response to drugs not only have practical importance for the choice and dose of drugs but should also alert physicians to the important underlying genetic determinants of drug response" (2001, pp. 1394–95).

It is interesting to note that Wood first ascribes differences in drug responses to a combination of race and ethnicity, but concludes by suggesting that race alone, independent of ethnicity, can be used effectively to predict response to a drug. Wood suggests that there are clear genetic differences between races, and that these genetic differences are tied directly to differences in the body's response to certain drugs. In tying racial groups to underlying genetic differences, Wood reflects one side of the debate over what does (or does not) distinguish a race.

In response, Schwartz argued that "race is a social construct, not a scientific classification" and suggested that the use of racial categories in medical care is both inaccurate and dangerous. "A racial designation in the context of medical management not only defies everything we have learned from biology, genetics, and history but also opens the door to inequities in medical care. ... Instruction in medical genetics should emphasize the fallacy of race as a scientific concept and the dangers inherent in practicing race-based medicine" (2001, pp. 1392–93).

The article by Exner and colleagues and the editorial responses by Wood and Schwartz contributed to a growing controversy in the medical literature about whether, in the context of medical care, different races should be seen as having predictable genetic differences that are tied to differences in the way the body reacts to certain treatments.

To address this and related questions, in 2003 the federal government sponsored a conference at which genetic and medical researchers from around the country were brought together and asked to address the following question: "What does the current body of scientific information say about the connections among race, ethnicity, genetics, and health?" (Patrinos 2004). A series of researchers contributed papers to this national conference, which were published in 2004 in a special issue of the journal *Nature Genetics.* In an introduction to that issue, the representative of the federal agency that sponsored the conference commented that "the term 'race' does not describe most of us with the subtlety and complexity required to capture and appreciate our genetic diversity. ... Oversimplified concepts of race don't work in any objective realm. It's bad medicine and it's bad science" (Patrinos 2004, pp. S1–S2).

There appears to be general consensus among the authors of the papers coming out of the conference that there are identifiable genetic differences among people whose ancestors came from different continents. After reviewing the genetic evolution of the human species from its origins in East Africa, Tishkoff and Kidd conclude that "populations do, generally, cluster by broad geographic regions that correspond with common racial classification (Africa, Europe, Asia, Oceania, Americas)" (2004, p. S26). However, the amount of genetic variation that occurs among groups with differing continental origins is tiny compared to the amount of genetic similarity that exists among all people, regardless of ancestry. Jorde and Wooding (2004) estimate that less than 1 percent of the DNA structure of humans differs across individuals. Of this 1 percent of difference, 85 to 90 percent occurs at the level of the individual in ways that have no association with ancestral continent. Only 10 to 15 percent of the less than 1 percent of difference occurs in ways that can be tied to continent of origin. Thus, it is certainly true that a person of European ancestry and a person of sub-Saharan African ancestry will have clear differences in appearance, and these differences will be due to underlying genetic differences. A person with light skin and light hair will have differences in the structure of the genes for skin color and hair color from a person with dark skin and dark hair. The same will be true for facial structure. The genes that create these differences in surface appearance are so few compared to the genes that create the structural and functional similarity among all humans that they have little association with important biologic characteristics.

This is not to say that people of different races (that is, differing continent of origin) will not, as a group, have differing frequencies of certain genes. It is simply that the differences in underlying frequencies are insufficient to define the group as a race. Take, for example, the genetic mutation that is associated with sickle cell disease. This mutation is found in a higher frequency among individuals whose ancestors came from Africa than in individuals whose ancestors came from Europe. Yet the presence of the sickle cell mutation does not define a person as belonging to a certain race. There are subpopulations among those of European ancestry (for example, those of certain Mediterranean ancestral groups) that also have an increased frequency of the sickle cell mutation. As summarized by Jorde and Wooding, "[Genetic] clustering of individuals is correlated with geographic origin or ancestry. These clusters are also correlated with some traditional concepts of race, but the correlations are imperfect" (p. S28).

Part of the problem in deriving genetic associations from racial classifications appears to come from the different ways in which the concept of race has been approached by different scientific disciplines. Keita and colleagues (2004) argue that there is a scientifically accurate way to approach race—by categorizing variations that occur in animal species that create genetically different groups without creating a new species. Using race in this context is scientifically valid. However, dividing the human species into subgroups based on continent of origin is not scientifically consistent with dividing the human species based on clear genetic differences. Using race to separate groups based on continental origin has little scientific basis. Rather, this use of the concept of race is a social construction—that is, it is based on a common understanding that evolves over time among a particular social group, and that is not grounded in science. In describing this concept of race, Keita and colleagues conclude: "'Race' is 'socially constructed' when the word is incorrectly used as the covering term for social or demographic groups. Broadly designated groups, such as 'Hispanic' or 'European American' do not meet the classical or phylogenetic criteria for subspecies or the criterion for a breeding population. ... 'Race' is a legitimate taxonomic concept that works for chimpanzees but does not apply to humans" (pp. S18–S19).

The History of the Use of "Race" as a Category in the United States

Recall from our discussion above that race is an explicit category used to categorize the population of the United States but that it is not used by the Canadian government to categorize its population. Similarly, the national census of Japan asks each resident to identify his or her nationality, but asks no questions about race (Japan, Statistics Bureau 2006). Why does the United States use the category of race, while other industrialized countries, both Western and Eastern, do not?

The concept of race as it is used in the United States has its origins in Western Europe. As European explorers were able to visit new parts of the globe, they recognized that the people they encountered often had a very different physical appearance than themselves. Since these physical differences were most striking when people from different continents were compared, the explorers came to distinguish human groups based on their continent of origin. Africans appeared quite distinct from Europeans. Those from Central and East Asia had their own distinct physical appearance, as did the native inhabitants of the Americas. Each time European explorers experienced the people of a new continent, they identified these people as a group distinct from their own.

The racial categories used by the United States have their origins in the eighteenth century. A Swedish naturalist named Carl Linnaeus made an exhaustive study of both plants and animals, seeking to establish a taxonomy of all animal life. In 1735 he first published *Systema Naturae,* a small pamphlet describing his understanding of the divisions of life on earth. Over a period of several years he gradually expanded this work into a multivolume publication. In it, he identified what he believed to be the four subspecies of humans:

1. *Afer niger* (African black): impassive, lazy, crafty, slow, foolish
2. *Americanus rubescus* (American red): ill-tempered, subjugated, obstinate
3. *Asiaticus luridus* (Asian yellow): melancholy, greedy, severe, haughty
4. *Europaeus albus* (European white): serious, strong, active, very smart, inventive

It should be apparent that the categories of subspecies identified by Linnaeus are nearly identical to the racial categories used by the U.S. government. For much of the twentieth century, before 1997 when the "Native Hawaiian and other Pacific Islander" category was separated from "Asian," the U.S. system of racial categorization was identical to that proposed by Linnaeus.

Linnaeus did not stop at naming the subspecies of *Homo sapiens*. He also ascribed predominant behavioral characteristics to them. American reds (that is, American Indians) he described as "obstinate, and regulated by custom"; Asians were "severe, ruled by opinion"; Africans were "crafty, governed by caprice"; Europeans were "gentle, governed by law" (Marks 1995; Lee and colleagues 2001, p. 38).

It is interesting to note that another scientist who was a contemporary of Linnaeus differed somewhat in his human taxonomy. Writing in 1781, Johan Blumenbach suggested that, in addition to the four categories identified by Linnaeus, there was a fifth category—the Malay, now often referred to as the people of Oceania and corresponding largely to the Native Hawaiian and Other Pacific Islander category used by the U.S. Census Bureau (Marks 1995). However, Blumenbach created these categories based purely on physical appearance. He ascribed no behavioral or psychological characteristics to these groups.

While Linnaeus and Blumenbach were in substantial agreement regarding most of the system of racial classification, they differed as to whether to include the peoples of Oceania as a separate racial category. How many human races were there: four or five? The answer depended on whether one adopted Linnaeus's view or that of Blumenbach. The view proposed by Linnaeus came to predominate, and was the system of racial categorization used by the U.S. government for most of the twentieth century. In the U.S. census conducted in 1990, there were four racial categories from which to choose: white, black, Asian/Pacific Islander, or Native American. In 1997 the government officially changed its policy of racial categorization, decreeing that Native Hawaiian and other Pacific Islander was the fifth race (Lee 2001). They did not do so because of Blumenbach—they did so for a set of reasons specific to the late twentieth century. It is interesting to note that, in making that change, the government was switching from the racial categories proposed by Linnaeus in 1758 to the categories proposed by Blumenbach in 1781.

Is There a Genetic Basis for Race?

While the consensus of the geneticists contributing papers to the federally sponsored conference discussed above is that race as a social category is very imprecise, they consistently acknowledge that there are genetic differences among population groups with differing continents of ancestral origin. A paper by Rosenberg and colleagues (2002) added substantially to our understanding of the genetic similarities and differences of different ancestral groups. They were able to obtain DNA samples from 1,056 individuals, representing 52 distinct populations around the globe. Each population had remained geographically stable for a number of generations. They tested each sample to determine the genetic structure of 377 different microsatellites—small segments of DNA without any known function. They asked themselves the following question. Without knowing the geographic origin of the samples, is it possible to sort the samples into groups based on genetic similarities that correspond to the geographic regions commonly associated with race as the concept is used in the United States?

To undertake this task, a computer was programmed to look at minute differences in microsatellite structure (sometimes as small as a single nucleotide), and to use an algorithm contained within a computer program to sort the samples into groups, such that the sorting maximized the overall difference in genetic structure among the groups. A key aspect of this sorting algorithm is that the computer does not determine the number of groups into which the samples will be sorted—a human selects this number and enters it into the computer. Based on this arbitrary number of groups, the computer groups the samples so as to maximize the genetic differences among the groups. The scientists ran this test five times, first sorting the samples into two groups, then three groups, and so on up to a maximum of six groups.

Once the DNA samples had been sorted into the specified number of groups based on genetic structure, the scientists looked at the geographic locations from which the samples within a group had been drawn. They wanted to know if the locations associated with a genetic group were also associated in some larger geographic area. They found that there was a fairly clear geographic patterning to the groups, and that the patterning overlapped substantially (but not completely) with the recognized continents. As stated by the authors, "Genetic clusters often correspond closely to predefined regional or population groups" (p. 2384). In fact, when the computer was programmed to divide the samples into four groups, the resulting groups corresponded largely to the four racial categories originally identified by Linnaeus.

— Group 1: Europe, Middle East, Central Asia, and South Asia
— Group 2: Sub-Saharan Africa
— Group 3: East Asia and Oceania
— Group 4: Americas (American Indians and other people indigenous to the Americas)

It is interesting to note what happened when the scientists programmed the computer to identify five genetic groups rather than four. When so instructed, the computer split East Asia and Oceania into separate groups, thus essentially re-creating the five racial groups identified in 1781 by Linnaeus's contemporary, Blumenbach.

Who was more accurate in their classification scheme, Linnaeus or Blumenbach? Do humans exist as four inherent groups or five? The answer to this question is entirely arbitrary. The peoples of Oceania are both genetically similar to, and genetically distinct from the peoples of East Asia. Do we focus on their similarity or their difference?

Rosenberg and colleagues were able to reproduce the findings summarized above by Jorde and Wooding: of the small amount of genetic variation that was identified among the samples (most of the DNA structure was identical), 93 to 95 percent of that variation occurred at the level of the individual, with no association with the group from which the individual is drawn. Only 3 to 5 percent of the variation they found in genetic structure occurred among geographic groups. Nonetheless, this tiny amount of genetic variation was enough for the computer to do its task of sorting the samples into groups. Instructing the computer in how many groups to use will change the outcome of that sorting process. Unless there is a scientific basis for selecting that number of groups, the number will be arbitrary.

What if the computer is instructed to sort the samples into two groups? We get the following results.

— Group 1: Sub-Saharan Africa, Europe, Middle East, Central Asia, and South Asia
— Group 2: East Asia and Oceania and the Americas

This division has sorted the human population into two recognizable groups: Westerners and Easterners. It has essentially cleaved the globe in two along a line of longitude. By this sorting, sub-Saharan Africans are more genetically similar to Europeans than they are genetically different, analogous to the Asia/Oceania situation discussed above.

What happens when we ask the computer to sort the samples into three groups? Sub-Saharan Africa is separated out from its previous group, and we have:

— Group 1: Sub-Saharan Africa
— Group 2: Europe, Middle East, Central Asia, and South Asia
— Group 3: East Asia and Oceania and the Americas

Instructed to sort the samples into six groups, how will the computer respond? What will be the sixth group, and will it correspond to any racial category? (After all, the U.S. Census Bureau stopped at five categories.) What we find is very interesting.

— Group 1: Europe, Middle East, Central Asia, and South Asia
— Group 2: Sub-Saharan Africa
— Group 3: East Asia
— Group 4: Oceania
— Group 5: Americas
— Group 6: Kalash

The sixth group identified by the computer is the Kalash, a tribal group of about 4,000 people living in northwestern Pakistan. There is a small amount of genetic difference between the Kalash and the surrounding peoples of Central Asia that is sufficient for the computer to distinguish the two groups as different, once the remainder of the world's population has been sorted into five groups. Do the Kalash constitute a race? Of course not! They are a distinct ethnic group with their own culture and geography, but are nearly identical on a genetic basis to other groups surrounding them.

Many who read the Rosenberg study focused on only the sorting that took place when the computer was programmed to identify four groups. They argued that these results confirmed that there is a biologic basis for the historical racial categories of white, black, Asian, and American Indian. There is enough similarity within these groups and enough difference among these groups to consider them genetically distinct. What are we to make of this assertion? To answer this question, let us imagine what might happen if, instead of sorting human DNA samples, we asked the computer to sort a deck of cards into groups based on similarities and differences among the cards.

As in the Rosenberg study, we would first program the computer to sort the cards into two groups. Using digital analysis of color scans of the cards, we would expect the computer to sort the deck into the red cards and the black cards. If we program the computer to sort the deck into three groups, we might get something like this: one group containing all the face cards, one group containing all the red-numbered cards, and one group containing all the black-numbered cards. Instructing the computer to sort the deck into four groups will likely result in groups made up of the four suits: spades, hearts, diamonds, and clubs.

Which is the most scientific way to sort the cards? There is no single answer to this question. The science in the sorting process was in the way we scanned the cards into digital images and the protocol we instructed the computer to use in analyzing those images. Each result—two groups, three groups, or four groups—is equally scientific, as each used the same sorting process.

However, in playing a game of cards, we are not principally concerned with the scientific nature of the cards. We are concerned primarily with understanding the rules of the game. For most card games played in the Western world, the cards are sorted according to suits. Why don't we play the same games using two suits, or three? Simple—because the rules say there are four suits. Where did the rules come from? In the case of card games, many of the rules came from an Englishman by the name of Edmond Hoyle, who lived in the eighteenth century. As described on the website hoylegaming. com, Hoyle "was best known as an expert on the rules and strategies behind card games and board games including chess and backgammon, memorializing the common phrase 'According to Hoyle.'" In 1770 Hoyle published his book, *Hoyles Games*, describing the rules by which card games were to be played. The 2001 version of the book is titled *Hoyle's Rules of Games*.

Why do we play card games with four suits rather than two? Because that's what the rules say. Over a period of several centuries we have come to a widely accepted consensus to play the game with four suits. Playing a game of cards with four suits rather than three is a social convention. In the words of sociologists, the suits in a deck of cards have been "socially constructed."

Let us use this same reasoning to ask which of the results of the Rosenberg study we should focus on. Should we consider the peoples of Oceania to be similar to or distinct from the peoples of East Asia? Should we consider the peoples of sub-Saharan Africa to be similar to (the result when sorting into two groups) or distinct from (the result when sorting into more than two groups) the peoples of Europe? Few would argue that sub-Saharan Africans should be considered to be of the same race as Europeans. However, this argument is not based on science, but on the social construction of racial categories that developed in much of Europe in the eighteenth century and before. Why are there four races rather than two? Because that's what the rules say. Just as people have come to agree on the rules of a card game, people (at least in the United States) also have come to agree on the "rules" of our society. Approaching the world's population as containing four races, as we did in the United States prior to 1997, was a social convention, just as dividing a deck of cards into four suits rather than two is a social convention. Changing from four races to five, as the U.S. government elected to do in 1997, simply changed the rules, adopting the categories originally suggested by Blumenbach as compared to those suggested by Linnaeus.

There are other examples in history of ethnic groups—people linked by a common language, culture, and ancestry—having been assigned to one racial group by social convention, only to have their perceived race change as the social convention changes. To provide an example of this phenomenon, I offer again some history from my own family. Figure 3.3.2 shows photos of my mother and father when they were young. It should be apparent that, by today's standards, my mother and father are members of the same race—white.

FIGURE 3.3.2 The author's mother and father.

My father was born in 1897, and his father was Irish. His father's family had emigrated to Nova Scotia at the time of the potato famine, and eventually settled in British Columbia. My mother was of Anglo-Saxon descent, with ancestors dating to the *Mayflower*. In the 1890s many in a position of power and authority in the United States did not consider a person of Irish ancestry to be a member of the white race (Roediger 1999). Among these were Senator Henry Cabot Lodge, of Massachusetts, who in the same year my father was born argued on the floor of the U.S. Senate that the immigration of Irish and other European groups to the United States was becoming a threat to the white race and should be limited. "Surely it is not too much to sift now the hordes that pour out of every European steamship unsifted, uncounted, unchecked. ... The races that built up this country come in diminishing numbers. New races, utterly alien, come in ever increasing numbers. What we now seek to accomplish by the pending bill is to sift this immigration and restrict it" (Lodge 1897, p. 1432). Based on these comments, Senator Lodge and many others like him would have considered my mother, whose ancestors were members of "the race that built up this country," to be white by race, but my father, whose ancestors fled Ireland in the nineteenth century, to be members of a "new race, utterly alien," and therefore not part of the white race.

To categorize the race of a child of Irish Canadian and English American descent (that is, the author's race) as anything other than white would be very unusual today. When my father was born a common social convention excluded those of Irish ancestry from the white race. Today that same convention includes the Irish within the white race. The social construction of race—the rules of the game—has changed in regards to the Irish, as it has for Jews, Italians, and other immigrant groups.

We should recognize some additional questions raised by the genetic data presented by Rosenberg and colleagues. The 1,056 subjects of their research were all from distinct population groups that had remained geographically stable for multiple generations. Rosenberg also looked at the genetic structure of certain populations in which there had been substantial geographic migration and resulting "admixture"—intermarriage and interbreeding. The genetic structures of many ethnic groups living in the Middle East, for example, are so heterogeneous that it was impossible for the computer to make any type of reliable separation. Similarly, a number of geographic groups were excluded from the study because they represented populations that were transitional between regions. For example, individuals from Ethiopia and Somalia have a genetic structure that is midway between that of Europeans and sub-Saharan Africans. Similarly, much of the African American and Hispanic population of the United States has experienced high levels of admixture over time, making it very difficult to reliably assign individuals to a specific geographic group.

Finally, we should recognize that some of the population groups sorted in one way by the computer in the Rosenberg study are typically sorted in a different way when the concept of race as a social construction is applied. In particular, the subjects drawn from South Asia sort into a different group based on genetics than they do based on social convention. Subjects from India and Pakistan are typically considered to be Asian by race. The U.S. Census Bureau explicitly identifies those from the

Indian subcontinent as Asian. However, in the Rosenberg study, South Asians such as Indians and Pakistanis are more genetically similar to Europeans than they are to East Asians, and are included in the European group in all the iterations of the sorting process. Thus, South Asians are Asian by social convention but white by genetic sorting.

As a second example of the difference between social convention and genetic structure, let us imagine what might have happened if Othello had been included as a subject in the Rosenberg study. As Shakespeare described him, Othello was a superb military commander—so successful that the Duke of Venice hired him to lead the Venetian army into battle against an invasion by the Turks. Othello of course was not Venetian. He was a Moor from the historical area of Mauritania (an area of North Africa that includes present-day Algeria and Morocco). Because he was a Moor, Othello had a skin color that was considerably darker than that of his Venetian hosts. His skin color, and the cultural difference it signified, was to get Othello into trouble when he first fell in love with and then (secretly) married Desdemona, the daughter of Barbantio, one of Venice's leading citizens.

When Barbantio learns that his daughter has chosen to marry Othello, he goes in search of him. On finding Othello, he assails him with the following words (act 1, scene 2):

> O thou foul thief, where hast thou stow'd my daughter?
> Damn'd as thou art, thou hast enchanted her ... to [thy] sooty bosom.

Barbantio is extremely upset that his daughter has married a man with a "sooty bosom" (that is, with dark skin). At the time Shakespeare was writing *Othello,* Moors were considered to be black—in the same group as sub-Saharan Africans. Well into the twentieth century, this social convention persisted throughout much of Europe and the United States.

It turns out that Barbantio had less to worry about than he thought. Data from the Rosenberg study confirm that, genetically, Moors and other ethnic groups from North Africa cluster with Europeans, having more genetic similarity to Europeans than to sub-Saharan Africans. If we insist on dividing the Western hemisphere into two racial groups based on genetic similarities and differences, then Othello was white. Interestingly, the U.S. Census Bureau would also consider Othello to be white, as it includes North Africans and those from the Middle East in the white racial category.

If we consider the evolution of the human species, it makes sense that North Africans are more similar genetically to Europeans than they are to sub-Saharan Africans. The origins of the human species were in the area of the Horn of Africa—currently Ethiopia, Somalia, and Eritrea. Gradually the new human species migrated north into the regions of the Middle East and North Africa, and south to the regions south of the Saharan Desert. The presence of the Sahara as a geographic barrier meant that there was little admixture over time between the northern migrants and the southern migrants. Each group gradually developed its own set of genetic markers. The people of Europe have their evolutionary origins in the northern group of migrants—those inhabiting North Africa and the

Middle East. It thus makes sense that modern-day North Africans have more in common genetically with Europeans than they do with sub-Saharan Africans.

There is, however, an important caveat about the above discussion of the gene tic clustering of individuals from South Asia or from the Middle East/North Africa. The genetic clustering of these population groups with Europeans was based on Rosenberg and colleagues' study of microsatellites—segments of DNA containing multiple nucleotides. As an alternative, Li and colleagues (2008) analyzed the same genetic material studied by Rosenberg, only instead of using microsatellite structure they evaluated single nucleotide polymorphisms (SNP). As its name suggests, a SNP looks at which nucleotide is present in a specific location on a DNA molecule. By doing this at 650,000 different DNA locations, they were able to repeat the sorting into groups. Using SNPs and sorting the genetic material into five groups, they came up with the same grouping as Rosenberg. However, when the computer was then asked to sort the material into six groups based on SNPs, the sixth group was South Asians. (The Kalashi were no longer identified as a separate group.) Sorting the material into seven groups identified populations from the Middle East and North Africa as the seventh group. Thus, determining whether South Asians and North Africans differ genetically from Europeans depends on whether we use SNPs or microsatellites as our basis for comparison.

Problems in the Continued Use of Race to Measure Health Outcomes

As discussed above, the four (or five) racial categories that have been identified in the United States are based largely on a social construction of what constitutes race. The common social convention is to distinguish races such as white and black, and to report health outcomes separately, with the expectation that the racial differences identified will be important in identifying those individuals who are at highest risk of adverse health outcomes. Such an approach, however, has inherent problems. I illustrate these problems in a discussion of three important medical conditions: low birth weight, heart disease, and high blood pressure.

Low Birth Weight

In 2009 infants born to black mothers in the United States died before their first birthday at the rate of 12.4 for every 1,000 live births. For the same year, the **infant mortality** rate for babies born to white mothers was 5.3 per 1,000 live births. One of the main contributors to this difference in infant mortality is the much higher frequency with which babies born to black mothers are underweight—either low birth weight (LBW) (weighing less than 2,500 grams) or very-low birth weight (VLBW) (weighing less than 1,500 grams). Babies born at these weights are much more likely to die before their first birthday than babies with a normal birth weight. In 2009 13.6 percent of black infants weighed less than 2,500 grams, while 3.1 percent weighed less than 1,500 grams. In the same year, 7.2 percent of white infants were less than 2,500 grams while 1.2 percent were less than 1,500 grams (U.S. Department of Health and Human Services, Centers for Disease Control and Prevention, National Center for Health Statistics 2012).

In 1997 David and Collins reported on a study of babies born in the state of Illinois between 1980 and 1995. They compared the weights of 44,000 babies born to white mothers and 46,000 babies born to black mothers. They separated the data on black infants based on whether the mother had been born in the United States or in Africa. When they did this, they found that the distribution of birth weights of the babies of African-born black mothers was nearly identical with that of U.S.-born white mothers, while the distribution of birth weights for the U.S.-born black mothers was significantly lower. The distribution of birth weights for the three groups is shown in Figure 3.3.3. The average birth weight and frequency of birth weight categories are shown in Table 3.3.1.

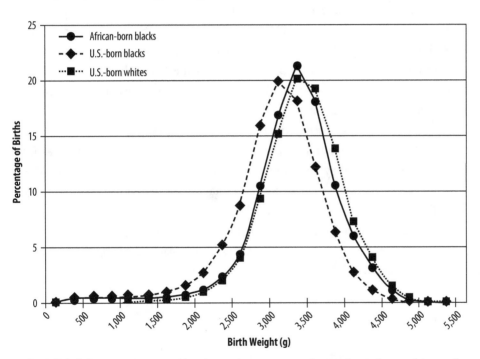

FIGURE 3.3.3 Distribution of birth weights among infants of U.S.-born white and black women and African-born black women in Illinois, 1980–1995. *Source:* R. J. David and J. W. Collins, "Differing Birth Weight among Infants of U.S.-Born Blacks, African-Born Blacks, and U.S.-Born Whites," *New England Journal of Medicine 337* (1997):1209–14. Copyright © 1997 Massachusetts Medical Society. All rights reserved.

TABLE 3.3.1 Average Birth Weight and Frequency of Low and Very Low Birth Weight among White, African-Born Black, and U.S.-Born Black Mothers in Illinois

	White	African-Born Black	U.S.-Born Black
Average birth weight (grams)	3,446	3,333	3,089
Low birth weight (1,500–2,500 grams), as a proportion of all births	3.6%	4.8%	10.6%
Very low birth weight (<1,500 grams), as a proportion of all births	0.7%	2.3%	2.6%

Source: David and Collins (1997).

While the rate of VLBW infants was higher among the African-born black mothers than the U.S.-born white mothers (2.3 percent as compared to 0.7 percent), the rate of LBW infants was similar (4.8 percent compared to 3.6 percent) and the average birth weight was only 3 percent lower (3,333 grams for African-born black mothers, 3,446 grams for U.S.-born white mothers). U.S.-born black mothers, on the other hand, had both VLBW and LBW infants at a higher rate than whites— 2.6 percent and 10.6 percent, respectively—and had infants that weighed on average 3,089 grams, or more than 10 percent less than white infants.

Comparing rates of LBW and the associated risk of infant mortality only by the race of the mother may yield inaccurate information and lead to inappropriate treatment decisions. If a doctor assumes that, because black mothers have many more tiny infants than white mothers, a black mother is therefore at increased risk of giving birth to a tiny child, that doctor would have inappropriately looked at the patient's race rather than her ethnicity. A U.S.-born black mother is in the same race as an African-born black mother. However, the ethnic characteristics of these two women is likely to be very different. In the David and Collins study, the African-born black mothers, when compared to the U.S.-born black mothers, were:

- older
- more likely to be married
- more highly educated
- less likely to have been late in starting prenatal care.

The social and economic differences between these two ethnic communities of black women are substantial. To know her risk of having a premature or underweight baby, you would have to know to which ethnic group a black woman in Illinois belongs.

Elo and Culhane (2010) found similar differences in a comparison of pregnant black women in Philadelphia. They compared behaviors associated with birth outcomes in women born in the United States, Africa, or the Caribbean. The foreign born women were less likely to engage in risky behaviors, and in addition had better self-reported health status, with the difference somewhat more pronounced in African-born women as compared to those born in the Caribbean. These ethnic differences persisted after controlling for SES.

Heart Disease

Fang and colleagues (1996) published a study comparing the risk of death from cardiovascular disease among white and black residents of New York City. Overall, New York City had a substantially higher rate of death from all causes than the rest of the country at that time. In addition, the overall death rate among blacks in New York was substantially higher than the rate for whites. These data are shown in Table 3.3.2.

Cardiovascular disease was the most common cause of death, accounting for 34 percent of deaths among blacks in New York and 52 percent of deaths among whites. Imagine that you are a doctor and two new adult male patients have come to see you,

TABLE 3.3.2 Age-Adjusted Annual Death Rates from All Causes, New York City, 1988–92

	Male	Female
United States, all races	680.2	387.9
New York, all races	878.9	456.8
New York, white	721.4	393.1
New York, black	1,224.8	593.7

Source: Fang et al. (1996).
Note: Deaths per 100,000 population.

one white and the other black. You reason that, because the death rate for cardiovascular disease is higher among blacks than among whites, your new black patient will be at a higher risk of death than your white patient. However, in arriving at such a conclusion, you would have made a fundamental error. Because the average death rate for black males is higher than that for white males, it does not necessarily follow that any black man will be at a higher risk of death than any white man.

The black community of New York City represents a variety of distinct ethnic groups, each with unique cultural characteristics. Three of the largest groups are blacks who were born in the Southeast of the United States, blacks born in the Northeast of the United States, and blacks born in the Caribbean. The diet, educational levels, behaviors, and other cultural characteristics of these three ethnic communities may have important differences. These ethnic differences may contribute to health status and to death rates. This is precisely what Fang and colleagues found. When they compared the cardiovascular death rates for these three ethnic groups with that of whites in New York, they found a very interesting pattern, as illustrated in Figure 3.3.4.

The cardiovascular death rate for blacks born in the Southeast was by far the highest of all the groups, for both men and women. Among men, the *lowest* cardiovascular death rate was among blacks born in the Caribbean. For women, rates for blacks born in the Northeast, blacks born in the

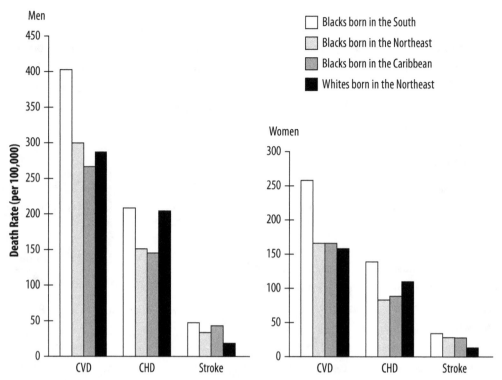

FIGURE 3.3.4 Age-adjusted annual rates of death from selected cardiovascular diseases in non-Hispanic blacks and whites in New York City, according to birthplace, 1988–1992. CVD = cardiovascular disease; CHD = coronary heart disease. *Source:* J. Fang, S. Madhavan, and M. Alderman, "The Association between Birthplace and Mortality from Cardiovascular Causes among Black and White Residents of New York City," *New England Journal of Medicine* 335 (1996):1545–51. Copyright © 1997 Massachusetts Medical Society. All rights reserved.

Caribbean, and whites born in the Northeast were almost indistinguishable. Looking only at deaths from coronary heart disease (for example, heart attacks), the rate among blacks born in the Southeast remained substantially higher than that of whites, but the rates for northeastern blacks and Caribbean blacks were substantially lower than for whites. For deaths from stroke, all three black groups had higher rates than whites.

In assessing the risk of death from cardiovascular disease in general, or coronary heart disease in particular, for any individual, it is not sufficient to know that the person is black. The physician must know the patient's ethnicity before being able to accurately predict and treat the risk of disease. As was the case in the genetic sorting of global populations in the Rosenberg study, and the distribution of birth weights in the David study, these authors found that there is more variation within races than there is between races. Race alone provides relatively little information about an individual's health risks.

High Blood Pressure

The National Center for Health Statistics reported that in 2011, 31 percent of the adult population in the United States had high blood pressure. However, the prevalence of high blood pressure is quite different among different racial and ethnic groups, as shown in Table 3.3.3.

The highest rate of high blood pressure is among black women—a rate that is nearly 50 percent greater than the comparable rate for white women. The rate for black men is 27 percent greater than that of white men. The lowest rate is for Mexican American men, with Mexican American women having the second lowest rate. (It is interesting to note that in this report,

TABLE 3.3.3 Age-Adjusted Percent of High Blood Pressure in the U.S. Population, by Race, Ethnicity, and Gender, 2011

	Male	Female
All races	34.1	32.7
White (not Hispanic)	33.9	31.3
Black (not Hispanic)	43.0	45.7
Mexican Americans	27.8	28.9

Source: National Center for Health Statistics, *High Blood Pressure Facts, 2011.*

the federal government reported rates not for Hispanics, but only for Mexican Americans. Below I discuss the importance of the heterogeneity of the category Hispanic.)

Given the strikingly different prevalence of high blood pressure between blacks and whites in the United States, it is crucially important to approach the treatment of high blood pressure in a manner that is supported by scientific data. In 2003 a national panel of high blood pressure researchers studied the scientific literature and published a consensus statement on the optimal approach to treating high blood pressure in African Americans (Douglas et al. 2003). They noted that two drugs often used as first-line treatment for high blood pressure in whites—beta-blockers and ACE-I—"may produce less blood-pressure lowering effect in African Americans than in whites" (p. 537). An accompanying editorial went somewhat further, stating that "these drugs should not be used as initial single-drug therapies for African Americans" (Materson 2003, p. 522). This recommendation—that these two drugs be used as first-line treatment in whites but not in blacks—has been echoed in a number of other publications and adopted by many physicians as best medical practice.

From the discussion above, we might want to question the assumption that all people who are black by race will have the same response to certain medications. This is precisely the question Mokwe and colleagues (2004) posed in a study of the use of one particular ACE-I drug in treating comparable samples of blacks and whites with high blood pressure. When they looked only at each subject's race without considering individual characteristics such as obesity, kidney function, and the presence of diabetes, they identified a lesser response to treatment among the blacks compared to the whites. However, when they took into account differences between the black subjects and the white subjects in the rates of these confounding conditions, they found that most of the difference in blood pressure response went away, leading them to conclude that "a large source of variability of blood pressure response to treatment is within, not between, racial groups, and that factors that vary at the level of the individual contribute to apparent racial differences in response to treatment" (p. 1202). These authors went on to caution physicians about using race to decide treatment choices. "Our results question the wisdom of using black race, per se, as a major criterion on which to base decisions regarding ACE inhibitor monotherapy because of their presumed lack of effectiveness for lowering BP. Race differences in *group* BP responses to monotherapy with ACE inhibitors are an inaccurate means of predicting the magnitude of BP-lowering with an ACE inhibitor in individual patients of either race because of the near-complete overlap of the BP response distributions of blacks and whites, and because a significant portion of the race difference in BP response is attributable to factors that vary at the level of the individual" (p. 1206).

Sehgal mirrored this conclusion in his review of 15 different studies comparing a variety of drugs for the treatment of high blood pressure in blacks and whites. He found that, while the average change in blood pressure was statistically lower in blacks than in whites, the difference in average response for the two groups was very small (between 0.6 mm and 3.0 mm out of a typical systolic blood pressure of 140–160), and that this difference in average group response was due to differences in response by a small subset of blacks. He found that "80% to 95% of whites and blacks have similar responses to commonly used antihypertensive drugs" (p. 569). After reviewing these fifteen different scientific studies Sehgal concluded that "race has little value in predicting antihypertensive drug response, because whites and blacks overlap greatly in their response to all categories of drugs. These findings are consistent with other work demonstrating that most genetic diversity exists within and not between races and that race is a poor predictor of drug-metabolizing enzymes (which in turn influence drug response)" (p. 570).

In following birth weight and associated infant mortality, in comparing death rates from cardio-vascular disease, and in selecting a treatment for high blood pressure, we find a consistent sequence of conclusions that are supported by scientific evidence.

- In comparing blacks and whites as racial groups, it is often possible to document significant differences in the mean (average) outcome.
- Once individual characteristics of group members are taken into account (for example, ethnicity, rates of other illness) most of the observed difference goes away.
- There is consistently more variation in these outcomes within racial groups than there is between racial groups.
- A person's race taken alone provides little information about and acts as a poor predictor of health outcomes.

Can We Use Hispanic Ethnicity to Predict Health Status?

In its report on **death rates** in the U.S. population for 2010, the federal government's National Center for Health Statistics reported that the age-adjusted death rate per 100,000 population was 755 for the non-Hispanic white population and 559 for the Hispanic population. From these data it would be technically accurate to state that the death rate for Hispanics is 25 percent lower than that of whites.

However, as was the case with race as a category, simply knowing that a person is Hispanic will tell you little about his or her risk of death relative to whites. Recall from the discussion of the U.S. census above that, for those who indicate that they are of Hispanic ethnicity, they are then asked to indicate which subgroup within Hispanic they belong to, with the largest three groups identified: Mexican, Puerto Rican, and Cuban.

Looking again at the data on deaths in 2010, we find that the age-adjusted death rate for these three groups is quite different:

- Mexican, 546
- Puerto Rican, 673
- Cuban, 575

While the death rate for all three groups is less than that of whites, there is substantial variation among the groups, with the rate for Cubans being 24 percent less than that of whites and the rate of Puerto Ricans being only 11 percent less than whites. It appears that, as with race, there is substantially more variation in health status within the Hispanic ethnicity than there is between Hispanics and non-Hispanic whites.

EDITOR'S NOTES

death rate: measures of the frequency of death in a defined population during a specified period of time.

References

David, R. J., and Collins, J. W. 1997. Differing birth weight among infants of U.S.-born blacks, African-born blacks, and U.S.-born whites. *New England Journal of Medicine* 337:1209–14.

Douglas, J. C., Bakris, G. L., Epstein, M., et al. 2003. Management of high blood pressure in African Americans. *Archives of Internal Medicine* 163:525–41.

Elo, I. T., Culhane, J. F. 2010. Variations in health and health behaviors by nativity among pregnant Black women in Philadelphia. *American Journal of Public Health* 100:2185–92.

Exner, D. V., Dries, D. L., Domanski, M. J., and Cohn, J. N. 2001. Lesser response to angiotensin-converting-enzyme inhibitor therapy in black as compared with white patients with left ventricular dysfunction. *New England Journal of Medicine* 344: 1351–57.

Fang, J., Madhavan, S., and Alderman, M. 1996. The association between birthplace and mortality from cardiovascular causes among black and white residents of New York City. *New England Journal of Medicine* 335:1545–51.

History of Hoyle. Available at http://www.hoylegaming.com/c-9-history-of-hoyle.aspx (accessed July 17, 2013).

Japan, Statistics Bureau, Ministry of Internal Affairs and Communication. Concerning the 2005 Population Census. Available at www.stat.go.jp/English/data/kokusei/e_cen_en.htm.

Jorde, L. B., Wooding, S. P. 2004. Genetic variation, classification, and "race." *Nature Genetics* 36(11 Suppl.):S28–33.

Keita, S. O. Y., Kittles, R. A., Royal, C. D. M., et al. 2004. Conceptualizing human variation. *Nature Genetics* 36(11 Suppl.):S17–20.

Lee, S. M. 2001. Using the New Racial Categories in the 2000 Census. Annie E. Casey Foundation and Population Reference Bureau. Available at www.aecf.org/kidscount/racia12000.pdf.

Lee, S. S., Mountain, J., Koenig, B. A. 2001. The meanings of "race" in the new genomics: Implications for health disparities research. *Yale Journal of Health Policy, Law, and Ethics* I: 33–75.

Li, J. Z., Absher, D. M., Tang, H., et al. 2008. Worldwide human relationships inferred from genome-wide patterns of variation. *Science.* 319(5866):1100–4.

Linnaeus, C. 1956. *Systema naturae.* Photographic facsimile of the first volume of the 10th ed. (1758), originally published under the name Carl von Linné. London: British Museum of Natural History.

Lodge, H. C. 1897. Senate speech, February 2. Congressional Record, 54th Congress, 2nd Session, vol. 29, part 2, p. 1432.

Marks, J. 1995. *Human Biodiversity: Genes, Race, and History.* New York: Aldine de Gruyter.

Materson, B. J. 2003. High blood pressure in African Americans. *Archives of Internal Medicine* 163:521–22.

Mokwe, E., Ohmit, S. E., Nasser, S. A., et al. 2004. Determinants of blood pressure response to Quinapril in black and white hypertensive patients. *Hypertension* 43:1202–7.

Oxford English Dictionary. Available at www.oed.com.

Patrinos, A. 2004. "Race" and the human genome. *Nature Genetics* 36(11 Suppl.):S1–2.

Risch, N., Burchard, E., Ziv, E., Tang, H. 2002. Categorization of humans in biomedical research: Genes, race, and disease. *Genome Biology* 3(7): comment 2007, pp. 1–12.

Roediger, D. R. 1999. *The Wages of Whiteness: Race and the Making of the American Working Class.* New York: Verso.

Rosenberg, N. A., Pritchard, J. K., Weber, J. L., et al. 2002. Genetic structure of human populations. *Science* 298:2381–85.

Schwartz, R. S. 2001. Racial profiling in medical research. *New England Journal of Medicine* 344:1392–93.

Sehgal, A. R. 2004. Overlap between whites and blacks in response to antihypertensive drugs. *Hypertension* 43:566–72.

Tishkoff, S. A., Kidd, K. K. 2004. Implications of biogeography of human populations for "race" and medicine. *Nature Genetics* 36(11 Suppl.):S21–26.

U.S. Census Bureau. 2010. Census Briefs—Overview of Race and Hispanic Origin: 2010. March 2011.

U.S. Census Bureau. 2010. Overview of Race and Hispanic Origin, 2010. Available at http://www.census.gov/prod/cen2010/briefs/c2010br-02.pdf.

U.S. Department of Health and Human Services, Centers for Disease Control and Prevention, National Center for Health Statistics. 2012. Deaths: Preliminary data for 2011. *National Vital Statistics Reports* 61(6), October 10, 2012.

U.S. Department of Health and Human Services, Centers for Disease Control and Prevention, National Center for Health Statistics. 2013. Births: Final data for 2011. *National Vital Statistics Reports* 62(1).

U.S. Department of Health and Human Services, Centers for Disease Control and Prevention, National Center for Health Statistics. High Blood Pressure Facts—2011. Available at http://www.cdc.gov/bloodpressure/facts.htm (accessed July 16, 2013).

Wood, A. J. 2001. Racial differences in the response to drugs: Pointers to genetic differences. *New England Journal of Medicine* 344:1393–96.

CRITICAL THINKING QUESTIONS

1. Define *race* and *ethnicity*. Then refer to the article by Barr to identify and discuss your own race and/or ethnicity as it is defined by the US Census and in Canada. Why is it important to know about race and ethnicity in healthcare studies? Use the article to provide at least one example and discuss.

2. What are *integrated interventions* and why are they important in the research and practice of healthcare? Provide at least one example from the readings to illustrate and discuss your answer.

3. Identify and discuss the types and causes of heath disparities between women and men. Be sure to address disparities at both the global and local levels. Use examples from Reading 3.1 to illustrate your discussion.

UNIT 4
Social Structures Affecting Health

••

Editor's Introduction

The purpose of unit IV is to illustrate many of the ways inequalities in health and healthcare can be *structural* in nature. Prior units have provided a hint of this. For instance, in Barr's comparison of the US and Canadian healthcare systems and the cultural traits that supported these (in unit II), we clearly glimpsed how more micro-level phenomena, like values, impact the development of the macro-level structures of healthcare for an entire nation.

In Barrett's article in unit II, we encountered the ways in which structures of religion and economy combine to impact the interpersonal lives of not only the people with Hansen's Disease, but also the people who know them. In unit III, Mercado et al. pointed out that, without the structural support of economic equity, access to healthcare, healthy foods, and fairly priced housing, the health of urban poor people is at very high risk. These readings depicted the myriad ways that culture, social stratification, and social structure interact.

In recent years, the Black Lives Matter movement has called for an end to a variety of structural inequalities affecting the lives of Black persons across the United States. As mentioned in unit III, when we think of racial and ethnic inequality in the United States, we tend to think of it in an individual or interpersonal sense, that racist real estate marketing is due to racist brokers alone, that racist banking is due to racist bankers alone. What does it mean that inequality can be structural? To answer this question, the readings in this unit build on Mercados et al.'s work on urban poor persons and describe the ways in which urban poverty is reproduced in the lives of Black Americans *without one person necessarily having to behave in a racist manner*. This is critical to Black health, illness, and healthcare because, as Mercado et al. point out, urban areas are among the highest-risk geographies and poverty puts one at high risk of morbidity and mortality. In both urban areas and high levels of poverty, Black Americans are overrepresented or, put another way, geography, poverty, and race *intersect*[1]

---

1 Erica E. Meade, "Overview of Community Characteristics in Areas with Concentrated Poverty. Racial and Ethnic Minorities are Overrepresented in the Concentrated Poverty Population, and Concentrated Poor Communities in Metropolitan Areas are Often Highly Segregated," Report of the Office of the Assistant Secretary for Planning and Evaluation for the U.S. Department of Health and Human Services (May 1, 2014), https://aspe.hhs.gov/system/files/pdf/40651/rb_concentratedpoverty.pdf.

In the United States, public schools are heavily funded through property taxes and these are distributed according to neighborhood. In neighborhoods where property values are higher, schools will be funded at higher levels and, conversely, in neighborhoods where property values are lower the schools will be funded at lower levels. Poorly funded schools tend to have poorer outcomes, such as low literacy and graduation rates, which result in poor job skills and opportunities. Poor neighborhoods tend to be less safe, due to lack of recreational, walking, and biking spaces; increased risk of violence; and environmental hazards, such as the pollution from nearby factories, and buildings that do not meet safety codes. All of these factors intersect, among others, to result in a next generation that is unable to move away from the poor neighborhood and will send its children to the same poor schools, resulting in poor job opportunities and an inability to afford housing in areas that support life more robustly. It is impossible to blame any one person for these conditions, but these factors highlight how the whole system or structure of urban poverty is maintained and reproduced. This is *structural inequality* as opposed to interpersonal or individual inequality. Many of the "isms" we encounter (e.g., racism, sexism, classism, ageism, etc.) have significant structural components that are never discussed because U.S. culture is so intent on the individual.

The readings in unit IV are clear and organized in their presentation of structural inequalities resulting in poor health outcomes. In "Today's 'Eat More' Environment: The Role of the Food Industry," Marion Nestle and Malden Nesheim examine factors related to the increase in American obesity since the 1980s. The evidence they present indicates that increases in calorie intake have played a key role in rising rates of obesity in the United States over the last sixty years. Nestle and Nesheim investigate where the calories come from and illustrate how new *agricultural policies* in the late 1970s encouraged farmers to plant more, while at the same time Wall Street was undergoing a shift to increase *shareholder values*. These variables resulted in a significant increase in the number of calories available and increased competition to package and market them to Americans. The cultural impact of these changes has been massive and changed the very structure of our food system, making food—especially nutritiously empty junk food—available everywhere for low prices. While humans have a hard time gauging their caloric intake to begin with, the changes brought about by these policy shifts, such as marketing empty calories as "no trans fat" or "organic," has made it even more difficult for people to discern. In the end, these structural factors played a significant role in the increase of obesity in the United States.

In "Globalizing the Chronicities of Modernity: Diabetes and the Metabolic Syndrome," Dennis Wiedman does a creditable job of laying out and supporting his *chronicities of modernity* theory by investigating *metabolic syndrome* (MetS), which is summarily defined as the variety of conditions related to diabetes and heart disease (e.g., high cholesterol, glucose intolerance, hypertension, etc.). Historically, diabetes increased significantly when humans moved from rural to urban locations; from non-westernized to westernized nations; among Pacific Islanders, among those more acculturated to colonizers; and among North American Indigenous populations when they were confined to reservations or poor rural areas. Wiedman discusses his own research with Cherokee from the Oklahoman Ozarks. In the shift from an agricultural to a cash economy, the cultural changes were drastic and left virtually no part of life untouched. Weidman discusses how diabetes was virtually unknown among the Cherokee until the 1960s, when it became epidemic. Wiedman traces this to the replacement of agriculture with a cash economy, which changes the jobs people do (with jobs in town being more sedentary), modes of transportation, and ways households are organized to work, all leading to decreases in physical activity and increases in caloric intake, and resulting in increased obesity, heart disease, and diabetes. These truly are *chronicities of modernity*.

American cultural values encourage looking to the individual for answers to health problems (e.g., behavioral, mental health, genetic, etc.) but much research has uncovered the social and, particularly, structural factors that impact people's health. The readings in unit IV illustrate how social structure impacts global health. The passage of major legislation, the promotion of new farming methods, the shift from an agricultural to a cash economy, and more all have clear ties to increases in poor health outcomes for many across the world.

Today's "Eat More" Environment

The Role of the Food Industry

By Marion Nestle and Malden Nesheim

··

W eight gain, as we keep saying, is caused by eating more, moving less, or doing both. Rates of overweight and obesity began to rise sharply in the United States in the early 1980s. Did Americans start becoming less active at that time? Did they begin to eat more? Or, as is widely believed, did both things happen simultaneously? Let's take a look.

Trend: Calories Expended in Physical Activity

Practically anyone you ask will tell you that people in general and kids in particular are less active now than they were in recent decades. Kids hardly ever take physical education classes, walk or ride bicycles to school, or play spontaneous sports. If enrolled in organized sports, they spend more time hanging around than running around. You cannot tear them away from computers, video games, or other sedentary online entertainment. On this basis, some researchers insist that declining levels of physical activity—not eating more calories—must be the chief cause of today's obesity crisis.[1]

We wish we had compelling reasons to believe this idea to be correct, but we do not. If anything, research shows the opposite. Doubly labeled water studies indicate a slight *increase* in physical activity since the early 1980s. Even research based on self-reports, which tend to exaggerate the most healthful practices, finds practically no change in calorie expenditures since 1980. The CDC, for example, conducts periodic surveys of physical activity levels based on self-reports. These show a slight increase in reported activity levels from 1990 to 1998. The CDC also asks questions about leisure-time sedentary behavior. The responses indicate a slight decline in inactivity from 1988 to 2008, as shown in figure 4.1.1.[2]

Additional CDC surveys record small increases in physical activity among men and women from 2001 to 2005. But other investigators report slight decreases in activity and slight increases in inactivity among ninth- and tenth-grade boys and among both black and white girls between the ages of nine and nineteen. The studies finding such results used different methods, age groups, and time periods and are not easily compared. To try to make sense of the conflicting data, Australian

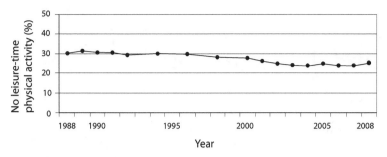

FIGURE 4.1.1 Rates of self-reported leisure-time inactivity, 1988–2008. If inactivity is declining slightly, activity levels must be increasing slightly. *Source:* CDC, 2010 (see note 2).

TABLE 4.1.1 Trends in Self-Reported Calorie Intake, 1971–2008, Per Capita Per Day

Year	Men	Women
1971–1974	2,450	1,540
1976–1980	2,440	1,520
1988–1994	2,670	1,800
1999–2000	2,620	1,880
2001–2002	2,620	1,845
2003–2004	2,610	1,850
2005–2006	2,640	1,785
2007–2008	2,510	1,770

Sources: 1971–2000 figures are from National Health and Nutrition Examination Surveys of people ages 20–74 (CDC, 2004; see note 5); 2001–2008 figures come from *What We Eat in America* surveys, ages 20–74+ (USDA, 2010; see note 6).
Note: Calories rounded off to the nearest 5.

investigators reviewed every study they could find on levels of physical activity but observed that almost none had collected baseline data on childhood activity from the earlier years. Without a baseline, they could not identify a trend.

They noted, however, that today's declining rates of active transport (walking, cycling), school physical education, and organized sports constitute what they call an "activity toxic" environment for kids. Kids want to be active but are constrained by school policies and curricula, parental concerns about safety and convenience, and the almost universal lack of sidewalks, bike paths, and safe places to play.[3]

Years ago kids were watching television and reading comic books. Are they really less active now? Without better data we cannot agree that declining physical activity is the more important cause of rising rates of overweight, especially because most data are self-reported. We did find one longitudinal study that measured baseline calorie intake and expenditure with doubly labeled water. Baseline total energy intake and resting energy expenditure predicted subsequent obesity, but energy expenditure from physical activity did not.[4] Overall, the available evidence points to calorie intake as a more important cause of obesity than calorie output.

Trend: Calorie Intake

Studies of calorie intake are much less ambiguous. For them, we have baseline data. Compared to studies dating back to the early 1970s, recent studies show a clear increase in calorie intake, as shown in table 4.1.1.[5]

These figures require some interpretation. They were obtained from self-reports of one-day diet recalls, cover different age groups, may not represent average daily intake, and undoubtedly underreport calories. Taking the results at face value, men in recent years reported eating about 200 more calories per day than men in 1971–74. For women, the increase for the same time period is more than 300 calories a day. Since 2000, reported calorie intake has declined somewhat, possibly as a result of extending the age range of participants (older people eat less). But whatever the exact number, calorie intakes seem to have increased.[6] Why? To answer this question, let's look at concurrent changes in the food environment.

Calories in the Food Environment

Since the early 1980s the U.S. food environment has changed in ways that encourage eating in more places at more times of day in larger portions.[7] We attribute these changes to food industry responses to a sharp increase in the number of calories available in the food supply. For more than seventy years, from the early 1900s to the early 1980s, the U.S. food supply provided an average of about 3,200 calories per person per day, with a variation of plus or minus 200 calories. But by 2000 the available calories had increased to 3,900 per person per day, in parallel with rising rates of obesity. We illustrate these trends in figure 4.1.2.

Although calories in the food supply have increased by 700 per person per day since 1980 or so, the constituent proportions of protein (11 percent of calories), fat (41 percent), and carbohydrate

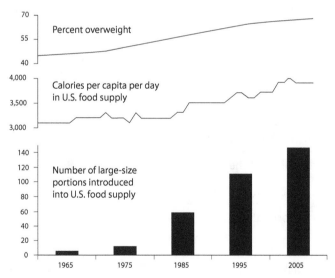

FIGURE 4.1.2 Calories in the food supply and large portions increased in tandem with rates of obesity from 1960 to 2005: trends in overweight (top panel), calories in the food supply per capita per day (middle panel), and introduction of larger food portions (bottom panel). Figure courtesy of Dr. Lisa Young.

(48 percent) show no evident change during that period. The mix of sources within those categories also did not change, except for the replacement of some fats from meat and dairy products with those from liquid oils. Calories from proteins, fats, and carbohydrates increased in direct proportion to total calories.[8]

Nevertheless, the kinds of foods that deliver many of the calories to American diets are a matter of considerable concern. The National Health and Nutrition Examination Survey (NHANES) collects data on dietary intake that can be used to identify the foods that are leading sources of calories in American diets. Table 4.1.2 summarizes data from the 2005–2006 NHANES. The leading contributors are desserts (grain-based and dairy), sodas, pizza, chips, and burgers. Chicken appears as the number three source, no doubt because the category includes fried chicken and McNuggets. These are largely foods of low nutrient density and high calorie density—junk foods. Worse, the top *three* food sources

TABLE 4.1.2 Top 15 Sources of Calories in U.S. Diets, People Ages 2 and Older

Rank	Calorie Source	Calories per Day from that Source
1	Grain-based desserts (cakes, cookies, pies, donuts)	138
2	Yeast breads	129
3	Chicken and chicken mixed dishes	121
4	Sodas, energy and sports drinks, sweetened waters	114
5	Pizza	98
6	Alcoholic beverages	82
7	Pasta and pasta dishes	81
8	Tortillas, burritos, tacos, nachos	80
9	Beef and beef mixed dishes	64
10	Dairy desserts (ice cream, sherbet, pudding)	62
11	Chips: potato, corn, other	56
12	Burgers	53
13	Reduced-fat milk	51
14	Cheese	49
15	Ready-to-eat cereals	49

Source: USDA, HHS, 2010 (see note 9).

of calories for children ages 2 to 18 are grain-based desserts (138 calories per day), pizza (136 calories), and sodas and energy and sports drinks (118 calories). Together these three food sources contribute one-fourth of a child's daily calorie intake. NHANES figures are national averages; some children obtain even more of their calories from such foods.[9]

Sugary drinks are of special concern. A later analysis of NHANES data from 2005 to 2008 reports that boys ages 12 to 19 consume nearly 300 calories a day from sugary drinks alone, and that 5 percent of the U.S. population consumes nearly 570 calories a day from such drinks. These contain sugars but no or few nutrients and are as low in nutrient density as you can get.[10]

The Causes

Why more calories became available is a matter of some conjecture. One frequently cited cause is the influx of women into the workforce, creating demands for convenience. But before blaming women for causing obesity, consider the labor statistics. These suggest that while women in the workforce—and longer working hours—may be contributing factors, the timing isn't quite right. By the early 1980s, half of working-age women had already entered the workforce, and from 1981 to 2007 the percentage only increased from 52 to 60 percent.[11] In any case, women can hardly be blamed for the food industry's creation of high-calorie, low-nutrient-density convenience foods. We think the evidence points more strongly to two other causes: agriculture policies and the advent of the "shareholder value" movement, which changed the way Wall Street evaluates publicly traded corporations.

Agricultural Policies. In 1973 and 1977, Congress passed laws that reversed long-standing farm policies aimed at protecting prices by controlling production. These policies paid farmers to set aside acres, but that changed when Earl Butz, a former dean of agriculture at Purdue, became USDA secretary and reportedly urged them to plant "fencerow to fencerow." Whether Butz really said this or not—no source has ever been found for the statement—the new policies encouraged farmers to plant as much as they possibly could. Food production increased, and so did calories in the food supply. The addition of 700 calories a day per capita made the food industry even more competitive. Food companies now had to find new ways to sell products in an environment that offered a vast excess of calories over the needs of the population. Even if, as the USDA maintains, Americans waste a third of available calories, the food supply is still highly overabundant.[12]

The "Shareholder Value" Movement. The onset of a movement to force corporations to produce more immediate and higher returns on investment especially increased competitive pressures on food companies. The movement's start is attributed to a speech given by Jack Welch, then head of General Electric, in 1981. Corporations, Welch said, owed more to their shareholders. His company would now focus on producing faster growth and higher profit margins and returns to investors. The movement caught on quickly, and Wall Street soon began to press companies to report not only profit but also increased *growth* on a quarterly basis. Food companies were having enough trouble producing profits in an overabundant food economy. Now they had to demonstrate profit growth every ninety days.[13]

The Consequences

Competitive pressures forced food companies to consolidate, become larger, and seek new markets and ways to expand sales in existing markets. The collateral result was a changed society. Today, in contrast to the early 1980s, it is socially acceptable to eat in more places, more frequently, and in larger amounts, and for children to regularly consume fast foods, snacks, and sodas—changes that singly and together promote higher calorie intakes. Here we highlight just a few of the ways in which the altered food environment promotes overeating.[14]

Foods away from Home. An abundance of food creates a cheap food supply, making it less expensive for people to eat foods prepared outside the home. Beginning in the late 1970s, spending on away-from-home foods rose from about one-third of total food expenditures to about one-half. The proportion of calories obtained from away-from-home foods rose from less than 20 to more than 30 percent, with much of the increase coming from fast food. Among children, the percentage of daily energy eaten away from home increased from 23 to 34 percent. According to an analysis of national food consumption surveys, children get more of their daily calories from fast-food outlets than they do from schools, and fast food is the largest contributor to the calories they consume outside the home. USDA economists say that the average meal eaten away from home by adults adds 134 calories to daily intakes, and one meal a week eaten at a restaurant can account for a two-pound annual weight gain.[15]

New Products. The low cost of basic food commodities has encouraged food companies to make new forms of tasty packaged food products. Manufacturers introduce nearly 20,000 new products into the food supply each year, nearly half of them candies, gums, snacks, and sodas. The habitual consumption of such foods is associated with long-term increases in calorie intake and body weight, and 40 percent of the calories in the diets of children and adolescents are reported to derive from high-calorie sweets and snack foods.[16]

Larger Portions. Once food became relatively cheap, restaurants, fast-food chains, and major food companies could offer foods and beverages in larger sizes to attract customers. Larger portions have more calories. They also encourage people to eat more and to underestimate the number of calories in their food by larger percentages. The increase in portion sizes is sufficient to explain rising levels of obesity (see figure 4.1.2).[17]

Ubiquity. We like to ask the question "When did it become acceptable to eat in bookstores?" Today snack foods are sold in 96 percent of pharmacies, 94 percent of gasoline stations, 22 percent of furniture stores, and 16 percent of apparel stores. Research shows that if food is at hand, people will eat it.[18]

Frequency. Nibbling may seem like a good idea, but the more times a day people eat junk foods, the more calories they are likely to consume. It now seems normal to snack and drink sodas throughout the day. Surveys find that children eat an average of three snacks per day, most of them high-calorie desserts, junk foods, and sweetened beverages of poor nutritional quality.[19]

Proximity. The mere location of fast-food restaurants near schools has been shown to promote fast-food consumption as well as overweight, even when corrected for community characteristics.

Cornell professor Brian Wansink and his colleagues have demonstrated the calorie-promoting effects of having food close at hand. The closer the candy dish, the more candy consumed. The mere presence of vending machines encourages kids to buy high-calorie foods, which explains why health advocates would like to see vending machines removed from schools.[20]

Low Prices. Adam Drewnowski and his team at the University of Washington have shown that on a per-calorie basis, junk foods are cheaper than healthier foods. They estimate that following federal dietary advice to increase intake of fruits and vegetables would raise one's food costs by several hundred dollars a year. If fruits and vegetables appear more expensive than junk foods, it's because they are. The Consumer Price Index indicates an increase of about 40 percent in the relative cost of fruits and vegetables since the early 1980s, whereas the indexed price of desserts, snack foods, and sodas has declined by 20 to 30 percent. Lower prices encourage people to eat more. Higher prices discourage food purchases.[21] For example, as part of its contribution to obesity prevention, Coca-Cola now offers drinks in 7.5-ounce cans but prices them higher than 12-ounce sodas. As a retailing executive once explained to us, if customers want smaller portions, they ought to be willing to pay for them.

Marketing Health. The food industry spends billions of dollars a year to encourage people to buy its products, but foods marketed as "healthy" particularly encourage greater calorie intake. Professor Wansink's experiments show that people eat more calories from snack foods labeled low fat, no trans fat, or organic. Most people, he says, are "blissfully unaware" of how the food environment influences what they eat. People take in excessive calories "not because of hunger but because of family and friends, packages and plates, names and numbers, labels and lights, colors and candles, shapes and smells. … The list is almost as endless as it's invisible."[22]

Invisible to consumers, yes, but not to food marketers. The result of constant exposure to today's "eat more" food environment, as David Kessler explains in *The End of Overeating,* has been to drive people to desire high-calorie foods and to become "conditioned overeaters."[23] The power of this food environment to promote greater calorie intake is so great that even educated eaters have trouble dealing with it. If you as an educated eater have trouble managing "eat more" pressures it is because it is virtually impossible for individuals to judge the number of calories they are eating […].

Notes

1. Blair SN, Leermaker EA. Exercise and weight management. In: Wadden TA, Stunkard AJ, eds. *Handbook of Obesity Treatment.* New York: Guilford Press, 2004:283–300. Church TS, et al. Trends over 5 decades in U.S. occupation-related physical activity and their associations with obesity. *PLoS One* 2011;6(5):e19657.

2. Westerterp KR, Speakman JR. Physical activity energy expenditure has not declined since the 1980s and matches energy expenditures of wild animals. *Int'l J Obesity* 2008;32:1256–63. CDC. Physical activity trends—United States, 1990–1998. *Morbidity and Mortality Weekly Report* 2001;50:166–69. CDC. Physical activity statistics, updated February 2, 2010, at www.cdc.gov/nccdphp/dnpa/physical/stats/.

3. CDC. Prevalence of regular physical activity among adults—United States, 2001 and 2005. *Morbidity and Mortality Weekly Report* 2007;56:1209–12. Adams J. Trends in physical activity and inactivity amongst US 14–18 year olds by gender, school grade and race, 1993–2003: Evidence from the youth risk behavior survey. *BMC Public Health* 2006;6:57, online at www.biomedcentral.com/1471-2458/6/57. Kimm SYS, et al. Decline in physical activity in black girls and white girls during adolescence. *NEJM* 2002;347:709–15. Dollman J, Norton K, Norton L. Evidence for secular trends in children's physical activity behavior. *British J Sports Medicine* 2005;39:892–97.

4. Tataranni PA, et al. Body weight gain in free-living Pima Indians: Effect of energy intake vs. expenditure. *Int'l J Obesity* 2003;27:1578–83.

5. CDC. Trends in intake of energy and macronutrients—United States, 1971–2000. *Morbidity and Mortality Weekly Report* 2004;53:80–82.

6. USDA. Data tables from *What We Eat in America,* NHANES 2007–2008, revised August 2010, available at www.ars.usda.gov/Services/docs.htm?docid=18349. Kant AK, Graubard BI. Secular trends in patterns of self-reported food consumption of American adults: NHANES 1971–1975 to NHANES 1999–2002. *AJCN* 2006;84:1215–23.

7. Swinburn BA, Sacks G, Ravussin E. Increased food energy supply is more than sufficient to explain the US epidemic of obesity. *AJCN* 2009;90:1453–56.

8. Percentages are calculated using Atwater Values from figures in the USDA Food Availability (Per Capita) Data System, at www.ers.usda.gov/data/foodconsumption. These data show no change in the availability of sugars as a percent of calories from 1980 to 2000. The data sets do not distinguish whole from refined grains, but daily fiber availability increased by 5 grams per day during that period, perhaps indicating some increase in the availability of whole grains.

9. USDA, HHS. *Dietary Guidelines* for *Americans,* 2010, at www.dietaryguide lines.gov. The NHANES data are analyzed in National Cancer Institute. Food sources of energy among U.S. population, 2005–06. National Cancer Institute, May 21, 2010, at http://riskfactor.cancer.gov/diet/foodsources.

10. Ogden CL, et al. Consumption of sugar drinks in the United States, 2005–2008. NCHS Data Brief No. 71, August 2011, at www.cdc.gov/nchs/data/databriefs/db71.htm.

11. Rupert P, Stepanczuk C. Economic trends: Women in the workforce. Federal Reserve Bank of Cleveland website, March 15, 2007, at www.clevelandfed.org/research/trends/2007/0407/03ecoact_031407.cfm.

12. Breimyer HF. *Over-fulfilled Expectations: A Life in Rural America.* Ames: Iowa State U Press, 1991. USDA, Economic Research Service. Data sets: Loss-adjusted food availability: Spreadsheets, updated March 17, 2010, at www.ers.usda.gov/data/foodconsumption/FoodGuideSpreadsheets.htm.

13. Morris B. The new rules. *Fortune,* July 24, 2006. Welch's speech was titled "Growing Fast in a Slow-Growth Economy." The shareholder value movement is usually traced to the work of Alfred Rappaport, editor

of *Information for Decision Making: Quantitative and Behavioral Dimensions* (Prentice-Hall, 1975). The book contains Rappaport's chapter on discounted cash flow, the point of which is to maximize the immediate value of investment projects "subject to the constraint that the earnings of the company must grow at a stipulated rate." Also see Swinburn BA, et al. The global obesity pandemic: Shaped by global drivers and local environments. *Lancet* 2011;378:804–14.

14. Nestle M. *Food Politics: How the Food Industry Influences Nutrition and Health,* revised edition. Berkeley: U California Press, 2007. Nestle M, et al. Behavioral and social influences on food choice. *Nutrition Reviews* 1998;56(5):s50–s74.

15. Rosenheck R. Fast food consumption and increased caloric intake: A systematic review of a trajectory towards weight gain and obesity risk. *Obesity Reviews* 2008;9:535–37. Potti JM, Popkin BM. Trends in energy intake among US children by eating location and food source. *JADA* 2011;111:1156–64. Todd JE, Mancino L, Lin B-H. The impact of food away from home on diet quality. USDA Economic Research Report No. 90, February 2010.

16. USDA. Food marketing system in the U.S.: New product introductions, May 21, 2010, at www.ers.usda. gov/Briefing/FoodMarketingSystem/new_product.htm. Reedy J, Krebs-Smith SM. Dietary sources of energy, solid fats, and added sugars among children and adolescents in the United States. *JADA* 2010;110:1477–84.

17. Young LR, Nestle M. The contribution of increasing portion sizes to the obesity epidemic. *Am J Public Health* 2002;92:246–49. Young LR, Nestle M. Portion sizes and obesity: Responses of the fast-food companies. *J Public Health Policy* 2007;28:238–48. Rolls BJ, Morris EL, Roe LS. Portion size of food affects energy intake in normal-weight and overweight men and women. *AJCN* 2002;76:1207–13. Wansink B, van Ittersum K. Portion size me: Downsizing our consumption norms. *JADA* 2007;107:1103–6. Diliberti N, et al. Increased portion size leads to increased energy intake in a restaurant meal. *Obesity Res* 2004;12:562–68.

18. Farley TA, et al. The ubiquity of energy-dense snack foods: A national multicity study. *Am J Public Health* 2010;100:306–11.

19. Piernas C, Popkin BM. Trends in snacking among U.S. children. *Health Affairs* 2010;29(3):398–404. Duffey KJ, Popkin BM. Energy density, portion size, and eating occasions: Contributions to increased energy intake in the United States, 1977–2006. *PLoS Medicine* 8(6):e1001050, June 28, 2011.

20. Davis B, Carpenter C. Proximity of fast-food restaurants to schools and adolescent obesity. *Am J Public Health* 2009;99:505–10. Painter JE, Wansink B, Hieggelke JB. How visibility and convenience influence candy consumption. *Appetite* 2002;38(3):237–38. Anonymous. Dispensing junk: How school vending undermines efforts to feed children well. CSPI, May 2004, online at www.cspinet.org/new/pdf/dispensing_junk.pdf.

21. Monsivais P, Aggarwal A, Drewnowski A. Following federal guidelines to increase nutrient consumption may lead to higher food costs for consumers. *Health Affairs* 2011;30(8):1–7. Leonhardt D. Sodas a tempting

tax target. *NYT,* May 19, 2009, at www.nytimes.com/2009/05/20/business/economy/20leonhardt.html, and What's wrong with this chart? *NYT,* May 20, 2009, at http://economix.blogs.nytimes.com/2009/05/20/whats-wrong-with-this-chart. But see Kuchler F, Stewart H. Price trends are similar for fruit, vegetables, and snack foods. USDA, Economic Research Service, Economic Research Report No. 55, March 2008, available at www.ers.usda.gov/publications/err55/err55.pdf. These USDA economists argue that Consumer Price Index data overstate the rise in the indexed price of fruits and vegetables. Andreyeva T, Brownell KD. The impact of food prices on consumption: A systematic review of research on the price elasticity of demand for food. *Am J Public Health* 2010;100:216–22.

22. 100 leading national advertisers, 2010. *Advertising Age,* June 20, 2010. Wansink B, Chandon P. Can "low-fat" nutrition labels lead to obesity? *J Marketing Res* 2006;43:605–17. Wansink B. *Mindless Eating: Why We Eat More than We Think.* New York: Bantam, 2006:1.

23. Kessler DA. *The End of Overeating.* Emmaus, PA: Rodale, 2009.

Globalizing the Chronicities of Modernity

Diabetes and the Metabolic Syndrome

By Dennis Wiedman

F or most of human history as hunters, gatherers, and agriculturalists, humans maintained an active physical lifestyle that varied with seasonal resources and promoted cardiovascular and metabolic fitness. But for the past five hundred years, since early European imperialism, there have been major changes in everyday life and, in consequence, in health. Early **industrialization** and globalization **diffused** commodities and labor-saving technologies for work and home throughout the world. In recent decades, this process has gained extraordinary momentum: With **modernity**, large numbers of people now live a life of low physical activity, consistent energy intake from foods, and chronic levels of psychosocial stress. These in turn result in an array of metabolic disorders: including diabetes mellitus and associated chronic conditions. In ancient Greece, diabetes as a disease was associated with the elite managerial class; by the 1970s it was characterized as a "disease of civilization," affecting mostly lower classes and ethnic minorities. Once blamed on the genetic, mental, and cultural maladaptations of indigenous peoples, ethnic minorities, and inner-city poor, it now affects the full spectrum of social classes and ethnic groups. Thirty years later, diabetes is associated with the metabolic syndrome (MetS), the co-epidemic of obesity and heart and kidney disease that is increasingly prevalent in developed and developing nations.

No particular foods, genes, socioeconomic class, ethnicity, or other inequality can consistently explain the initiation of metabolic disorders in modernizing populations worldwide. In this chapter, I develop a

> **EDITOR'S NOTES**
>
> **industrialization:** the introduction, maintenance, and growth of manufacturing and technical enterprise in a society.

> **EDITOR'S NOTES**
>
> **cultural diffusion:** the transmission of culture (e.g., norms, technologies, values, etc.) from one place to another.

> **EDITOR'S NOTES**
>
> **modernity:** an era in human history generally characterized by advances in science and technology, industrialization and capitalism, as well as significant social inequalities.

theory of chronicity to reconceptualize and explain the global pandemic of MetS, by arguing that its underlying cause is the dramatic shift from "seasonality" of hunters, gatherers, and agriculturalists to the "chronicities of modernity." This perspective builds upon Susan Estroff's use of *chronicity* "to refer to the persistence in time of limitations and suffering that results in disabilities as they are socially and culturally defined and lived" (Estroff 1993; 250). This theory of chronicity focuses on sociocultural explanations for metabolic disorders, rather than the current genetic and biological explanations that are predominant today. As an embodiment of modernity, the chronic metabolic disorders reflect the physical body's response to the chronicities of modernity.

Metabolic Syndrome Defined

Diabetes mellitus and associated chronic metabolic disorders were relatively unknown prior to modernization, even though the physical characteristics of diabetes were mentioned as early as 1500 BC in Egyptian medical writings and a Greek physician provided the first complete clinical description of diabetes in the second century AD. His patient was the manager of a granary, an elite member of the community (Fapaspyros 1964: 4–6). Like our knowledge of most diseases, the biopathological understanding of metabolic disorders began in the mid-nineteenth century. In 1849 Claude Bernard identified glycogen in the human body as similar to the sugar in grapes and found in the urine of those with diabetes. In 1869, the pancreas was associated with the metabolism of carbohydrates. In 1921, the extracted hormone *insulin* from the pancreas was discovered to lower blood sugar. By 1923 a test was being used to determine blood sugar levels and insulin was being used to treat diabetes. This led to the identification of insulin resistance as type 2 diabetes, and subsequently, in the early 1950s, to the development of oral hypoglycemic medicines (Papaspyros 1964). A significant paradigm shift in the scientific explanation for diabetes followed Kelly West's comparative study of twelve different nations of the world (West 1978). Finding a consistent association of diabetes with body fat, irrespective of the source of calories, West shifted the theoretical paradigm that diabetes was the result of "sugar consumption" to the most often used explanation today: "obesity" (West 1974a).

The clustering of risk factors for obesity, diabetes, dyslipidemia, gall bladder disease, and hypertension has focused researchers on portraying these as metabolic disorders with a common defect. Over the years, these were variously conceptualized as "Insulin Resistance Syndrome," "Syndrome X" (Reaven 1988), "New World Syndrome" (Weiss et al. 1984), and "Multiple Metabolic Syndrome" (Young et al. 2002). In 1999, the World Health Organization (WHO) reconceptualized the cluster of the disorders as MetS. The International Forum on Diabetes in 2005 defined the core components of MetS as central body obesity plus two of the following: raised blood lipids, hypertension, glucose intolerance, or reduced high-density lipoprotein (HDL) cholesterol (Alberti and Zimmet 2005; Alberti et al. 2006; International Diabetes Federation 2005).

This reconceptualization and refinement of MetS as a world health problem and public health priority stimulated a broad array of medical research and national public health initiatives. These included the WHO's 2007 Declaration of Diet and Physical Activity (WHO 20072), which urged national governments to promote healthy diets and regular, adequate physical activity as major factors in the promotion and maintenance of good health throughout the entire life course.

The emergence of scientific and public attention to MetS is a recurrent political and economic phenomenon, where little attention is paid to a health issue when it affects the poor, minorities, and underprivileged. However, once it affects the privileged class, actions begin to be taken with enhanced public health funding, biomedical research, and prevention programs. Like Farmer's (1999) reflections on emerging infectious disease, chronic metabolic diseases have been "discovered" only once they had an impact on those who have economic power. A recent article in the *New England Journal of Medicine*, "Obesity and Diabetes in the Developing World—A Growing Challenge," summarizes this emergent perspective: "Diabetes is rapidly emerging as a global healthcare problem that threatens to reach pandemic levels by 2030: the number of people with diabetes worldwide is projected to increase from 171 million in 2000, to 366 million by 2030" (Hossain et al. 2007: 214). In developing countries this increase is from 84 to 228 million (ibid.). Similarly, the world level of hypertension prevalence was estimated to be one billion in 2000, and predicted to rise to 1.56 billion in 2025 (Kearney et al. 2005). Yet from all the research to date, no nation or community anywhere, worldwide, has reported success in leveling or reducing the MetS epidemic.

Modernity as a Critical Juncture for MetS

In the late 1960s and early 1970s, researchers began to report that the prevalence of diabetes increased significantly as populations moved from rural to urban locations (1969), migrated from non-Western to Westernized nations, lived at greater levels of acculturation on Pacific islands, or, in the case of indigenous peoples, when confined to reservations and in poor rural communities (Cohen et al. 1972). Maori migrating from Polynesian atolls to urban New Zealand, for example, exhibited diabetes within a few years (Prior 1974). This correlation of diabetes with modernization was epitomized by Prior (1971) as "the price of civilization" (see also Eaton 1977).

Data from the United States further illustrate the association of modernization, culture change, and diabetes. Diabetes was unknown prior to 1940 among Oklahoma Native Americans, yet by the 1960s, it had reached epidemic proportions; and prevalence rates continue to rise (West 1974b). To identify the social and cultural factors for the onset of this epidemic, I compiled a 150-year cultural and demographic history of Cherokee living in an eighty square mile area of the Oklahoma Ozarks. Ethno historic research methods, including archaeology, ethnography, oral history interviews, kinship, and historic document analysis, provide details of the critical juncture of modernity among this population living in one location for over 150 years (Wiedman 1979, 1987).

The Cherokee had been farmers of corn, beans, and squash for more than three thousand years in the southern Appalachians of Georgia and the Carolinas. After forced removal to Indian Territory and the Ozark Mountains of eastern Oklahoma in the 1830s, they continued to farm and hunt, in a very similar physical environment as the southern Appalachians. The Cherokee who moved into this forested area dispersed their homes and farms throughout the hills and valleys. In the 1890s, a railroad passed thirty miles south of the valley, facilitating the planting and export of cotton by the Cherokee as a cash crop to the world market. Following the U.S. Indian Allotment Act in 1903, each Cherokee individual was deeded 160 acres of land. With population increases and smaller parcels of land for farming, more land was cleared of trees for cultivation and a greater percentage of the desirable river bottom lands were planted with cotton. Each spring more and more soil eroded and filled the rivers. Droughts led to the first farm failures in 1936, and by 1946 no families were able to live by subsistence farming. Purchased by outsiders, farms were consolidated into a few very large cattle ranches. Cherokee then moved to California or along a new gravel road that winded through the valley. In a matter of ten years, house sites and settlement patterns changed dramatically, and scattered homesteads were replaced by concentration residences near the improved road. Cherokee men began to work for cash on the new cattle ranches or logged trees for export. Small stores along the roads carried a wider array of products, and roads facilitated residents' travel to nearby towns and cities to purchase manufactured products.

With the shift to a cash economy, Cherokee were freed from the restraints of the seasonality of the immediate natural resources and could purchase foods and other products obtained from a variety of environments. Horse-drawn wagons and plows were replaced with cars, trucks, and tractors. Adults reduced body energy expenditure as they drove to nearby towns and cities to work in jobs. Reconfigured house floor plans and domestic technological changes significantly reduced both male and female physical activity levels. Cooking and bathrooms, once outside in separate buildings, were moved into the main house. Electric and gas stoves controlled fire, heat, and smoke better, while dramatically expanding cooking methods, especially baking and frying. Electricity allowed for refrigerators that enabled larger amounts and kinds of foods to be stored for longer periods of time. This reduced the need for an exterior smokehouse and root cellar for food storage. With house pipes and faucets, the energy expended in carrying water for cooking and bathing was reduced. Indoor bathrooms with flush toilets further reduced walking to an outhouse. Radios, then televisions, connected people to the national and global news, and to commercials advertising industrially produced foods and other items. One example of the impact of these trends was the change in energy expended to prepare whole ground cornmeal, which served as the basic food item for thousands of years, Traditionally, women would spend time each morning vigorously pounding corn for that day's use, to be cooked by fuel and with water, both carried to the cooking area. One cup of cornmeal contains eighty-seven grams of carbohydrates. In contrast, degermed and enriched cornmeal, purchased from a supermarket, contains 114 grams per cup (increased carbohydrates by 25 percent), and, with piped water and electricity or gas for cooking, demands little work in preparation.

This summary ethnohistory, reflecting the rapidity of the demographic and cultural transition, portrays the critical juncture of modernity as populations transition from subsistence agriculture to a cash economy, from self-produced foods to store-bought foods, from vigorous household chores to the comforts of household appliances, and from actively walking to riding in cars and trucks (Wiedznan 1979, 1987, 1989). Other studies, conducted in diverse settings throughout the world, further document this transition to modernity. Douglas Crews and P. C. Mackeen (1982) reported on the modernizing population of American Samoa, Young (1988) among Native Canadians, Teri Hall and colleagues (1992) with the Navajo, and Sharon Bruce (2000) on the Canadian Métis transition in the 1980s and 1990s. The Pima of Arizona, who have the highest rates of diabetes in the world, underwent this critical juncture in the 1930s and 1940s as their water supply for farming was increasingly restricted for commercial agriculture and urban development (Smith-Morris 2006b). In developing countries too, evidence from population-based surveys of seventy-five communities in thirty-two developing countries demonstrate that those who have undergone Westernization and industrialization, and especially urbanization, are at high risk of diabetes, with a 14 to 20 percent prevalence (Hossain, Kawar, and El Nahas 2007). In contrast, where a traditional lifestyle has been preserved, diabetes is rare.

China and India provide a contemporary example, at a mass national scale, of rapid transition to a modern lifestyle concurrent with rapid economic development (Prentice 2006; Reddy and Yusai 1998; Yach et al. 2004). Between 1992 and 2002, overweight and obese Chinese individuals increased from 14.6 percent to 21.8 percent throughout the nation, affecting all gender and age-groups in all geographic areas (Wang et al. 2007). Between 1993 and 2003, infectious diseases decreased while the prevalence of chronic diseases such us diabetes and cardiovascular disease increased. Depending on the criteria used, 13.7 percent to 24.8 percent of all Chinese adults aged thirty-five to seventy-four were said to have MetS. Overall, urban residents (those not engaged in farming who lived within cities and towns) had the highest rates of obesity compared to rural farmers. In urban areas, men had higher rates than women. This was reversed in rural areas where women are more likely to be obese than men. Here, men are responsible for the energy-intensive farmwork that maintains cardiovascular fitness and body weights; women tend to have the less labor-intensive work of food processing, cooking, and distribution. There may also be social pressure for women to gain weight as a sign of household affluence. In these ten years many Chinese have moved from rural to urban locations for employment and higher pay, leading to a shift from physically active agricultural labor to less labor-demanding occupations with long hours, limited movements, and little time to get up and walk around. In urban areas the bicycle was the main form of transportation ten years ago, now many more use cars, taxis, and mass transportation (Wang et al. 2007).

MetS has catastrophic cost implications for developing nations. In China, diet-related chronic diseases account for the deaths of 2.6 million people annually—42 percent of all deaths. In 1998, total hospital spending for these chronic diseases was estimated at $11.7 billion U.S. dollars, which is 23 percent of all hospital costs and 1.6 percent of China's gross national product (Wang et al. 2007).

Seasonality and Metabolic Fitness

The multifactorial basis of these disorders makes the manifestations of MetS appear highly variable among various human groups, confounding our understanding of the commonalities. I propose that we view the chronicities of the modern lifestyle as the commonality and the primary cause of MetS. Humans, and all mammals, living in a natural setting experience annual cycles of seasonal changes that produce variation in activity levels and caloric intake from food resources. For millions of years as hunters and gatherers, humans lived active food production lifestyles that produced daily and seasonal variation promoting cardiovascular and metabolic fitness (Hurtado and Hill 1990; Wilmsen 1978). Seasonal physical activity levels and metabolic rates have been documented among pastoral nomads (Beall et al. 1996) as well as agricultural populations based on cash crops (Huss-Ashmore et al. 1989). Heart and metabolic rates varied from day to day and seasonally as required to survive. Adjustments in metabolic rates are primarily physiological responses to needs of the moment. Prior to modernity, variability of the metabolic system was the norm. With transition to a modern lifestyle, food is relatively constant throughout the year, and daily physical activities are routinized to a relatively low level. The chronicities of the modern lifestyle are embodied by infrequent metabolic variation and overconsumption of calories leading to obesity. By not regularly increasing and decreasing our metabolic rates in our everyday lives, chronic metabolic disorders appear. This affects individuals while in the fetal environment of their mothers, and is compounded as they age from childhood to adult and then elder.

The dominant genetic explanation for diabetes is James Neel's (1962, 1999, 1982) "thrifty genotype theory," based on the proposition that for 99 percent of human existence we were hunters and gatherers living a life of feast and famine. Cycles of food deprivation selected for individuals who could quickly metabolize food into fat stores. This thrifty gene would be detrimental when populations modernized to a plentiful food supply. Decades of research question this assumption of Neel's thrifty gene hypothesis, even suggesting that famines are more frequent in recent agricultural societies.

An early cross-cultural analysis by Lee (1968) found that of the fifty-eight documented societies who were hunters and gatherers, half emphasized gathering of vegetable items more than hunting, one-third emphasized fishing, and only one-sixth of the cases depended mostly on hunting. Women, as the primary collectors of vegetable materials, often supplied more consistent calories to the diet than did men. The Khoisan of the Kalahari Desert in Southern Africa, who reside in a particularly harsh environment, actually have more leisure time than people in developed countries. In general, hunters and gatherers are physically active mobile populations using a wide variety of food resources. This enables them to exploit resources that are seasonally abundant in some areas while not abundant in others.

A meta-analysis of nutritional studies of hunters and gatherers and agriculturalists concluded that the overall food securities of recent foragers and pre-industrial agriculturalists are very similar to one another. These results "offer no support for the thrifty genotype proposition that past foraging populations likely had access to less food, and experienced particularly severe and frequent feast and famine cycles of nutrition, thereby providing a selective advantage to thrifty genotypes" (Benyshek and Watson 2006: 124–125). The chronicities of modernity theory is an alternative to the thrifty gene hypothesis, since it does not rely on selective advantages for a genetic predisposition for these metabolic disorders. Human and mammal populations experience similar metabolic disorders with the shift from seasonality to chronicity.

The important role of seasonality is illustrated with two studies in which I have been involved, comparing people in rural and urban Alaska. Remote communities continuing to live a food production lifestyle of hunting and fishing, based on the seasonal variation in weather and food resources, have low rates of diabetes and heart disease. In the first study (Smith et al. 2004), five rural communities were selected, one from each of the major Native cultural areas. All had a population of 250 to 800 people and they had no roads connecting them to other communities. Although they were active subsistence hunters and fishers, they were served by modern schools, medical clinics, and satellite television communications. Globally produced foods and products were imported via small airplanes or occasional boats. Rapid ethnographic assessment and structured interviews showed that a wide variety of community members were involved in food procurement, processing, and distribution. Although a few individuals were hunters or fishers, an array of ages and genders participated in cutting, smoking, packaging, storing, and cooking subsistence foods. Based on their particular geographic location, salmon, halibut, whale, moose, and seal were major protein sources. The comparable urban population was also consumers of subsistence foods; they received these as gifts and were much less involved in the food production process that promoted daily activities. The rural population had greater body weights and consumed more calories than the urban population, but had lower levels of blood glucose, cholesterol, and hypertension. Ninety-six percent of the rural respondents had blood sugar readings within normal range compared to 89 percent of the urban; for cholesterol 90 percent of rural and 69 percent of urban dwellers were within the normal range. Systolic blood pressure was within normal range for 94 percent of the rural and 87 percent for urban. Those within normal range for diastolic blood pressure were 100 percent for rural and 88 percent for urban (Smith et al. 2008). In the second more refined study, Native elders of two subsistence-based rural communities in northwest Alaska were compared with elders from the same communities who had moved to an urban area. Once again the rural elders had higher levels of physical and mental well-being and lower levels of diabetes and heart disease. We concluded that those who live in rural communities have better mental and physical health indicators (Smith et al. 2009a, 2009b).

These studies point to a food production lifestyle, where daily activities change with the seasons, as the normal human condition; low levels of daily physical activity with consistent sources of calories from food is the abnormal human condition.

Health Consequences of the Chronicities of Modernity and Globalization

Globalization has reshaped societies, nations, and identities for the past five hundred years, since the first expansion of European colonization and imperialism. With the growth of capitalism and the Industrial Revolution in the eighteenth century, new technologies developed supporting dramatic growths in human population. The culture of capitalism and scientism—characterized as the "Spirit of Capitalism" (Weber 1958)—changes social, economic, and spiritual life in very specific ways. As Eric Wolf (1982) demonstrated, European capitalism dramatically changed economic and power relationships among non-European peoples by introducing trade and the selective harvest of salable natural resources. Intensification of worldwide social relations now link distant localities in such a way that local processes are shaped by events occurring many miles away and vice versa. Production, distribution, transportation, communication, and financial systems link the local to the global. As the number of connections increase, there is a decrease in the time it takes to move people, products, and ideas—space and time are reorganized (Appadurai 1996; Inda and Renato 2007).

With globalization, governments and corporations attempt to stabilize, standardize, and routinize their bureaucratic routines as the number of people they involve grow. As individuals interact with or become part of these social structures and economies their behaviors become less diverse and more uniform. Wallace (1970) portrayed this cultural process as the organization of diversity and the replication of uniformity. Foucault (1977) writes about this as modern institutions controlling bodies through systems of power and knowledge, and Bourdieu's (1977) "habitus" portrays these as socially acquired everyday routines of thoughts and actions. Indigenous peoples confined to reservations are examples of how governments create, maintain, and impose chronicities on specific populations. U.S. reservation communities are not only the earliest populations to embody MetS, they continue to have the highest rates of MetS morbidity and mortality. By being forcibly contained politically, economically, and bodily to small resource areas, history shows that they quickly became limited in their physical activities and dependent upon the U.S. government for energy-dense, industrially processed food.

More broadly speaking, as populations are brought into global systems, individual behaviors are increasingly patterned by similar calendars and schedules based on clocks, daily routines, workweeks, and annual cycles of events. A cognitive focus on harvesting the changing seasonal food resources is replaced by a focus on a workday, defined by society rather than the natural environment. Large numbers of people move in synchronicity with a globalized time that patterns when to eat, sleep, and work. As transactions occur in less time and in greater numbers, there is a sense that time is moving at a faster pace from the present into the future. This shift from environmental seasonality to the embodiment of socially constructed time is a major element in the chronicities of modernity that affects the onset of MetS.

Diffusion of medical technologies and vaccines reduces childhood deaths from communicable diseases while increasing life expectancies and chronic disorders (Armelagos and Harper 2005). But at the same time, aspects of globalisation jeopardize health by eroding family-based social systems, denigrating the environment with pollution of the water, air, and land, and by disseminating consumerism accentuating the gap between the rich and the poor (Guest and Jones 2005). Delocalization of foods and resources create powerful economic forces influencing people to move to urban centers for employment and health services. Low-wage workers migrate transnationally to take advantage of employment opportunities, creating communities with poor health and working conditions. Those continuing to live in local communities become dependent upon foods and goods produced elsewhere in the world. Relatively inexpensive commodities are widely advertized and distributed through the world markets controlled by multinational corporations.

This profound cultural transformation of the capitalist nation-state encourages the development of a myriad of rules, regulations, values, and laws. The culture of capitalism encourages the conversion of items and activities into objects that can be bought and sold in the marketplace (Robbins 2005). Even for items and activities with no clear boundaries, science socially produces objects with clear boundaries in well-defined hierarchies of cause and effect (Latour 2004: 22). For example, healthcare activities once associated with family, kin, and tribe become the role of professionalized healers where health care is converted into monetary activities. Based upon capitalism and scientism, the biomedical professions reframe and transform the human body, disease, and time into measurable objects. The physician counts body weights and blood sugar levels while the nutritionist measures the calories and nutrients consumed. What is measured and counted significantly differs from what the local communities perceive as important to their overall health and well-being. Yet, these economic and scientifically measured objects influence policies at the state, national, and global levels. These socially constructed measures formulated by transnational health organizations now supersede national healthcare systems, furthering the spread of the chronicities of modernity that set parameters on the everyday lives of local peoples.

In these ways, social and cultural institutions promote low physical activity, consistent energy intake from foods, and chronic levels of psychosocial stress. Wherever there is a conjuncture of these three factors on the life situations of individuals, the risk for MetS is greatly increased.

Chronicities of Physical Activity

Recent controlled studies demonstrate that chronicities of the modern lifestyle can be modified, thus giving hope that MetS can be prevented. The Finnish Diabetes Prevention Study, for example, shows that 30 to 67 percent of people with impaired glucose tolerance can reduce their progress toward detrimental manifestations through adherence to lifestyle interventions emphasizing body weight control, physical activity, and dietary modification. A seven-year follow-up study of the participants showed that sustained risk reduction continued in 43 percent, even after discontinuation of active counseling (Lindstrom et al. 2003). A continuing study showed that even low-impact exercise and walking conferred benefits (Laaksonen et al. 2005, 2007). Vigorous physical leisure time activities, including sports and weight resistance as well as moderate activities such as housework, home improvements, gardening, and walking to and from places of work, have also been shown to reduce risk (Rennie et al. 2003).

Similarly, in the Fels Longitudinal Study in Ohio (Remsberg et al. 2007), habitual physical activity reduced the risks among young adults, mostly for men and less for women. Extensive **anthropometric** measurements collected from 237 men and 249 women aged eighteen to forty years were correlated with self-reported levels for work, sport, nonsport leisure, and total physical fitness. Being physically active was shown to be a primary prevention for MetS for both men and women (see also Irwin et al. 2002).

Based on these and other recent studies, the 2005 Consensus Statement from the International Diabetes Federation proposed that moderate physical activity for 180 minutes per week would reduce the risk of MetS by 50 percent, only sixty minutes was necessary with more rigorous exercise (Alberti and Zimmet 2005: 477). These data show that diabetes and the chronic disorders are reversible through social and cultural changes. For those who have the motivation and life situation to implement and continue this positive change to a healthy lifestyle, the benefits are great. Now that we have controlled studies showing that low, moderate, and intensive lifestyle intervention does reverse or prevent the progress toward diabetic symptoms, the public health challenge is to forestall the MetS epidemic by influencing a large proportion of a population to live a healthy active lifestyle. However, prevention programs face enormous challenges. A third of the Finnish intervention subjects, for example, attained none or only one of the predefined goals after one year into the study. Lifestyle change and medications focus on the individual, and decades of a biomedical focus on individual counseling and regimen control has not worked. The approach presumes that individuals have a choice about what they eat, how they live, and how they work, and that they have resources to implement change.

The chronicities of modernity theory challenges us to look beyond the individual to the larger parameters of life situations: family dynamics, political and economic inequalities, architectural building designs, transportation systems, and dominant cultural themes and ideologies.

Chronicities of Food

The general direction of transformations in food use throughout the world, especially in the past two or three centuries, has involved an increasingly rapid delocalization of food production and distribution. Food varieties, production methods, and consumption patterns are disseminated throughout the world in an ever-increasing and intensifying network of socioeconomic and political interdependency. For individual and community health, delocalization shifts the provision of food, energy sources, and services from the local setting to points of market exchange outside the local area. These shifts reconfigure social relations of production (Pelto and Pelto 1983). The effects tend to be more positive for the developed world, the populations of which have greater access to a wider range of food products. For local food-producing communities, this leads to drastic changes in daily life, as the loss of control over food production and distribution systems causes a restructuring of social relationships and daily physical activities.

Development of industrial technologies enables mass production and the rapid distribution of high-calorie, energy-dense foods. In Europe by the late 1700s, wheat and cereal grains were produced, milled, and stored in large quantities for urban consumption. Ships transported these grains from the United States and Russia to European ports while smaller boats distributed grains along rivers and through canals (Pelizzon 1994). With the building of cross-continental railroads in the late 1800s these carbohydrates became the dietary foundation, replacing locally produced foods in many communities. By the 1930s, industrially refined, highly processed, energy-dense foods had been developed: Edible liquid fats and oleomargarines were used in cooking, for instance; high-fructose corn syrup was used as a drink sweetener (Popkin and Nielson 2003). A "nutrition transition" occurred as food industries produced relatively inexpensive, energy-dense foods that were widely advertised and distributed through the world markets (Popkin et al. 2001). Popkin (2004) reports that in China, over a matter of twenty years from 1980 to 2000, large shifts had occurred toward increased edible oil intake and increased sweetening of the diet, leading to the consistent availability and overconsumption of high-calorie, energy-dense foods.

The decade-long Strong Heart Study (SHS) among three Native populations in Arizona, Oklahoma, and the Dakotas provides further longitudinal data that challenge received wisdom of the role of nutrition and specific foods as a cause for cardiovascular disease and diabetes. Many published reports from the SHS have appeared in the literature over the past decade, comparing three American

Indian populations to the average U.S. population of NHANES III, the National Health and Nutrition Examination Survey (U.S. Department of Agriculture 2006). Stang and colleagues (2005) found that nutrient intakes varied little between the three populations, and overall few differences were noted compared to the U.S. national averages for the NHANES III participants. Their most notable conclusion was that energy intake differences between NHANES III and SHS participants were not consistent with the dramatic increase in cardiovascular disease and diabetes. Simply stated, these dietary data did not account for the dramatic increase in heart disease, obesity, or diabetes (Wiedman 2005a). Compared with an earlier Phase 1 SHS report (Welty et al. 2002), small changes in calorie energy intake did not explain the astounding increases in cardiovascular disease or diabetes. Various types of dietary fats and carbohydrates have been discounted as causal factors (Hu et al. 2001; Willett 2002). These data indicate that no single food or nutrient is responsible for MetS. These studies also reveal the methodological complications of assessing the nutrient content of composite foods derived from a combination of globally produced foods (Smith and Wiedman 2001).

Composite foods like pizza and American Indian fry bread combine global food products into hybridized meals that replace traditional meals. For example, cornmeal was the traditional Indian food; this was replaced by wheat flour during the reservation years when the U.S. government issued food rations of flour and bacon. Fry bread, a mix of flour and water cooked in bacon grease, provided a stable diet during near starvation days and continues today as a symbol of Indian identity and a pervasive Native North American food. However, from a survey of Indian fry breads, Smith and Wiedman (2001) documented that the caloric content of this energy-dense food, even though it is made from just a few ingredients, is highly variable according to cooking conditions.

Industrially produced foods that are transported quickly through global commodity chains controlled by multinational corporations enable large populations of people to have a consistent supply of high-calorie, energy-dense, and relatively inexpensive foods throughout the year. This homogenizing of local diets to a few consistently available food components diminishes seasonal dietary variety and the physical activities related to producing local foods.

Chronicities of Stress

MetS is the embodiment of the chronicities of the modern lifestyle especially when viewed as the body's physiological response to emotional suffering from adverse, traumatic stresses. Social and economic inequalities, traumatic historical experiences, daily occupational situations, and individual psychosocial stresses place specific population segments at greater risk for MetS.

Stress and cortisol levels are now linked to many physical disorders, including MetS. Stress produces observable changes in the neuroendocrine system, affecting the production and circulation of the hormones cortisol, glucagons, catecholamines, and insulin that control blood pressure, blood glucose levels, and heart rate. Culture and the individual's perception of stress influence what is threatening and potentially stressful and the physiological and social responses, which can be either adaptive or damaging. Stress involves the brain and the cardiovascular, immune, and other systems through neural and endocrine mechanisms. Acute stress initiates the fight-or-flight response that was selected for throughout human evolution. During these acute events the body produces the hormone cortisol, needed to release energy to escape predators. Modernity brings together an array of everyday events that produce chronic stresses that lead over time to wear and tear on the body (McEwen 2007).

A number of studies conducted in the United States illustrate these connections. Jo Scheder (1988), for example, examined life conditions of Mexican farm laborers in Wisconsin through ethnographic, psychological, and biochemical methods. She correlated diabetes with workers who spent more years in migrant labor and reported greater numbers of stressful life events. Another example is provided by Maria Yellow Horse Brave Heart, in her work linking post-traumatic stress syndrome caused from "historic trauma," the long history of domination and oppression to diabetes, cardiovascular diseases, and related health disorders among Native Americans (Brave Heart 1999). Multiple generations of stressful events are associated with continued loss of identity, demoralization, and ongoing emotional suffering, key elements that maintain the chronic stresses resulting in metabolic disorders (Ferreira and Lang 2006). From a biocultural perspective, William Dressler and colleagues (Dressler 1995) developed the Cultural Consonance model linking social status inconsistencies with chronic diseases such as hypertension and circulating levels of stress hormones, the catecholamines (Gravlee and Dressler 2005). This correlation has been replicated among the Caribbean islanders of St. Lucia and black Americans in Alabama and in various communities in North and South America (Dressler et al. 2007). And as a final example, Raikkonen, Matthews, and Kuller (2007) link psychosocial factors to alterations in the autonomic nervous system such as elevated heart rate, reduced heart rate variability, and elevated cortisol level leading in turn to MetS. This fifteen-year population-based prospective cohort study included healthy middle-aged women in the United States with symptoms of depression and very stressful life events. Frequent and intense feelings of anger and tension were associated with the cumulative prevalence and increased risk for developing MetS. A low physical activity level was associated with depression and the behavioral traits of heavier consumption of alcohol, smoking, anger, and anxiety.

A physiological response of "fight or flight" originally beneficial to protect the body in the short term is now with modernity embodied as a constant state of chronic stress increasing the risk of MetS for many individuals.

Global, Community, and Individual Chronicities

The chronicities of modernity is a theoretical perspective that hypothesizes the sociocultural processes at the global, individual, and local community are the causes of MetS. Higher risks for MetS appear wherever there is a conjuncture of social and cultural chronicities experienced by a particular segment of society and this varies greatly from nation to nation. The risk of MetS does increase with age, but what was once considered an adult disorder is now affecting children. The inner-city uneducated poor were at highest risk, but now it is increasingly common among the well educated with higher incomes. Women consistently have higher prevalence rates, but in some nations it is men. Urbanized populations have higher rates, but so do many rural areas and especially indigenous peoples restricted to reservations.

People whose lives are contained with few alternatives are at most risk for MetS. Those who face extreme poverty, unemployment, and environmental pollution have few alternatives to modify their individual behaviors. Persons on reservations, in remote communities, and poor inner cities do not have the wide array of food choices or physical activities that would enable them to change their daily lives even if they wanted. Urban workers, rich or poor, who work long hours do not have time or energy to exercise or take part in recreational activities that would promote metabolic fitness. The risk would be greater for persons confined to an office cubical answering phones or looking at a computer screen all day. Women with household responsibilities are often restricted in these same ways. Urban and suburban neighborhoods often do not have pedestrian-friendly walkways or green spaces for physical activities. In many localities high crime rates influence children to limit their activities to indoors. Extensive hours involved with the television and video and computer games further reduce metabolic fitness. These are some social and cultural behaviors that a community and nation would need to address in order to reduce the MetS epidemic.

Building upon Estroff's outline of chronicity (1993: 274), a scenario of the person with MetS can be portrayed at the micro level of individual, family, and healthcare provider. Physicians and caregivers, in response to patient's chronic metabolic disorders, make arrangements to stabilize, regulate, and control the amount and type of behaviors, foods, and physical activities that are acceptable regimens. Daily "variability" is transformed to a life of daily chronicity as a person transitions from being an active commodity producer to being dependent, regulated, and controlled. Social structures of institutions and family caregivers increasingly stabilize and routinize everyday life as the individual becomes more dependent. With hospitalization or institutionalization, everyday life becomes even less variable and less physically active. Persons who have never exhibited the symptoms of MetS are at greater risk when they become home-bound, hospitalized, or placed in nursing homes for other disorders. From the perspective of chronicity theory, healthcare systems and institutionalization increases the risks for MetS. In these cases MetS results from social and cultural iatrogenic causes.

Implications

The theory of chronicity prioritizes cardiovascular fitness, nutritional balance, and reasonable stress levels as ways to address the chronic metabolic disorders of MetS. First and foremost is to enhance cardiovascular and metabolic fitness by promoting a variety of physical activities in the daily and weekly lives of individuals. The MetS epidemic will have to be addressed at a multitude of levels: at international, national, regional, community, family, and individual levels (Nishida et al. 2004). This can only be accomplished with a multisectoral and broad-based public health approach to prevention (Kumanyika et al. 1998).

For decades healthcare providers and medical researchers have actively pursued ways to educate and counsel patients on health, diet, and exercise. Individual patient education and counseling in the clinical setting has not made a large difference in reducing these health disparities. This "blaming the victim" approach has not produced results, thus a shift to the larger social, cultural, and global factors is necessary.

Communities are beginning to develop innovative programs to promote metabolic wellness, although not conventionally spoken of in these terms. Rural and indigenous communities should be supported in their pursuit to retain self-sufficiency in the production, distribution, and local consumption of nutrient-rich foods such as fishing, hunting, and farming of fruits, vegetables, and grains (LaDuke 2005; Reddy 2002). As Ferreira and Lang (2006) contend, the chronic stresses of emotional suffering and historic trauma can be addressed through community empowerment by building emotional liberty. Building healthy self-sustaining communities is possible, as our research documented for Alaskan subsistence communities; the local food production lifestyle promotes metabolic fitness, nutritional, mental, and spiritual wellness.

National and local policy makers can influence companies, stores, government agencies, schools, university dormitories, cafeterias, and other organizations to make wise decisions affecting the availability of quality food and drink. Consumers should be motivated to make healthy purchasing decisions. A shift in perspectives is needed to promote the daily physical activity of people through the design of buildings, transportation systems, and recreational areas.

By promoting the positives of healthy communities and by addressing the necessary structural changes, rather than the negatives of disease prevention and individual regimens, community empowerment could reduce the pandemic of chronic diseases associated with the industrial lifestyle (Wiedman 2005b). It is imperative that metabolic fitness, good nutrition, and reasonable psychosocial stress levels be emphasized at the individual, community, national, and international levels. Efforts at multiple levels should empower communities and leadership with MetS knowledge presented in understandable and culturally appropriate ways to (a) influence accessibility to affordable and healthy choices of foods in local communities; (b) enhance activity levels with designs of transportation systems, work, exercise, and recreational facilities; and (c) promote the redevelopment of local food production lifestyles in communities that want to farm, garden, ranch, hunt, or fish.

Like the reconceptualization of MetS as a diverse set of physical disorders that cluster together, with the concept of chronicity we can now better understand sociocultural aspects of the modern lifestyle that cluster together as a set of causes for these chronic metabolic disorders. Implications for future research are many as this theory of chronicity focuses investigations on sociocultural systems, rather than solely on genetic and biological explanations.

Note

1. I thank nutritionists Dr. Janell Smith and Dr. Rena Quinton for working with me over the years to integrate nutritional science and anthropology into our collaborative research. Alicia Diaz assisted greatly in assembling the recent literature. Also, my heartfelt thanks to Felicia Wiedman; without her daily attention to life's details, this research would not be possible. This chapter was first presented at the American Anthropology meeting in Washington DC, December 1, 2007, at a presidential invited session of the Society for Medical Anthropology titled Inequalities, Chronic Illness and Chronicity: Dedicated to the Memory of Gay Becker, organized by Lenore Manderson and Carolyn Smith-Morris.

References

Alberti, George, and Paul Zimmet.

2005 The Metabolic Syndrome—A New Worldwide Definition. Lancet 366:1059–1062.

Alberti, George, Paul Zimmet, and Jonathan Shaw

2006 Metabolic syndrome—a new world-wide definition. A consensus statement from the International Diabetes Federation. Diabetes Medicine 23:469–480.

Appadurai, Arjun

1996 Modernity at Large: Cultural Dimensions of Globalization. Minneapolis, London: University of Minnesota Press.

Armelagos, George L., and Kristin N. Harper

2005 Disease Globalization in the Third Epidemiological Transition. In Globalization, Health, and the Environment. G. Guest, ed. New York: Altamira Press.

Beall, Cynthia, et al.

1996 Basal metabolic rate and dietary seasonality among Tibetan nomads. American Journal of Human Biology 8:361–370.

Benyshek, Daniel C., and James T. Watson

2006 Exploring the Thrifty Genotype's food-shortage assumptions: A cross cultural comparison of ethnographic accounts of food security among foraging and agricultural societies. American journal of physical anthropology 131:120–126.

Bourdieu, Pierre

1977 Outline of a Theory of Practice. R. Nice, transl. New York: Cambridge University Press.

Brave Heart, Maria Yellow Horse

1999 Gender differences in the historical trauma response among the Lakota. Journal of Health and Social Policy 10(4): 1–21.

Bruce, Sharon G.

2000 Prevalence and determinants of diabetes mellitus among the Métis of Western Canada. American Journal of Human Biology 12(4):542–551.

Cleave, Thomas, and George Campbell

1969 Diabetes, Coronary Thrombosis arid Saccharine Disease. Bristol: John Wright and Sons.

Cohen, A.M., A. Teitelbaum, and R. Saliternik

1972 Genetics and diet as factors in development of diabetes mellitus. Metabolism 21:235–240.

Crews, Douglas, and P.C. Mackeen

1982 Mortality related to cardiovascular disease and diabetes mellitus in a modernizing population. Social Science & Medicine 16:175–181.

Dressler, William

1995 Modeling biocultural interactions: examples from studies of stress and cardiovascular disease. Yearbook of Physical Anthropology 38:27–56.

Dressler, William, et al.

2007 Cultural consonance and psychological distress: Examining the associations in multiple cultural domains. Culture Medicine and Psychiatry 31(2):195–224.

Estroff, Sue E.

1993 Identity, disability, and schizophrenia: The problem of chronicity. In Knowledge, Power, and Practice: The Anthropology of Medicine and Everyday Life. S. Lindenbaum and M. Lock, eds. Pp. 247–286. Berkeley & Los Angeles: University of California Press.

Farmer, Paul

1999 Infections and Inequities: The Modern Plagues. Berkeley: University of California Press.

Ferreira, Mariana K. Leal, and Gretchen Chesley Lang

2006 Indigenous Peoples and Diabetes: Community Empowerment and Wellness. Durham, N.C.: Carolina Academic Press.

Foucault, Michel

1977 Discipline and Punish: The Birth of the Prison A. Sheridan, transl. New York: Pantheon Books.

Gravlee, Clarence C., and William W. Dressler

2005 Skin pigmentation, self-perceived color, and arterial blood pressure in Puerto Rico. American Journal of Human Biology 17(2):195–206.

Guest, Greg, and Eric Jones

2005 Globalization, Health, and the Environment: An Introduction. In Globalization, Health, and the Environment: An integrated Perspective. G. Guest, ed. New York: AltaMira.

Hall, Teri R., Martin E. Hickey, and Terry B. Young

1992 Evidence for recent increases in obesity and non-insulin-dependent diabetes-mellitus in a Navajo community. American Journal of Human Biology 4(4):547–553.

Hossain, Parvez, Bisher Kawar, and Meguid El Nahas

2007 Obesity and diabetes in the developing world—a growing challenge. New England Journal of Medicine 356(3):213–215.

Hu, F. B., R. M. van Dam, and S. Liu

2001 Diet and Risk of Type II Diabetes: The Role of Types of Fat and Carbohydrates. Diabetologia 44:805–817.

Hurtado, Magdalena, and Kim Hill

1990 Seasonality in a foraging society: Variation in diet, work effort, fertility and sexual division of labor among the Hiwi of Venezuela. Journal of Anthropological Research 46:293–236.

Huss-Ashmore, Rebecca, John J. Curry, and Robert Hitchock

1989 Coping with Seasonal Constraints. MASCA Research Papers in Science and Archaeology. Volume 5. Philadelphia: University of Pennsylvania.

Inda, Jonathan Xavier, and Rosaldo Renato

2007 The Anthropology of Globalization: A Reader. Oxford: Blackwell.

International Diabetes Federation

2005 The IDF Consensus Worldwide Definition of Metabolic Syndrome. Brussels, Belgium: International Diabetes Federation. http://www.idf.org/webdata/docs/metac_syndrome_def.pdf.

Irwin, Melinda, et al.

2002 Physical activity and the metabolic syndrome in a tri-ethnic sample of women. Obesity Research 10(10):1030–1037.

Kearney, Patricia, et al.

2005 Global Burden of Hypertension: Analysis of Worldwide Data. Lancet 365:212–23.

Kumanyika, Shiriki, et al.

1998 The international obesity task force: Its role in public health prevention. Appetite 31(3):426–428.

Laaksonen, D.E., et al.

2005 Physical Activity in the prevention of Type 2 Diabetes—The Finnish Diabetes Prevention Study. Diabetes 54(1):158–165.

———

2007 Increased physical activity is a cornerstone in the prevention of Type 2 Diabetes in high-risk individuals. Diabetologia 50(12):2607–2608.

LaDuke, Winona

2005 Recovering the Sacred: The Power of Naming and Claiming. Cambridge, MA: South End Press.

Latour, Bruno

2004 Politics of Nature: How to Bring the Sciences into Democracy. Cambridge, Mass.: Harvard University Press.

Lee, Richard

1968 What Hunters Do for a Living, or, How to make Out on Scarse Resources. In Man the Hunter. R. Lee and I. Devore, eds. Pp. 30–48. Chicago: Aldine Publishing Co.

Lindstrom, J., et al.

2003 Prevention of diabetes mellitus in subjects with impaired glucose tolerance in the Finnish Diabetes Prevention Study: Results from a randomized clinical trial. Journal of the American Society of Nephrology 14(7):S108–S113.

McEwen, Bruce S.

2007 Physiology and neurobiology of stress and adaptation: Central role of the brain. Physiological Review 87(3):873–904.

Neel, James V.

1962 Diabetes Mellitus: A "Thrifty" Genotype Rendered Detrimental by "Progress." American Journal of Human Genetics 14:353–362.

———

1982 The Thrifty Gene Revisited. In The Genetics of Diabetes Mellitus. J. Kobberling and J. Tattersall, eds. New York: Academic Press.

———

1999 The Thrifty Genotype in 1999. Nutrition Review 57:2–9.

Nishida, Chizuru, et al.

2004 The Joint WHO/FAO Expert Consultation on Diet, Nutrition and the Prevention of Chronic Diseases: Process, product and policy implications. Public Health Nutrition Feb;7(1A):245–250.

Papaspyros, Nick Spyros

1964 The History of Diabetes Mellitus. Stuttgart: Georg Thieme Verlag.

Pelizzon, Sheila

1994 The Grain Flour Commodity Chain, 1590–1790. In Commodity Chains and Global Capitalism. G. Gereffi and M. Korzeniewicz, eds. Pp. 34–47. Westport, Connecticut: Praeger.

Pelto, Gretel H., and Pertti J. Pelto

1983 Diet and delocalization—Dietary changes since 1750. Journal of Interdisciplinary History 14(2):507–528.

Popkin, Barry M.

2004 The nutrition transition: An overview of world patterns of change. Nutrition Reviews 62(7):S140–S143.

Popkin, Barry M., Susan Horton, and Soowon Kim

2001 The nutrition transition and prevention of diet-related diseases in Asia and the Pacific. Food and Nutrition Bulletin 22(4).

Popkin, Barry M., and Samara Joy Nielson

2003 The sweetening of the world's diet. Obesity Research 11(11):1325–1332.

Prentice, Andrew

2006 The emerging epidemic of obesity in developing nations. International Journal of Epidemiology 35:93–99.

Prior, I.A.M.

1971 The price of civilization. Nutrition Today 6:2–11.

———

1974 Diabetes in the South Pacific In Is the Risk of Becoming Diabetes Affected by Sugar Consumption? Eight International Sugar Research Symposium, Pp. 4–13.

Raikkonen, Katri, Karen Matthews, and Lewis Kuller

2007 Depressive symptoms and stressful life events predict metabolic syndrome among middle-aged women: A comparison of World Health Organization, Adult Treatment Panel III, and International Diabetes Foundation definitions. Diabetes Care 30(l0):2761–2761.

Reaven, Gerald

1988 Role of insulin resistance in human disease. Diabetes 37(1595–1607).

Reddy, K. Srinath

2002 Cardiovascular diseases in the developing countries: Dimensions, determinants, dynamics and directions for public health action. Public Health Nutrition 5(1A):231–238.

Reddy, K. Srinath, and Salim Yusaf

1998 Emerging epidemic of cardiovascular disease in developing countries. Circulation 97:596–601.

Remsberg, Karen, et al.

2007 Sex differences in young adulthood metabolic syndrome and physical activity: The Fels Longitudinal Study. American Journal of Human Biology 19:544–550.

Rennie, Kirsten, et al.

2003 Association of metabolic syndrome with both vigorous and moderate physical activity. International Journal of Epidemiology 32:600–606.

Robbins, Richard

2005 Global Problems and the Culture of Capitalism. Boston: Pearson Education.

Scheder, Jo C.

1988 A Sickly-Sweet Harvest: Farmworker Diabetes and Social (In)Equality. Medical Anthropology Quarterly 2(3):251–277.

Smith-Morris, Carolyn

2006 Diabetes among the Pima: Stories of Survival. Tuscon: University of Arizona Press.

Smith, Janell, Penelope Easton, Dennis Wiedman, Nancy Rody, Karl Hamrick, Elizebeth Nobmann, Emma Widmark, Diane Peck, Jennifer Cipra.

2004 Comparison of BMI and Body Fat Determinations in Rural Alaska Women: Results of the WIC Healthy Mom Survey, Summer 2001. Alaska Medicine 46(1):18–27.

Smith, Janell, Paulette Johnson, Penelope S. Easton, Dennis Wiedman, Ema Widmark.

2008 Food Customs of Alaska Women of Childbearing Age: The Alaska WIC Healthy Moms Survey. Ecology of Food and Nutrition 47:485–517.

Smith, Janell, Penelope Easton, Brian Saylor, Dennis Wiedman, and Jim LaBelle, Sr.

2009a Harvested Food Customs and their Influences on Valuable Functioning of Alaska Native Elders. Alaska Journal of Anthropology 7(1):101–121.

Smith, Janell, Brian Saylor, Penelope Easton, Dennis Wiedman and the Elders from the Alaska Villages of Buckland and Deering

2009b Measurable Benefits of Traditional Food Customs in the Lives of Rural and Urban Alaska Inupiaq Elders. Alaska Journal of Anthropology 7(l):89–99.

Smith, Janell, and Dennis Wiedman

2001 Fat Content of South Florida Indian Frybread: Health Implications for a Pervasive Native-American Food. Journal of the American Dietetic Association 101(5):582–585.

Stang, J., et al.

2005 Dietary intakes of nutrients thought to modify cardiovascular risk from three groups of American Indians: The Strong Heart Dietary Study, Phase II. Journal of the American Dietetic Association 105(12):1895–1903.

U.S. Department of Agriculture, Agriculture Research Service.

2006 What We Eat In America, NHANES 2003–2004: Documentation and Data Files.

Wallace, Anthony

1970 Culture and Personality. New York: Randon House.

Wang, Y., et al.

2007 Is China facing an obesity epidemic and the consequences? The trends in obesity and chronic disease. International Journal of Obesity 31:177–188.

Weber, Max

1958 The Protestant Ethic and the Spirit of Capitalism. New York: Scribner.

Weiss, Kenneth M., Robert E. Ferrell, and Craig L. Hanis

1984 A new world syndrome of metabolic diseases with a genetic and evolutionary basis. Yearbook of Physical Anthropology 27:153–178.

Welty, Thomas, et al.

2002 Changes in cardiovascular disease risk factors among American Indians. The Strong Heart Study. Annals of Epidemiology 12(2):97–106.

West, Kelly

1974 Diabetes in American Indians and other native populations of the new world. Diabetes 23:841–855.

———

1978 Epidemiology of Diabetes and Its Vascular Lesions. Holland: Elsevier.

WHO

2007 A Guide for Population-Based Approaches to Increasing Levels of Physical Activity: Implementation of the WHO Global Strategy on Diet, Physical Activity and Health. Geneva: World Health Organization.

Wiedman, Dennis

1979 Diabetes Mellitus and Oklahoma Native Americans; A Case Study of Culture Change in Oklahoma Cherokee. Ph.D. Dissertation, University of Oklahoma. Ann Arbor: University Microfilms International.

———

1987 Type II Diabetes Mellitus, Technological Development and the Oklahoma Cherokee. In Encounters in Biomedicine: Case Studies in Medical Anthropology. H. Baer, ed. New York: Gordon and Breach.

———

1989 Adiposity or longevity: Which factor accounts for the increase in Type II Diabetes Mellitus when populations acculturate to an industrial technology? Medical Anthropology 11(3):237–254.

———

2005 American Indian Diets and Nutritional Research: Implications of the Strong Heart Dietary Study, Phase II for Cardiovascular Disease and Diabetes. Journal of the American Dietetic Association 105(12):1874–1880.

Willett, W. C.
2002 Dietary Fat Plays a Major Role in Obesity: No. The International Association for the Study of Obesity. Obesity Reviews 3:59–68.

Wilmsen, Edwin N.
1978 Seasonal effects of dietary intake on Kalahari San, Federation Proceedings 37:65–72.

Wise, P.H., et al.
1970 Hyperglycaemia in the urbanized Aboriginal, Medical Journal of Australia 2:1001–1006.

Wolf, Eric R.
1982 Europe and the People Without History. Berkeley: University of California Press.

Yach, Derek, et al.
2004 The global burden of chronic diseases. Journal of the American Medical Association 291 (21):2616–2622.

Young, T. Kue
1988 Are subarctic Indians undergoing the epidemiological transition? Social Science & Medicine 26:659–671.

Young, T. Kue, Daniel Chateau, and Min Zhang
2002 Factor analysis of ethnic variation in the multiple metabolic (insulin resistance) syndrome in three Canadian populations. American Journal of Human Biology 14(5):649–658.

CRITICAL THINKING QUESTIONS

1. Discuss how agricultural policies and shareholder values have impacted people's health since the 1980s. Please use examples from the reading by Nestle and Nesheim. Define pertinent concepts when applicable.

2. What does Wiedman mean by *chronicities of modernity*?

3. What is *MetS*? How has it arisen over time? Identify one or more factors related to increases in metabolic disease and discuss. Please use examples from the article.

4. Think of your own experiences in the healthcare system and identify a structural problem. Describe the history of the problem. Are there any policies or laws that have affected the problem, for example? Who participates in the problem (e.g., doctors, patients, nurses, politicians, etc.)? What is their experience and how do they typically cope? What part of the healthcare structure can be changed to make conditions better? How?

The Practice of Medicine

··

Editor's Introduction

The purpose of unit V is to provide you with a snapshot of medical practices, including *both* Western and non-Western paradigms. Currently, in the United States and most other developed nations, medicine is divided into two camps: traditional Western medicine and complementary and alternative therapies. The titles of these categories are a bit nonsensical as many of the complementary and alternative therapies are much older (many by thousands of years) than traditional Western medicine and they arose complementary and alternative to nothing, since Western medicine is the new kid on the block. *These seemingly insignificant word choices are, however, reflections of power differentials for which the Western medical industry has studiously worked.* The readings in unit V illustrate norms and practices identifiable in both Western and non-Western forms of medicine.

In "Training for Efficiency: Work, Time, and Systems-Based Practice in Medical Residency," Julia E. Szymczak and Charles L. Bosk explore how the meaning and performance of *efficiency* in medical residency has changed since sociological studies of the 1950s to 1980s. While the residents in their study were responsible for about the same number of patients as residents of the earlier era, they are now expected to care for them in a shorter amount of time, in a crowded technological environment that is more highly controlled by formal organizational protocols (such as multiple documentations). The authors find that efficiency is very important to contemporary physician socialization, even though its practice leads to anxiety due to the unpredictability of people's health and healthcare settings. Szymczak and Bosk identify and discuss a variety of barriers to the attainment of efficiency, such as the poor interaction between multiple systems requiring attention and care.

This study of efficiency is reminiscent of a greater body of work on *McDonaldization* by George Ritzer.[1] Ritzer defines McDonaldization as "the process by which the principles of the fast-food restaurant are coming to dominate more and more sectors of American society as well as of the rest of the world." Ritzer identifies five major themes in the McDonalization process. The first of

---

1   George Ritzer, *The McDonaldization of Society: An Investigation into the Changing Character of Contemporary Social Life* (Thousand Oaks, CA: Pine Forge Press, 1996).

these is *efficiency*, or the choosing of means to minimize cost and effort in order to meet a particular goal, which in our case is health diagnosis and treatment. Second of the themes is *calculability*, or the emphasizing of things that can be calculated, counted, and quantified. The third theme is *predictability*, or the attempt to structure the environment so that nothing different encroaches on people's experience. The fourth theme is *a high level of control by substitution of non-human for human technology*. In healthcare, this means predetermined treatment modalities for every diagnosis, for example. Physicians wishing to explore options that fit patients' needs and wishes must fight insurance companies or simply forego presenting options to patients. Finally, the fifth theme in the McDonaldization process, which Ritzer refers to as "the irrationality of rationality," is perhaps the most poignant. Ritzer writes, "irrationality means that rational systems are unreasonable systems. By that I mean that they deny the basic humanity, the human reason, of the people who work within or are served by them."[2] In tying this them back to the article by Szymczak and Bosk, one of the most interesting findings is that residents do not experience themselves as a part of the system in which such high degrees of efficiency are demanded and, as a result, do little to fight the status quo.

In "Understanding Folk Medicine," Bonnie B. O'Connor and David J. Hufford illustrate folk medicines in broad strokes to show their commonalities and to debunk the myths that they are irrational, dangerous, and disorganized. O'Connor and Hufford propose that one of the reasons folk medicine is called *folk* relates to the power of the mainstream system to which folk medicine is compared. In the United States, mainstream Western medicine has much power. It is the only perspective taught in public schools; it is overwhelmingly predominant in the insurance industry; it is the basis of all health information; and it is the only medicine taught in medical school. Mainstream Western medicine typically responds to folk medicine in a number of ways. Doctors often point out that folk medicine is not scientific and suggest that this makes it dangerous to the public. Western medical practitioners have also suggested that patients are being fooled by the false promises of folk medicine practitioners. The American Medical Association (AMA) has undertaken educational campaigns to warn patients against folk medicines and has used its lobbying powers to restrict the legitimate use of folk medicine. Additionally, most Western medical practitioners refuse to work with folk practitioners. From the perspective of critical sociology, Western medical practitioners benefit from this because these strategies solidify their position in the culture and act to lessen competition for patients and for governmental and nongovernmental funding. O'Connor and Hufford respond to the various campaigns against folk medicine by suggesting that people are not so easily led and that if folk medicine did not have the capacity to bring health and well-being, no one would use it. Furthermore, they do a thorough job of describing the wonderful complexities and organization of folk medicines, laying out how folk medicines are "organized into complex and coherent systems of thought, action, and content." They touch on the common characteristics of folk medicine systems, disease and illness classifications, folk practitioners, common therapeutic practices, and their interactions with other systems of medicine.

---

2   Ritzer, *The McDonaldization of Society.*

In "Big and Little Moon Peyotism as Healthcare Delivery Systems," Dennis Wiedman takes us from the macro perspective of O'Connor and Hufford to the specific example of Cherokee in the Oklahoma Ozarks who practice Big and Little Moon Peyotism. Wiedman provides a history of the Cherokee in the region and their relationship to the peyote plant, considered sacred, and its use in two variations of a major religion and healing system practiced by Indigenous persons across the United States. Using ethnographic methods, Wiedman records the details of ceremonies in the two churches and every way health and healing is addressed by the ceremonies. Wiedman takes us through the political and legislative histories, as well as the cultural changes that built Big and Little Moon Peyotism at the time of his writing. Firmly establishing Big and, especially Little Moon Peyotism as healthcare delivery systems, he positions the healthcare system within the Cherokee Nation, within Native American tribes in North America, and in relation to other healthcare systems that the Cherokee use to maintain health.

Western and non-Western healthcare systems are complex and dynamic. Practitioners must be trained; the space in which healthcare takes place must be organized for the benefit of all; communications must be optimized; trust must be built between all parties, and so much more. These readings should give you a taste of that complexity and the richness of healthcare methods and organization across cultures.

Training for Efficiency

Work, Time, and Systems-Based Practice in Medical Residency

By Julia E. Szymczak and Charles L. Bosk

Abstract: Medical residency is a period of intense socialization with a heavy workload. Previous sociological studies have identified efficiency as a practical skill necessary for success. However, many contextual features of the training environment have undergone dramatic change since these studies were conducted. What are the consequences of these changes for the socialization of residents to time management and the development of a professional identity? Based on observations of and interviews with internal medicine residents at three training programs, we find that efficiency is both a social norm and strategy that residents employ to manage a workload for which the demand for work exceeds the supply of time available to accomplish it. We found that residents struggle to be efficient in the face of seemingly intractable "systems" problems. Residents work around these problems, and in doing so develop a tolerance for organizational vulnerabilities.

T he experience of medical education is arduous. During the years of formal training following medical school, young physicians, known as "residents," are primarily responsible for delivering care to patients in teaching hospitals. Both mass media presentations and the scholarly literature have identified residency as an exhausting experience (Mizrahi 1986; Shem 1978). Sociologists, interested in residency as socialization for a professional occupation, have explored the way residents cope with this experience and how that coping shapes professional identity (Bosk 1979; Bucher and Stelling 1977; Light 1980). One aspect of residents' shop floor culture described, but not typically the focal point of analysis, is efficiency.

Background
Efficiency and Time Management: Then

When efficiency is discussed in the literature on resident socialization, it is typically conceptualized in one of two ways. The first focuses on how trainees present information to peers, consultants, and senior physicians at rounds (Anspach 1988; Arluke 1980). Residents are socialized to be as efficient as possible in presenting a case—"a history should contain only those points deemed to be important,

Julia E. Szymczak and Charles L. Bosk, "Training for Efficiency: Work, Time, and Systems-Based Practice in Medical Residency," *Journal of Health and Social Behavior*, vol. 53, no. 3, pp. 344–358. Copyright © 2012 by SAGE Publications. Reprinted with permission.

with a minimum of wasted words" (Anspach 1988:362). This is also a theme in the literature on socialization in medical school. Students face an overwhelming amount of material to learn and must come to terms with incomplete mastery of medical knowledge (Fox 1957). They prioritize the knowledge that attending faculty need to hear in order to make treatment decisions and learn to present only that information and nothing more (Becker et al. 1961; Mumford 1970). Efficiency is an individual skill of self-presentation that trainees master to communicate effectively and signal competence.

Second, efficiency is conceptualized as a response to the stresses and strains of the residency experience. Residents attempt to control time both to retaliate against the brutal nature of their training and to maintain professional dominance (Freidson 1974; Light 1980). They metaphorically describe themselves as grunts in the trenches under combat conditions, doing battle against two enemies—patients and attending faculty (Mizrahi 1986). This portrayal of the residency experience, epitomized in the novel *The House of God* (Shem 1978), includes descriptions of residents "turfing" patients to other services, deflecting admissions, and doing as little as possible (Shem 1978). Efficiency in this conceptualization is a coping mechanism that embittered residents use to survive the training experience.

Dimensions of Change in American Health Care

Sociological studies of the professional socialization during residency primarily draw on data from the 1950s through the 1980s. Since these studies were conducted, the delivery of health care has changed radically (Fennell and Adams 2011). These changes have altered the socialization of residents, but their impact has been incompletely explored. A partial list of the factors that have changed the context for the delivery of inpatient care makes clear why an empirical revisiting and conceptual update of **medical socialization**, with a particular emphasis on time management and efficiency, are necessary.

First, the **discourse** surrounding, the modes of appraising, and the basic understanding of health care have shifted since the classic studies of medical socialization were conducted (Starr 1984). During this earlier era, academic health centers had abundant resources and experienced tremendous growth in income, size, and power (Ludmerer 1999).

The era of cost containment began in earnest in the mid-1980s with the introduction of Medicare's prospective payment system. To counter the threat to revenue posed by diagnosis-related groups (DRGs), lower reimbursement, and new restrictions on services, hospitals focused on increasing the volume of procedures they performed while decreasing patients' length of stay. Residents today are expected to see more hospitalized patients in less time and to discharge them faster than their predecessors (Edmond 2010). An early study comparing care before and after implementation of DRGs found a 24 percent reduction in length of inpatient stay (LOS), from 14.4 to 11 days between 1983 and 1986 (Kahn et al. 1990). In 2009, the average LOS in U.S. hospitals was 4.8 days (Hall et al. 2010).

Second, measures of efficiency, quality, and safety have become more managerial and subject to external oversight. Despite progress in treating acutely ill patients, unexpected deaths and complications remain a commonplace feature of hospital life (Landrigan et al. 2010). Residents still need to provide those supervising them with acceptable reasons for unacceptable outcomes. Mastering this skill has become more difficult as medical care has become more corporate and measures of quality and efficiency have become more objective and standardized. These measures exist at an organizational level: LOS, readmissions within 30 days, rates of hospital-acquired infections, number of serious safety events, and patient satisfaction. Efficiency is also measured at an individual level: rates of patients screened for certain cancers, compliance with duty-hour limits, and appropriate antibiotic prescribing behavior. Efficiency is now a major organizing principle of health care management and hospital administration.

Third, new regulations limit the amount of time residents are allowed to work. In 2003, the Accreditation Council for Graduate Medical Education (ACGME)[1] implemented a set of rules that limit the total amount of time residents can work per week (80 hours) and per shift (30 hours). Revised in July 2011, the regulations became more stringent, further reducing the number of consecutive hours that residents (particularly those in the first year) are permitted to work (Iglehart 2010). Residency programs that violate these rules risk losing their accreditation, which has important financial ramifications.[2] These rules have been controversial, and programs have struggled to adapt (Romano and Volpp 2012). Duty-hour limits represent a significant change in the context and organization of work for residents. While there are numerous surveys of resident and attending faculty perceptions of the impact of these regulations (i.e., Antiel et al. 2011), the literature describing how residents actually behave in response to them and how this response impacts professional socialization is scant (Kellogg 2009; Szymczak et al. 2010).

In this article, we explore how the meaning and enactment of efficiency in medical residency has changed since the sociological studies of the 1950s to 1980s. Through an analysis of ethnographic and interview data, we explore the work of internal medicine residents in three training programs and provide an examination of the meaning and enactment of "efficiency" on the shop floor of the hospital. Our data enable a "conceptual updating" (Glaser and Strauss 1967; Timmermans and Angell 2001) of earlier sociological studies of resident socialization toward time and its management by revisiting the typical site of previous studies of the socialization of residents: the hospital inpatient ward. Unlike other themes in the "training for" literature, we find that efficiency is not focused on mastering skills that are specific to being a physician (mastering uncertainty-riddled biomedical knowledge, the maintenance of professional dominance, the management of error, and the existential crisis of dealing with death); rather it is about learning to labor within a complex health care system.

Data and Methods

The qualitative data presented are part of a larger study on the influence of duty-hour regulations on residency programs. We conducted ethnographic observation and in-depth interviews with internal medicine residents affiliated with three training programs in the eastern United States. These data were collected intermittently over the course of two years (2008–2010, Table 5.1.1). The institutional review board (IRB) at all hospitals approved our study protocol.

Phase 1—Preliminary Data Collection at Franklin

We spent the majority of our time at Franklin, a large, elite residency program. The program takes three years to complete and residents participate in a number of different rotations and practice settings spread out over three hospitals. Our research team, comprising one professor of sociology (a project P.I.) and four graduate students, spent three months in the summer of 2008 observing residents as they went about their everyday work. We observed multiple teams of internal medicine residents as they provided care on a general medicine inpatient ward at the Franklin Veteran's Affairs (VA) hospital (10 weeks) and Franklin Hospital (three weeks).

Each team member spent approximately two weeks at a time shadowing individual residents on a team. We attempted to tie our observation period to scheduled shifts of target residents, focusing on daily work. We arrived at and left the hospital with them, saw patients, went to attending rounds, attended didactic conferences, observed procedures, and sat with them while they entered notes into computers. We observed their work on nights, weekends, and holidays, including spending the night at the hospital as part of their on-call responsibilities. We shadowed 12 internal medicine residents. Since residents work together in teams, we invariably spent time interacting frequently with other members of the team (typically a junior or senior resident, medical student, and attending physician).

We told residents we were interested in learning about the experience of their day-to-day work. As observers, we attempted to be as unobtrusive as possible but found that residents actively engaged with us. Each observer took jottings while observing and wrote fieldnotes at the end of each day, or as soon as possible given the constraints of scheduling. The research team met weekly to discuss ongoing data collection and emergent themes.

TABLE 5.1.1 Data Collection Strategy

	Franklin (Franklin and VA Hospitals)	Lark Hospital	Able Memorial Hospital
Observation period	June–August 2008 • Immersive observations at Franklin and VA Hospitals • January–May 2009 • 1 day/week observing at Franklin • November 2009 and April 2010 • 3 nights observing night float resident at VA and Franklin • May 2009 and 2010 • Observations at New Resident Orientation	December 2009 3 days of observation, 2 days of interviews	June 2010 3 days of observation, 2 days of interviews
Number of interviews conducted (with whom, year in program)	10 Residents: 7 Interns 2 Senior residents 1 Chief residents	20 Residents: 8 Interns[a] 10 Senior residents[a] 2 Chief residents	5 Residents: 3 Interns 2 Chief residents
Number of beds	Franklin Hospital-776 beds; large academic medical center; VA Hospital-145 beds	331 beds; small community hospital	665 beds; midsize, regional referral center

a. Focus group.

Using a semi-structured format that grew inductively from observations, we conducted indepth interviews with 10 Franklin residents in early Fall 2008. We conducted the interviews after we finished our summer observations, which allowed us to ask more nuanced questions and to reflect on specific events we observed. Interviews ranged in length from one to three hours.

Phase 2—Additional Data Collection at Franklin, Site Visits at Lark and Able Memorial

After the initial round of data collection we sought to validate our findings by expanding the range of our observations. To do this we continued our observations of residents in the Franklin program at different times during the year (Table 5.1.1). We also selected two additional residency programs in the vicinity of Franklin—Lark and Able Memorial Hospital—that differed in size and structure. We visited each program for one week. During these site visits, our research team spent three days observing internal medicine residents as they worked on a general medicine inpatient ward. We also spent two days conducting in-depth interviews with residents.

Scheduling interviews was challenging. At Lark, for example, we decided that for scheduling purposes we would conduct two focus groups, one with junior and senior residents and one with interns, instead of interviews. The program administration at Lark was receptive to our project and facilitated the scheduling of the focus groups. We encountered more resistance from Able Memorial and correspondingly had a much lower rate of participation. Although the time spent at these two additional sites was limited and the number of residents interviewed was not large, we feel that exposure to programs different from Franklin's allows us to explore potential sources of variation and the prevalence of an emphasis on efficiency.

Data Analysis

All interviews were digitally recorded and transcribed. Fieldnotes and interview transcripts were uploaded to QSR's NVivo 8 qualitative data analysis software. Analysis was largely inductive. We approached the data with an interest in resident norms about work, time, and efficiency that informed the creation of code categories. The first author coded the documents and reviewed evolving themes in meetings and memos with the second author. All names used here are pseudonyms.

Results

Organization of Work for Residents—General Medicine Inpatient Services at Three Hospitals

The daily schedules for residents at Franklin, Lark, and Able Memorial largely depend on their year in the program, hospital, and rotation, but include a mix of patient care and formal didactics. The labor of patient care involves all of the work that must be done when patients are admitted to the hospital: taking a history and performing a physical exam, formulating a diagnosis, coming up with a treatment plan, putting in medical orders (blood work, laboratory tests, imaging studies, administration of medication, dietary needs, physical therapy, etc.), doing procedures (lumbar puncture, placing a central line, etc.), and writing notes that document all of the aforementioned for the medical record. Residents work together in teams to provide patient care. First-year residents, known as interns, have the most intense schedule and shoulder the largest share of the labor. They are supervised by a senior (second- or third-year) resident and confer with the attending physician at rounds each day and occasionally by phone or in informal interactions throughout the day.

The workflow at each program depends on how new patient admissions are assigned to residents. The flow at the Franklin program is different from that at Lark and Able Memorial because of the way the schedule is organized (Tables 5.1.2 and 5.1.3).

At Franklin, new admissions are assigned to residents every fourth day, when their teams are "on call." A team is made up of one senior resident, two interns, and two medical students. The interns accept primary responsibility for the team's patients while the senior resident supervises, assists with tasks as needed, and conducts informal teaching. At the time of our observations, each intern was permitted to carry up to 12 patients at a time, for a cap of 24 per team.[3] During their "call day," teams admit new patients up to 9:30 pm or until they reach 24 total patients. These patients become the intern's primary responsibility, as are the still hospitalized patients admitted from prior calls. The senior resident stays at the hospital until 10:00 pm, at which point the interns provide care for the team's patients overnight.

TABLE 5.1.2 Intern Work Week—Q4 Call System at Franklin, 2008

Day 1	Day 2	Day 3	Day 4	Day 5	Day 6	Day 7
On call; receives new admissions until 9:30 pm	Post-call; leaves hospital by 1:00 pm	7:00 am to 6:00 pm; manage patients	7:00 am to 6:00 pm; manage patients	On call; receives new admissions until 9:30 pm	Post-call; leaves hospital by 1:00 pm	Day off (1 day off every 7 days averaged over a rotation)

TABLE 5.1.3 Intern Work Week—No Overnight Call System at Lark and Able Memorial Hospital, 2009–2010

Day 1	Day 2	Day 3	Day 4	Day 5	Day 6	Day 7
7:00 am to 6:00 pm; manage patients and get new admissions (the same through Day 6)	7:00 am to 6:00 pm	7:00 am to 6:00 pm	7:00 am to 6:00 pm	7:00 am to 6:00 pm	7:00 am to 6:00 pm	Day off (1 day off every 7 days averaged over a rotation)

As a result of duty-hour regulations, the program has implemented a "night float" system. The night float resident comes to the hospital in the evening and is responsible for admitting patients that arrive between 9:30 pm and 8:00 am. Interns "inherit" the patient that the night float admitted and become responsible for their care. To comply with duty-hour regulations, interns are required to leave the hospital by 1:00 pm on their "post call" day. Their senior resident provides care for the team's patients after 1:00 pm.

In addition to admitting new patients, interns, while on call, are responsible for "cross coverage." When cross covering, residents are responsible not only for their patients but also the patients of the other residents rotating on their service. For example, on the general medicine ward at Franklin VA, there are four teams of residents caring for patients. Each night, three of the teams go home and "hand off" or "sign out" the responsibility for their patients to the on-call team. Each intern becomes responsible for up to 30 "cross-cover" patients in addition to their mix of newly and previously admitted patients. When on call, interns cover as many as 40 patients.

Lark and Able Memorial have a similar structure and schedule with the exception of overnight call. Teams are made up of one senior resident, one intern, and two medical students. Residents do not take overnight calls. Teams can get newly admitted patients at any time during their workday (7:00 am to 5:00/6:00 pm). At Able Memorial, interns are paged when a new patient comes in and go to the emergency department to perform the initial admission examination. At Lark, teams do not perform the initial admission examination. Instead, there is a senior resident (known as the 4555 resident because of their pager number) who works in the emergency room performing the admission work-up and assigning patients to teams on the general medical floor. At both programs there is a dedicated team of night float residents who accept admissions and cross cover overnight.

Cross coverage is a major part of the organization of work at all three programs. The transfer of responsibility for a patient marks the beginning and end of each workday. Residents "sign out," communicating information necessary for care of patients to the team assuming responsibility. The formal transfer of responsibility for patients between teams or to a night float is a major change in the social organization of work since the classic studies of resident socialization (Miller 1970). Today's residents must leave the hospital at a certain time and are faced with the challenge of knowing what work to hand over and how to communicate it. This feature of the training environment structures how residents understand and enact efficiency.

The Nature of Time

The residents we observed and interviewed at all three programs felt overwhelmed with their workload and did not feel that time was something they could control. That residents are overwhelmed does not represent a change in the experience of training. What has changed is the pace of work. The residents in our study were responsible for approximately the same number of patients as residents of an earlier era—12 to 14—yet are expected to care for them in a shorter amount of time in a crowded technological environment that is more tightly controlled by formal organizational protocols (see Note 3). The interaction of these factors makes the workday feel frenzied and unpredictable for residents. For example, here is an excerpt from our Lark Hospital fieldnotes:

> It is 2:53 pm and we are rounding with the team. Sally (second year) gets a page, groans and says "it's 4555." She finds a phone to return the page. When it becomes clear that the team is going to get a new admission the attending Dr. D says to me "this is a major new source of stress for residents. The workload is so intense and the unpredictability and uncertainty of the admissions system makes planning work and carrying it out very challenging. It wasn't like this when I was training—we were at least protected from admissions some of the time."

The nature of work on an inpatient general medicine ward makes it very hard to transition from what a resident is doing at one moment to something completely different at the next, especially if it is nonemergent and unrelated to patient care. This includes attending morning report, arriving at rounds on time, eating, using the bathroom, and leaving the hospital on time. For example, these Franklin residents struggled with leaving even though they knew that not doing so by 1:00 pm violated duty-hour rules:

> I'm at the bay with Sarah [second year resident] and Peter [first year]. It is 2:00 pm. They are working on getting their sign-outs in order so they can go home. Sarah is on the phone with someone who asks her if she is still at work "I'm trying not to be here, but yes, I'm here."

To cope with the unpredictable workflow, accomplish required tasks, and comply with the constraints imposed by duty-hour regulations, residents prioritize efficiency.

Training for Efficiency

In what follows we describe aspects of a culture of efficiency that we observed in three residency programs. We did not observe variation in an overarching emphasis on efficiency or in its operational definition: the ability to prioritize, to anticipate problems, and to take action in order to accomplish tasks. While it is possible that this lack of variation is due to the limitations of our data, we believe it is more likely that efficiency is a group norm. The residents we observed exhibited a strong peer and group orientation. Being efficient in residency is no longer simply an individual skill of self-presentation whose mastery signals one's competence. We observed a considerable degree of cooperation among residents in all three programs around managing work.

That physicians in training exhibit a group orientation toward work is not a new finding—Becker et al. (1961) describe the importance in medical school of making sure that any one student does not increase the workload that all must bear and of avoiding being seen as "goldbricking." Both Miller

(1970) and Mizrahi (1986:89) describe "sloughing behavior, that is sloppy or lazy management of patients ... so that it [becomes] the responsibility of another fellow house officer to complete or rectify" as "an imposition on a colleague and, as such, an unforgivable social sin."

What conflict we did observe among residents around workload was unrelated to sloughing behavior. Instead, spending too much time with patients or taking too much time to accomplish tasks became an issue for contestation. An example from our Franklin fieldnotes stands out:

> Around noon, in the resident workroom: a senior resident, Beth, asks her intern Matt if he has finished his work. He says, "Yes, I'm done, just working on these discharge instructions." Beth says, "You need to leave if you are ready to sign out. You are post call. I can take over for you." Matt protests, "I'm almost done, I can finish!" Beth, her voice raised, says, "You need to learn to LET GO!"

We observed that a major topic of the teaching and practical wisdom passed down from resident to intern concerned the style in which they should work. Residents were critical of interns when they spent too much time with patients:

> Peter, a Franklin intern, is seeing his patients. After we finish, the husband of a patient approaches him and says that his wife cannot swallow her potassium pill. He asks Peter to consult the pharmacy to explore how she can get her potassium in a more tolerable formula. We are interrupted by a call from Sarah, Peter's senior resident, who tells him to come up to the ninth floor immediately. Assuming an emergency, Peter excuses himself and we run upstairs. We find Sarah casually leaning against the bay; there is no emergency. She tells Peter that the urgent call was a ruse. She heard he was "being tortured" by the husband of Mrs. X. She tells Peter that he is "too empathic" and to increase his efficiency he can't spend time dealing with every little complaint.

Sarah's criticism of Peter for being "too empathic" is reminiscent of the process involved in "training for detached concern" (Fox 1988; Lief and Fox 1963) except that now emotional detachment is a tool of efficiency—being emotionally invested in a patient takes too much time.

While we did observe that residents tried to avoid spending too much time with patients and families, they did not adopt an oppositional, angry attitude like Mizrahi's (1986) residents. One Franklin senior resident reflected on the challenges of reprimanding a junior colleague who spent too much time working:

> I had this intern, an excellent physician ... he could be my doctor any day. He would break duty hours left and right and I was his senior resident, so I was freaking out, because I'm

always trying to get people home at noon ... he'd be two hours over. But what was he doing? He was calling their primary care doctors, making sure they knew what happened to their patient ... he would call the family members, the kind of things that people want doctors to do for them, he did them all. ... This was not a lazy person who was wasting time ... I had to speak to [program director] about it and I said "people call him inefficient. It's really because he is doing what we all should be doing but there was not time to do it."

Throughout the summer at Franklin we observed new interns struggle with the tension between needing to be efficient and wanting to be thorough.

We also observed residents reflecting on their own performance in terms of how efficiently they worked. Much of this reflection took on a self-critical tone. We observed the following at Lark Hospital:

We are sitting in the resident workroom at a bank of computers. Sally, the second year resident that I am shadowing, says out loud and unprompted as she types notes in the computer, "I find it hard to step back as a second year. I feel like I am a better intern than second year" (note: it is six months into Sally's junior year). Her intern, Neil laughs and says, "that is because you are too thorough." Sally continues, "I guess I have a hard time letting go. ..." She says that in the second year she should be focusing on "stepping back" and thinking about patient problems from a level above day-to-day management. She says, "I am worried that by focusing so much on the details of the everyday I might be missing the forest for the trees."

Much of Sally's self-evaluation reflects on the operational meaning of efficiency, which we found to have greater social salience than previous studies of medical residents suggested.

Being Efficient

Residents have a more nuanced understanding of what it means to be efficient than simply providing a concise patient presentation at rounds or turfing patients to other services. During interviews, we probed residents for their operational definitions of efficiency. For our informants, efficiency involves prioritization, the anticipation of problems, and taking action to accomplish tasks. Residents identify the ability to prioritize the always multiple and competing demands on their time as a key part of being efficient. A Franklin chief resident explains:

There are so many competing tasks in a limited amount of time, that when we say efficiency what we mean, or what we often take as a surrogate of that is prioritization and so, if you address every task and every call and every page equally you could get nothing done. So efficiency is being able to say, "This is important now, I finish this now. This is a sick patient I need to deal with now. Taking the social history on this patient and finishing the note can take the back burner." So, it's the ability to dispense your time, which is limited, appropriately. ... If you don't prioritize and you don't give more time to more important things and less time to less important things then you'll never get anything done.

One third-year Franklin resident reflects on the meaning of efficiency:

You start realizing that what efficiency is, is making sure you pay the right amount of attention for the right degree of severity ... learning the sick versus not sick. And knowing who you really have to pay attention to, or red flags, or warning signs.

This explanation highlights the other component of efficiency that a resident is required to master: anticipation.

We observed that much of the informal teaching surrounding the pathophysiology of hospitalized patients is concerned with predicting and preventing emergent situations. One Franklin senior resident impresses the following on her two interns during an informal lesson late one night on call:

She stresses the importance of paying attention to urine and fecal retention. Patients who are unable to urinate become a "major problem and quickly." She recounts a story of a patient who couldn't urinate for 30+ hours. The nursing staff couldn't get a foley (catheter) in him and he started to crump (become acutely unwell). Eventually, they had to call a urologist who performed a surgical procedure. She says that the patient recovered completely after he was able to void and that urine retention, a common cause of crumping, is to be avoided.

We observed that residents communicate the importance of anticipation by using various code words. The phrase "to crump" signals rapid deterioration in a patient (Coombs et al. 1993). Residents at all three programs discussed "sick" versus "not sick" patients. When we first heard this term used in the context of a routine sign out ("Is anybody on your list sick?" was a common question asked by the resident coming on duty), we were confused. Wasn't everyone in the hospital sick? We came to learn that "sick" was a code word for "might crump any minute." A "sick" patient became an object of heightened attention and concern. "Sick" is a linguistic red flag that allows residents to anticipate and prioritize tasks in the face of limited time.

Residents found resuscitation situations highly stressful and attempted to stave them off by keeping attuned to subtle changes in a "sick" patient's vital signs and proactively managing cardiopulmonary distress, or by being alert to signs that an otherwise stable patient might "crump." Avoiding emergent situations has become an important external quality metric. "Failure to rescue" patients with unexpected clinical deterioration is receiving increased attention as a measure of the quality of inpatient care (Silber et al. 2007). During our time observing at Lark hospital, a young patient with sickle cell disease developed worsening acute chest syndrome overnight that remained unidentified until he went into cardiopulmonary arrest. He was successfully transferred to the ICU and survived.

This incident occurred on the first day, and sense-making (Weick, Sutcliffe, and Obstfeld 2005) around this event reverberated through our time there. Sally, the junior resident caring for the patient, was especially distraught. From our fieldnotes:

> Sally and her attending, Dr. D, talk about what happened. Sally says she feels very badly about what happened and that it is her fault. Dr. D reassures her that she did everything that she could. Dr. D asks Sally how she signed out the patient with sickle cell disease to the night float. She asks, "Did you use the word 'sick' to describe him? Because sometimes that alerts the person getting sign out to pay extra close attention to the patient." Sally says, "Well, I didn't really think he was sick last night. He had been noncompliant with his oxygen all day so I assumed his breathing trouble was related to that." She tells Dr. D that the only thing she signed out on this patient was that if he were to develop a fever the night float should do a pan culture. She says she ordered a chest X-ray before she left and put it on the list of things to do overnight, but she didn't stress it. The night float did not follow up on the results overnight, as the patient got progressively worse.

Being efficient is both a social norm and a strategy that residents employ to cope with a workload whose accomplishment in the time allotted is uncertain.

Systemic Threats to Efficiency

When coding our fieldnotes we found that residents at each of the three programs would use the term "systems problem" to explain why they have difficulty being efficient. From our analysis of those utterances we found that "the system" is a catchall term that encompasses a variety of features of organizational life. Instead of developing an oppositional attitude to patients (Mizrahi 1986), residents conceptualize "the system" as an entity that works against them in their efforts to prioritize and anticipate. Through an analysis of those places where the system caused problems for residents and how they handled them, we can see how physicians in training are socialized to think about the pressures of working in a complex organization and how system problems become accepted, taken for granted, and seen as par for the course in the provision of care (Dixon-Woods 2010; Waring 2007).

People are components of the system—the consultant physician who takes hours to call back, the nurse who does not record vital signs consistently, or the social worker who refuses to put in a request for a patient to be discharged to a nursing home—threaten efficiency. Technology is also part of the system—the unfamiliar blood pressure machine whose operation is opaque, the broken electronic informed consent machines that delay completion of procedures, and the printer that will not print sign out sheets, delaying a timely exit—all of these frustrate residents' best efforts to act efficiently.

New communication technologies like cell phones are a feature of the system that challenges the enactment of efficiency (even though they are often heralded as efficiency promoting; Wu et al. 2010). Residents at Franklin and Able Memorial carry program-issued cell phones that they are required to answer regardless of what they are doing. Administrative rules prohibit residents from setting up voicemail accounts.

During our observations at Franklin and Able Memorial, cell phones rang constantly. They interrupted formal didactics; attending rounds; physical exams; procedures; conversations with patients, their families, nurses, and ancillary staff; sign outs; and casual conversations between residents. For example, the Franklin program has an educational conference for residents from noon to 1:00 pm three times a week. When we observed at these conferences, we noted each time any attendee's phone rang. We attended 19 noon conferences and observed an average of 10 phone calls per conference, with a high of 20 and a low of 6. In one report, the same intern was called 6 times. A similar event was observed at Able Memorial when the resident we were shadowing was called out of a small lecture on diabetic ketoacidosis nine times. These data are not systematic and we cannot say for sure how generalizable they are. However, it is instructive to compare the frequency of phone calls we observed to the average frequency of pages per hour found in a 1988 study of internal medicine residents: one (Katz and Schroeder 1988).

Handoffs were also very vulnerable to being interrupted by cell phone calls, as this Franklin fieldnote suggests:

> I am in the tiny call room with Jen, an intern. She is on call and getting sign-out from Alice, an intern. We sit on the bottom bunk bed as Alice briefs us on the patients and the things that need to get done. As Alice is talking she is interrupted by three phone calls. The first from her senior resident with a question, the second from a nurse wanting an order put in (which Alice does quickly on the computer in the room, "before I forget"), and the third from the ophthalmology fellow following up on one of her patients. The fellow wants Alice to order intravitreal antibiotics [medication injected directly into the eye] and he wants them "STAT to the bedside." Alice hangs up and rolls her eyes sarcastically, "what a perfect call. STAT intravitreous antibiotics. The pharmacy is totally going to get on my case about this." She tells Jen she will be back to finish up the handoff later, because she has to go manage this situation. She does eventually complete the handoff about an hour later.

Hospital handoffs have received steadily increasing regulatory and research attention in the past five years (Cohen and Hilligoss 2010). There is a push to standardize handoffs to reduce the likelihood of non- or miscommunication of patient data (Starmer et al. 2012). Our observations suggest that future research and policymaking should take into account the vulnerabilities that arise due to the environment in which the handoff occurs.

Franklin and Able Memorial residents had mixed opinions about cell phones. Some liked that they cut down on the "phone tag" required by pagers, while others felt that they interfered with prioritization and anticipation. The presence of cell phones encouraged the nesting of tasks within time, as the previous fieldnote excerpt illustrates. Nesting occurred when a resident working on a task was interrupted by a cell phone call requesting her to do another task, which she must decide to attend to at that moment or at a later point. Tasks accumulate over time. Nesting contributes to the intensity of the workload and is a major threat to efficiency because keeping situational and attentional focus becomes problematic as the number of tasks multiplies. Nesting is not merely a matter of interruption, it is also a matter of tasks that require different levels of attention and action arising rapidly and unexpectedly.

The spatial and socio-temporal rhythms of the hospital as a complex organization are another barrier to the efficiency that residents strive to achieve. Examples that we observed include: the code call that demands an immediate response, received while seeing patients in another building three blocks away that cannot be reached by the normal route because access is blocked by new construction; the STAT CT scan that cannot be ordered on a holiday weekend; or the phlebotomy team that refuses to draw blood on a patient if called after 4:30 pm, even though they are supposed to be on call until 5:00 pm.

Residents at both Lark and Able Memorial identified the way the hospital assigned new admissions to teams (Table 5.1.3) and the night float cross coverage model as problematic aspects of "the system." These challenges, all of which we observed or were told were a "systems problem," highlight why residents often express uncertainty about whether they are able to achieve what is expected of them in the time required. The residents in our study still train for uncertainty (Fox 1957), but the uncertainty that they must learn to manage primarily arises from the process of moving patients through a fragmented and complex health care system, rather than from epistemic quandaries.

The poor meshing of multiple interacting systems has been identified as a major contributor to medical error in the human factors approach to improving patient safety (Peters and Peters 2007). Systems discourse is the main way hospital policies concerning adverse events are organized and communicated. Residents in our study use systems language to describe the problems that come from working in a complex health care organization, as well as for making sense of specific incidents (Waring 2007). Tom, an intern, describes the challenges of working efficiently at Franklin:

> I think it's mainly in the hospital settings that knowing who to call is the big issue for my efficiency. I don't know all the right numbers to call. I don't know who's the right person to contact if I need to get something done. I still struggle with that because ... I'm not sure why I still struggle with it. I've been there for a while now. But I think this hospital is so big

and it's such a lumbering beast … there's so many people making decisions that it's hard to figure out who to call. *That's a systems problem and not an intern problem.*

By suggesting that his confusion over whom to call is a systems problem and not an intern problem, Tom locates interns outside of and against "the system."

This kind of oppositional thinking toward the challenges posed by the system permeates the culture of efficiency we observed. The latent message here is that while physicians must work within the system, they are not a part of it. As a result, residents do not feel responsible for enacting change within the system. Instead, they attempt to maneuver within the constraints that the system presents.

Linda, a Franklin medical student, expressed the futility of trying to change the system during a discussion of a near miss on rounds: "As an individual you feel very futile with these system level errors. I'm only here for a few weeks, what can I do?" This feature of the residency experience encourages the development of a "learned tolerance" of systems problems that leads to the acceptance of adverse events as normal, natural troubles of providing inpatient care (Dixon-Woods et al. 2009; Waring 2007).

In order to cope with systemic threats to efficiency, residents learn to master workarounds to problems caused by "the system." A basic example from our Franklin fieldnotes concerns the acquisition of supplies for a patient:

> I see Nate (an intern) come into the resident room with two opened packages of chux (absorbent pads), which he puts in his locker. He says, "I'm stealing these for one of my patients who needs them." Anne (an intern), who is sitting at a computer, says "you know you can go through outpatient meds for that." Nate says "yeah, but I'm not going to go through that."

In this case "going through that" involves logging on to a computer to place a formal order; for Nate, pilfering from the supply room takes less time and ensures the chux are available when needed.

Other workarounds concerned the problems encountered when trying to communicate with consultants from other departments. Residents employed a number of strategies to get consultants to call back more quickly:

> I am sitting in the workroom with Lana, an intern and Eric, her senior resident. Lana has been on hold for 10 minutes. She needs to get a cardiology consult to prescribe one of her patients a specific medication. She is having a hard time getting a return call and needs an answer sooner rather than later. Eric tells her to ask them to write a quick note authorizing the medication. He explains that this will get them down here faster because they won't write the note without doing the consult. Lana says "oh, clever!"

While these workarounds on the surface seem to be shortcuts that residents take to get their work done, we argue instead that they represent teachable moments in which lessons about accountability, the feasibility of system improvement, and professional identity are imparted.

Discussion

In this ethnographic study of internal medicine residents from three different training programs, we find that a "training for efficiency" (TFE) ethos is the predominant value organizing the professional and occupational culture of residency. The TFE ethos, unlike other themes in the "training for" literature, is not focused on mastering skills that are specific to being a physician (mastering uncertainty-riddled biomedical knowledge, the maintenance of professional dominance, the management of error, and the existential crisis of dealing with death); rather it is about learning to labor within a complex health care system. While the mastery of these skills remains important, they become manifest within the context of systems challenges that make efficiency a primary emphasis in displaying competence. For example, while the residents in our study still needed to come to terms with the inherent uncertainty of biomedical knowledge and impossibility of learning everything, both concerns blended into the background of our observations. In those instances where residents were unsure about what dosage of a medication to order or how to manage a clinical problem, they would reference UpToDate, an online clinical decision support system. Technology has partially mitigated the stress of epistemic uncertainty. These earlier identified dynamics are not absent from the current socialization experience of residents; rather, they manifest in new and different ways because the context of providing inpatient care has changed. This analysis is an effort to update these concepts so our understanding of medical socialization is better aligned with the changed context of inpatient hospital care.

We illustrate how the meaning of efficiency has changed since the classic studies of resident socialization. While efficiency has always been an important part of resident performance, it has gained greater social salience. The dramatic changes to the delivery of inpatient hospital care in the United States in the past 20 years have in all likelihood played a role in the redefinition of efficiency. In previous sociological literature, efficiency was conceptualized on an individual level. We illustrate that efficiency has evolved into a group norm that residents use to critique themselves and others about the style in which they should work. We also show that efficiency entails a set of cognitive and interactional skills—prioritization and anticipation—that are necessary to overcome the challenges of providing care in a complex organization with a limited amount of time.

There is a theme in much of the sociological literature on resident socialization that depicts residents developing antagonistic feelings toward certain patients because they are challenging to deal with and symbolize the absurdity of many aspects of hospital care (Mizrahi 1986). In our study, we did not find that residents held antagonistic feelings toward patients and instead depicted themselves primarily in opposition to "the system." "Systems" constraints pose the biggest threat to efficiency that are outside residents' control. Residents direct their resentment to a complex set of demands that are embedded in an opaque system and respond to these barriers to efficiency by working around them. Workarounds may well have negative unintended consequences. Things get dropped in the space between the formal and informal ways of doing things (Dixon-Woods et al. 2009). Clean supplies stored in a locker, not in the always-locked-and-difficult-to-access sterile central processing unit, could become contaminated and lead to a hospital-acquired infection (HAI).

When residents employ workarounds to deal with "systems issues," no matter how small, they implicitly accept problems in the way that care is delivered. Implicit acceptance of these problems encourages complacency about vulnerabilities in the provision of hospital care that may have serious consequences for patient safety. As hospitals look to apply principles of high reliability organizing to improve patient safety and quality, it is worthwhile to consider the way physicians in training are socialized to think about the barriers to providing patient care in complex health care organizations (Hines et al. 2008).

A tolerance of "systems issues" also has implications for the professional identity of young physicians and their orientation toward efforts at organizational change in their future practice. Many hospitals in the United States are actively engaged in improvement work to make the care they provide safer and of higher quality. For example, there is a national push to reduce the rates of HAI through the implementation of basic infection prevention practices. Although simple, these changed practices require considerable engagement, commitment, and buy-in from frontline clinical staff (Dixon-Woods et al. 2011). The literature on quality improvement in health care documents how difficult it is to obtain this engagement from physicians (Taitz, Lee, and Sequist 2011). Our findings suggest that the explanation for physician resistance to quality improvement work may not only be a function of the fact that they feel they do not have enough time. The ways that young physicians are socialized into medical culture in complex health care organizations influence the way they define their responsibility for change.

Our study has limitations. The primary drawbacks include a short amount of time in the field at two of the program sites and limited interview sample size. Although we only spent a short amount of time at Lark and Able Memorial, we felt confident that we developed a thorough sense of the way residents approached and thought of their workflow. We were able to ask more focused questions to refine the themes we had found at Franklin and to determine if the emphasis on efficiency was a product of Franklin's elite status or the size of its hospital and complexity of patients. In our extended time observing at Franklin, we made an effort to search for negative cases and checked back to see if the interns we had shadowed in the summer had developed any new ways of understanding efficiency. Another limitation of our study is a limited interview sample size. Our close relationships with many of the respondents from Franklin and from those residents at Lark and Able Memorial that we shadowed during our three-day period encouraged open and honest conversation in the interviews and focus groups.

Despite these limitations, our data provide important insight into the way medical residents are socialized to think about work, time, and efficiency in hospital settings in which reduced costs, improved efficiency, and greater safety are all organizational goals. More work is needed in other settings and across specialties to assess the extent of the TFE ethos, describe its forms in a broader range of health care institutions, and clarify how specific regulations shape physician socialization.

Funding

The authors disclosed receipt of the following financial support for the research, authorship, and/or publication of this article: This study was supported by the U.S. Department of Veterans Affairs, Veterans Health Administration, Office of Research and Development grant SHP 08-178 and the National Heart, Lung and Blood Institute grant 5R01HL094593-03. Charles L. Bosk received additional support from a Robert Wood Johnson Health Investigator Award.

Notes

1. The Accreditation Council for Graduate Medical Education (ACGME) is a national organization responsible for the accreditation of post-MD medical training programs in the United States.

2. Medicare provides approximately $9.5 billion a year in support for accredited residency programs (Association of American Medical Colleges 2011).

3. The 2011 revisions to duty-hour regulations reduced the cap for interns to 10 patients.

References

Anspach, Renee R. 1988. "Notes on the Sociology of Medical Discourse: The Language of Case Presentation." *Journal of Health and Social Behavior* 29:357–75.

Antiel, Ryan M., Scott M. Thompson, Frederic W. Hafferty, Katherine M. James, Jon C. Tilburt, Michael P. Bannon, Philip R. Fischer, David R. Farley, and Darcy A. Reed. 2011. "Duty Hour Recommendations and the Implications for Meeting the ACGME Core Competencies: Views of Residency Directors." *Mayo Clinic Proceedings* 86:185–91.

Arluke, Arnold. 1980. "Roundsmanship: Inherent Control on a Medical Teaching Ward." *Social Science and Medicine* 14:297–302.

Association of American Medical Colleges. 2011. "What Does Medicare Have to Do with Graduate Education?" Washington, DC: Association of American Medical Colleges. Retrieved January 26, 2012 (https://www.aamc.org/initiatives/gmefunding/factsheets/253372/medicare-gme.html).

Becker, Howard S., Blanche Geer, Everett C. Hughes, and Anselm L. Strauss. 1961. *Boys in White: Student Culture in Medical School.* Chicago, IL: The University of Chicago Press.

Bosk, Charles L. 1979. *Forgive and Remember: Managing Medical Failure.* Chicago, IL: The University of Chicago Press.

Bucher, Rue and Joan Stelling. 1977. *Becoming Professionals.* Beverly Hills, CA: Sage.

Cohen, Michael D. and P. Brian Hilligoss. 2010. "The Published Literature on Handoffs in Hospitals: Deficiencies Identified in an Extensive Review." *Quality and Safety in Healthcare* 19:493–97.

Coombs, Robert H., Sangeeta Chopra, Debra R. Schenk, and Elaine Yutan. 1993. "Medical Slang and Its Functions." *Social Science and Medicine* 36:987–98.

Dixon-Woods, Mary. 2010. "Why Is Patient Safety So Hard?" *Journal of Health Services Research and Policy* 15(suppl):11–16.

Dixon-Woods, Mary, Charles L. Bosk, Emma L. Aveling, Christine A. Goeschel, and Peter J. Pronovost. 2011. "Explaining Michigan: Developing an Ex Post Theory of a Quality Improvement Program." *The Milbank Quarterly* 89:167–205.

Dixon-Woods, Mary, Anu Suokas, Emma Pitchforth, and Carolyn Tarrant. 2009. "An Ethnographic Study of Classifying and Accounting for Risk at the Sharp End of Medical Wards." *Social Science and Medicine* 69:362–69.

Edmond, Michael B. 2010. "Taylorized Medicine." *Annals of Internal Medicine* 153:845–46.

Fennell, Mary L. and Crystal M. Adams. 2011. "U.S. Health-Care Organizations: Complexity, Turbulence, and Multilevel Change." *Annual Review of Sociology* 37:205–19.

Fox, Renée C. 1957. "Training for Uncertainty" Pp. 207–41 in *The Student Physician*, edited by R. K. Merton, G. Reader, and P. L. Kendall. Cambridge, MA: Harvard University Press.

Fox, Renée C. 1988. *Essays in Medical Sociology: Journeys into the Field.* New York, NY: John Wiley & Sons.

Freidson, Elliot. 1974. *Professional Dominance: The Social Structure of Medical Care.* Chicago, IL: Aldine.

Glaser, Barney and Anselm Strauss. 1967. *The Discovery of Grounded Theory.* New York: Aldine de Gruyter.

Hall, Margaret Jean, Carol J. DeFrances, Sonja N. Williams, Aleksandr Golosinskiy, and Alexander Schwartzman. 2010. "National Hospital Discharge Survey: 2007 Summary." *National Health Statistics Reports* 29(October 26):1–24.

Hines, Stephen, Katie Luna, Jennifer Lofthus, Michael Marquardt, and Dana Stelmokas. 2008. "Becoming a Highly Reliable Organization: Operational Advice for Hospital Leaders" (AHRQ Publication No. 08-0022). Rockville, MD: Agency for Healthcare Research and Quality.

Iglehart, John K. 2010. "The ACGME's Final Duty-Hour Standards—Special PGY-1 Limits and Strategic Napping." *The New England Journal of Medicine* 363:1589–1591.

Kahn, Katherine L., Lisa V. Rubenstein, David Draper, Jacquelin Kosecoff, William H. Rogers, Emmett B. Keeler, and Robert H. Brook. 1990. "The Effects of the DRG-Based Prospective Payment System on Quality of Care for Hospitalized Medicare Patients." *Journal of the American Medical Association* 264:1953–55.

Katz, Mitchell H. and Steven A. Schroeder. 1988. "The Sounds of the Hospital." *The New England Journal of Medicine* 319:1585–89.

Kellogg, Katherine C. 2009. "Operating Room: Relational Spaces and Microinstitutional Change in Surgery." *American Journal of Sociology* 115:657–711.

Landrigan, Christopher P., Gareth J. Parry, Catherine B. Bones, Andrew D. Hackbarth, Donald A. Goldmann, and Paul J. Sharek. 2010. "Temporal Trends in Rate of Patient Harm Resulting from Medical Care." *The New England Journal of Medicine* 363:2124–34.

Lief, Harold I. and Renee C. Fox. 1963. "The Medical Student's Training for Detached Concern." Pp. 111–23 in *The Psychological Basis of Medical Practice*, edited by H. I. Lief, V. F. Lief, and N. R. Lief. New York, NY: Harper and Row.

Light, Donald. 1980. *Becoming Psychiatrists: The Professional Transformation of Self*. New York, NY: WW Norton.

Ludmerer, Kenneth. 1999. *Time to Heal: American Medical Education from the Turn of the Century to the Era of Managed Care*. Oxford: Oxford University Press.

Miller, Stephen J. 1970. *Prescription for Leadership: Training for the Medical Elite*. Chicago, IL: Aldine Publishing Company.

Mizrahi, Terri. 1986. *Getting Rid of Patients: Contradictions in the Socialization of Physicians*. New Brunswick, NJ: Rutgers University Press.

Mumford, Emily. 1970. *Interns: From Students to Physicians*. Cambridge, MA: Harvard University Press.

Peters, George A. and Barbara J. Peters. 2007. *Medical Errors and Patient Safety: Human Factors in Medicine*. Boca Raton, FL: Taylor & Francis Group.

Romano, Patrick S. and Kevin Volpp. 2012. "The ACGME's 2011 Changes to Resident Duty Hours: Are They an Unfunded Mandate on Teaching Hospitals?" *Journal of General Internal Medicine* 27:136–38.

Shem, Samuel. 1978. *The House of God*. New York, NY: Dell Publishing.

Silber, Jeffrey H., Patrick S. Romano, Amy K. Rosen, Yanli Wang, Orit Even-Shoshan, and Kevin G. Volpp. 2007. "Failure-to-Rescue: Comparing Definitions to Measure Quality of Care." *Medical Care* 45:918–25.

Starmer, Amy J., Nancy D. Spector, Rajendu Srivastava, April D. Allen, Christopher P. Landrigan, Theodore C. Sectish, and the I-PASS Study Group. 2012. "I-PASS, a Mnemonic to Standardize Verbal Hand-offs." *Pediatrics* 129:1–3.

Starr, Paul. 1984. *The Social Transformation of American Medicine*. New York, NY: Basic Books.

Szymczak, Julia E., Joanna V. Brooks, Kevin G. Volpp, and Charles L. Bosk. 2010. "To Leave or to Lie? Are Concerns about a Shift-Work Mentality and Eroding Professionalism as a Result of Duty-Hour Rules Justified?" *The Milbank Quarterly* 88:350–81.

Taitz, Jonathan M., Thomas H. Lee, and Thomas D. Sequist. 2011. "A Framework for Engaging Physicians in Quality and Safety." *BMJ Quality and Safety in Healthcare,* published online July 14, doi: 10.1136/bmjqs-2011-000167.

Timmermans, Stefan and Alison Angell. 2001. "Evidence-Based Medicine, Clinical Uncertainty, and Learning to Doctor." *Journal of Health and Social Behavior* 42:342–59.

Waring, Justin J. 2007. "Doctors' Thinking about 'the System' as a Threat to Patient Safety." *Health* 11:29–46.

Weick, Karl E., Kathleen M. Sutcliffe, and David Obstfeld. 2005. "Organizing and the Process of Sense making." *Organization Science* 16:409–21.

Wu, Robert C., Dante Morra, Sherman Quan, Sannie Lai, Samira Zanjani, Howard Abrams, and Peter G. Rossos. 2010. "The Use of Smartphones for Clinical Communication on Internal Medicine Wards." *Journal of Hospital Medicine* 5:553–59.

Understanding Folk Medicine

By Bonnie B. O'Connor and David J. Hufford

Introduction

Both the term "folk medicine" and the conceptual category to which it refers are academic constructs that identify a particular subset of healing and health care practice. The most common interpretation of folk medicine in both popular and professional thought is that it represents a body of belief and practice isolated in various ways from the social and cultural "mainstream" and intriguingly unaffected by "modern" knowledge, with which it is frequently compared on the apparent presumption that "folk" and "modern" are mutually exclusive classifications. Folk medicine thus tends to be conceptualized within a hierarchical model of knowledge and sophistication of thought, in which it is typically located in a sort of lower midsection between official, scientific medicine at the hierarchical pinnacle and "primitive" medicine on the bottom stratum.

In part this schema is a product of the widely influential nineteenth-century Anglo-European theory of cultural evolution. From this perspective, medicine, like the rest of culture, was presumed to have developed "upward" in a largely linear and unidirectional progression from its crudest, most primitive form into its modern, Western, highly sophisticated state. All that was most effective, according to this theory, was retained and improved upon during this ascent, while discarded and obsolete ideas and practices drifted "downward" and were preserved in the "lower layers" of culture (somewhat tautologically identified by their difference from or incongruence with the social class and cultural heritage membership of those who articulated the theory). This model remains very influential in current popular and professional thought, despite the fact that the evolutionary view of culture on which it was based has been largely dismissed by most modern scholars of culture.

The simple evolutionary model leads almost inevitably to the erroneous conclusion that folk medical resources are by definition outdated and uninformed, and to the equally erroneous presumption that they are likely to be replaced by conventional biomedicine through improved access, together with the processes of education and **acculturation**. (Until quite recently this was the typical medical and academic perception of all the health care resources now gaining increasing popularity

EDITOR'S NOTES

acculturation: the process and results that occur when two or more cultures come into contact.

and legitimacy, under the general heading of complementary and alternative medicine, and it remains most persistent with respect to those nonbiomedical systems and modalities classified as "folk.") On the other hand, there are also those who romanticize folk medicine, inverting the value structure to portray it as an important repository of once-universal human knowledge and talents abandoned or forgotten in the push for progress and increasingly complex technological development (Fulder 1982; Grossinger 1982). The romantic view leads to misattributions to, and misinterpretations of, folk medical traditions. Neither of these models is an accurate or sufficient depiction of the nature of folk medicine, of its robust persistence in modern times, or of the complexity of the interactions between folk medicine and other health and healing resources—both through history and in the present day.

Defining Folk Medicine

What makes some medicine "folk" is not the particular content of the system of knowledge and practice, but the mode of transmission together with the status of the system by comparison with whatever other medical system is recognized as "official" in the local context (Yoder 1972; Press 1978). Folklorists generally consider a heavy reliance on oral transmission to be a definitive feature of all aspects of folk culture. By this standard, folk medical systems are those learned and maintained primarily through oral channels. Because in the United States there is at present practically no cultural or identity group that is entirely independent of print and other technological media, the criterion of oral transmission is relative; that is, folk healing traditions have greater reliance on orality by comparison with other healing systems that rely primarily on (usually fairly standardized) printed information sources. Unofficial status, with respect to "official" dominant cultural forms, is another defining feature of folk knowledge and practice. These two characteristics—unofficial status and strong reliance on oral transmission—therefore interact in defining folk medicine.

Oral traditions involve relatively direct communication among individuals who share enough values and meanings for the communication to be accurately and easily interpreted, and for responses to have a direct and immediate impact. Thus folk medical traditions tend to show regional variation and to accommodate specific local conditions, as well as to be closely tied to groups or populations who share important identity-defining features such as a particular ethnicity (for example, the Pennsylvania German *Bräuche* or powwow tradition), a broadly shared cultural heritage (like the recognition by many distinct Latino populations of a hot/cold classificatory index for foods, medicines, and bodily states), or common regional influences (for instance, both blacks and whites in the Appalachian South share many aspects of regional folk herbalism and its related worldview and theories of disease causation).

Particularly in the present day, oral traditions often supplement direct, face-to-face speech with additional communicative media. In the United States these occasionally include use of telephones and circulation of audio-and videotapes to disseminate and maintain the vigor of traditional knowledge and practice and to accomplish or facilitate diagnostic and therapeutic ends, as well as exchanges of self-care information and recommendations by phone, fax, and internet. In addition, most do include some written source materials. For example, many refer closely to various religious scriptural sources and several include handwritten or printed books of recipes, formulae, verbal charms and prayers, and interpretive dicta.

Pragmatic and Systematic Nature of Folk Medicine

Several significant oversights have characterized the study of folk medicine until quite recently. For example, although folk medicine, like all medicine, carries both benefits and risks, the effectiveness of folk medical practices has seldom been studied (with the exception of some ethnobotanical studies of medicinal plants), tending rather to be dismissed a priori as improbable. (One consequence of this persistent academic blind spot is that we have no independently verifiable record of the benefits or detriments of the majority of folk medical practices, or of their effects on health outcomes.) The precepts and practices of folk medicine have usually been presumed to be erroneous, and therefore thought to survive mainly through unexamined habitual usage or cultural custom. However, it is precisely the health promoting capacities of any system or therapeutic modality that are of greatest importance to its proponents and users. People dealing with health problems are typically quite pragmatic in approaching and evaluating any form of treatment or remedy: if it seems not to work, or produces effects that are too unpleasant, it tends to be rejected; if it seems to work, it tends to be supported and retained in the repertoire of healing resources likely to be tried again (and recommended to others). This pragmatism operates at both individual and collective levels. Folk healing traditions' reputations for efficacy, based on aggregate observation and experience, are central to their persistence and continued vitality.

Folk medicine has historically been viewed as a rather random aggregation of disparate ideas and practices. The presumed randomness and fragmentation, however, are attributions based largely on insufficient depth of study and unexamined assumptions. In fact, folk medical beliefs and practices are typically organized into complex and coherent systems of thought, action, and content (Hufford 1988a, 1992, 1994). Folk medical systems encompass, for example, complex bodies of knowledge and belief, specific modes of knowledge production (intuition, introspection, experimentation), evaluative processes applied in assessing the effectiveness of interventions and the qualifications of practitioners, definitions and categories of health and illness, explanatory models (Kleinman 1975, 1984) of disease **etiology** and human function, theories relating cause and nature of illness to preventive and therapeutic choices, specific repertoires of diagnostic and therapeutic actions and materia medica, generalist and specialist practitioners and the means to their training and legitimation within the system (apprenticeship, cross-gender training, supernatural selection), self-care modalities, and generative principles for formulating system-consistent responses to new input arising from

EDITOR'S NOTES

EDITOR'S NOTES

etiology: the study of cause or origination, in this case of disease.

EDITOR'S NOTES

systematization: the organization of something into a systematic rationale.

confronting novel situations (O'Connor 1995a) and from interactions with other systems, including biomedicine.

One significant reason that the systematic organization of folk medicine has been overlooked for so long is the fact that in modern Western society **systematization** is a characteristic explicitly associated with official status. In conventional biomedicine, for example, the use of textbooks and specified curricula; the development of professional societies, standardized practice guidelines, licensure requirements, and regulatory legislation; the establishment of third-party payor systems following minutely articulated reimbursement criteria; and a host of other features of official culture foster the development and articulation of explicit systematization. In addition, these interconnecting features cause the systematization to be socially visible and prominently displayed in institutional forms—clearly enough, in fact, that ordinary people commonly refer to the entire aggregate as "the [health care] System."

Folk medicine, by contrast, generally relies more heavily on oral than printed transmission; is passed on more by observation and apprenticeship than by collective instruction in institutional settings; does not follow specific curricular formulations; does not seek or generate formal licensure or legal sanctions; does not give rise to professional publications or practitioner associations, or establish ties with external payors; and functions without internal or external requirements of standardization. These characteristics do not generate the explicit display of a systematic framework of organization. However, the lack of such visible expression is not an indication that no systematization exists. Within any folk healing tradition, the ways in which practitioners are selected, trained, and recognized as legitimate and qualified are interconnected, and are articulated with such other aspects of the system as help-seeking patterns (from self-care to seeking the services of a practitioner), understandings of illness causation, modes of recompense for services, and so forth.

For example, in spiritist healing traditions, practitioners are often identified initially through some form of supernatural indication or selection, and acquire their specialized knowledge through a combination of apprenticeship with recognized healers and mystically or intuitively acquired knowledge. Their "credentials," consisting of their communities' collective evaluations of them, derive in part from the reputations of those with whom they have trained, and in part from their cumulative personal reputations for proper and successful practice. Clients dealing with health problems are aware of a range of possible causes of illness, from environmental factors to spiritual or supernatural ones. The client or patient who believes an illness to be mild, or to have only material causes, typically begins with self-treatment through widely familiar home remedies, may move to consultation with an herbalist who has more specialized knowledge if results are not satisfactory, and upon suspecting that the illness has a spiritual cause, then may seek the services of the spiritist healer. The healer, having acquired his or her abilities as supernatural or divine gifts, may refuse to charge for services rendered, though the patient or a close relative may nevertheless leave an offering of goods or money in exchange or in gratitude. All of these features are systematically linked through shared bodies of knowledge and principles of action that form a coherent and integrated whole. Members of the system may nevertheless be unable to describe it in much detail, to identify its many components, or to articulate the principles by which these features are interconnected: they can *do* it, even if they cannot *say* precisely how and why.

The most useful explanatory analogy is language. Official ("correct") English has a rigorous and highly complex systematic structure that is codified in books. There are official English speakers and teachers who can recite the rules and correct inaccurate usages. Practically all American children are exposed to much of this official system, and some even learn it, though most do not achieve proficiency in articulating its structural elements and principles. Folk language (for instance local dialects and vernaculars, or slang) does not have such a prominent codified system, but linguists have amply demonstrated that a complex system is nonetheless present and is consistently acted upon. Speakers speak their particular linguistic forms correctly (with varying degrees of individual competence) and recognize errors, but they generally find it difficult to state the rules behind the distinctions. A linguist can infer the rules, however, through observation, analysis, and the questioning of speakers, and can construct an accurate descriptive grammar on the basis of these inferences.

Systems of folk medical belief and practice operate in the same fashion. Believers vary both in the scope of their traditional knowledge and in their competence to act within the system. Some, for example, folk healers, may be able to state the theoretical basis or directly describe substantial portions of the system, but the entire system is rarely available for direct inspection. The natural form for the expression of folk medical knowledge is in actions and in narratives about events. The theories and complex content of the systems must therefore at least in part be inferred from observing and listening to those who act within them. Then, like linguistic inferences, they can be checked with "insiders" for validity and situational applicability.

Core Concepts and Characteristics

Folk medicine in the United States comprises a very large and diverse array of health practices and beliefs. Because of the ethnic and cultural heterogeneity of the U.S. population, American folk medicine bears the influences of healing traditions and practices from all over the world. Although the range of distinct folk medical systems and modalities in the United States is enormous, many of these systems do share a number of fundamental concepts that can be broadly identified—so long as one bears in mind that the fine points of specific interpretations and the precise combinations in which they are found vary from system to system.

Characteristics of Folk Medical Systems

- Transmission primarily through oral means, coupled with unofficial status
- Health as harmony or balance
- Interrelation of body, mind, spirit
- Vitalism
- Magical or supernatural elements
- Thoughts and emotions as etiologic factors
- Concern with underlying causes
- Positive/negative energies; transference of energies
- Moral tone; meaning of illness

Health as harmony or balance. Most folk medical systems define health in terms of some form of harmony or balance. This balance can be among bodily humors or regulatory substances; innate properties such as heat and cold or yin and yang; forces such as upward and downward or inward and outward motion; states of the blood or other vehicles of internal bodily nourishment and cleansing; or periods of activity and rest. The spectrum of health practices is informed by this concept of balance. Many Latino, Caribbean, Asian, and Southeast Asian folk traditions, for example, incorporate a balance between hot and cold properties of foods, medicaments, and symptoms or bodily states. Cold conditions are offset with hot foods and medicines; hot conditions with cool ones. The goal of preventive and therapeutic actions is to maintain or restore health by moving toward a neutral center, usually with a preference for remaining slightly on the warm side (Harwood 1971, 1981; Schreiber and Homiak 1981; Duong 1987; LaGuerre 1987; Assanand et al. 1990; Gleave and Manes 1990).

In addition to internal states of equilibrium, harmony between the individual and external factors such as social, environmental, spiritual, and cosmological elements may affect health. For example, times of seasonal change are typically regarded as times of particular vulnerability to illness, and may require special protective steps such as seasonal "tonics," specific foods to be taken or avoided, and attention to health-promoting dress. Protection from exposure to cold, particularly in the form of cold air, drafts, and wind is a common preventive measure against ill health (indeed, it is difficult to find a person of *any* background or persuasion who did not grow up with some form of routine familial advice concerning protection from cold for reasons of health maintenance and disease prevention). This concern accompanies a pervasive conviction that cold can enter the body and accumulate, causing or contributing to a large variety of illnesses both immediately and in the (even quite distant) future (Snow 1974; Helman 1978; Ragucci 1981; Duong 1987). Cosmological factors such as lunar and astrological cycles may also be identified as affecting health or vitality in a variety of ways. These may call for behavioral adjustments to maintain a healthful balance or reduce health risk, and may be factored into the planting, harvesting, and preparation of medicinal plants and other substances (Snow 1977; Crellin and Philpott 1990).

Interrelation of body, mind, and spirit. Most folk healing systems assume a complex interconnectedness of body, mind, and spirit (Harwood 1977; Trotter and Chavira 1981; Reimensnyder 1982; Hufford 1985, 1993; Duong 1987; LaGuerre 1987; Hufford and Chilton 1996). The balance and harmony that define health incorporate all of these aspects of persons, and disturbances in any of the aspects can produce sickness and symptoms in any of the others. Physical injury or sickness may bring about mental, emotional, or spiritual unwellness; emotional disturbance and mental unrest or worry may cause or exacerbate physical illness and disease. Spiritual well-being and harmony may be crucial aspects of health, and are variously defined in terms of an individual's inner state as well as in terms of relationships between human individuals and spiritual entities understood to interact with the material world and to influence personal health and more general well-being (success, prosperity, happiness, social relations) in a variety of ways.

Vital force or essence. The human body is understood in most folk medical systems to be animated and sustained by a special type of force, energy, or essence whose presence and proper activity are essential to life and health. The nature, source, behavior, and manipulability of this life-sustaining force are variously defined across systems. There is a wide range of spiritual and metaphysical interpretations of this vital force, including, in some systems, connection of each individual's vital force with universal or cosmological fonts or reservoirs (Davis 1988). Damage to or disturbance, obstruction, or capture of the vital force leads to illness; restoration of its proper embodiment, freedom, and function promotes healing.

Magical and supernatural elements. A significant number of folk medical systems recognize magical and supernatural elements in disease etiology. These may include, for example, sin as a direct cause of illness and disharmony; interventions by deities or spirit entities causing illness as retribution or reminder; undesirable states of spirit possession or intrusion (Duong 1987); spiritual causes such as soul loss or capture (Harwood 1981; Trotter and Chavira 1981; Rubel et al. 1984; Davis 1988; Dinh et al. 1990; Stephenson 1995); and malign human agency such as cursing, hexing witchcraft, and sorcery (Harwood 1977, 1981; Ragucci 1981; Reimensnyder 1982; LaGuerre 1987; Davis 1988; Brainard and Zaharlick 1989).

In some systems there are illness types that are specific to supernatural or magical causation. In addition, many systems recognize the possibility of variable causation, including supernatural elements, for *any* type of disease or illness (mental illnesses, infectious diseases, cancers, et cetera). Particular developments or details of an illness episode may suggest that supernatural causal factors are involved. In Haitian and Haitian-American folk healing tradition, for example, a magical or supernatural origin for disease may be suggested by sudden and severe onset, or by an unusually protracted course (LaGuerre 1987); in many Latino cultures, by either lengthy duration or failure to respond to standard (folk or conventional) treatment (Harwood 1977, 1981; Schreiber and Homiak 1981; Trotter and Chavira 1981); in African-American folk healing, by inability of a medical doctor to arrive at a diagnosis or identify a cause for troubling symptoms, or by a continual worsening of symptoms in spite of medical treatment (Snow 1974).

Treatment of illnesses that have supernatural or magical causal factors may involve simultaneous use of conventional biomedicine and one or more folk healing systems. Herbal remedies or conventional medicine may be the system used for symptom relief or to handle illnesses that seem serious. Whenever magical or supernatural causes are determined to be involved, however, these must also be properly addressed in the healing effort or else illness can be expected to recur, even if symptoms abate for the near term. Some of these types of healing measures can be carried out on one's own or in the context of the family, for example, through prayer, offerings, ritual baths and cleansings, use of specific medicaments and other protective and therapeutic substances, and so forth. Others require the interventions of a specialist practitioner, such as a *curandera,* shaman, rootworker, powwow, religious authority, or spiritual healer.

Thoughts and emotions as etiologic factors. Obsessive, fearful, or negative thoughts, mental unrest and worry, and extremes of emotion (especially strong and negative emotions, such as anger or envy) are regarded as direct etiologic factors for illness in a number of systems. These factors too may be considered contributory in any type of disease or illness process (not just in mental and emotional illness), and again require that appropriate therapeutic action be taken to address them in order for healing to be complete or lasting.

One example common to many systems is envy as a possible etiologic factor in illness, both for the envious person and for those who are objects of the envy. Symptoms (for either person) may include headache, sleep disturbance, nightmares, fatigue or lassitude, loss of appetite, and gastric distress, among others. Envy as a direct cause of illness in others may be mediated through the envious or covetous gaze or the evil eye, which may be cast both intentionally and unintentionally (Foulks et al. 1977; Dundes 1981; Harwood 1981; Ragucci 1981; Assanand et al. 1990). Evil eye beliefs form a part of many American folk medical systems. Babies and children may be considered especially susceptible, and protective charms and amulets are commonly worn by children and adults alike as a preventive measure.

Concern with underlying causes. Most folk medical systems seek to identify and treat underlying as well as immediate causes of disease. Underlying causes help to establish the conditions under which illness may develop or disease take hold, and may represent some type of fundamental imbalance or disharmony. This view generally accommodates conventional medical views quite readily, for example, accepting medical etiologies as identifying certain immediate causes. Thus, a germ may be accepted as the immediate cause of a disease, but it is understood to have caused it in a particular person at a particular time because of, for example, internal disequilibrium (hot/cold, or yin/yang), a buildup of toxins in the body, individual sinfulness, violation of dietary requirements (which in some instances may itself be a sin), diminished vital energy, and so forth (Hufford 1993; O'Connor 1995a). From the perspective of the folk medical system, diseases, and the body's susceptibility to their pathological agents, are often considered to be symptoms of underlying imbalances that require redress. This attention to underlying causes commonly leads proponents to feel that folk medicine treats the *causes* of ill health, while conventional medicine addresses itself primarily or exclusively to the *symptoms*. This view furnishes a conceptual framework in which the two kinds of healing systems can readily be integrated together in treating disease and promoting health.

Energies and transference. An emphasis on various kinds of "energy" is almost universal in folk medical systems, beginning, as previously noted, with the recognition of an animating energy or vital force. Folk medicine often involves several kinds of positive energies in promoting healing, and these are frequently contrasted with negative, life-destroying energies. Disease may result from imbalances in or the loss or theft of vital energy, but it may also be caused by the presence or intrusion of negative energies. These energies may be implicated in both natural and supernatural concepts of disease etiology. For example, improper preparation or cooking of foods may destroy their energetic vitality (natural), or witchcraft may steal it (supernatural), resulting in food that appears good but cannot nourish. Either circumstance can lead to illness.

A transference of positive energy from healer to patient is a characteristic of those systems in which a practitioner's hands are used therapeutically on or near the patient's body. In secular interpretations, this healing energy may be understood to come from within the healer's own vital energy stores or to pass through the healer from a cosmic source. In religious or spiritual interpretations, the healing energy is usually considered to be of divine origin; healers stress that it is God (or another powerful spiritual figure, depending on the system) who does the actual healing, while the practitioner is but an intermediary.

Many of the folk beliefs interpreted by scholars as based on the principle of "magical contagion" imply the exchange of such energies. Material objects may be endowed with negative energies and placed in the victim's environment; or the residue of a victim's unique life force in hair, nail parings, or an object long worn on his or her body may serve to focus the transmission of negative force, as in malign magical assault using figurines or magical packets. (These techniques are found, for example, in rootwork, a part of African-American folk tradition, and in some forms of Pennsylvania-German hexing.) In some traditions of prayer healing and psychic healing, conversely, personal objects still resonant with the sick person's life force serve to focus "distant healing." Disease, as a negative energy, may be transferred out of a person and into another living organism (such as a tree or an animal), or onto another object—as a wart is transferred onto a potato or a silver coin in some folk wart cures, later to wither away as the potato decays, or to be transferred to a new host along with the coin (Hand 1980). Conversely, positive energies and innate qualities (serenity, courage, vigor) may be imbibed with specific therapeutic substances and contribute in this nonpharmacologic way to the restoration or maintenance of health.

Moral tone. Folk healing systems generally incorporate a strong moral element such as a presumption of the inherent goodness of Nature, or a sense of personal responsibility for right behavior and health-protecting actions. Together with the high value placed on harmony and balance, these moral elements underscore the interconnectedness of personal health with the community, the physical environment, and the cosmos, and integrate the experience of sickness and health within a comprehensive and meaningful view of the world. This accounts for the characteristic way in which folk medical systems address the meaning of disease and suffering alongside attention to causation and cure, helping to furnish explanations for the always urgent questions that seriously sick people have of why (in the moral or metaphysical sense) they are sick, why in this way, and why now.

Disease and Illness Classifications

Folk medical systems include illness taxonomies which tend, on the whole, to classify illnesses according to causation. In systems that incorporate a hot/cold index, one way of classifying diseases (or specific symptoms) is by their hot or cold type. Folk medical systems of Southeast-Asian historical origin may classify diseases and syndromes as caused primarily by "wind," "fire," or other elements in the body. Across a number of systems, two broad categories indicate natural or supernatural causation. In several systems, as mentioned, any disease or illness may entail natural and/or supernatural causality, and features of the particular illness episode and its progression will help to determine which factors are implicated and in which ways.

In African-American folk tradition, sickness can be broadly classified as natural or unnatural. Natural illnesses occur in accordance with the proper workings of Nature (or, in a religious interpretation, in accordance with God's laws); unnatural ones are brought on by means that in some way violate God's will (in religious terms) or the natural order (in secular terms), such as sickness caused by sorcery or by excessive worry or mental unrest (Snow 1974, 1977). Both natural and unnatural sicknesses may have material causes (such as germs), or may have divine causal elements such as punishment for sin, or illness sent as a test or reminder of faith and religious duty.

Across folk medical systems, some types of illness may be specific to one category while for others a variable type of causation is possible, and etiology may differ in specific instances of the same disease. Causality may also be mixed, or one type may establish the imbalance or disharmony (underlying cause) that makes a person vulnerable to another form of (immediate) causal agent or circumstance. Treatment is in accordance with the nature and causes of the disease. As new information is gained in the course of the illness, or as prior treatment strategies are deemed ineffective or inappropriate, substitutions or additions will be made in the treatment strategy—both within the folk medical system and by incorporation of other treatment forms such as elements from other systems, including conventional medicine.

Folk Illnesses

Folk healing systems generally include recognition of some types of illness that are not recognized as disease categories in the biomedical diagnostic canon. These illnesses are referred to by scholars and health professionals as "folk illnesses," sometimes also called "culture-bound syndromes" (Simons and Hughes 1985; Hufford 1988b; Pang 1990; American Psychiatric Association 1994). The concept of "folk illness" is an academic construct which takes the diagnostic and etiological categories of biomedicine as its reference point. The implication of the label is that an illness so referenced is not "real," or at least is not "really" what people who accept it as real believe it to be. This is an etic viewpoint that is of course not shared by members of and believers in the folk medical systems in which these illness categories are found. Cultural insiders likewise do not use the term "folk illness," referring instead to each such illness by its own culturally supplied name (Snow 1977; Harwood 1981; Schreiber and Homiak 1981; Trotter and Chavira 1981; Hufford 1982; Rubel et al. 1984; Duong 1987).

Folk illnesses, like other illnesses, have recognized etiologies, particular constellations of symptoms, diagnostic criteria, identified sequelae, and specified preventive and therapeutic measures. Some folk illnesses appear to represent local names or varied symptom patterns of currently recognized medical disorders (Rubel et al. 1984; Hufford 1992), while others do not seem to have medical correlates (although they are frequently—and often erroneously—reinterpreted in psychiatric terms by health professionals and researchers). In either case, some aspects of the explanatory model of folk illnesses will depart from the conventional medical model, and treatment will follow the system-congruent reasoning: cooling excess heat, restoring proper motion of vital force, dispelling cold or toxins accumulated in the body, extirpating evil influences, and so on. Folk medical causality and therapeutics are not confined solely to folk illnesses, however, but are also applied to medically recognized diseases. This is another element that helps to account for the fact that folk healing traditions are frequently combined as therapeutic options both with biomedicine and with other unofficial systems or modalities with which particular individuals may be familiar.

Some folk illnesses are closely tied to specific populations or healing traditions, while others are widely recognized across cultures and systems. Of these, perhaps the most ubiquitous is soul loss, called by a variety of system-specific names, and sometimes academically referred to as "magical fright" or "fright illness" (Simons and Hughes 1985). The fundamental pathogenic factor in soul loss is inappropriate, undesirable, or unintentional separation of a living person's soul from the body. Soul loss (perhaps most familiar to academics and researchers by its Spanish name, *susto* [Rubel et al. 1984]) is recognized across a number of systems as most commonly being caused by severe fright, trauma, or emotional shock. This may be precipitated by experiencing (or even witnessing) a frightening accident or incident of violence or brutality, receiving sudden bad news for which one is unprepared, experiencing extended extreme hardship, or being caught up in terrifying natural events such as earthquakes and other natural disasters. Some systems also recognize the possibility of soul loss through capture by human sorcerers (Davis 1988) or malicious spirits (Geddes 1976).

Like many medically recognized conditions, soul loss is considered both a sickness in itself, and a contributing factor in other illnesses. Soul loss is always serious, and if not properly treated can lead to death. Indications are that treatment outcomes for at least some folk illnesses, including susto, are best when the appropriate traditional remedies are used or the indicated folk healers provide the treatment (Rubel et al. 1984). It is important that health professionals not dismiss or trivialize folk illnesses since, for at least some of them, there is also evidence that their sufferers are at increased risk for general morbidity and mortality (Rubel et al. 1984), and in some cases traditional treatments may also have important clinical consequences, both positive and negative (Trotter 1981a, 1981b, 1985; Lazar and O'Connor 1997).

Folk Practitioners

Self-care or family care and home-based first aid account for a great proportion of health behavior in both folk tradition and "mainstream" practice. Household staples such as eggs, lemons, garlic, chicken soup, rice, and other foodstuffs are used preventively and therapeutically across populations and traditions, together with common medicinal plants and herbs; and their proper preparation and applications tend to be matters of general knowledge. Many households maintain a small herb or medicine garden, or keep a few of the "standards" potted indoors. Dietary and behavioral patterns may or may not explicitly be considered parts of "health care," yet still may constitute important health behaviors within the system and follow system-consistent organizing principles.

Generalist and specialist practitioners are also found in most folk medical systems. Across several traditions these include midwives, massagers, bonesetters, blood stoppers, wart curers, thrush or "thrash" doctors (for infants and children), healers of burns and other skin conditions, religious, magical, and spiritual specialists of various kinds, and herbalists. Selection as a practitioner occurs in a number of ways. Common among these are birth order or other birth circumstances; conferring of divine or other supernaturally bestowed gifts and callings; special life circumstances; transformative personal experiences, including experiences of serious illness and healing; familial inheritance; and of course self-selection for reasons of personal desire or interest (Hand 1980).

Seventh children—especially seventh sons—are widely believed to be born with special powers and abilities, and among these may be the gift of healing. (Variations on this theme include the seventh same-sex child with no intervening opposite sex births, or the seventh son of a seventh son.) The gift does not usually become active until near adulthood, though there are instances of child healers in many folk systems. Twins may have innate healing abilities, and if one twin dies the "left twin" (the one left behind) is especially likely subsequently to be able to heal. Posthumous children (those born after the death of their mothers—usually a death in childbirth, but also deaths from other circumstances such as illness or accident, following which the child is taken alive from the womb) are often considered born healers, either with general healing abilities, or with a particular capacity to heal thrush and other diseases of infancy and childhood (Hand 1980). Children born with a veil or caul (a portion of the amniotic membrane covering the face or eyes) may be believed destined to be healers, and sometimes also to have "second sight" or clairvoyant abilities, which may also be used in their healing vocations.

Ordinary individuals may be singled out to become healers by receipt of a divine or other supernatural gift or calling. The indication of this calling can come in a number of ways, including mystical experience, notification in dreams or visions, direct cognitive awareness, human messenger (often another person with special abilities), or a series of subtle signs whose cumulative import gradually becomes clear. It is common in a number of traditions for individuals singled out in this way to find the gift or calling burdensome, and to try to ignore or reject it—especially as acting on it may require substantial changes in behavior and lifestyle. Typically the attempt to refuse such a calling results in an escalating series of illnesses and other misfortunes that befall the designee, until he or she reaches the point of determining that the gift or calling is truly an imperative and must be accepted. Acceptance and the accompanying change in life direction resolve the preceding state of disruption of the healer's life.

Special life circumstances such as widowhood or childlessness may confer healing ability or simply make a (potential) healer readily identifiable (Hand 1980). Transformative life experiences, including mystical and visionary experiences, religious conversion, and instances of sudden and extreme good or bad fortune may prompt a person to become a healer, or provide a sign of a calling. Serious illness which subsequently resolves or is healed by specific means (including biomedical ones), together with accidents that leave the victim permanently changed in some way, also figure prominently among these transformative experiences. In some cases this may be simply because harsh personal experience yields insight and empathy and a desire to help others; in others, the illness experience includes receipt of special information or mystical insight. Shamanic healers may in the course of their illness enter the spirit world and there be instructed, tested, assaulted, or even spiritually killed and resurrected, and return to consciousness and the material world redirected to become healers (Eliade 1964). Supernatural selection may be implied in the occurrence of any transformative experience, including illness. The likelihood of such selection may or may not run in families. Selection or calling to become a healer may itself bestow healing abilities directly upon the designee, or these may have to be acquired through a period of apprenticeship—sometimes quite long and arduous—with an established healer.

Common Therapeutic Practices

The enormous diversity of American folk medicine makes it impossible to enumerate every therapeutic practice found in every system. There are, however, broad common categories of preventive and therapeutic modalities in use across systems, including physically applied therapies, medicinal herbs and other naturally derived substances, sacramental objects, and prayers and other religious and spiritual actions. It is important to note that these are not mutually exclusive categories. Indeed, it is most common to find considerable overlap among them, for example, medicinal herbs used in a mash physically applied to the body, with accompanying prayer, for the purpose of bringing about spiritual purification as a step in the healing process.

Of course, particular theories of the modes of action of these therapies, and of the relationship between a particular therapy and the specific health condition or individual illness episode for which it is applied, vary across healing traditions in keeping with system-specific explanatory models of health and illness and care. Because standardization is not a feature of folk medicine, it is also quite common to find significant variation from region to region, or from healer to healer, in the interpretation and applications of even those practices most fundamental to a given system.

Religious, spiritual, and magical actions and sacramental objects. Spiritual and magicoreligious actions commonly used to promote health and healing include prayer; reading or recitation of sacred texts; pious ejaculations (for example "Ave María" among Spanish-speaking Catholics, or "Good Saint Anne, protect us!"); recitation of verbal charms and brief formulaic utterances (such as "knock wood" or "*kain ein horeh*") to ward off misfortune or evil influences; protective gestures such as making the sign of the cross, or spitting between the first two fingers or extending the index and little fingers to ward off the evil eye; meditation and spiritual contemplation of a variety of types; laying on of hands or use of the hands near the body to remove illness and negative influences or energies; petitions and offerings to or bargaining with spiritual entities; visits to holy sites and healing shrines; temporary internment in places of worship or spiritual contemplation; burning of incense and of "spirit money" or joss paper; spiritual cleansings of a variety of types (including herbal baths, and "sweepings" with plant and animal substances); soul callings and restorations; preparation of figurines and magical packets; and use of amulets and other protective items, among innumerable other possibilities. Prescription or administration of botanical and other natural medicaments, as mentioned, may occur in a religious healing setting, with spiritual instruction or guidance, or with spiritual or metaphysical health outcomes in mind.

Natural substances. Ethnic and regional cultures almost without exception have developed a materia medica of locally available natural substances—botanical, animal, and mineral. Therapeutic goals and modes of use of these natural medicines are determined by the tenets of a wide variety of theoretical models, and pharmacological and biochemical models do not necessarily apply (O'Connor 1986). Herbs and other natural medicinals are used for their physical actions and effects, but also (among other purposes) for metaphysical properties such as hot and cold or yin and yang qualities and effects; for spiritual qualities with which they are associated, such as purity, patience, inner strength, or calm; for effects they will have on the quality and function of the body's vital energy; or for their capacity to absorb and carry away negative influences.

Natural medicants are taken orally as teas or soups and are cooked into foods, both primarily as medicines, and as culinary herbs intended to provide both gustatory and salutary benefits. They are used as inhalants and as ingredients in baths, sweats, and steamings; in ointments, linaments, and salves, ear and eye drops, douches and enemas, poultices, wet or dry packs, massage compounds; and in moxibustion (the burning on or very near the skin surface of tiny amounts of dried compressed plant material). Specific substances may be used to "sweep" the body in ritual cleansings, drawing out disease-causing malignancies. Eggs or small live animals are also used for this purpose in many settings, because their life force may successfully substitute for the vital essence of the patient as a target for malign forces, possessing spirits, and other agents of ill health which may be transferrable out of the patient.

Any natural substances, in any of their multitudinous modes of use, may be used to achieve physical, mental, emotional, or spiritual healing objectives. An herb taken internally is as likely to be intended to bring about changes in the state or motion of vital energy, to imbue a quality of character or state of mind, or to enhance or restrain specific bodily functions, for example, as it is to alleviate a physical symptom. An herbal rubdown or sweeping may be used to draw out a fever or put an end to respiratory distress as well as to deal with spiritual or metaphysical aspects of illness.

Physical therapies. Various forms of massage, stroking, and rubbing are physical therapies found in numerous folk medical traditions. As with herbs and other natural medicinals, the therapeutic goals are varied. For example, abdominal massage is used in Mexican-American folk healing to achieve specific physical ends: alleviation of intestinal gas or of muscle pain and cramping, or release of "stuck" digestive products that are thought to adhere to the stomach lining, causing the folk illness *empacho* (Schreiber and Homiak 1981; Trotter 1981a, 1985). Pinching and lifting of the skin may serve a similar purpose, while other forms of massage and physical manipulation are intended to ameliorate the flow and functional status of vital energy, or to promote states of physical relaxation or mental or emotional calm or clarity. In some Southeast-Asian traditions, dermabrasive techniques such as rubbing the skin with a lubricated metal utensil or coin (hence the English name, "coining") have as their goal the release of "wind" (Yeatman and Dang 1980; Duong 1987), an etiologic factor in a variety of illness states. Cupping is used in folk medical traditions of a wide range of ethnic and cultural origins. This entails placing on the skin (most commonly on the back and upper shoulders) small cups or jars which adhere by means of a vacuum created when they are first heated. Depending on the tradition within which this treatment is undertaken, it is intended to draw impurities, excess humors, "bad blood," or "wind" out of the body; if blood is specifically to be released, small cuts may be made in the skin before placement of the cups.

A number of folk medical traditions also include physical actions which are intended to achieve their therapeutic ends through essentially magical or metaphysical means. These include such practices as "measuring" (sometimes using a specific type or color of ribbon or string), and "passing through," a practice in which the sick person (most often a child) is passed through a fork or other opening in a tree, during which process it is intended that the sickness or other negative energy or undesirable influence will be drawn out (Hand 1980).

Interactions with Other Systems

Most people—even those for whom a single health care system is dominant—use a wide variety of home treatment and prevention strategies far more often than they seek the services of any kind of practitioner (Levin et al. 1976; Dean 1981). If they do consult a doctor or other healer, these self-care practices often continue in some way to be used together with newly prescribed regimens. The herb teas taken to promote relaxation or sleep during an episode of disabling back pain, for example, are not necessarily replaced by the treatments of a chiropractor, the prescriptions of a physician, or the ministrations of a religious healer, but used concurrently with the practitioner's services. Indeed, *all* of these resources may be used simultaneously without causing any sense of dissonance or conflict for the patient: each may be seen to address a specific aspect of the problem, or all may be felt to complement and support each other in a well-rounded therapeutic plan (Hufford 1992; O'Connor 1995a, 1995b).

Self-care efforts are typically informed by a mixture of folk and "official" belief, gleaned during an individual's life through a variety of exposures and experiences. These are incorporated together into a coherent, if sometimes quite eclectic, personal system (Hufford 1988a), and involve beliefs that shape the manner in which any practitioner's advice is interpreted and pursued. For example, for adherents of a folk healing system incorporating a hot-cold theory, use of a medical doctor or other healer is common. If an herbal or pharmaceutical medication classified according to the folk taxonomy as "hot" is prescribed for a disease or symptom classified as "cold," it is likely to be accepted readily because its use is consonant with the patient's model of healthful balance. If "hot" symptoms or side effects then develop, however, it is likely that the dosage will be reduced or the medication discontinued: the hot medicine may be thought to be creating too much internal heat in the body (Harwood 1971), or the hot symptoms may be an indication that the body's balance has shifted and it is time to stop the treatment. If other types of treatments provided by a folk or "alternative" practitioner produce symptoms or reactions indicating disturbance of hot/cold balance, these too are likely to be suspended or amended to become congruent with the individual's dominant model.

For different patients the number of resources and the order in which they are brought to bear will vary depending on the availability of each option and other features of the sickness context, including the advice and opinions of trusted others and the nature and severity of the illness. The same person is likely to activate different health resources, or to come to them in a different order, for each particular health problem. Many people will try a folk remedy or have a folk healer treat them for warts much more readily than they will seek out a physician for the same purpose. The same individual may see a chiropractor for neck pain or chronic headaches but never for severe gastrointestinal symptoms, which are instead presented to a medical doctor. The services of the folk healer may be (re-)added if other treatments seem not to be working. If a diagnosis or prognosis is sufficiently alarming, it may move the patient to use modalities or practitioners which have been a part of his or her broader cultural repertoire, but of which he/she was previously fearful or skeptical. Entirely new and previously unfamiliar options may be sought out if new information has recently been acquired through the media, or through the patient's social network—a source of abundant health-related information and advice at almost any time, but especially so when one is known to have a health problem.

The precise patterns of folk medical use are highly individualized and case-specific. Folk medical systems have constant interactions with conventional medicine, though often without the knowledge of the medical profession. Many folk healers freely refer clients to medical doctors, even insist that they go, and they sometimes come into hospitals to continue to provide treatments for their patients (Hufford 1988a). The conventional medical model can be incorporated rather easily along with folk models of illness, and in some instances may even serve to reinforce them (Helman 1978).

Predictions that folk medicine would (even "should") die out in the face of scientific medical advances have been made in the United States for well over a century. They clearly have not been borne out to date, and there is no reason to suppose that they will be realized in the future. These healing systems are dynamic and flexible, readily incorporating new content and adapting to changing conditions while preserving many traditional elements, including some ideas and practices considered outmoded in parallel healing traditions. Folk medicine remains vigorously active in the United States, continually attracting new proponents who find the systems effective, broadly accessible, and often comfortably consonant with their general worldviews. It is fair to say that folk medicine is an important part of the total pool of health care resources upon which people draw for both therapeutic and preventive purposes. From herbalism to food customs to the use of prayer in preserving and restoring health, folk medicine is in fact the most basic and persistent dimension of the pluralistic health culture of the United States.

References

American Psychiatric Association. 1994. *Diagnostic and statistical manual of mental disorders (DSM-IV)*. Washington, D.C.: American Psychiatric Association.

Assanand, S., M. Dias, E. Richardson, and N. Waxler-Morrison. 1990. The south Asians. In *Cross-cultural caring: A handbook for health professionals in western Canada*, ed. N. Waxler-Morrison, J. M. Anderson, and E. Richardson, 141–80. Vancouver: University of British Columbia Press.

Brainard. J., and A. Zaharlick. 1989. Changing health beliefs and behaviors of resettled Laotian refugees: Ethnic variation in adaptation. *Social Science and Medicine* 29: 845–52.

Crellin, J. K., and J. Philpott. 1990. *Herbal medicine past and present*. Vol. 1, *Trying to give ease*. Durham, North Carolina: Duke University Press.

Davis, E. W. 1988. *Passage of darkness: The ethnobiology of the Haitian zombie*. Chapel Hill: University of North Carolina Press.

Dean, K. 1981. Self-care responses to illness: A selected review. *Social Science and Medicine* 15A: 673–87.

Dinh, D.-K., S. Ganesan, and N. Waxler-Morrison. 1990. The Vietnamese. In *Cross-cultural Caring: A handbook for health professionals in western Canada*, ed. N. Waxler-Morrison, J. M. Anderson, and E. Richardson, 181–213. Vancouver: University of British Columbia Press.

Dundes, A., ed. 1981. *The evil eye: A folklore casebook*. New York: Garland Publishing.

Duong, V. H. 1987. The Indochinese patient. In *Urban family medicine*, ed. R. B. Birrer, 238–42. New York: Springer-Verlag.

Eliade, M. 1964. *Shamanism: Archaic techniques of ecstasy*. Princeton, New Jersey: Princeton University Press.

Foulks, E., D. Freeman, F. Kaslow, and L. Madow. 1977. The Italian evil eye: *Mal occhio*. *Journal of Operational Psychiatry* 8 (2): 28–34.

Fulder, S. 1982. *The tao of medicine: Ginseng, Oriental remedies, and the pharmacology of harmony*. New York: Destiny Books.

Geddes, W. R. 1976. *Migrants of the mountains: The cultural ecology of the Blue Miao (Hmong Njua) of Thailand*. Oxford: Clarendon Press and Oxford University Press.

Gleave, D., and A. S. Manes. 1990. The Central Americans. In *Cross-cultural caring: A handbook for health professionals in western Canada*, ed. N. Waxler-Morrison, J. M. Anderson, and E. Richardson, 36–67. Vancouver: University of British Columbia Press.

Grossinger, R. 1982. *Planet medicine: From Stone Age shamanism to post-Industrial healing*. Revised edition. Boston: Shambhala Publications.

Hand, Wayland D. 1980. *Magical medicine: The folkloric component of medicine in the folk belief, custom, and ritual of the peoples of Europe and America. Selected essays of Wayland D. Hand*. Berkeley and Los Angeles: University of California Press.

Harwood, A. 1971. The hot/cold theory of disease: Implications for the treatment of Puerto Rican patients. *Journal of the American Medical Association* 216: 1153–58.

———. 1977. *Rx: Spiritist as needed: A study of a Puerto Rican community mental health resource.* Ithaca: Cornell University Press.

———. 1981. Mainland Puerto Ricans. In *Ethnicity and medical care*, ed. A. Harwood, 397–481. Cambridge, Massachusetts: Harvard University Press.

Helman, C. G. 1978. "Feed a cold, starve a fever": Folk models of infection in an English suburban community, and their relationship to medical treatment. *Culture, Medicine, and Psychiatry* 2: 107–37.

Hufford, David J. 1982. *The terror that comes in the night: An experience-centered study of supernatural assault traditions.* Philadelphia: University of Pennsylvania Press.

———. 1985. Sainte Anne de Beaupré: Roman Catholic pilgrimage and healing. *Western Folklore* 44: 194–207.

———. 1988a. Contemporary folk medicine. In *Other healers: Unorthodox medicine in America*, ed. N. Gevitz, 228–64. Baltimore: Johns Hopkins University Press.

———. 1988b. Inclusionism vs. reductionism in the study of the culture bound syndromes. *Culture, Medicine, and Psychiatry* 12: 503.

———. 1992. Folk medicine in contemporary America. In *Herbal and magical medicine: Traditional healing today*, ed. James Kirkland, Holly F. Mathews, C. W. Sullivan III, and Karen Baldwin, 14–31. Durham, North Carolina: Duke University Press.

———. 1993. Epistemologies of religious healing. *Journal of Medicine and Philosophy* 18: 175–94.

———. 1994. Folklore and medicine. In *Putting folklore to use: From health to human welfare*, ed. Michael Owen Jones, 117–35. Lexington: University Press of Kentucky.

Hufford, David J., and M. Chilton. 1996. Politics, spirituality, and environmental healing. In *The ecology of health: Issues and alternatives*, ed. J. Chesworth, 59–71. Thousand Oaks, California: Sage.

Kleinman, A. 1975. Explanatory models in health care relationships. In *Health of the family*, 159–72. Washington, D.C.: National Council for International Health.

———. 1984. Indigenous systems of healing: Questions for professional, popular, and folk care. In *Alternative medicines: Popular and policy perspectives*, ed. J. W. Salmon, 251–58. New York: Tavistock.

LaGuerre, M. S. 1987. *Afro-Caribbean folk medicine.* South Hadley, Massachusetts: Bergin and Garvey Publishers.

Lazar, J. S., and Bonnie Blair O'Connor. 1997. Talking with patients about their use of alternative therapies. *Primary Care: Clinics in Office Practice* 24 (4): 699–714.

Levin, L. S., A. H. Katz, and E. Holst. 1976. *Self-care: Lay initiatives in health.* New York: Prodist.

O'Connor, Bonnie Blair. 1986. Material and immaterial essences in herbal healing. Unpublished paper, delivered at the American Folklore Society annual meeting, Baltimore, Maryland.

———. 1995a. *Healing traditions: Alternative medicine and the health professions.* Philadelphia: University of Pennsylvania Press.

———. 1995b. Vernacular health care responses to HIV and AIDS. *Alternative Therapies in Health and Medicine* 1 (5): 35–52.

———. 1998. Healing practices. In *Handbook of immigrant health*, ed. S. Loue. New York: Plenum Press.

Pang, K. Y. C. 1990. *Hwabyung:* The construction of a Korean popular illness among Korean elderly immigrant women in the United States. *Culture, Medicine, and Psychiatry* 14: 495–512.

Press, I. 1978. Urban folk medicine: A functional overview. *American Anthropologist* 80: 71–84.

Ragucci, A. J. 1981. Italian Americans. In *Ethnicity and medical care*, ed. A. Harwood, 211–63. Cambridge, Massachusetts: Harvard University Press.

Reimensnyder, B. 1982. Powwowing in Union County. Ph.D. diss. Philadelphia: University of Pennsylvania.

Rubel, A. J., C. O'Nell, and R. Collado-Ardon. 1984. *Susto: A folk illness.* Berkeley: University of California Press.

Schreiber, J. M., and J. P. Homiak. 1981. Mexican Americans. In *Ethnicity and medical care*, ed. A. Harwood, 264–336. Cambridge, Massachusetts: Harvard University Press.

Simons, R. C., and C. C. Hughes. 1985. *The culture-bound syndromes: Folk illnesses of psychiatric and anthropological interest.* Dordrecht: D. Reidel Publishing Company.

Snow, L. 1974. Folk medical beliefs and their implications for care of patients: A review based on studies among black Americans. *Annals of Internal Medicine* 81: 82–96.

———. 1977. Popular medicine in a black neighborhood. In *Ethnic medicine in the Southwest*, ed. E. Spicer, 19–98. Tucson: University of Arizona Press.

Stephenson, P. H. 1995. Vietnamese refugees in Victoria, B.C.: An overview of immigrant and refugee health care in a medium-sized Canadian urban centre. *Social Science and Medicine* 40 (12): 1631–42.

Trotter, R. T., III. 1981a. Folk remedies as indicators of common illnesses: Examples from the United States-Mexican border. *Journal of Ethnopharmacology* 4: 207–21.

———. 1981b. *Remedios caseros:* Mexican American home remedies and community health problems. *Social Science and Medicine* 15B: 107–14.

———. 1985. Folk medicine in the Southwest: Myths and medical facts. *Postgraduate Medicine* 78 (8): 167–79.

Trotter, R. T., III, and J. A. Chavira. 1981. *Curanderismo: Mexican American folk healing.* Athens: University of Georgia Press.

Yeatman, G. W., and V. V. Dang. 1980. *Cao gio* (coin rubbing): Vietnamese attitudes towards health care. *Journal of the American Medical Association* 244: 2748–49.

Yoder, D. 1972. Folk medicine. In *Folklore and folklife: An introduction*, ed. Richard M. Dorson, 191–215. Chicago: University of Chicago Press.

Big and Little Moon Peyotism as Health Care Delivery Systems

By Dennis Wiedman

Big Moon Peyotism was introduced in the 1880s to the Delaware, Osage and Quapaw of Northeast Oklahoma by John Wilson, a Delaware-Caddo from Southwest Oklahoma. This form of Peyotism and the Little Moon ritual developed by the Apache, Kiowa, and Comanche of Southwest Oklahoma formed the basis of the two major variations of this religion as practiced by Native Americans throughout North America. An ethnographic and historic comparison of these religious traditions in Northeast Oklahoma presents these as health care delivery systems and highlights the importance of health care as a factor in the acceptance and persistence of Peyotism.

Introduction

The use of peyote for health care purposes was noted by the Spaniards, who recorded its use among the Aztec (Slotkin 1955, 1956), but few scholars have focused on health care as an explanation for the acceptance and persistence of Peyotism, the largest intertribal religion practiced by more than 125,000 North American Indians. Ethnographic fieldwork among Delaware in Northeast Oklahoma indicates that the majority of Peyote meetings were specifically for health care purposes.

From 1885 to the 1920s, when Peyotism and traditional Delaware ceremonies were practiced simultaneously, Peyotism added an important aspect to Delaware life that the traditional religion did not. During these years United States Government Indian Agents and Christian missionaries actively denounced traditional Indian religions, dances, languages, and customs. United States Government policy promoted Western medicine through Indian hospitals and physicians while not recognizing the activities of medicine men and other traditional healers. This transition also mirrored the changes which had occurred throughout the United States, where the medical care system had been transformed from a home-oriented, family-centered system into a **stratified** system associated with the new social and economic urban centers (Knox, Bohland, and Shumsky 1983).

Dennis Wiedman, "Big and Little Moon Peyotism as Health Care Delivery Systems," *Medical Anthropology*, vol. 12, no. 4, pp. 371–387. Copyright © 1990 by Taylor & Francis Group. Reprinted with permission.

EDITOR'S NOTES

social stratification: a system of inequality based upon the ranking of people according to wealth, prestige, power, and other variables.

Peyotism as an organized intertribal religion, with Christian elements and a legal charter as a church, was a direct response to this development and federal policy. Even though traditional Delaware ceremonies continued to take place until the 1920s, they followed the traditional ritual cycle, with the major Big House ceremony held only for twelve days each fall. An annual healing ceremony, the Doll Dance, ceased to be held in the 1930s (Weslager 1973; Prewitt 1981). Peyote meetings, however, could be called at any time an individual had an immediate social, spiritual, or health need. From this perspective, Peyotism became the most prevalent religious and healing system among the Delaware because the traditional religious system and healers did not meet Delaware health needs

The primary purpose of this paper is to present Peyotism as a religious system, which provides moral and spiritual needs, while also functioning as a health care system in providing for its members' physical and mental well-being. This paper will also highlight the importance of the health care aspects of Peyotism in the acceptance and persistence of two major ritual forms among the Delaware: Big Moon and Little Moon Peyotism.

History of Peyotism as a Religion

Legally recognized in Oklahoma since 1918 as the Native American Church, the Peyote religion is based upon the sacramental use of peyote, a small spineless cactus. Peyotists believe God placed this cactus on earth for use by Indians, and they consider it a teacher of the correct way of life, a helper in times of need, and a medicine in times of sickness (Wiedman 1985).

After the forced settlement of many tribes to Indian and Oklahoma Territory in the late 1800s, the use of peyote was formalized into a structured ritual incorporating Native American and Christian concepts. Two major variations, or Peyote Ways, developed in Southwestern Oklahoma by 1885: the Kiowa, Comanche, and Apache developed the Little Moon ritual, and the Delaware-Caddo developed Big Moon Peyotism (La Barre 1967).

Compared with Little Moon Peyotism, Big Moon Peyotism incorporated additional ritual **roles**, material items, and symbols. Big and Little Moon Peyotism as developed in Oklahoma, form the basis of

EDITOR'S NOTES

role: the cultural expectations for persons holding particular social positions.

the two major variations of this religion as practiced by Indian tribes throughout North America. Among the northern tribes Little Moon Peyotism is known as "Half Moon" or the "Tipi Way." In Oklahoma, Big Moon is also known as "Wilson Moon," while the northern and western tribes know it as the "Cross Fire" because of lines drawn on the altar forming a cross (Petrullo 1934:79; Stewart 1987). Stewart (1987:209) noted that both versions "remained dedicated to curing, to sobriety, and to Christian ideals."

Although the Cross Fire ritual of the northern tribes derived from the Wilson Moon, this form of Peyotism is nowhere practiced in the complexity that developed in Northeastern Oklahoma. This paper focuses upon Northeast Oklahoma Delaware Peyotism, which distinguishes most notably between the two variations.

Ritual Structure of Delaware Big Moon and Little Moon Peyotism

When the ritual, social, material, and belief structures of Big and Little Moon Peyotism are compared, there is a common basic structure. Generally speaking, the basic structure of Peyotism involves the communal consumption of peyote during an all-night ceremony, during which time a participant's attention should be focused on peyote and the purpose of the meeting. A basic belief is that peyote can each the proper way of life and that it can cure illnesses. During the ceremony, the participants sit around a crescent moon-shaped altar constructed on the ground. A line extends along the moon from point to point, indicating the "peyote road," or the "road of life," and a large peyote is placed on this line midway between its points. All the participants face towards this "grandfather" peyote and are led by a "road-man" or "road chief," who sits closest to it. The roadman is assisted by a drum chief to his right and a fireman, who sits on the opposite side of the moon near the door The ritual items consist of a staff, fan, rattle, drum, and drumstick (Wiedman 1985). The ceremony is highlighted by five events: the start, midnight, morning, breakfast, and conclusion. Between these events each man takes his turn singing four songs while shaking the rattle and holding the staff and fan. He is accompanied on the drum by a man to his right. After completing his songs, he passes the ritual items to his left, so that they pass clockwise around the altar throughout the night. Following the ceremony, participants, family, and friends eat a dinner prepared by the women.

Upon this basic structure Big and Little Moon Peyotism were founded. Since the standardization of these two variations in the 1880s only minor additions have been made to accommodate the belief and ritual systems of the various Native communities of North America (Wiedman and Greene 1988). The additions include social, material, and symbolic elements, which primarily concern the construction of the ceremonial altar, the addition of ritual officials, the decoration of the ritual items, etiquette during the ceremony, and distinctions in beliefs about prayer and the individual's relation to the roadman, peyote, and God.

Petrullo (1975 [1934]), La Barre (1967), Stewart (1987) and Wiedman (1988a and 1988b) provide descriptions and illustrations of these two religious traditions. Briefly stated, the major differences between these two variations as practiced by the Delaware were:

Little Moon Peyotism

1. Crescent moon-shaped altar made of earth.

2. Four officials: roadman, drum chief, fireman, and cedarman.

3. Singer accompanied on a drum by man who sits to his right, or another man invited to drum by singer.

4. Water outside of *tipi* can be drunk only after special events.

5. Five events in the ceremony:

   A. Start: Statement of purpose. Prayer with tobacco smoked by all. Peyote consumed by all. Four songs by roadman.

   B. Midnight: Water bucket brought in by fireman. Coals from fire spread and cedar incense placed on coals. Eagle whistle blown outside of tipi in four directions by roadman.

   C. Morning: Water brought in by woman who says prayer while smoking tobacco.

   D. Breakfast: Woman brings in water, meat, corn, and fruit.

   E. Quitting: Four songs by roadman shortly after breakfast, or after four complete circles of altar by staff during night.

6. Participants can go outside tipi during night, preferably after midnight, by requesting permission from roadman. On return they can go directly to their seats.

7. When not in use, staff, fan, rattle, and drum are laid on a cloth in front, and slightly to the left, of the roadman.

8. Staff is property of roadman, who uses it wherever he leads a meeting.

Big Moon Peyotism

1. Altar is in the form of a large crescent moon with ground recessed between its points. A line runs along edge of recessed area forming "Peyote Road." Two lines form a cross on the altar. A line runs from the grandfather peyote to sun in the shape of a globe on eastern edge of altar, and a line across the altar forms a crossmark.

2. Eight officials: In addition to four major officials there are two additional firemen and two crossmark men, one sits at each end of the line which forms the cross on the altar.

3. A fireman drums for all singers.

4. Water is inside and is distributed by a fireman on request.

5. Five events in ceremony:

    A. Start: Purpose stated. Prayer with tobacco smoked only by roadman. Peyote consumed by all. Four songs by roadman.

    B. Midnight: Coals from fire are spread. Four songs Sung by roadman.

    C. Morning: Person sponsoring meeting or person who is being healed stands in recessed area between fire and sun. He or she is fanned with eagle fan. Fanning of others, if they so desire.

    D. Breakfast: Brought in and placed in recessed area of altar. Water, meat, corn, and fruit.

    E. Conclusion: Four songs sung by roadman at noon.

6. The staff, which is ornately decorated with draped ribbons, is never laid down. When not in use it is placed upright before the roadman, its tip placed in a hole in the ground.

7. The staff is passed clockwise throughout the night; however, when there is a second row of persons, the staff is passed from the left of a front-row person to a person in the second row. After blessing himself by passing his hands over the staff, second-row person returns staff to next person in front row, to left of person who passed it originally.

8. When a person wishes to go outside, he must get attention of a crossmark man, who signals the roadman to allow the person to exit. On return, before he can take his seat, he stands in recessed area facing the fire and grandfather peyote and is fanned by a fireman with an eagle fan. He then passes to left or right of altar according to side on which he is seated, and walks along edge of recessed area to grandfather peyote. He touches grandfather peyote and then returns to his seat.

9. Anyone who desires to say a prayer out loud with tobacco addresses roadman and communicates his or her needs. Roadman then rolls a tobacco cigarette and prays for individual.

10. Sponsor of meeting or person for whom meeting is held takes a sweatbath directed by roadman at noon before meeting.

11. In most cases recessed altar is made of concrete. Osage and Quapaw built large round houses containing permanent altar; however, Delaware used tipi, no houses were built.

12. Staff stays with owners of permanent altar. Although different roadmen are asked to lead meetings, they use staff which is associated with altar.

History of Delaware Peyotism

The Delaware tribe was originally located in present-day New Jersey, Pennsylvania, and Delaware. After many forced displacements the largest group of 985 settled in Northeastern Oklahoma along the

Caney River in 1867, and a smaller number, 83, settled with the Caddo near Anadarko in Southwestern Oklahoma. In Northeastern Oklahoma the Delaware purchased lands from the Cherokee equal to 160 acres for each Delaware man and they became members of the Cherokee Nation with the same rights and immunities as native Cherokees (Weslager 1972:426–430). In the 1970s, the nearly 8,000 Delaware lived primarily near Dewey and Bartlesville in Washington County (Weslager 1978). By 1990, the Delaware tribal office reports a total of 11,000 members.

The two forms of Peyotism were introduced to the Northeastern Delaware within one year of each other: Little Moon in 1884 and Big Moon in 1885. Elk Hair, a prominent Delaware leader, was the primary adherent of the Kiowa-Comanche Little Moon ritual, while at the same time he was a leader in traditional Delaware ceremonies (Speck 1933).

John Wilson, a Delaware-Caddo also known as Moonhead, was the originator of Big Moon Peyotism and the person who introduced this ritual into Northeastern Oklahoma. Ethnologist James Mooney interviewed John Wilson in 1891. He reported that Wilson: "… assumes the occult powers of authority of a great medicineman, all the powers claimed by him being freely conceded by his people" (Mooney 1965:161).

From about 1885 until his death in 1902, Moonhead regularly visited the Delaware, Osage, and Quapaw among whom he established many peyote churches. Speck (1907:171) reports that by 1902 most of the Osage had taken up Big Moon Peyotism and had become devoted to it. In the 1920s and 1930s, ethnologists Vincenzo Petrullo and Frank Speck wrote that the Delaware primarily practiced Big Moon Peyotism (La Barre 1967:115; Speck 1931, 1937).

George Anderson, the primary Delaware Big Moon leader, related to Speck that Wilson taught his followers that:

> sincere devotion to the sacred rites and teachings revealed would result in the curing of disease by administration of Peyote when taken in the right spirit during the meetings by believers sincere in purpose and observant of the regulations imposed upon them. [Speck 1933:543]

Ethnologist Newcomb visited the Delaware in 1955 and recorded that "Most Delaware peyotists belong to the more liberal and Christianized sect which has been termed Big Moon; a few are adherents to the Little Moon sect" (Newcomb 1955:1042; 1956).

When I began my fieldwork in 1970, I found that the Delaware continued to have great respect for Moonhead, something that was emphasized by the fact that four families claimed a kinship relationship to him. But it was puzzling to find that the leading Delaware roadman and inheritor of Big Moon Peyotism practiced Little Moon Peyotism.

Delaware Peyotism in the 1970s

In 1970, only the Osage practiced the elaborate Big Moon ritual in large wooden houses with concrete altars. The Quapaw, who at one time had as many as nine permanent Big Moon altars, had no active roadman. The last Delaware Big Moon ceremony had been held in 1969.

This does not mean that Peyotism had completely disappeared among the Delaware. The Little Moon ritual had taken its place. For five years, from 1970 to 1975, I participated in Delaware activities. From August of 1972 to August of 1973, my wife and I spent a complete year as participant-observers of daily activities of the leading Delaware peyote families whose homes were the church grounds for Peyote meetings.

Two rented wooden houses separated by about three hundred yards of trees, brush, and hilly ravines were the homes of the extended-family households related through brother and sister. Wood burning stoves heated the homes and kept a man in each household busy chopping, hauling, and splitting firewood. Bottled propane gas was used for cooking in the house, wood fires for cooking outside. One house had an indoor toilet; however, residents and visitors used outside toilets. Water was obtained from rain-filled cisterns; piped in water and a toilet were later installed in one of the houses. Each house had a specially prepared and maintained ground within a hundred feet of the house where the peyote tipi was set up. The nearest neighbors could barely distinguish the all-night drumbeats from the clank-clank-clank of the oil wells, which constantly broke the silence of the oak-and-blackjack-covered hillside.

The Delaware roadman had married a Pawnee woman; his sister, who lived in the other house, had married a Comanche roadman. Both households were identified as Delaware even though the non-Delaware spouses were from prominent peyote families in their own tribes. Delaware and other tribal members from throughout Northeast Oklahoma came to these households to ask for them to have a meeting for their purpose. This intertribal congregation of the Native American Church was known over a wide area and at each Peyote meeting there were persons from tribes throughout Oklahoma. Regular members represented the Delaware, Pawnee, Comanche, Shawnee, Omaha, Quapaw, and Seneca.

Peyote meetings took place throughout the year except for the cold months of December through mid-March. Most of the fifteen meetings were held in a tipi except for one house meeting in November and one in March, when cold weather was extreme. The ceremony usually took place on Saturday night, but when needed it was held any night. During a special time of need, as many as four meetings were held in a two-week period.

An average of seventeen participants (between six and twenty-five) were in attendance at each meeting. Participants ranged in age from twenty-five to seventy-six years old, not including the small children, who slept through the night behind their parents or joined their parents in the morning. A total of eighty-six different people took part in at least one meeting that year. If we consider that for every participant, two additional people attended the dinner the following day, about 250 people took part in the church activities.

When there was no weekend meeting at these locations, core members traveled to one of the surrounding Peyote churches. On nine occasions the core members of this church traveled by car 30 to 250 miles, but usually within 50 miles. On most of these occasions the meetings were planned well in advance, and members were invited as the roadman, other ritual officials, or as special guests. They included meeting places among the Shawnee, Yuchi, Pawnee, Comanche, Ponca, and Cheyenne. The core group did not attend intertribal pow-wows, as they considered them to be a different religious way.

An indication of the intertribal participation in this church is the fact that six different roadmen led the fifteen meetings that year. Besides the Delaware roadman and his Comanche brother-in-law, these included Comanche and Yuchi roadmen.

Each meeting had a purpose that was specified when persons were invited to the meeting. This purpose was the focal point of attention during the ceremony. Four types of purposes were given that year: for a holiday, for a social problem, for rites of passage, and for health problems.

More specifically, one meeting was for the holiday of Thanksgiving, one for a social problem relating to children and separated parents, and three meetings were for rites of passage: a wedding, a birthday, and the end of a mourning period. However the majority of meetings, 66 percent, focused upon specific physical health problems.

Meetings planned well in advance were the rites of passage, Thanksgiving, wedding, birthday, and end of mourning. These were attended by a great number of people as compared to those for health purposes. Four meetings are considered necessary to cure a serious ailment. Since the onset of ailments was often abrupt, first meetings were not planned in advance, and the following three occurred as needed, sometimes giving only one- or two-day notice to the participants. A small group of participants is considered more effective when a specific cure is desired; thus, everyone can focus on the one purpose.

Peyotism and Health Care Delivery

Regardless of the primary purpose, at every meeting some participants brought to the roadman's attention their own problems and health care needs, or those of a family member or a friend. The roadman acted upon these requests by including them in the prayers: by rolling a tobacco cigarette for a special prayer, by preparing peyote for special consumption by the ill person, by fanning the person with an eagle feather and cedar incense, or, in a few cases, by sucking a foreign object from the ill person.

Meetings for health purposes included cases of blindness, a hernia, high blood pressure, and congestive heart failure. In all these major cases the affected person was also being treated by physicians at Claremore Indian Health Service Hospital, a distance of sixty miles by car.

Persons were not only using Peyotism, they used the Indian Health Service, local physicians, and traditional healers. They also readily used patent medicines and home remedies of traditional

Delaware and Western origin. Traditional Delaware recognized two types of healing roles: those who used the power within himself to heal and doctor sick people; and the herbal healer. The power of these healers was obtained through visions granted by the large number of spiritual beings who were subordinate to the creator. To understand the visions, to talk to the medicinal plants, to pray, and to heal in the traditional way, one must be a fluent speaker of the Lenape language (Twaddle 1988:7).

Delaware medicinal plants have been well-documented by Weslager (1973) and Hill (1971). Like pharmaceutical medicines, these plants and the persons familiar with them are specialists in the treatment of specific ailments.

During this study, several Delaware were known for their healing powers and knowledge of a wide variety of plants used as medicines. When a Delaware was not available for the treatment of a person's sickness, members of other tribes were sought out for their expertise. One case was known to have been treated by a Seminole medicine man seventy miles away.

This use of the various health care systems, Peyotism, traditional medicine, and biomedicine, shows that in times of illness many pathways to health care are followed. Although these various health care systems operate independently of one another within this health culture, seldom is one the exclusive provider of care to an individual. Although it was often stated that peyote could cure most ailments, it was considered ineffective for diseases like cancer and diabetes, which were considered to have been brought by the white man (Wiedman 1987, 1989).

Like health care systems in general (Rosser and Mossberg 1977:25), Peyotism was deliberately formed to perform a set of functions, one of which is health care delivery: "the attainment of optimal physical, mental, and social well-being, and not the mere absence of discernible disease" (Weinerman 1971). As detailed in this paper, Peyotism has an organizational structure and specific roles which manage the participants, knowledge, facilities, and commodities, the primary characteristics of a health care delivery system (Roemer 1986).

Many explanations have been proposed in the literature for the acceptance and persistence of Peyotism; however, few have had sufficient participant-observation fieldwork to document the importance of health care as a major factor.

Shonle (1925) explained its appeal as due to diffusion through a culture area with an underlying belief in the supernatural origins of visions. Peyotism has also been analyzed as a revitalization movement, or in strictly sociofunctional terms by Barber (1941) and Hurt (1960). While Weston La Barre did present its psycho-therapeutic aspects, he considered the therapeutic possibilities to be unimpressive (La Barre 1967:147). David Aberle's (1966) study of Navaho Peyotism accounted for the differential acceptance of Peyotism in terms of relative deprivation. The pharmacological study by Edward Anderson (1980:90) clearly notes the medicinal use of peyote by North and Central American Indians, but he states that the curative nature of the plant is due to its psychoactive properties rather than healing chemical substances (Anderson 1980:102).

When data collected over the years are reinterpreted from the health care perspective, they give new meaning to health aspects of Peyotism. Aberle's work is suggestive in this regard. On the basis of interviews with over a hundred Navajo individuals, Aberle found that:

> In the vast majority of cases, initial recourse to peyotism is for the purpose of being cured, or occurs when a member of one's family of orientation or of procreation is ill and is taken to a peyote ceremony. This is true of both members, former members, and people who tried peyote only once or twice. Curing one's self or a family member accounts for about three-quarters of all instances. [Aberle 1966:183]

Thereafter, as they become involved in peyotist activities, they come to see the Native American Church as a combination of cure, ethical code, and inspiration for life. [Aberle 1966:189]

The use of peyote as a medicine is also reflected in the words of the Comanche medicine woman Sanapia: " … some of the Indians call it a sacrament like white peoples who are Christian. God gave that peyote to the Indians to help them when they got sickness." She goes on to say: "It's a medicine and that's the way I use it. Peyote gives me power to make people well" (Jones 1972:23). Additional evidence, and support of this view, comes from botanist Richard Evans Schultes, who studied peyote from the botanical, pharmacological, and cultural perspective. He concluded that the "principal appeal of peyote has been and continues to be centered around the therapeutic and stimulating properties of the plant …" (Schultes 1938).

Morris Opler, although not proposing health care as a factor in Peyotism's acceptance and persistence, did document its early curing aspects. He claims that in the early 1800s, as peyote was used by the Carrizo and Lipan Apache, curing was not a central motive. However, when later adopted by the Mescalero Apache, it was emphasized as a curative rite (Opler 1936). The Mescalero may have had an influence on the curative use of Peyote by the Kiowa, Comanche, and Kiowa-Apache in the 1870s (see Stewart 1987:50).

With the forced settlement of the Southern Plains tribes onto reservations in Southwestern Oklahoma, their economic, social, political, religious, and healing systems underwent dramatic transformations. As a result of the influences of Christian missionaries, their religious belief in **animism** (the belief that all things animate and inanimate possess a spirit or power) was transformed into a greater emphasis on a monotheistic belief in a single, all-powerful God. This change is also reflected by the transformation of the broad use of medicinal plants and substances (Jones 1972) into the Peyotists' increased use of a single medicinal plant and source of spiritual power: peyote. By 1885, the Big Moon and Little Moon ritual had become standardized (Wiedman and Greene 1988), incorporating many new rules which formalized the structure and refined peyote's use as a medicine for the sick (Opler 1938:284).

After seventy-five years many factors affected Big Moon Peyotism's decline in Northeast Oklahoma, including Delaware intermarriage with Euroamericans, acculturation to urban life, and acceptance of Western medical care. With each passing generation the land upon which the permanent Big Moon altars were built was divided among the heirs who, in many cases, were non-Peyotists. For this same reason, Big Moon staffs, which remain with the altar, also passed to non-Peyotists. Furthermore, Big Moon Peyotism, with its complex ritual and added officials, became increasingly structured as a religious system and less effective as a health care delivery system.

Petrullo noted this de-emphasis of medicinal aspects of peyote by Delaware Big Moon Peyotists (Petrullo 1975[1934]:171). This is clearly stated by Willie Long Bone in the early 1930s.

> I don't use Peyote as a medicine. I use it to follow in the footsteps of Jesus. Were it not for this I wouldn't use it at all. It is difficult to use it. It is not at all pleasant, but we have to suffer anyway, the way Jesus did, if we want to go to our Father. There are many other medicines for sickness, but I don't believe in using Peyote that way. [Petrullo 1975[1934]:109]

The leading Delaware roadman during my fieldwork gave several reasons for the decline of Big Moon Peyotism. To him, the Big Moon ceremony was an important occasion with many people involved, and it needed to be planned several weeks in advance. Little Moon meetings, on the other hand, could be called whenever there was a purpose, sometimes the same night (Wiedman fieldnotes).

Although Omer Stewart and others have noted the use of tobacco as one of the ritual differences between Big and Little Moon Peyotism, the social and symbolic differences regarding the use of tobacco with prayer has not been clearly presented. In my view, this is a critical issue which requires further examination. As stated in my fieldnotes the Delaware roadman mentioned:

> that he does not like the Big Moon way because they do not allow an individual to pray with tobacco, or allow talks to be heard for any duration. They are less personal. He believes that the reason for people to go into a meeting is for them to pray and to say what is on their mind and bothering them. This is the way it should be or he would not even be in there.

EDITOR'S NOTES

animism: the belief that all things animate and inanimate possess a spirit or power.

His father ran meetings Big Moon way and the first meetings he attended were Big Moon. But Little Moon is now his preference. [Wiedman fieldnotes 9-8-72]

This difference was succinctly stated by the Comanche roadman:

No one could pray to that peyote for another and have a cure occur. In order for a person to be cured he has to tell that peyote what he wants. [Wiedman fieldnotes 6-20-73]

Cultural interpretation is warranted here. For example, a basic rule applies during both Little Moon and Big Moon peyote meetings. Whenever a person is about to consume peyote or is eating peyote, no one should pass between the person and the grandfather peyote placed on the altar. This rule is strictly enforced by the ritual leaders, and if broken, often leads to disputes in the meetings. To break it is considered a bad omen.

This ritual procedure reflects Peyotism's basic cultural theme of the individual's power and the belief that no person should come between an individual and God. This belief could be interpreted as being derived from the individualism of Southern Plains Indian religion, in which an individual was to have a personal power experience and his or her own vision. When Peyotism was formulated, the Apache, Kiowa, and Comanche combined this belief with monotheism, limiting power-seeking to one power through peyote as a representation of God or Jesus. The Big Moon ritual elaborated on this common philosophy by maintaining the rule that no one should physically pass between an individual consuming peyote and the grandfather peyote. However, since Big Moon procedures are complex and often attended by greater numbers of people than Little Moon ceremonies, four additional officials are needed to maintain the ritual rules: two crossmark men and two additional firemen. Whenever a person wants a special prayer, he communicates his needs to the roadman, who at the appropriate time rolls a tobacco cigarette and prays. By restricting formal prayer and the smoking of tobacco to the roadman and his officials, the Big Moon ritual incorporated a social stratification which symbolically placed an intermediary between an individual and God. Thus, in the view of the Delaware roadman, this reduced the power of prayer and the curing power of peyote.

Certainly, this field research among the Delaware affirms that this religious system has a strong emphasis on health and wellness. Not only could the health care aspects of Peyotism be a major factor in its acceptance and persistence, but conversely, a de-emphasis on health care could also be cause for its decline.

Health-Related Aspects of Peyotism

Although it is not the primary purpose of this paper to present the basis for the healing efficacy of Peyotism, a review of health-related aspects of Peyotism may further our understanding of the dynamics involved. These can be presented at several levels: psychotherapeutic, social, nutritional, psychochemical, and physical. Psychotherapeutic effects of Peyotism have been well presented by Weston La Barre. Suggestive techniques used by the healer influence the patient to develop new patterns of thought and behavior. La Barre portrayed the open prayers as confession and a form of cathartic therapy (La Barre 1947).

The altered state of consciousness produced by the ritual and peyote may be an effective means of altering the individual's cognitive paradigm. Following Wallace's 1966 concept of **mazeway resynthesis**, Peyotism may effectively restructure symbolic meanings or cognitive map. In this way, maladaptive behaviors can be modified, and the morals and principles of Peyotism re-emphasized. In cases when a Western doctor has informed an Indian patient that he is sick because of complex biochemical reactions, the Indian may not understand these terms. But he can undergo symbolic healing by having his ailments, and the doctor's words, reinterpreted during the peyote meeting in such a way that they are understandable. Thus, he is better able to respond to the Western medical system's requests for medication use and dietary and behavioral restrictions. During the year of observation, all the major physical diseases were under a physician's care, and the reinterpretation and explanation of the illnesses were taking place in the Peyote meeting. It might be said that the Western physician treats the "disease," the malfunctioning of biological and/or psychological processes, while the Peyote healer treats the "illness," the psychosocial experience and meaning of perceived disease (cf. Fabrega 1974; Kleinman 1980:72). Thus, the two health care systems are not in conflict or competition with one another; they are complementary and symbiotic.

Prayers spoken in ritual context also serve as information to the participants about social relations and problem-solving. During these symbolic transactions, stress-producing individual, group, and inter-group behaviors are brought to the group's attention in prayers spoken out loud. The evening before and the morning after the meeting are times when participants and visitors carry on casual conversations in small groups. These conversations are often interspersed with jokes and stories about incidents in previous meetings, famous characters, and historic individuals. These abstract conversations often directly relate to a personal problem mentioned in the meeting or to the behavior of

EDITOR'S NOTES

mazeway resynthesis: a psychological process through which a person reorganizes their values, ethics, and sense of self and place in the world.

an individual. These public statements are ways of conveying advice or opinions without directly talking to the person at whom it is aimed.

Social support systems are of great importance to wellness. Church participation and kin-group involvement provide a sense of identity and social solidarity, a setting to meet and make friends, while participating in an important cultural ritual. This type of participation and kin group involvement has been shown to have a positive effect on physiology, most notably hypertension (Janes 1986:196; Walsh 1980). Participants in need benefit from renewed social support and the restructuring of social relations, important aspects of symbolic healing (Dow 1986).

The sharing of information and social support also results in more efficient resource distribution as well as reduced social and psychological stress. Attendance at Peyote meetings as a participant at the ceremony, as a visitor, or as worker at the home includes the ritual consumption of a supper the evening of the meeting and a complete dinner the next afternoon. The remaining food is often taken home by visitors, especially by the elderly. For elderly males who live alone, this may be the only time during the week they eat complete home-cooked meals, and the leftovers provide two or three more meals for them during the week. For the single elderly male and for low-income families, regular attendance at these dinners and the food taken home provide an important nutritional supplement.

Although still speculative, symbolic healing through trance and altered states of consciousness may have an effect on the immunological system by the release of endorphins, which are pain reducers. Research suggests that chronic stress causes the adrenal gland to pump increased amounts of corticosteroids into the bloodstream and these hormones inhibit immune function (Glaser et al. 1987). Stress reduction, on the other hand, has a positive effect on cortisol levels (McGrady et al. 1987). Chemical properties of peyote are structurally similar to the neurohormone epinephrine (Anderson 1980:126). Further research on how immune molecules affect the physiology and metabolism of the brain and body is needed before it is understood how peyote affects the immune system, which, in turn may prevent disease and repair damaged tissue (see Mandler et al. 1986; McClelland and Jemmott 1980; Antonie 1987).

The taste of peyote is so nauseating that to consume any amount requires enormous self-control and a heightened awareness of bodily functions in order to prevent vomiting. The Peyotist also needs firm self-control to restrict movement to a sitting position for nearly twelve hours. Fasting in the form of limited food and water intake during the ceremony also requires control of emotions and behaviors. For the Peyotist who regularly attends meetings, this exercise of concentrated willpower promotes the individual's ability to control his emotions, bodily functions, and possibly his immune system.

Discussion

Because it has had a standardized organization and ritual structure for over a hundred years, Peyotism must be considered successful in meeting its members' needs. Curing and health care, as well as religious concerns, are its primary functions, as evidenced by oral testimony, the literature, and an observed annual ritual cycle, during which two-thirds of all the meetings had the stated purpose of dealing with physical health care problems.

The health culture of a society can be broadly defined as a system of ideas, practices, roles, technologies, and organizations which deal with the problems of health and illness (see Lee 1982:629). Every population has a health culture which incorporates particular ways of meeting its members' health needs. These are a society's repertoire of patterns for cognition, affect, and behavior "which relate specifically to the maintenance of well-being and problems of sickness with which people cope in traditional ways within their own social networks and institutional structures" (Weidman 1988:263). Throughout human evolution it has been necessary for the health culture of a population to be composed of one or more health care delivery systems containing specialized knowledge, medicinal substances technological items, explanations about bodily functions, and social roles for the success of the population.

A population that lacked a properly functioning health care delivery system, in which this specialized knowledge was passed from one generation to another, would be at an adaptive disadvantage.

Native American traditional health culture was woven into religious beliefs and curing practices. Health care delivery was often the role of the religious specialist, the medicine man or a group of individuals in a medicine society. When Native American tribes were forcibly settled on reservations in Oklahoma, their language, social, economic, religious, health culture, and health care systems were greatly impacted. Under these conditions, Peyotism developed as a structured religious and health care system. As one of the health care delivery systems available, Peyotism provides its benefits by assisting its members psychologically, socially, physically, and nutritionally, as well as spiritually and morally. Like physicians, the peyote healer focuses on pathophysiological and social problems. With peyote churches dispersed from at least thirty to fifty miles apart in all but Southeast Oklahoma and the western Panhandle, it is accessible to most participants within an hour's drive.

Anthony Wallace argued that when a population's needs are not met, these stressful conditions lead to a **revitalization movement**: a conscious organized attempt to change cultural behaviors and beliefs (Wallace

1966:158). In his view, this revitalization process explains the development of new religions. Peyotism can also be placed into this theoretical paradigm, especially if it is viewed as a therapeutic movement which reduces stress and physical ailments. Once established, however, a therapeutic movement must maintain its level of effectiveness or it will decline. This change in overall health culture is part of the intricate process by which populations adapt to their environments (Alland 1970).

Within this theoretical framework, we would have to argue that, given health care as its major professed and observed purposes, if Peyotism did not succeed in efficiently providing a positive health outcome, it would lose its members and cease to be a recognized church and health care delivery system. This has not happened. Peyotism continues to be practiced throughout the United States and Canada. In Northeastern Oklahoma, however, where two health care systems based on peyote developed, Big Moon Peyotism became more structured as a religious system and church with less emphasis on providing health care. Consequently, its membership decreased and it ceased to be practiced among the Delaware and Quapaw.

On the basis of this ethnographic and historical analysis, it is clear that Peyotism, like traditional Native American cultures, combines religion and health care in a cultural whole. Within this cultural context, Peyotism functions as a health care delivery system by addressing health needs which are not fully met by the biomedical approach of orthodox medicine, or other traditional healing systems. Following this, it might be predicted that, as a health care delivery system Peyotism will continue to thrive as long as it efficiently and effectively reaches the population, and as long as real or perceived health outcomes result.

Notes

1. This paper is dedicated to Allan and Grace Dale, who dedicated their lives to Peyote and Indian religious freedom. As President of the Native American Church of North America, Allan actively spoke for the Indian use of peyote and its spiritual powers before many courts in the United States. He strongly believed in peyote's healing power and the right of Indians to practice this religion and use this medicine. This paper reflects his life's work of continually educating people to peyote's benefits for the Indian people.

2. I sincerely thank Morris Opler of the University of Oklahoma, and Hazel Weidman of the University of Miami School of Medicine. They not only read this paper, and contributed to its refinement, but also inspired me to pursue its completion. The initial fieldwork was directed by Charles Fairbanks at the University of Florida. During the intensive fieldwork period, occasional visits with Garrick Bailey at the University of Tulsa provided a welcome return to the anthropological perspective.

3. A version of this paper was presented at the Annual Meeting of the American Anthropological Association, November 1988, in Phoenix, Arizona. In a paper, "History and Ethnology of Delaware Peyotism," presented at the Delaware Indian Cultural Exchange Symposium, in June 1988, I provided a detailed ethnographic and historic comparison of Big and Little Moon Peyotism in Northeast Oklahoma, At that time I proposed the importance of health care as a factor in the persistence and success of Peyotism.

References

Aberle, D.

   1966   The Peyote Religion Among the Navaho. Chicago: Aldine.

Alland, A.

   1970   Adaptation in Cultural Evolution: An Approach to Medical Anthropology. New York: Columbia University Press.

Anderson, E.

   1980   Peyote: The Divine Cactus. Tucson: University of Arizona Press.

Antonie, M.

   1987   Neuroendocrine Influences in Psychoimmunology and Neoplasia: A Review. Psychology and Health 1:3–24.

Barber, B.

   1941   A Socio-cultural Interpretation of the Peyote Cult. American Anthropologist 43:673–675.

Csordas, T

   1988   Elements of Charismatic Healing. Medical Anthropology Quarterly, New Series 2(2):121–142.

Dow, J.

   1986   Universal Aspects of Symbolic Healing: A Theoretical Synthesis. American Anthropologist 88:56–69.

Duffy, J.

   1979   The Healers: A History of American Medicine. Urbana: University of Illinois Press.

Fabrega. H.

   1974   Disease and Social Behavior: An Interdisciplinary Perspective. Cambridge, MA: M.I.T. Press.

Glaser, R., J. Rice, J. Sheridan, R. Fertel, et al.

   1987   Stress-Related Immune Suppression: Health Implications. Brain, Behavior, and Immunity 1:7–20.

Hill, G.

   1971   Delaware Ethnobotany. Oklahoma Anthropological Society Newsletter 19(3):3–18.

Hurt, W.

   1960   Factors for the Persistence of Peyote in the Northern Plains. Plains Anthropologist 5:16–27.

Janes, C.

   1986   Migration and Hypertension: An Ethnography of Disease Risk in an Urban Samoan Community. *In* Anthropology and Epidemiology: Interdisciplinary Approaches to the Study of Health and Disease. C. Janes, R. Stall, and S. Gifford, eds. Pp. 175–211. Boston: D. Reidel.

Jones, D.

   1972   Sanapia: Comanche Medicine Women. New York: Holt, Rinehart and Winston.

Kleinman, A.

   1980   Patient and Healers in the Context of Culture: An Exploration of the Borderland Between Anthropology, Medicine, and Psychiatry. Berkeley: University of California Press.

Knox, P, J. Bohland, and N. Shumsky

1983   Urban Transition and the Evaluation of Medical Care Delivery Systems in America. Social Science and Medicine 17:37–43.

La Barre, W.

1947   Primitive Psychotherapy in Native American Cultures: Peyotism and Confession. Journal of Abnormal and Social Psychology 42(3):294–309.

1967   The Peyote Cult. Connecticut: The Shoe String Press. (Reprint of 1938 Yale University Publications in Anthropology No 19.)

Lee, R.

1982   Comparative Studies of Health Care Systems. Social Science and Medicine 16:629–642. Mandler, R., W. Biddison, R.

Mander, and S. Serrate

1986   Beta-Endorphin Augments the Cytolytic Activity and Interferon Production of Natural Killer Cells. Journal of Immunology 136:934–939.

McClelland, D., and J. Jemmott

1980   Power Motivation, Stress and Physical Illness. Journal of Human Stress 6:6–15.

McGrady, A., M. Woerner, G. Bernal, and J. Higgins

1987   Effect of Biofeedback-Assisted Relaxation on Blood Pressure and Cortisol Levels in Normotensives and Hypertensives. Journal of Behavioral Medicine 10:301–310.

Mooney, J.

1965   The Ghost-Dance Religion and the Sioux Outbreak of 1890. Chicago: University of Chicago Press. Reprint of 1896 14th Annual Report of the Bureau of American Ethnology for 1892–1893, Part 2.

Newcomb, W. W.

1955   A Note on Cherokee-Delaware Pan Indianism. American Anthropologist 57:1041–1045. 1956 The Culture and Acculturation of the Delaware Indians. University of Michigan, Museum of Anthropology, Anthropological Papers, 10:113–122.

Olper, M.

1936   The Influence of Aboriginal Pattern and White Contact on a Recently Introduced Ceremony, the Mescalero Peyote Rite. Journal of American Folklore 191 & 192:143–166.

1938   The Use of Peyote by the Carrizo and Lipan Apache Tribes. American Anthropologist 40(2):271–285.

Petrullo, V.

1975   (1934] The Diabolic Root: A Study of Peyotism, the New Indian Religion, Among the Delawares. New York: Octagon Books.

Prewitt, T.

1981   Tradition and Culture, Change in the Oklahoma Delaware Big House Community: 1867–1924. University of Tulsa Laboratory of Archeology, Contributions in Archeology #9.

Roemer, M.

1986   Introduction to the U.S. Health Care System. New York: Springer.

Rosser, J., and H. Mossberg

1977   An Analysis of Health Care Delivery, New York: John Wiley, and Sons.

Schultes, R. E.

1938   The Appeal of Peyote as a Medicine. American Anthropologist 40:698.

Shonie, R.

1925   Peyote: The Giver of Visions. American Anthropologist 27:53–75.

Slotkin, J. S.

1955   Peyotism, 1521–1891. American Anthropologist 57:202–230.

1956   The Peyote Religion: A Study in Indian-White Relations. Glencoe, IL: The Free Press.

Speck, F. G.

1907   Notes on the Ethnology of the Osage Indians. University of Pennsylvania, Transactions of the University Museum 2(2):159–171.

1931   A Study of the Delaware Big House Ceremony. Publications of the Pennsylvania Historical Commission. #2 Harrisburg.

1933   Notes on the Life of John Wilson, the Revealer of Peyote, as Recalled by his Nephew, George Anderson. General Magazine and Historical Chronicle 35:539–556.

1937   Oklahoma Delaware Ceremonies, Feasts and Dances. Philadelphia: The American Philosophical Society.

Stewart, 0.

1987   Peyote Religion: A History. Norman: University of Oklahoma Press.

Twaddle, A.

1988   Traditional Healing Practices of the Delaware. Paper presented at the Delaware Indian Cultural Exchange Symposium, June 1988. New Philadelphia, Ohio: Kent State University.

Wallace, A.

1966   Religion: An Anthropological View. New York: Random House.

Walsh, A.

1980   The Prophylactic Effect of Religion on Blood Pressure Levels Among a Sample of Migrants. Social Science and Medicine 14B:59–64.

Weslager, C. A.

1972   The Delaware Indians: A History. New Brunswick: Rutgers University Press.

1973   Magic Medicines of the Indians. Somerset, NJ: Middle Atlantic Press.

1978   Delaware Indian Westward Migration. Somerset, NJ: Middle Atlantic Press.

Weidman, H.

1988   A Transcultural Perspective on Health Behavior. In Health Behavior: Emerging Research Perspectives. D. Gochman, ed. New York: Plenum.

Weinerman, E. R.

1971   Research on Comparative Health Service Systems. Medical Care 9:272–290.

Wiedman, D.

1985   Staff, Fan, Rattle, and Drum: Spiritual and Artistic Expressions of Oklahoma Peyotists. American Indian Art Magazine 10(3):38–45.

1987   Type II Diabetes Mellitus, Technological Development and Oklahoma Cherokee. *In* Encounters with Biomedicine: Case Studies in Medical Anthropology. H. Baer, ed. Pp. 43–71. New York: Gordon and Breach Science Publishers.

1988a   The History and Ethnology of Delaware Peyotism. Paper presented at the Delaware Indian Cultural Exchange Symposium, June 1988. New Philadelphia, Ohio: Kent State University.

1988b   Big and Little Moon Peyotism as Health Care Delivery Systems. Paper presented at the Annual Meeting of the American Anthropological Association, Phoenix, Arizona, November 1988.

1989   Adiposity or Longevity: Which Factor Accounts for the Increase in Type II Diabetes Mellitus When Populations Acculturate to an Industrial Technology? Medical Anthropology 11(3):237–253. n. d. Unpublished fieldnotes 1970–1973.

Wiedman, D., and C. Greene

1988   Early Kiowa Peyote Ritual and Symbolism: The 1891 Drawing Books of Silverhorn (Haungooh). American Indian Art Magazine 13(4):32–41.

CRITICAL THINKING QUESTIONS

1. Identify and discuss the characteristics of folk medicinal systems as outlined by O'Connor and Hufford. Use the other readings from this unit to illustrate your discussion.

2. Why is efficiency so important to medical residents? Identify and discuss at least two barriers that residents experience when trying to be efficient. To what do residents attribute their failures to be efficient? Please discuss and use examples from the article by Szymczak and Bosk.

3. Wiedman states that "Peyotism has an organizational structure and specific roles which manage the participants, knowledge, facilities, and commodities, the primary characteristics of a health care delivery system." Provide an example of each of these characteristics from the reading and discuss them.

UNIT 6
Medical Technology

··

Editor's Introduction

The purposes of unit VI are to highlight the breadth of technology use in medicine, to introduce the sociological perspective on this topic, and to illustrate some of the ways medical technologies and humans interact. In sociology, **technology** is part of material culture and refers to any objects used to perform a task and the processes involved in their use. For example, a pacemaker, the processes used to determine its use, and its actual use are all pacemaker-related technology. In medicine, technology refers to everything from Band-Aids to cardiac stents to complex, computerized medical records systems.

technology: any objects used to perform a task and the processes involved in their use.

It is always important to study the cultural system in which technology occurs in order to determine how it will be used, by whom, and for what purposes. *Technology in and of itself is benign but can be helpful or harmful depending upon how it is used.* The development and maintenance of medical technology is a political process involving the needs, desires, and powers of various stakeholders, such as pharmaceutical companies, patients, doctors, insurance companies, politicians, and more. This confusing and constrained process sometimes results in unnecessary technology being developed, while needed technology goes undeveloped.

Rose Weitz[1] reviews of cardiopulmonary resuscitation (CPR) from the **critical perspective** in sociology. The purpose of this technology is to resuscitate someone whose lungs and heart have stopped, typically resulting in sudden death. Prior to modern medicine, people were

critical perspective: a theoretical perspective in sociology in which the focus is on the assessment and critique of social phenomena in light of power relations.

---

1 Rose Weitz. *The Sociology of Health, Illness, and Healthcare: A Critical Approach*, 7th ed. (Boston, MA: Cengage Learning Custom Publishing, 2017).

generally accepting of death, often explaining it as "God's will." However, in modern medicine, doctors have become increasingly interested in restoring life to those who have died suddenly. Sudden death is quite common and mostly due to stroke or heart disease. Cardiopulmonary resuscitation is most successful when performed on people who have drowned or been struck by lightning. Sadly, those who have died suddenly from stroke or heart disease fare less well when CPR is applied due to a variety of concurrent conditions, as well as the application of CPR itself. The average person receiving CPR has a 1–3 percent chance of surviving, at an estimated cost of about $500,000 dollars per person. Survival may be brief and accompanied by significant neurological damage. *In the end, CPR demonstrates the cultural, political, and economic variables that are at the root of the social construction of technology.* CPR would not have become popular if corporations did not have a vested interest in it. Additionally, CPR would not have become so widely used if corporations had to prove its efficacy. In and of itself, CPR is benign, but it can be helpful or harmful depending upon how it is used.

Beginning with a broad view, the article "Medical Sociology and Technology: Critical Engagements," by Monica J. Casper and Daniel R. Morrison, provides a "snapshot" of sociology related to biomedical technology developed and managed over the last fifty years. Their review focuses on three areas, the first being *how medical technology has shaped medical practices*. They illustrate their findings with a fine history of the use of ultrasound, which diversified medical jobs due to the need for sonographers. Over the past fifty years, ultrasound has impacted the ways we define fetuses, pregnancy, personhood, life, and patient-hood. It has also altered people's perceptions of what *good* mothers should do. Second, Casper and Morrison focus on *how medical technology has reconfigured human bodies*, raising important issues. For instance, they discuss how the definitions of bipolar disorder have had to be standardized across cultures so that the pharmaceutical industry could treat bipolar disorder globally. They conclude that pharmaceuticals often come first, through the machinations of global capitalism seeking new patients, bodies, or markets to treat. Finally, they focus on *how technology has been key to the emergence of new medical social movements*. We can all think of examples of this, such as the breast cancer movement and, more recently, the movement that has arisen around water safety due to pollution of the water in Flint, Michigan. Medical sociology scholars have investigated the emergence, development, and maintenance of movements based on health status. Medical sociologists have made tremendous contributions to social science, having broad-reaching impacts, even outside the field.

In narrowing our view of the sociology of medical technology, the article "The Sociological Concomitants of the Pharmaceutical Industry and Medications" by John Abraham speaks specifically to the issues regarding expansions in the pharmaceutical industry and in prescribing medications. Abraham challenges the *biomedical thesis*, which posits that these increases are due to the response of biomedical science to new and growing health needs. To support this challenge, Abraham investigates the pharmaceutical industry, the drug regulatory state, and patients as organized interests. These mutually interacting variables play a significant part in what he calls *pharmaceuticalization*, or the process by which social, behavioral, or bodily conditions are treated or deemed to be in need of treatment or intervention with pharmaceuticals by doctors, patients, or both. Abraham supports his thesis with a review of the condition ADHD, which convincingly illustrates the ways in which pharmaceuticalization is superior to the biomedical thesis as an explanatory concept. He writes a thorough discussion of the impact of pharmaceutical advertising on people's health, which has grown significantly more than research and development in the industry. He soundly grounds the concept of pharmaceuticalization within the medicalization milieu and demonstrates its superiority over the biomedical thesis for explaining increases in production and prescription of pharmaceuticals.

Sociology is uniquely suited to investigate medical technology because of the field's broad perspectives, organizational analysis, and attention to power relations. Casper and Morrison present a wide-ranging view of the field in their article, reviewing fifty years of study related to how medical technology shapes medical practice, how it influences and reconfigures human bodies, and how it inspires social movements. Abraham introduces the concept of pharmaceuticalization and contrasts it with the traditional biomedical thesis. Together, the readings in unit VI provide a glimpse of the both the breadth and depth the discipline of medical sociology has to offer.

Medical Sociology and Technology

Critical Engagements

By Monica J. Casper and Daniel R. Morrison

Abstract: In this selective review of the literature on medical sociology's engagement with technology, we outline the concurrent developments of the American Sociological Association section on medicine and advances in medical treatment. We then describe theoretical and epistemological issues with scholars' treatment of technology in medicine. Using symbolic interactionist concepts, as well as work from the interdisciplinary field of science and technology studies, we review and synthesize critical connections in and across sociology's intellectual relationship with medical technology. Next, we discuss key findings in these literatures, noting a shift from a focus on the effects of technology on practice to a reconfiguration of human bodies. We also look toward the future, focusing on connections between technoscientific identities and embodied health movements. Finally, we call for greater engagement by medical sociologists in studying medical technology and the process of policy-making—two areas central to debates in health economics and public policy.

T he Medical Sociology Section of the American Sociological Association was founded in 1959, at the turn of a decade that had witnessed tremendous advances in medical technology. Cardiopulmonary resuscitation was innovated, and the first pacemaker was developed. Penicillin was chemically synthesized in the 1940s, ushering in an era of mass production of antibiotics. Salk fashioned a polio vaccine in 1952, and by 1955 it was being distributed to American schoolchildren (Oshinsky 2005). The first kidney transplants were performed, and dialysis was innovated to treat kidney failure. Heart transplants followed. Scientists researched the birth control pill in a shifting context of sexual politics, successfully but under ethically dubious conditions (Briggs 2002). The price of hospital care doubled in the 1950s, and national health expenditures grew to 4.5 percent of the gross national product (GNP) (Starr 1982). Health insurance companies began to spread across the United States, inaugurating employer-based benefits, and limited private coverage for people who could afford it (Murray 2007; Quadagno 2006).

In 2009, 50 years later, health care accounted for 16 percent of the **gross domestic product (GDP)**, the highest ratio among industrialized

> **EDITOR'S NOTES**
>
> **gross domestic product (GDP):** the total monetary value of all the goods and services produced within a country in a specific time period.

Monica J. Casper and Daniel R. Morrison, "Medical Sociology and Technology: Critical Engagements," *Journal of Health and Social Behavior*, vol. 51, pp. S120–S132. Copyright © 2010 by SAGE Publications. Reprinted with permission.

nations (Robert Wood Johnson Foundation 2009). And according to the American Public Health Association, approximately 47 million Americans (many employed at least part-time) were uninsured. The new millennium brought expanded use of genetic technologies, growth in nanotechnology, diffusion of knowledge produced by the Human Genome Project (HGP), a booming transnational pharmaceutical industry, new reproductive technologies, standardization of care, and escalating visualization and digitalization of medicine. The twenty-first century ushered in biomedicalization across sectors (Clarke et al. 2003, 2010), new health movements (e.g., Brown et al. 2004; Brown 2007; Epstein 1996, 2008; Klawiter 2004, 2008), and translational research (the practical application of scientific research) (Wainwright et al. 2006)—alongside ongoing contention about U.S. health care. The 2008 election of President Obama, whose campaign platform emphasized health reform, deepened public debates.

Across the half-century lifespan of the Medical Sociology Section, during which sweeping changes have impacted American society as a whole, technologies have changed dramatically, too, from large "machines at the bedside" to tiny pills and devices that enter into and transform human bodies, and information technologies that have altered if not restructured health care provision. These have been central to health care practices and financing (or lack thereof), politics of reform, health outcomes, and scholarship. Medical sociologists have investigated both the category of technology writ large and specific drugs, devices, digital innovations, and technical practices such as neonatal intensive care (e.g., Anspach 1993; Zetka 2003). Many scholars explore the essential "nature" of technology; contestation surrounds the term and its application to specific devices, techniques, and practices (Nye 2006).

The substantive and theoretical questions medical sociologists have pursued are as complex and capacious as the shifting technological landscape itself—far too extensive to fully document here. In offering a half-century "snapshot" of research on biomedical technology, we briefly profile three major foci: how technologies have reshaped medical practices; how technologies have reconfigured human bodies and our conceptions of them; and how technologies have been crucial to the emergence of new health social movements. While there has been major work on medical technologies, until the turn of this century sociologists did not attend thoroughly to technical aspects of medical practice. Only within a theoretical paradigm in which technology was considered peripheral could we get an account of the social transformation of American medicine that little discusses the role of key technologies (much less science) in professionalization (Starr 1982).

Theoretical Developments

Part of our charge for this issue of *JHSB*, and the ASA session from which it originated in 2009, was to articulate our key findings about technology. Yet *what* we know is inextricably bound up with *how* we know. Technologies have varied across 50 years; so, too, have theories, concepts, and methods for understanding them. Thus, we cannot discuss shifts in our knowledge about technologies without chronicling the myriad ways in which scholars have approached the topic. These **epistemological** developments have contributed to our collective knowledge about technology, advancing medical sociology while also broadening its connections to other scholarly areas. Concepts such as medicalization and biomedicalization and a range of perspectives (e.g., symbolic interactionist, feminist, constructionist, and social movement approaches) have significantly reconfigured what "technology" means, under what conditions, and for whom.

In the mid-twentieth century and beyond, nascent sociologists of health and medicine were interested in the impact of particular technologies, as medical professionals used them "at the bedside" (Reiser and Anbar 1984). These technologies, often framed as external to meatier intellectual topics, were studied to understand the social order of medical work and the people who engaged in it as practitioners and patients. The focus was not on technology per se, but rather on the practices altered by introduction of new devices. Theoretically, the goal was to elucidate the contours of biomedicine itself, and not necessarily the tools of the trade or their unique, varied technical histories (e.g., Strauss et al. 1985).

Medical technologies have long been criticized as one form of medicalization (Zola 1972), a potentially dehumanizing process that restricts the autonomy of both experts and nonexperts as they confront pain, suffering, and death. Illich (1975) claimed that interventions intended to make sick people well in fact made sick people sicker, turning progress into pathogenesis. Technologies designed to alleviate symptoms of disease, according to this view, prolong suffering needlessly, and at exorbitant cost. Illich's concern with iatrogenic diseases, medicalization, and the high costs and profits of pharmaceuticals and medical devices remain with us, and they constitute a subtext of contemporary debates about health care. Other scholars of the political economy of health care extended these debates (McKinlay 1984; Navarro 1986). Medical machinery now monitors fetuses during delivery, while magnetic resonance imaging (MRI) maps our brains—each technology one step in the process of defining (or divining) the normal and the pathological (Canguilhem 1991; Foucault 1994, 2008).

EDITOR'S NOTES

epistemology: a branch of philosophy concerned with knowing.

Further developments, such as more complicated understandings of medicalization and stratification, were spurred by women's health movements of the 1970s (Lorber and Moore 2002). Feminist scholarship has both celebrated and critiqued the medical profession and its practices and technologies (Clarke and Olesen 1999; Ruzek, Olesen, and Clarke 1997). These studies underscored power relations embedded in medical technologies, and their differential impact on women relative to men. Indeed, research on women's health has long emphasized that health care is stratified (Ginsburg and Rapp 1995), as are medicalization experiences (Bell 1995, 2009; Riessman 1983). Some women (usually white, middle-class women) receive too much care and unnecessary interventions while many other women (especially poor women and women of color) receive too little. This chronic tension has provided diverse perspectives on, and varying levels of appreciation for, women's health care.

Symbolic interactionists, rooted in **pragmatism** and the Chicago School, created an early and vital home within the sociology of medicine. These contributions have focused, in part, on social interactions within medicine (e.g., hospitals, clinics, nursing homes) as forms of work (Strauss et al. 1985). This approach led to surprising findings about ways in which doctors, nurses, and other health professionals make the work of others easier, for example smoothing out ruffled emotions or preparing families for bad news (Star and Strauss 1999; Strauss 1988). Symbolic interactionists also analyzed medical practices in terms that highlight processes instead of outcomes. From Glaser and Strauss's (1965) early work on dying, to Charmaz's (1991) portrait of chronic illness, to Timmermans's (1999) study of cardiopulmonary resuscitation (CPR), symbolic interactionists have documented and theorized medical work, technologies, and care, refreshing such stalwart sociological concepts as trajectory.

Strauss and colleagues analyzed uses of machines for diagnosis and treatment, including laboratory tests, mobile X-ray machines, and heart rate monitors, as well as the growing army of technicians who do the **"articulation work"** between human patients and medical technologies (Strauss et al. 1985; Wiener et al. 1997). Chronic illness, they found, led to a growing reliance on medical technologies for monitoring and maintaining health. The major thrust of this research investigated the

EDITOR'S NOTES

pragmatism: a philosophical approach that assesses the strength of theories and beliefs based upon their practical application.

EDITOR'S NOTES

articulation work: labor done by technicians that mediates between the user (in this case, a doctor) and technology.

role of technology in changing practices. How, for example, did doctors, nurses, and patients respond to new technologies? How did technologies affect patients' illness experiences? What was the relationship between technologies and new systems of professional knowledge? How did technology impact conceptions of the patient and his or her illness? These questions continue to drive sociological research on health care technologies (Conrad and Gabe 1999; Franklin 2007).

Working at the intersection of medical sociology and science and technology studies, scholars developed other concepts (Clarke and Star 2007). For example, Star and Griesemer (1989) theorized **boundary objects**, or those objects (such as fetuses, genes, and brains) whose meanings are common and flexible enough to be intelligible across social arenas, but distinct and obdurate enough to carry specific localized meanings. Cultural and material characteristics of these objects, both within and across social arenas, make shared understandings, collaboration, and work itself possible. For example, Williams et al. (2008) show how human embryos as boundary objects link the biomedical worlds of embryonic stem cells and pre-implantation genetic diagnosis. Similarly, Fujimura's (1988, 1996) notion of "bandwagons" in clinical research made possible new understandings of the theory and method packages that clinicians and scientists use in advancing their work. And Clarke and Fujimura's (1992) theoretical elaboration of "the right tools for the job" offered new material, symbolic, and institutional parameters for locating technologies in practice. This body of work allowed scholars to see how previously invisible technologies *work* in the practical accomplishment of science.

Scholars have also generated new ideas about classification as an organizing concept for scientific and biomedical practice, and they also have shown how classification systems are themselves technologies. By unpacking the processes by which classification systems are created and sustained, Bowker and Star (2000) demonstrate the social and political impulses that animate these. Their work also illustrates the ways in which messy, complex practices are conceptually narrowed in order to "fit" within existing knowledge systems. These classification systems as technologies are crucial for organizing knowledge and practice. For example, proposed revisions to the *Diagnostic and Statistical Manual of Mental Disorders* (DSM) would remove Asperger's Syndrome, placing

EDITOR'S NOTES

boundary objects: objects and information that can be used in different ways by different communities.

it under the more general "autism spectrum disorders" (ASD). Such changes have real consequences for patients, who often define themselves as distinct from people with autism (Grinker 2010; Tanner 2010).

Timmermans and Berg (2003) critique evidence-based medicine as a type of technology that provides (or claims to provide) "gold standard" care. Similar classification practices occur for large-scale projects, such as the "International Classification of Diseases," "Nursing Interventions Classification" (Bowker and Star 2000), and the DSM (Horwitz 2002). Clarke and Casper (1996; see also Casper and Clarke 1998) focus on practices of reading and classifying pap smears. Simple diagnostic practices allow many tests to be analyzed per day, while at the same time rendering classification more difficult for lab technicians who meticulously examine specimens and slides. Classification schemes thus attempt to make sense of nebulous biological material (Keating and Cambrosio 2002, 2003).

Clarke and colleagues (2003, 2010) reformulated a central concept in medical sociology—medicalization—that was not routinely associated with technology, turning our attention toward contemporary, cutting-edge forms of "biomedicalization." This term encompasses both old and new practices, such as genome-wide association studies, nanoscale medicine that upends common sense distinctions between organic and inorganic matter, and devices made to alter electrical signals within the brain. To some degree, biomedicalization brings us full-circle to earlier notions of medicalization (Zola 1972; Conrad 2005, 2007), but the concept is updated and expanded theoretically for the twenty-first century. Biomedicalization is inflected with characteristic symbolic interactionist and science and technology studies attention to (1) processes and knowledge, (2) an interweaving of medicine with science, (3) recognition of vertical and horizontal integration of health care markets and biocapital, (4) introduction of nascent technologies and reinventions of the old, and (5) new organotechnical configurations of human bodies (Cooper 2008).

Finally, medical sociologists have taken up Foucauldian concepts, including biopolitics, to theorize individual health in relation to governmentality and governance (Armstrong 1995; Cooper 2008; Waldby 1996, 2000). Others have utilized Foucault's notion of **biopower** to underscore the productive capacities of human bodies (Hatch 2009; Waldby and

Mitchell 2006). While Foucault's work has been highly influential, he did not address the specific role of technologies (e.g., tests, prosthetics, drugs) in and on biopolitical processes. Rather, he focused on knowledge as a kind of social apparatus or technology that shaped systems of governance and attempted control over life. He described other social technologies, such as the panopticon, a prison system designed such that one guard could survey all prisoners without himself being seen (Foucault 1995). This form of governance, with its imagined (or real) surveillance, ultimately affected notions of human health and well-being. More recent Foucauldian work considers twenty-first century technologies in relation to new discursive and institutional formations, and the consequences of these for human bodies and lives (Casper and Moore 2009; Lakoff 2005; Talley 2008).

In sum, in mid-twentieth century theoretical paradigms, technologies were often black-boxed. That is, the object of analysis was not technology per se, but rather practices surrounding the technology and people who both used it and on whom it was used. Political, economic, and early feminist perspectives recognized the intensely political valence of technologies, yet these perspectives saw technology as fairly static. Technologies were conceptualized as inert, ahistorical objects, uninteresting in and of themselves but with a dynamic capacity to reshape social practices and reorganize human bodies. Symbolic interactionist, feminist, and science and technology studies approaches, while highlighting practices, began to focus on technologies themselves. Previously black-boxed medical technologies were dissected and their historical, cultural, and political innards examined. In newer approaches, there is vivid and sustained recognition that technologies, health care practices, bodies, and identities are continually and mutually shaped, with innumerable consequences for human lives.

Key Findings

Impact of Technologies in and on Practice

Over the past 20 years, a major shift has occurred in the organization and goals of medicine, in which technical innovations have reshaped the contours of practice (Clarke et al. 2003, 2010). Medical sociologists have engaged with technology, using a "technology in practice" perspective, akin to the "science in practice" perspectives utilized by science and technology scholars (Pickering 1992). They have shown how professionals, patients, and others interact with and through medical technologies (and with each other via technologies) while also showing how new and old technologies influence health care practices and other aspects of social life. Through these interactions, new meanings and categories—of patienthood, humanity, disease, risk, and health—are forged. These shifts mark a move from enhanced control over external nature to the harnessing and transformation of internal nature, often rebuilding life itself (Franklin 2000; Rose 2007), along with its fundamental properties.

Thompson (2005), for example, shows how women undergoing in vitro fertilization mobilize different forms of argument, reflection, and dialogue to account for success or failure. Instead of lacking agency, we see agency made operative through objectification. This "**ontological** choreography," as Thompson (2005) termed it, describes the development of actions and ideas that link persons with (and through) reproductive technologies in domains of practice. Dumit (2003), by contrast, shows how positron emission tomography (PET) brain imaging technologies are used to bolster professional accounts of "knowing" human types or persons, tracking the technology from development to implementation to cultural impact. These studies are exemplary in their descriptions and analyses of people and medical technologies interacting.

The history of ultrasound is also revealing. Ultrasound was developed for detecting icebergs after the sinking of the Titanic, expanded into naval warfare during World War I, and later used in manufacturing of metals (Yoxen 1987). Early twentieth century practitioners believed ultrasound could destroy tumors, and subsequent use grew exponentially between the 1930s and 1950s. Visual mapping of the body was infinitely more appealing as the hazards of X-rays became known (Caufield 1989). In the 1970s, ultrasound was central to the emerging field of fetal medicine as clinicians attempted to locate the "unborn" patient, thus advancing the field and playing a key role in the evolution of fetal surgery (Blizzard 2007; Casper 1998). Critics debate benefits vis-à-vis measurable risks, yet ultrasound has become a normal, even highly anticipated part of prenatal care in the United States, offering pregnant women their first "baby" snapshots to hang on the refrigerator (Taylor 2000). Ultrasound has significantly transformed medical practice, creating new forms of work (e.g., increasing the need for sonographers) across the past half-century; making possible new cultural meanings of fetuses, pregnancy, personhood, life, and patienthood; and altering public and private perceptions of what "good" mothers should do (e.g., abstain from alcohol, certain recreational activities, and sex) (Burri and Dumit 2008; Casper 1998; Oakley 1984; Taylor 2008).

In the new millennium, other technologies have become part of medical practice, transforming routine procedures, shifting contexts of care, and generating new meanings of expertise. For example, health care systems have increasingly relied on the Internet to connect patients and doctors across long (and even short) distances. Hospitals of all sizes and resource levels use electronic medical records to store patient information and log medical records, prognoses, and outcomes. These records have multiple uses beyond simple record-keeping. For example, genome-wide association studies integrate genetic information from patients with de-identified medical records in a search for correlations between certain genetic profiles and disease (Roden et al. 2008). **Biobanking**—the establishment of repositories of human biological material—is also changing medical practice, providing new forms of bio-data for clinical research and practice (Gottweis and Petersen 2008). Research on attitudes toward DNA biobanking found widespread support among a sample of patients (Pulley et al. 2008).

EDITOR'S NOTES

biobanking: (see definition in reading)

Such examples of technoscientific developments—from MRI (Joyce 2008) to personalized medicine (Hedgecoe 2004)—can be seen across health care delivery and research infrastructures. Of course, as with women's health care described above, these "advances" are stratified in their application: Elites everywhere receive "too much" boutique care, while impoverished people in both the global North and South lack even the most basic levels of nutrition and hygiene.

Reconfigurations of Human Bodies

Medicine in the early- to mid-twentieth century could be characterized by a mechanical notion of widespread application of technologies to human bodies and use of technical objects on bodies. Such technologies, many innovated in military contexts, unquestionably affected bodies, as they were designed to do, with the aim of improving human health. Serlin (2004), for example, nimbly traces the origins and impacts of an "engineering" model in postwar America that resulted in new cultural meanings of the prosthetic and collective recognition of our "replaceable" body parts. Yet a key shift in medical technology has been the introduction of novel pills, devices, and other objects, both small and large, which remake bodies, often from the inside out. Clarke (1995) described this move from technologies of control to technologies of transformation, marking an epochal shift from the "modern" to the "**postmodern**" period. These technical practices have produced variations in bodies across time and space, alongside new epistemological frameworks.

EDITOR'S NOTES

postmodernism: a theoretical perspective that addresses and challenges traditional ideologies of the modern era.

In 1989, Nelkin and Tancredi (1989) documented, in vaguely alarmist prose, the rise of "dangerous diagnostics"—a set of technologies, such as genetic testing for possible future maladies and IQ tests, that increasingly pervaded the social sphere and threatened individual bodies and rights. They analyzed genetic technologies and biological information in social context, but they did not delve into the historical and cultural configurations of the technologies themselves, or their impacts, on bodies. One such "dangerous diagnostic" is amniocentesis. As Rothman (1993) argued, use of this prenatal test spurred a new ontological embodied category, the "tentative pregnancy." She found that until a negative test result proved optimal health of a fetus, pregnant women could not fully accept their pregnancies. On the other hand, a positive diagnosis of genetic aberration created moral and bodily dilemmas; in the absence of prenatal treatment options and/or counseling, women with "defective" fetuses were confronted with the hollow "choice" of abortion. Rapp (2000) later explored these dynamics among a more ethnically and economically diverse group of women, finding a more intricate set of embodied politics.

Duster ([1990] 2003) presented a nuanced analysis of genetic technologies and risks posed to civil liberties and bodies by recycled explanations of science, heredity, and race. He suggested that genetic information reproduces structural inequalities, thus diluting any potential impact toward alleviation of human suffering. In Duster's story, the technologies have both histories and politics, as do the humans. In 2004, Hedgecoe offered an ethnographic account of genetics in practice, documenting the ascendance of personalized medicine and its impact on patients and practices. Wailoo and Pemberton (2006) then placed race, ethnicity, and racialized bodies front and center in their historical analysis of Tay-Sachs, cystic fibrosis, and sickle cell disease.

One of the most startling and instructive examples of old and very new technologies reshaping human bodies and lives is that of pharmaceuticals. A special issue of *Sociology of Health and Illness* (Williams, Gabe, and Davis 2008) explored multifaceted issues including direct-to-consumer advertising, sleep drugs, the human papillomavirus (HPV) vaccine, antiretroviral therapy, and stem cells. For example, Casper and Carpenter (2008) showed, with respect to the innovative and controversial HPV vaccine, that new technologies transform clinical practices: "the vaccine reveals gendered aspects of the doctor-patient relationship while creating new categories of patients and new pathways to medicalization of girls' bodies. ... New drugs may reorder or forge new health-care practices and markets" (p. 890). These transnational dynamics are increasingly played out on the bodies of women in developing nations, often those women most desperately in need of new preventive and healing technologies (Carpenter and Casper 2009).

Similarly, in their landmark volume, anthropologists Petryna, Lakoff, and Kleinman (2006) describe the state of affairs:

> Major pharmaceutical breakthroughs occurred during and after World War II ... After the war, the industry used sophisticated marketing methods to transform from a commodity

chemicals business ... to one heavily concentrated in several large firms and dependent on large investments in research and marketing. Global pharmaceutical spending reached almost $500 billion in 2003; approximately half of that was attributed to the United States and Canada." (p. 2)

As they also note, however, "behind these figures lies a morass of economic and moral paradoxes" (p. 2).

Biehl (2006) highlights such paradoxes in his investigation of the AIDS Program in Brazil, where state-supported production of antiretroviral medication has become a key strategy for controlling the epidemic. Drawing on ethnography geared toward making visible the "people missing in official data," he writes that "Brazil's policy of biotechnology for the people has dramatically reduced AIDS mortality and improved the quality of life for the patients covered" (p. 236).

Abundantly clear in the literature on pharmaceuticals is their profound impact on human bodies and experiences. Lakoff's (2005) compelling ethnography of mental illness showcases the transformative role of the multinational pharmaceutical industry in forging connections across psychiatric diagnostic categories in the United States and Argentina. In order for future pharmaceutical treatments to apply worldwide, the classification of bipolar disorder had to be standardized. The patients who populate the Buenos Aires clinic in Lakoff's study must negotiate the complex intersections of embodied personhood with "expert" medical knowledge, and of local experience with global formations. Lakoff's (2008) more recent work follows "pharmaceutical circuits" of regulation, technical standards, and struggles over inclusion and exclusion in finding the "right patients" for pharmaceutical clinical trials. Greene (2007) similarly argues that increasing reliance on measures such as blood pressure or cholesterol levels turns people without illnesses into those with "pre-disease" that doctors may feel obligated to treat.

One result of this over-reliance on tests is that drugs for the management of not-yet-illnesses are continuously used in human bodies, requiring ongoing monitoring and adjustment. Lovell (2006) states, "The history of buprenorphine, like that of psychotropics more generally, is a narrative of effects in search of an application" (p. 138). To state this more baldly, the pharmaceuticals often come first via the operations of global capitalism ("Big Pharma"), and diagnoses and patients follow as drug-makers seek new markets (and bodies) for their goods. Biehl (2006) notes, regarding the Brazilian program, "as the AIDS policy unfolded, Brazil attracted new investments, and novel public-private cooperation over access to medical technologies ensued" (p. 237). These arrangements resulted in expanded markets for pharmaceutical manufacturers and a marketing support infrastructure for the supply of "pharmaceutical intelligence" and forecasting (e.g., Piribo Limited 2010). New arrangements have also led to intensification of clinical research targeting human bodies conceptualized in terms of disease or predisease categories.

Use of cochlear implants provides a fascinating example of technical transformations of bodies and ensuing social consequences (Blume 2009). Advocates for Deaf culture have vigorously opposed the technological "solution" of cochlear implants on the grounds that deafness is not a difference in need of intervention, particularly in children (Hyde and Power 2006; Sparrow 2005). For these advocates, Deafness is a source of pride, an identity with a culture unified by its own unique language. Like medical sociologists, disability studies scholars have contested the biomedical model, arguing that "disability" is a socially constructed category (Shakespeare 1998). The biomedical model focuses on individual-level therapy and treatment, neglecting social conditions that lead to loss of mobility and social interaction that turns "impairment" into a disability. A constructionist stance toward disability has reframed bodily differences, such as deafness, to highlight abilities rather than deficits. Siebers (2006) has called for an embodied ontology as a theoretical ground for disability studies, echoing medical sociologists' call for attention to human bodies and embodiment.

In short, while we have learned much about how technologies remake human bodies, we need empirical and theoretical works on new biosubjectivities—work that can track formation of technoscientific identities alongside reconfigurations of bodies (Clarke et al. 2003, 2010; Sulik 2009). The questions then become bigger: In what ways, with what consequences, and by whom are these technoscientific identities constructed? In what ways and with what meanings and consequences do people take up such embodied identities? Sulik (2009), for example, found that women with breast cancer diagnoses formed one such identity as a result of their immersion in professional knowledge, placing themselves discursively within this technoscientific framework, receiving support in this identity from the medical system, and prioritizing official classification over their own suffering. Future work might investigate, for example, relations between humans and their brain implants (Morrison 2009), emergent pharmaceutical relations, new "biosocial" collective identities (Gibbon and Novas 2008; Rabinow 1992), and social movements associated with technologies (Kenny 2009).

Technologies and Embodied Health Movements

Since pioneering work by Epstein (1996), sociologists of medicine have theorized and examined connections among health, illness, and social movements—what Brown et al. (2004) call **embodied health movements (EHMs)**. These are social movements organized around health-related issues such as disease categories, access to care, illness experiences, and inequities. Regarding HIV/AIDS activism (Epstein

1996), diethylstilbestrol (DES) daughters (Bell 2009), environmental contaminants (Brown 2007), and other product- and practice-oriented movements (Hess 2005), scholars have analyzed connections between health statuses and movement formation, development, and activism. Communities have emerged on the basis of biosocial categories, deploying technoscientific identities and knowledge (Bell 2009; Epstein 2008). Scholars have analyzed novel group formations and strategies using terms such as "**biosociality**," "biological citizenship," and others that are Foucauldian in their understandings of power and dominance (Petryna 2002; Rabinow and Rose 2006; Rose and Novas 2005).

Klawiter's (2008) work on breast cancer, for example, shows how the breast cancer movement transformed fundamental terms of debate about the condition; coalitions of women, researchers, and funding agencies reshaped the landscape of scientific inquiry and lived experiences. Breast cancer has been transformed from an embodied experience of passive patienthood to active identification and solidarity with others, from victim to survivor. This solidarity, in turn, helps individuals take control of their health care decisions, while it also attempts to direct research funding at the federal level. Yet contestation surrounds the prioritizing of research on breast cancer treatment (including pharmaceuticals) at the expense of prevention (Ehrenreich 2001; Ley 2009). Screening mammographies had long been recommended for even very young women, enlarging the population of women considered "at risk" but who had not yet been diagnosed with cancer. New guidelines issued in 2009 by the U.S. Preventive Services Task Force recommended limiting routine mammography to women over 50 (Mandelblatt et al. 2009), sparking a firestorm of controversy (Rabin 2009).

Central to Klawiter's analysis, and to other work on breast cancer (e.g., Fosket 2004), is the figure of the "risky subject"—the woman who may carry a genetic marker predisposing her to breast cancer. Kenny's (2009) work on the "previvor" movement is one example of breast cancer activism that emerged from groups of women with the BRCA1 and BRCA2 gene mutations seeking support based on the knowledge that they are at greater risk for breast cancer. Previvors are women with the BRCA 1 and 2 genes but without the disease; marked with the "pre-disease," these women may ultimately make significant treatment decisions in the absence of actual symptoms (Koenig et al. 1998). This

EDITOR'S NOTES

biosociality: a phenomenon whereby persons diagnosed with a condition create their self-identity with that condition and may form social relations with the condition as the basis.

group of women is one of many who are advocating for research on young girls, seeking environmental causes for genetic variations even before birth (Ley 2009; Thomson 2009).

Policy Implications

What implications derive from this retrospective of a half-century of research on technology? Although policy has not been an explicit focus of the analyses discussed here, many of the works implicitly urge policy at local, national, and transnational levels. We want to stress that medical sociologists should continue to engage in critical analysis of medical practices and health policy (Harrington and Estes 2007; Mechanic 2007). Often this work takes the form of health disparities or health services research (e.g., Barr 2008); yet other fields in the discipline have much to offer. Medical sociologists interested in the effects of medical technology might, for example, examine the ways in which technologies such as electronic medical records, disease classification systems, and other artifacts and processes create and obscure certain forms of professional and lay work.

While medical sociologists will, of course, continue to produce intellectually rigorous, critical, and creative accounts of historical and contemporary medical practices, we also envision more sophisticated interdisciplinary work in the future. In forging links with bioethics and neuroethics, for example, medical sociologists may highlight inequities in resource allocation, informed consent, and institutional structures that obscure or make invisible the ethical practices of those who engage in medical work. Some sociologists practice "**empirical bioethics**" (De Vries and Kim 2008; Fisher 2009) while wearing the hat of faculty members in interdisciplinary academic centers for bioethics. These connections will become more important as new technologies enter the biomedical landscape, forging shifts in practice, innovative embodied identities, and as-yet-unknown social movements. As technologies become ever tinier—for example, nanotechnologies—scholars will need to attend to a host of issues concerning bodily integrity and autonomy, civil liberties, and the inner and outer reaches of medicine.

Medical sociologists play a substantial role in analyzing power relations within medicine, including the scope of medical authority, biopolitics, and health policy. Experts on medical technology should engage here as well. Despite passage of the federal Patient Protection and Affordable Care Act in March 2010, vociferous debates over health care reform in the United States continue at the time of this writing. Medical sociologists are poised to make key contributions to these debates, with the expertise to highlight connections between health economics and finance and inequalities in provision of services. Yet health disparities are not merely economic, in terms of too much or too little care; they also embody questions of social justice in distributing social resources. In an era when Americans spend too much money for care that is not equitably distributed, sociologists may highlight moral and ethical dimensions of this unequal distribution. Fears of rationing contribute to both public panic and political posturing instead of meaningful comparative analysis. Sociologists can contribute through studies of public and political discourse around policy change, as well as through empirical studies comparing health care systems locally, regionally, and nationally.

Additional research should be conducted transnationally and in dialogue with human rights theory and praxis (Gruskin 2006; Turner 2006). In the context of global flows of capital, bodies, and other resources, how do medical technologies, and the expertise it takes to use them, become distributed throughout the world? Who does what kinds of work, for whom, and with what consequences? What kinds of inequalities are created when MRI scans, X-rays, and other tests and techniques are performed in one location and analyzed in another? Some researchers have already documented the "outsourcing" of clinical trials research to the "Third World" (Cooper 2008; Sunder Rajan 2006). What kind of medicine do we get when drugs are created in the United States, tested abroad, and then marketed, sold, and consumed in wealthy nations? What kinds of technology do we get? Who benefits? Such questions of technology will continue to be at the core of medical sociology.

Acknowledgments

We gratefully acknowledge Lisa Jean Moore and two anonymous reviewers for their insightful comments on this manuscript. We dedicate this article to the memory of Susan Leigh Star, whose innovative work has influenced us in myriad ways.

References

Anspach, Renée R. 1993. *Deciding Who Lives: Fateful Choices in the Intensive-Care Nursery.* Berkeley: University of California Press.

Armstrong, David. 1995. "The Rise of Surveillance Medicine." *Sociology of Health and Illness* 17:393–404.

Barr, Michael S. 2008. "The Need to Test the Patient-Centered Medical Home." *Journal of the American Medical Association* 300:834–35.

Bell, Susan E. 1995. "Gendered Medical Science: Producing a Drug for Women." *Feminist Studies* 21:469–500.

———. 2009. *DES Daughters: Embodied Knowledge and the Transformation of Women's Health Politics.* Philadelphia, PA: Temple University Press.

Biehl, João. 2006. "Pharmaceutical Governance." Pp. 206–39 in *Global Pharmaceuticals: Ethics, Markets, Practices,* edited by A. Petryna, A. Lakoff, and A. Kleinman. Durham, NC: Duke University Press.

Blizzard, Deborah. 2007. *Looking Within: A Sociocultural Examination of Fetoscopy.* Cambridge, MA: MIT Press.

Blume, Stuart. 2009. *The Artificial Ear: Cochlear Implants and the Culture of Deafness.* New Brunswick, NJ: Rutgers University Press.

Bowker, Geoffrey C. and Susan Leigh Star. 2000. *Sorting Things Out: Classification and its Consequences.* Cambridge, MA: MIT Press.

Briggs, Laura. 2002. *Reproducing Empire: Race, Sex, Science, and U.S. Imperialism in Puerto Rico.* Berkeley: University of California Press.

Brown, Phil. 2007. *Toxic Exposures: Contested Illness and the Environmental Health Movement.* New York: Columbia University Press.

Brown, Phil, Stephen Zavestoski, Sabrina McCormick, Brian Mayer, Rachel Morello-Frosch, and Rebecca Gasior Altman. 2004. "Embodied Health Movements: New Approaches to Social Movements in Health." *Sociology of Health and Illness* 26:1–31.

Burri, Regula Valerie and Joseph Dumit. 2008. "Social Studies of Scientific Imaging and Visualization." Pp. 297–318 in *The Handbook of Science and Technology Studies,* edited by E. Hackett, O. Amsterdamska, M. Lynch, and J. Wajcman. Cambridge, MA: MIT Press.

Canguilhem, Georges. 1991. *The Normal and the Pathological.* New York: Zone Books.

Carpenter, Laura M. and Monica J. Casper. 2009. "Global Intimacies: Innovating the HPV Vaccine for Women's Health." *Women's Studies Quarterly* 37:80–100.

Casper, Monica J. 1998. *The Making of the Unborn Patient: A Social Anatomy of Fetal Surgery.* New Brunswick, NJ: Rutgers University Press.

Casper, Monica J. and Laura M. Carpenter. 2008. "Sex, Drugs, and Politics: The HPV Vaccine for Cervical Cancer." *Sociology of Health and Illness* 30:886–99.

Casper, Monica J. and Adele E. Clarke. 1998. "Making the Pap Smear into the Right Tool for the Job: Cervical Cancer Screening in the U.S., c1940–1995." *Social Studies of Science* 28:255–90.

Casper, Monica J. and Lisa Jean Moore. 2009. *Missing Bodies: The Politics of Visibility.* New York: New York University Press.

Caufield, Catherine. 1989. *Multiple Exposures: Chronicles of the Radiation Age.* Chicago, IL: University of Chicago Press.

Charmaz, Kathy C. 1991. *Good Days, Bad Days: The Self and Chronic Illness.* Piscataway, NJ: Rutgers University Press.

Clarke, Adele E. 1995. "Modernity, Postmodernity, and Reproductive Processes, ca 1890–1990: or, 'Mommy, Where do Cyborgs Come from Anyway?'" Pp. 139–56 in *The Cyborg Handbook*, edited by C. H. Gray, S. Mentor, and H. Figueroa-Sarriera. New York: Routledge.

Clarke, Adele E. and Monica Casper. 1996. "From Simple Technique to Complex System: Classification of Pap Smears, 1917–1990." *Medical Anthropology Quarterly* 10:601–23.

Clarke, Adele E. and Joan H. Fujimura. 1992. "What Tools? Which Jobs? Why Right?" Pp. 3–44 in *The Right Tools for the Job: At Work in Twentieth Century Life Sciences*, edited by A. E. Clarke and J. H. Fujimura. Princeton, NJ: Princeton University Press.

Clarke, Adele E. and Virginia L. Olesen. 1999. *Revisioning Women, Health, and Healing: Feminist, Cultural, and Technoscience Perspectives*. New York: Routledge.

Clarke, Adele E., Janet K. Shim, Laura Mamo, Jennifer Ruth Fosket, and Jennifer R. Fishman. 2003. "Biomedicalization: Technoscientific Transformations of Health, Illness, and U.S. Biomedicine" *American Sociological Review* 68:161–94.

———. 2010. *Biomedicalization: Technoscience and Transformations of Health and Illness in the U.S.* Durham, NC: Duke University Press.

Clarke, Adele E. and Susan Leigh Star. 2007. "The Social Worlds/Arenas Framework: A Theory-Methods Package." Pp. 113–37 in *The Handbook of Science and Technology Studies*, edited by E. Hackett, O. Amsterdamska, M. Lynch, and J. Wajcman. Cambridge, MA: MIT Press.

Conrad, Peter. 2005. "The Shifting Engines of Medicalization." *Journal of Health and Social Behavior* 46:3–14.

———. 2007. *The Medicalization of Society: On the Transformation of Human Conditions into Treatable Disorders*. Baltimore, MD: Johns Hopkins University Press.

Conrad, Peter and Jonathan Gabe. 1999. *Sociological Perspectives on the New Genetics*. Oxford, England: Blackwell.

Cooper, Melinda. 2008. *Life as Surplus: Biotechnology and Capitalism in the Neoliberal Era*. Seattle: University of Washington Press.

De Vries, Raymond and Scott Kim. 2008. "Bioethics and the Sociology of Trust: Introduction to the Theme." *Medicine, Health Care and Philosophy* 11: 377–79.

Dumit, Joseph. 2003. *Picturing Personhood: Brain Scans and Biomedical Identity*. Princeton, NJ: Princeton University Press.

Duster, Troy. [1990] 2003. *Backdoor to Eugenics*. 2nd ed. New York: Routledge.

Ehrenreich, Barbara. 2001. "Welcome to Cancerland: A Mammogram Leads to a Cult of Pink Kitsch." *Harper's Magazine*, November 2001, pp. 43–53.

Epstein, Steven. 1996. *Impure Science: AIDS, Activism, and the Politics of Knowledge*. Berkeley: University of California Press.

———. 2008. "Patient Groups and Health Movements." Pp. 499–540 in *The Handbook of Science and Technology Studies*, edited by E. Hackett, O. Amsterdamska, M. Lynch, and J. Wajcman. Cambridge, MA: MIT Press.

Fisher, Jill A. 2009. *Medical Research for Hire: The Political Economy of Pharmaceutical Clinical Trials*. New Brunswick, NJ: Rutgers University Press.

Fosket, Jennifer R. 2004. "Constructing 'High Risk Women': The Development and Standardization of a Breast Cancer Risk Assessment Tool." *Science, Technology and Human Values* 29:291–313.

Foucault, Michel. 1994. *The Birth of the Clinic.* New York: Pantheon.

———. 1995. *Discipline and Punish: The Birth of the Prison.* New York: Vintage.

———. 2008. *The Birth of Biopolitics: Lectures at the College de France, 1978–1979.* New York: Palgrave Macmillan.

Franklin, Sarah. 2000. "Life Itself." Pp. 188–98 and 215–27 in *Global Nature/Global Culture*, edited by S. Franklin, C. Lurie, and J. Stacey. London, England: Sage.

———. 2007. *Dolly Mixtures: The Remaking of Genealogy.* Durham, NC: Duke University Press.

Fujimura, Joan H. 1988. "The Molecular Biological Bandwagon in Cancer Research: Where Social Worlds Meet." *Social Problems* 35:261–83.

———. 1996. *Crafting Science: A Sociohistory of the Quest for the Genetics of Cancer.* Cambridge, MA: Harvard University Press.

Gibbon, Sahra and Carlos Novas. 2008. *Biosocialities, Genetics, and the Social Sciences: Making Biologies and Identities.* London: Routledge.

Ginsburg, Faye D. and Rayna Rapp. 1995. *Conceiving the New World Order: The Global Politics of Reproduction.* Berkeley: University of California Press.

Glaser, Barney G. and Anselm Strauss. 1965. *Awareness of Dying.* Chicago, IL: Aldine.

Gottweis, Herbert and Alan Petersen. 2008. *Biobanks: Governance in Comparative Perspective.* New York: Routledge.

Greene, Jeremy A. 2007. *Prescribing by Numbers: Drugs and the Definition of Disease.* Baltimore, MD: Johns Hopkins University Press.

Grinker, Roy Richard. 2010. "Disorder out of Chaos." *New York Times*, February 9, P. A23. Retrieved March 2, 2010 (http://www.nytimes.com/2010/02/10/opinion/10grinker.html).

Gruskin, Sofia. 2006. "Rights-Based Approaches to Health: Something for Everyone." *Health and Human Rights* 9:5–9.

Harrington, Charlene and Carroll L. Estes. 2007. *Health Policy: Crisis and Reform in the U.S. Health Care Delivery System.* 5th ed. Sudbury, MA: Jones and Bartlett.

Hatch, Anthony R. 2009. "The Politics of Metabolism: The Metabolic Syndrome and the Reproduction of Race and Racism." PhD dissertation, Department of Sociology, University of Maryland, College Park, MD.

Hedgecoe, Adam. 2004. *The Politics of Personalised Medicine: Pharmacogenetics in the Clinic.* Cambridge, England: Cambridge University Press.

Hess, David J. 2005. "Technology- and Product-Oriented Movements: Approximating Social Movement Studies and Science and Technology Studies." *Science, Technology, and Human Values* 30:515–35.

Horwitz, Allan V. 2002. *Creating Mental Illness.* Chicago, IL: The University of Chicago Press.

Hyde, Merv and Des Power. 2006. "Some Ethical Dimensions of Cochlear Implantation for Deaf Children and Their Families." *Journal of Deaf Studies and Deaf Education* 11:102–11.

Illich, Ivan. 1975. *Medical Nemesis: The Expropriation of Health.* London, England: Calder & Boyars.

Joyce, Kelly A. 2008. *Magnetic Appeal: MRI and the Myth of Transparency*. Ithaca, NY: Cornell University Press.

Keating, Peter and Alberto Cambrosio. 2002. "From Screening to Clinical Research: The Cure of Leukemia and the Early Development of the Cooperative Oncology Groups, 1955–1966." *Bulletin of the History of Medicine* 76:299–334.

———. 2003. *Biomedical Platforms: Realigning the Normal and the Pathological in Late-Twentieth Century Medicine*. Cambridge, MA: MIT Press.

Kenny, Katherine E. 2009. "Breast Cancer Activism and the 'Previvor' Movement: Embodiment, Citizenship, and the Genetically 'at Risk.'" Presented at the meeting of the Society for the Social Studies of Science, Washington, DC, October 31.

Klawiter, Maren. 2004. "Breast Cancer in Two Regimes: The Impact of Social Movements on Illness Experience." *Sociology of Health and Illness* 26: 845–74.

———. 2008. *The Biopolitics of Breast Cancer: Changing Cultures of Disease and Activism*. Minneapolis: University of Minnesota Press.

Koenig, Barbara A., Henry T. Greely, Laura M. McConnell, Heather L. Silverberg, Thomas A. Raffin, and the Members of the Breast Cancer Working Group of the Stanford Program in Genomics, Ethics, and Society. 1998. "Genetic Testing for BRCA1 and BRCA2: Recommendations of the Stanford Program in Genomics, Ethics, and Society." *Journal of Women's Health* 7:531–45.

Lakoff, Andrew. 2005. *Pharmaceutical Reason: Knowledge and Value in Global Psychiatry*. Cambridge, England: Cambridge University Press.

———. 2008. "The Right Patient for the Drug: Pharmaceutical Circuits and the Codification of Illness." Pp. 741–60 in *The Social Construction of Technological Systems*, edited by W. E. Bijker, T. P. Hughes, and T. Pinch. Cambridge, MA: MIT Press.

Ley, Barbara L. 2009. *From Pink to Green: Disease Prevention and the Environmental Breast Cancer Movement*. New Brunswick, NJ: Rutgers University Press.

Lorber, Judith and Lisa Jean Moore. 2002. *Gender and the Social Construction of Illness*. 2nd ed. Walnut Creek, CA: Rowman Altamira.

Lovell, Anne M. 2006. "Addiction Markets: The Case of High-Dose Buprenorphine in France." Pp. 136–70 in *Global Pharmaceuticals: Ethics, Markets, Practices*, edited by A. Petryna, A. Lakoff, and A. Kleinman. Durham, NC: Duke University Press.

Mandelblatt, Jeanne, Kathleen A. Cronin, Stephanie Bailey, Donald A. Berry, Harry J. de Koning, Gerrit Draisma, Hui Huang, Sandra J. Lee, Mark Munsell, Sylvia K. Pleveritis, Peter Ravdin, Clyde B. Schechter, Bronislava Sigal, Michael A. Stoto, Satasha K. Stout, Nicolien T. van Ravesteyn, John Venier, Marvin Zelen, Eric J. Feuer, and for the Breast Cancer Working Group of the Cancer Intervention and Surveillance Modeling Network (CISNET). 2009. "Effects of Mammography Screening Under Different Screening Schedules: Model Estimates of Potential Benefits and Harms." *Annals of Internal Medicine* 151:738–47.

McKinlay, John B. 1984. *Issues in the Political Economy of Health Care*. New York: Tavistock.

Mechanic, David. 2007. "Population Health: Challenges for Science and Society." *The Milbank Quarterly* 85:533–59.

Morrison, Daniel R. 2009. "Brain and Machine: Deep Brain Stimulation and the Self." Presented at the meeting of the Society for the Social Studies of Science, Washington, DC, October 31.

Murray, John E. 2007. *Origins of American Health Insurance: A History of Industrial Sickness Funds*. New Haven, CT: Yale University Press.

Navarro, Vicente. 1986. *Crisis, Health, and Medicine: A Social Critique*. New York: Tavistock.

Nelkin, Dorothy and Laurence Tancredi. 1989. *Dangerous Diagnostics: The Social Power of Biological Information*. New York: Basic Books.

Nye, David E. 2006. *Technology Matters: Questions to Live With*. Cambridge, MA: MIT Press.

Oakley, Ann. 1984. *The Captured Womb: A History of the Medical Care of Pregnant Women*. Oxford, England: Blackwell.

Oshinsky, David M. 2005. *Polio: An American Story*. New York: Oxford University Press.

Petryna, Adriana. 2002. *Life Exposed: Biological Citizens after Chernobyl*. Princeton, NJ: Princeton University Press.

Petryna, Adriana, Andrew Lakoff, and Arthur Kleinman. 2006. *Global Pharmaceuticals: Ethics, Markets, Practices*. Durham, NC: Duke University Press.

Pickering, Andrew. 1992. *Science as Practice and Culture*. Chicago, IL: The University of Chicago Press.

Piribo Limited. 2010. "About Piribo." Retrieved March 6, 2010 (http://www.piribo.com/about_us/index.html).

Pulley, Jill M., Margaret M. Brace, Gordon R. Bernard, and Dan R. Masys. 2008. "Attitudes and Perceptions of Patients towards Methods of Establishing a DNA Biobank." *Cell and Tissue Banking* 9:55–65.

Quadagno, Jill. 2006. *One Nation, Uninsured: Why the U.S. Has No National Health Insurance*. New York: Oxford University Press.

Rabin, Roni Caryn. 2009. "New Guidelines on Breast Cancer Draw Opposition." *New York Times*, November 16. Retrieved March 6, 2010 (http://www. nytimes.com/2009/11/17/health/17scre.html).

Rabinow, Paul. 1992. "Artificiality and Enlightenment: From Sociobiology to Biosociality." Pp. 234–52 in *Incorporations*, edited by J. Crary and S. Kwinter. New York: Zone.

Rabinow, Paul and Nikolas Rose. 2006. "Biopower Today." *Biosocieties* 1:195–217.

Rapp, Rayna. 2000. *Testing Women, Testing the Fetus: The Social Impact of Amniocentesis in America*. New York: Routledge.

Reiser, Stanley Joel and Michael Anbar. 1984. *The Machine at the Bedside: Strategies for Using Technology in Patient Care*. New York: Cambridge University Press.

Riessman, Catherine Kohler. 1983. "Women and Medicalization: A New Perspective." *Social Policy* 14:3–18.

Robert Wood Johnson Foundation. 2009. "Health Care Spending as Percentage of GDP." Talking About Quality Part 1: Health Care Today. Retrieved March 5, 2010 (http://www.rwjf.org/pr/product.jsp?id=45110).

Roden, Dan M., Jill Pulley, Melissa Basford, Gordon Bernard, Ellen Wright Clayton, Jeffrey Balser, and Dan Masys. 2008. "Development of a Large-Scale De-Identified DNA Biobank to Enable Personalized Medicine." *Clinical Pharmacology and Therapeutics* 84:362–69.

Rose, Nikolas S. 2007. *The Politics of Life Itself: Bio-medicine, Power, and Subjectivity in the Twenty-First Century.* Princeton, NJ: Princeton University Press.

Rose, Nikolas S. and Carlos Novas. 2005. "Biological Citizenship." Pp. 439–64 in *Global Assemblages: Technology, Politics, and Ethics as Anthropological Problems,* edited by A. Ong and S. J. Collier. Malden, MA: Blackwell.

Rothman, Barbara Katz. 1993. *The Tentative Pregnancy: How Amniocentesis Changes the Experience of Motherhood.* New York: W.W. Norton & Co.

Ruzek, Sheryl Burt, Virginia L. Olesen, and Adele E. Clarke. 1997. Women's Health: Complexities and Differences. Columbus: The Ohio State University Press.

Serlin, David H. 2004. *Replaceable You: Engineering the Body in Postwar America.* Chicago, IL: University of Chicago Press.

Shakespeare, Tom (ed.). 1998. The Disability Reader: Social Science Perspectives. London, England: Continuum.

Siebers, Tobin. 2006. "Disability in Theory: From Social Construction to the New Realism of the Body." Pp. 173–84 in The Disability Studies Reader, 2nd ed., edited by L. J. Davis. New York: Routledge.

Sparrow, Robert. 2005. "Defending Deaf Culture: The Case of Cochlear Implants." The Journal of Political Philosophy 13:135–52.

Star, Susan Leigh and James R. Griesemer. 1989. "Institutional Ecology, 'Translations' and Boundary Objects: Amateurs and Professionals in Berkeley's Museum of Vertebrate Zoology, 1907–39." Social Studies of Science 19:387–420.

Star, Susan Leigh and Anselm Strauss. 1999. "Layers of Silence, Arenas of Voice: The Ecology of Visible and Invisible Work." Computer Supported Cooperative Work 8:9–30.

Starr, Paul. 1982. The Social Transformation of American Medicine: The Rise of a Sovereign Profession and the Making of a Vast Industry. New York: Basic Books.

Strauss, Anselm. 1988. "The Articulation of Project Work." The Sociological Quarterly 29:163–78.

Strauss, Anselm L., Shizuko Fagerhaugh, Barbara Suczek, and Carolyn Wiener. 1985. Social Organization of Medical Work. Chicago, IL: University of Chicago Press.

Sulik, Gayle A. 2009. "Managing Biomedical Uncertainty: The Technoscientific Illness Identity." Sociology of Health and Illness 31:1059–76.

Sunder Rajan, Kaushik. 2006. Biocapital: The Constitution of Postgenomic Life. Durham, NC: Duke University Press.

Talley, Heather Laine. 2008. "Face Work: Cultural, Technical, and Surgical Interventions for Facial 'Disfigurement.'" PhD dissertation, Department of Sociology, Vanderbilt University, Nashville, TN.

Tanner, Lindsey. 2010. "Proposed Autism Diagnosis Changes Anger 'Aspies.'" Associated Press, February 10, 2010. Retrieved March 5, 2010 (http://www.apa.org/news/psycport/PsycPORTArticle.aspx?id=ap_2010_02_11_ap.online.all_D9DQ25C80_news_ap_org.anpa.xml).

Taylor, Janelle S. 2000. "Of Sonograms and Baby Prams: Prenatal Diagnosis, Pregnancy, and Consumption." Feminist Studies 26:391–418.

―――. 2008. The Public Life of the Fetal Sonogram: Technology, Consumption, and the Politics of Reproduction. New Brunswick, NJ: Rutgers University Press.

Thompson, Charis. 2005. Making Parents: The Ontological Choreography of Reproductive Technologies. Cambridge, MA: MIT Press.

Thomson, L. Katherine. 2009. "Transdisciplinary Knowledge Production of Endocrine Disruptors: 'Windows of Vulnerability' in Breast Cancer Risk." PhD dissertation, Department of Social and Behavioral Sciences, University of California, San Francisco, CA.

Timmermans, Stefan. 1999. Sudden Death and the Myth of CPR. Philadelphia, PA: Temple University Press.

Timmermans, Stefan and Marc Berg. 2003. The Gold Standard: The Challenge of Evidence-Based Medicine and Standardization in Health Care. Philadelphia, PA: Temple University Press.

Turner, Bryan S. 2006. Vulnerability and Human Rights: Essays on Human Rights. University Park, PA: The Pennsylvania State University Press.

Wailoo, Keith and Stephen Pemberton. 2006. The Troubled Dream of Genetic Medicine: Ethnicity and Innovation in Tay-Sachs, Cystic Fibrosis, and Sickle Cell Disease. Baltimore, MD: Johns Hopkins University Press.

Wainwright, Steven P., Clare Williams, Mike Michael, Bonnie Farsides, and Alan Cribb. 2006. "From Bench to Bedside? Biomedical Scientists' Expectations of Stem Cell Science as a Future Therapy for Diabetes." Social Science and Medicine 63:2052–64.

Waldby, Catherine. 1996. AIDS and the Body Politic: Bio-medicine and Sexual Difference. New York: Routledge.

―――. 2000. The Visible Human Project: Informatic Bodies and Posthuman Medicine. New York: Routledge.

Waldby, Catherine and Robert Mitchell. 2006. Tissue Economies: Blood, Organs, and Cell Lines in Late Capitalism. Durham, NC: Duke University Press.

Wiener, Carolyn, Anselm Strauss, Shizuko Fagerhaugh, and Barbara Suczek. 1997. "Trajectories, Biogra phies, and the Evolving Medical Technology Scene." Pp. 229–50 in Grounded Theory in Practice, edited by A. Strauss and J. Corbin. Thousand Oaks, CA: Sage. Williams, Clare, Steven P. Wainwright, Kathryn Ehrich, and Mike Michael. 2008. "Human Embryos as Boundary Objects: Some Reflections on the Biomedical Worlds of Embryonic Stem Cells and Pre-Implantation Genetic Diagnosis." New Genetics and Society 27:7–18.

Williams, Simon J., Jonathan Gabe, and Peter Davis. 2008. "The Sociology of Pharmaceuticals: Progress and Prospects." Sociology of Health and Illness 30:813–24.

Yoxen, Edward. 1987. "Seeing with Sound: A Study of the Development of Medical Images." Pp. 281–303 in The Social Construction of Technological Systems, edited by W. E. Bijker, T. P. Hughes, and T. Pinch. Cambridge, MA: MIT Press.

Zetka, James R. 2003. Surgeons and the Scope. Ithaca, NY: ILR Press/Cornell University Press.

Zola, Irving Kenneth. 1972. "Medicine as an Institution of Social Control." Sociological Review 20:487–504.

The Sociological Concomitants of the Pharmaceutical Industry and Medications

By John Abraham

....

Pharmaceuticals are pervasive in medicine and society. The transnational industrial nature and scale of pharmaceutical markets and the level of technoscientific sophistication in pharmaceutical development in the last twenty to twenty-five years are unprecedented. Between 1960 and the early 1980s, prescription-drug sales were almost static as a percentage of GDP in most of the major Western economies, including the United States, which alone makes up about half the world's prescription-drug sales.[1] However, from the early 1980s to 2002, prescription-drug sales tripled to nearly US$400 billion worldwide, and almost US$200 billion in the United States (Angell 2004, 1–5). By 2007, global sales were approaching US$600 billion (IMS Health 2008). Pharmaceuticals also seem to be more pervasive in public discourse and media outlets than in previous decades (Applbaum 2006). Many who speak for the pharmaceutical industry in drug companies, the scientific community, or within the media assert or give the impression that the expansion of pharmaceutical markets and prescribing over the last few decades is best understood as the innovative responses of biomedical science to growing and new health needs. I refer to this as the "**biomedicalism thesis**," which has long been a deep-seated part of the popular, commercial, and scientistic discourse about drug products.

Conventionally, the biomedicalism thesis has been challenged by the well-established sociological concept of **medicalization**—the making of the social medical. The medicalization thesis asserts that the growth in medical conditions partly reflects medical dominance in society and the significance of the "**sick role**" in redefining **social**

John Abraham, "The Sociological Concomitants of the Pharmaceutical Industry and Medications," *Handbook of Medical Sociology,* ed. Chloe E. Bird, Peter Conrad, Allen M. Fremont, and Stefan Timmermans, pp. 290–308. Copyright © 2010 by Vanderbilt University Press. Reprinted with permission.

EDITOR'S NOTES

social deviance: the violation of social or cultural norms.

EDITOR'S NOTES

pharmaceuticalization: (see definition in reading)

EDITOR'S NOTES

deregulation: the act of removing laws, rules, and restrictions related to an economy.

deviance or dysfunctionality (Conrad and Schneider 1992; Parsons 1951). One can envisage such medicalization leading to growth in drug treatment, but medicalization theorists focused primarily on interactions between the medical professions, patients, and health-care organizations. Until very recently, medicalization theorists paid very little attention to the pharmaceutical industry, the drug regulatory state, or patients as organized interests.

I contend that, while medicalization can account for some of the growth in pharmaceutical markets, it is only one of a constellation of sociological factors. To compensate for this, I introduce the new concept of "**pharmaceuticalization**," which I define as the process by which social, behavioral, or bodily conditions are treated, or deemed to be in need of treatment/intervention, with pharmaceuticals by doctors, patients, or both. For example, the treatment of mood with anxiolytics (tranquilizers and sleeping pills) or antidepressants; treatment of behavior such as attention deficit hyperactivity disorder (ADHD) with methylphenidate (Ritalin); treatment of erectile dysfunction with sildenafil (Viagra); or even treatment of heart-disease risk factors with cholesterol-lowering drugs, such as statins. Notably, not all pharmaceuticalization involves making the social medical. The appropriate treatment of bacterial infections, previously without effective drug remedies, with new antibiotics involves pharmaceuticalization, but not medicalization.

In this chapter I suggest that, in addition to medicalization, one needs to appreciate the salience of other sociological factors to explain pharmaceuticalization—specifically, the political economy of the pharmaceutical industry, consumerism, and **deregulatory** state ideology. I argue that these factors, while conceptually distinct, are empirically mutually interrelated, particularly by the pharmaceutical industry's power and influence in promoting its commercial interests. Overall, I conclude that these mutually interacting sociological factors almost certainly provide a better explanation for growing pharmaceuticalization than does the biomedicalism thesis.

Biomedicalism, Medicalization, and the Pharmaceuticalization of Medicine: Response to Need or Creation of Markets?

There is evidence that pharmaceuticalization is increasing along with the expansion of pharmaceutical markets. Between 1993 and 2002, National Health Service (NHS) prescriptions in England for the antidepressant drugs known as selective serotonin reuptake inhibitors (SSRIs) grew from 1,884,571 to 15,500,000; for Ritalin to treat ADHD, they grew from 3,500 to 161,800 (Department of Health 1994, 2003). In the United States, sales of the SSRI fluoxetine (Prozac) more than doubled between 1994 and 2000, sales of Viagra nearly doubled within four years of market release in 1998, and sales of Ritalin multiplied fivefold in the ten years after 1992 (Scripnews 1999, 1995; Drug Enforcement Administration 2001; Eli Lilly 2000; Timmerman 2003). In Canada, prescription of Ritalin grew fivefold between 1990 and 1995, while in New South Wales (Australia), treatment of children with drugs in 2000 was nine times the rate in 1990 (Phillips 2006, 433).

Some argue that growing pharmaceuticalization reflects advances in medical science which enable people with, say, ADHD, depression, or erectile dysfunction, who would previously have gone undiagnosed, to be treated (Castellanos 2002; Harding 2001). On this biomedicalist view, pharmaceuticalization corresponds to meeting health needs. For example, treatment of ADHD with Ritalin (and other drugs) depends on diagnosis of an identifiable condition amenable to *biochemical* intervention. ADHD is regarded as an organic brain dysfunction—either due to reduced metabolism and inhibition in regions of the brain associated with attention and motor activity, or due to dopamine deficiency (Barkley 1997, 2003; Castellanos 2002; Couvoisie and Hooper 2003; Diller 1998; Krause et al. 2003; Zametkin et al. 1990). Additionally or alternatively, other proponents of biomedicalism contend that increasing pharmaceuticalization is the result of more sophisticated *clinical* diagnostics.

Yet, these technoscientific advances declared by biomedicalism exhibited many uncertainties within the scientific literature itself. In the case of ADHD, the brain-imaging studies have lacked replicability and suffered from problems of small sample size and experimental rigor in matching the ages of the children in control and test groups (DeGrandpre 2000; Thambirajah 1998). The hypothesis that ADHD is caused by dopamine deficiency is derived from post hoc pharmaceutical intervention, because Ritalin has been observed to help some children with ADHD while it is simultaneously believed to increase dopamine levels in the brain. However, direct measurement of dopamine levels in the brain cannot be sampled from living people, so they have to be inferred from dopamine metabolites in the blood, urine, or cerebrospinal fluid. The validity of such measurement is questionable given the existence of dopamine in other parts of the body. For similar reasons, the setting of normal levels of dopamine in the brain, from which people diagnosed with ADHD are supposed to deviate, is also problematic (Yuwiler, Brammer, and Yuwiler 1994). Indeed, it is quite possible that Ritalin's effects on some ADHD children are via some mechanism other than dopamine increase (Glenmullen 2000). Thus, the biomedicalism claim that rising pharmaceuticalization, with respect to ADHD, is due to increased identification of people with biological markers of the disease is not convincing.

Nor is it compelling that pharmaceuticalization has been spreading because increasingly sensitive clinical diagnostics have discovered more people in need of drug treatment. For ADHD, diagnosis is based on nine criteria, of which six need to be present. Over the last forty years, the diagnostic criteria for ADHD have been consistently widened, making it virtually impossible to disentangle increased identification of ADHD sufferers from increased medicalization, and leading to concern that the threshold between normal behavior and ADHD has been set too low. For example, Goldman, Genel, and Bezman (1998) have estimated that the official diagnostic criteria for ADHD apply to almost 20 percent of school-age children in the United States. More fundamentally, the diagnostic criteria are problematic because of their overlap with normal experience or other psychiatric diagnoses. A large-scale epidemiological study found that nearly 50 percent of U.S. children satisfied the symptom-criteria for official ADHD diagnosis (Bird et al. 1990). Indeed, up to 70 percent of children in the United States diagnosed with ADHD are also diagnosed with "conduct disorder" or "oppositional defiant disorder" (Sharma, Halpern, and Newcorn 2000).

Furthermore, research in medical sociology and medicines policy over the last fifteen years has suggested that there is an alternative explanation to biomedicalism for pharmaceuticalization, namely socioinstitutional processes involving the marketing strategies of the pharmaceutical industry. Indeed, pharmaceuticalization may go hand in hand with the more established sociological concept of medicalization to form the "pharmaceuticalization-medicalization" complex, one aspect of the medical-industrial complex (Abraham 1995a). Doctors' prescribing of pharmaceuticals may increase because of widening diagnostic criteria of conditions for which new drugs are emerging or for which existing drugs may be repackaged for a new market (Conrad and Potter 2000). For example, the growth in prescriptions for antipsychotics in the West in recent decades is due to those drugs being redefined to also treat bipolar disorder—a condition whose medicalization is claimed to have increased fiftyfold since it first entered the *Diagnostic and Statistical Manual of Mental Disorders* (*DSM*) in 1980 (Healy 2006a). Simultaneously, the apparent clinical effects of a drug combined with a hypothesized mode of action may give rise to a medical diagnosis, such as "dopamine deficiency."

It should be recognized, however, that pharmaceutical firms can achieve much of this pharmaceuticalization only with the collaboration of key parts of the medical profession.

For example, the International Obesity Task Force is a group of medical experts who work with the World Health Organization (WHO) and was widely regarded as an independent think-tank on how to define, prevent, and manage obesity. The group was one of the driving forces behind boundary changes that broadened the definitions of childhood overweight and obesity. Yet this group allowed itself to be funded by up to £1 million by pharmaceutical companies, including major manufacturers of obesity drugs, such as Roche and Abbot (Moynihan 2006).

Similarly, the UK Defeat Depression Campaign (1992–1997), which was run through the Royal College of Psychiatrists and the Royal College of General Practitioners, was sponsored by the manufacturers of antidepressants, who provided about a third of the funding. The campaign targeted doctors to emphasize in particular that these drugs did not cause addiction or dependence. Those claims have since been disputed and warnings about withdrawal symptoms are now included on the labels of those antidepressants (HCHC 2005b, 70). These disease-awareness campaigns, involving an alliance between pharmaceutical manufacturers and the medical establishment, are vital to the process of pharmaceuticalization. That such pharmaceuticalization is merely a reflection of medical need is highly questionable given that major case studies from sociology and other policy research suggest that industry-sponsored disease-awareness campaigns aimed at doctors have exaggerated the benefits and neglected serious adverse effects of tranquilizers in the 1970s and 1980s, and of antidepressants since the early 1990s (Abraham and Sheppard 1999; Healy 2004; HCHC 2005b, 69–70; Medawar 1992; Medawar and Hardon 2004).

Disease-awareness campaigns are supported by the pharmaceutical industry because they invent, develop, and sustain markets for whole classes of drugs. However, pharmaceuticalization is also driven by the promotion and advertising of individual drug products by their manufacturers to the medical profession, which might involve little or no medicalization (e.g., the promotion of painkillers). Pharmaceutical advertising and promotion are huge enterprises, and growing at a much faster rate than are pharmaceutical research and development (R&D) in most Western industrialized countries. Between 1995 and 2005, research staff numbers in the UK pharmaceutical industry actually *fell* by 2 percent, while marketing staff numbers increased dramatically, by perhaps as much as 59 percent (HCHC 2005b, 58). Similarly, in the United States, industry expenditure on marketing is about double that on R&D—US$54 billion and US$26 billion in 2000, respectively (Angell 2004, 40, 120). Such findings cast further doubt on the veracity of the biomedicalism thesis, because if the major drivers of pharmaceuticalization were scientific discoveries that meet new medical needs, rather than socioeconomic forces, then one would expect clearer evidence of growth in R&D relative to marketing activities.

Subtle aspects of drug promotion include the integration of senior members of the medical profession and medical science into pharmaceutical marketing strategies by first paying them through grants or consultancies to be involved in the development of company products and then funding them to act as "opinion leaders" who speak favorably about the drug at various symposia attended by doctors. This assimilation of allies may be combined with publication via special supplements of journals, the editors of which are company sponsored and known to be sympathetic to the product (HCHC 2005b, 56–57). Before publication, significant editorial changes may be made to scientists' manuscripts with a view to portraying the drug more positively than the author intended (Abraham 1994b). Indeed, many industry-sponsored medical articles might be written not by the researchers under whose names they appear in publication, but rather by professional medical writers working for the manufacturer—so-called ghostwriters (HCHC 2005b; Healy 2006b). Ostensibly to save the time of busy medical experts, such ghostwriting may extend market size by promoting the off-label use of new drugs, as is believed to have occurred with the prescribing of SSRIs to children in some countries (HCHC 2005b, 54).[2]

After an article showing their drug in a positive light reaches publication, pharmaceutical companies may hire public relations firms to create an exaggerated, favorable media and professional reception. Conversely, they may delay publication of findings that reveal problems with their drug by demanding much higher standards of proof for "negative" results, such as "confirmatory" repeat studies by loyal internal company scientists (Abraham 1994a, 1995a). Frequently, negative findings about a drug are not published at all, leading to a systematic bias in the medical literature prescribing doctors read about that drug. This is mainly due to drug companies' reluctance to submit articles showing their products in an unfavorable light, though it is also partly due to journals' preference to publish positive results (HCHC 2005b, 55–56; Lexchin et al. 2003).

Doctors' continued prescribing of pharmaceutical products, and hence pharmaceuticalization, is also maintained by drug companies' strategies to contain criticism of their products as unsafe or ineffective. This may involve withdrawing funding from institutions that provide platforms for the critics' views; attempting to prevent further publication of critics' data; or using experts supportive of the company to undermine critics' concerns about the product (Abraham and Sheppard 1999; Healy 2004). For instance, internal memos of the pharmaceutical manufacturer Upjohn, released in open court, revealed that the company was willing to use what the judge called "cut-throat commercial tactics" to prevent doctors such as van der Kroef and Oswald from publicizing concerns about the dangers posed by the benzodiazepine sleeping pill triazolam (Halcion): "We [Upjohn] must stop further publication by van der Kroef in major journals. ... We must learn everything possible about van der Kroef, and be prepared to use the evidence. It should be clear that someone is going to get hurt and this is going to be a long and tough battle. ... Oswald paper indicated high percentage of Halcion users have problems. So far we have been successful in having it stopped" (cited in Abraham 2002, 1677, 1679).

Pharmaceuticalization and Consumerism

Alongside the growth in pharmaceuticalization has emerged rising consumerism characterized by greater reflexivity, expertise, and activism among patients. Two distinct types of consumerism vis-à-vis the medical-industrial complex can be identified: **injury-oriented adversary,** and **access-oriented collaborator**.[3] The former involves patients (or their surviving relatives, or both) who believe they have been harmed by particular drugs and who embark on campaigns and litigation against the pharmaceutical manufacturers of those drugs. Such adversarial consumerism has been more extensive and more successful in the United States than in any other country. For example, in the 1980s, plaintiffs claiming compensation against Eli Lilly for alleged injury from the antiarthritis drug benoxaprofen (marketed as Oraflex in the United States) were awarded many millions of dollars by the U.S. courts in punitive damages against the company. One plaintiff alone received US$6 million for the death of his wife from Oraflex (Abraham 1995b). Twenty years later, some U.S. plaintiffs received tens of millions of dollars of compensation in punitive damages against Merck for fatal and severe injuries allegedly caused by an antiarthritis drug marketed as Vioxx, though Merck's final payment of US$4.85 billion to settle 27,000 lawsuits claiming injury from Vioxx is generally regarded as a better outcome for the company than first expected (Berenson 2007). Even in the United States, there have been plenty of failed alleged injury cases against pharmaceutical companies. Eli Lilly won most of the cases (mostly suicide or homicide related) brought against it concerning Prozac, for instance (Cornwall 1996).

In Europe, there has been much less injury-oriented adversarial consumerism. When it has occurred, it has enjoyed much less success. For example, during the late 1980s, UK plaintiffs also embarked on extensive legal actions against Eli Lilly and the UK drug regulators following injuries associated with benoxaprofen (marketed as Opren in the UK). Similarly, patients took large-scale legal action in the early 1990s against the manufacturers of benzodiazepines, and a BBC TV *Panorama* documentary featured patients and medical experts attacking Upjohn for its handling of safety problems with Halcion. However, the Opren litigation dissipated into a low-cost out-of-court settlement offered by the company, with no blame attached to either the manufacturer or the regulators, and the legal action against benzodiazepine manufacturers collapsed, leaving many users of the drugs still without compensation, while Upjohn *won* a major libel action against the BBC regarding its documentary on Halcion (Abraham 1994b; Abraham and Sheppard 1999; HCHC 2005b, 65–66).

EDITOR'S NOTES

access-oriented collaborating consumerism: a type of consumerism involving actions by patients, often in collaboration with the producers of treatments, to medicalize a condition and make treatments available quickly.

There are several reasons for the different fortunes of adversarial consumerism in the United States and the UK (and much of Europe). The United States is a much more litigious society with an established no-win no-fees consumer-friendly legal philosophy, while plaintiffs must pay legal fees up front in the UK or seek legal aid, which is generally not substantial enough to support complex and extensive litigation against a colossal transnational company. Moreover, U.S. lawyers are much more likely to take on a case, because of the much greater freedom of information in the United States, which enables them to see more clearly at an early stage how they could build a prosecution. This is to be contrasted with the long-standing government secrecy in the UK, which has prevented British plaintiffs from realizing that there might even be a case to answer.[4] The landscape of consumer politics is also different. The United States is home to the largest public-health advocacy group on pharmaceuticals (Public Citizen) and the largest drug-industry regulator (FDA, the Food and Drug Administration) in the world. Public Citizen has its own legal staff with regular experience using the 1967 U.S. Freedom of Information Act (FOIA) to obtain detailed information about the safety of pharmaceuticals approved by the FDA and can help plaintiffs and lawyers taking action against pharmaceutical firms (Abraham 1995b). In some cases, such as the Oraflex litigation, FDA scientists testified on behalf of the plaintiffs. By contrast, public-health advocacy organizations concerned with pharmaceuticals in the UK (and other European countries) are tiny, and the UK regulatory authorities, traditionally much closer to the pharmaceutical industry than is the FDA, sided with Eli Lilly during the Opren litigation (Abraham and Lewis 2002).

While injury-oriented adversarial consumerism occasions the presence of pharmaceutical controversies in the courts and the mass media, it does not increase pharmaceuticalization. If anything, it is likely to raise doubts in the minds of doctors and prospective patients about the safety of drug products and hence reduce pharmaceutical prescription and use. Hence, there is generally an inverse relationship between pharmaceuticalization and injury-oriented adversarial consumerism. Access-oriented collaborative consumerism, however, increases pharmaceuticalization because it involves patient groups, often in alliance with pharmaceutical firms, who seek faster access to new drugs via accelerated marketing and cost-effectiveness approval by regulators. The main focus of this type of consumerism is generally not safety but expectations about the therapeutic efficacy of a new drug. Access-oriented consumerism has also often involved public campaigns and litigation, but in collaboration with pharmaceutical manufacturers and against the government. Unlike injury-oriented adversarial consumerism, access-oriented consumerism has enjoyed considerable success on both sides of the Atlantic.

In the United States, the recent growth in access-oriented consumerism probably has its roots in the activism of HIV/AIDS patients in the late 1980s. Significant numbers of people diagnosed with HIV/AIDS organized themselves into an effective social movement, which aggressively lobbied the FDA to allow patients faster access to HIV/AIDS drugs either by accelerating approval of such drugs for the market or permitting the drugs still in development to be made more widely available, despite more limited knowledge about safety and efficacy than FDA standards had previously required (Epstein 1996). Several authors have mistakenly pointed to this AIDS activism as the principal or sole cause of major subsequent changes in FDA policies that made provisions for accelerated approval of drugs for life-threatening diseases based on less data and less thorough testing (Carpenter 2004; Daemmrich and Krucken 2000; Edgar and Rothman 1990).[5] Rather, the crucial point is that the activism had considerable support from the pharmaceutical industry, who saw it as a way to reduce the FDA's regulatory barriers to pharmaceutical markets and to induce the regulatory agency to accelerate its approval of new drugs generally, not only for HIV/AIDS or life-threatening conditions. The activists also had the support of the Reagan and Bush Senior administrations, whose deregulatory political proclivities were already putting pressure on the FDA to reduce its regulatory "burden" on industry and "innovation" (Scripnews 1988).

Since the late 1980s, the FDA has introduced many policies designed to hasten regulatory review of all types of new drugs. Between 1993 and 2003, FDA cut regulatory review times by half, and these were based on cuts made in the very early 1990s (FDA 2004). Also, from 1992, the FDA established "accelerated-approval regulations," which permit the marketing approval of particular drug products that, compared with existing treatments, appear to provide meaningful therapeutic benefits to patients with serious or life-threatening illnesses on the basis of clinical trials demonstrating that the drug product has an effect on a surrogate endpoint (i.e., nonclinical measure) that is "reasonably likely" to predict clinical benefit (Code of Federal Regulations 1992). In these respects, U.S. access-oriented collaborative consumerism has been largely successful in making drug products available to patients sooner, though it is doubtful that such haste and fast-tracking development, which involve fewer regulatory checks on drug safety and efficacy, are in the interests of public health.

For example, tumor shrinkage by anticancer drugs is a surrogate endpoint for the clinical end-points/benefits of decreased mortality or morbidity of cancer patients, but tumor shrinkage does not necessarily deliver these clinical benefits. Thus the standard of efficacy for accelerated approval is lower than that for regular approval (Roberts and Chabner 2004). The consequence of fast tracking and accelerated approvals based on surrogate endpoints for some pharmaceuticals is a lack of data comparing the efficacy of the drugs with alternatives in relation to the relevant clinical conditions, such as mortality and morbidity. This has made it very difficult for physicians to know whether, or how, to use the drugs. The problem of not having this knowledge has been hugely compounded because some of these drugs have had serious adverse effects in some patients and, like the cancer drug Iressa, have had to be withdrawn from the market (HCHC 2005b). As Gale (2001) puts it: "Clinicians trade a known risk for an unknown risk only when there is reasonable expectation that the new therapy is better."

As the true effect on morbidity and mortality of products granted accelerated approval is unknown, approval under these regulations requires that companies must conduct postmarketing studies of the drug "to validate the surrogate endpoint or otherwise confirm the effect on the clinical endpoint" (FDA

1997). However, there is evidence that such confirmatory postmarketing studies, which are supposed to provide vital data to determine whether these new drugs do in fact have a positive benefit-risk profile, frequently have not been done. In 2004, it was reported that the FDA's Division of Oncology Drug Products had approved twenty-three new drug products or applications for new indications under the accelerated-approval legislation, but companies had completed postmarketing confirmatory studies for only six of them (Roberts and Chabner 2004). According to Fleming (2005), the average projected time for completion of these confirmatory studies for cancer drugs is ten years. This problem has not been confined to cancer drugs. According to Mitka (2003), only half of all accelerated-approval drugs had completed postmarketing confirmatory studies in the United States by May 2003.

In the UK, access-oriented collaborative consumerism has also enjoyed considerable victories in alliance with pharmaceutical firms. Much of the focus has been on patient access to new drugs on the NHS, which pays the full cost of drug treatment in the UK provided that the appropriate NHS authorities approve funding. A crucial body in this respect is the National Institute for Health and Clinical Excellence (NICE), which assesses the cost-effectiveness of many new drugs for use in the NHS after they have received marketing approval from UK drug-regulatory authorities, the Medicines and Healthcare products Regulatory Agency (MHRA). Access-oriented collaborative consumerism is a more recent phenomenon in the UK than in the United States but has grown significantly since the late 1990s.

For example, NICE recommended the use of the drug Herceptin on the NHS for advanced breast cancer in March 2002, but there was no such advice for its use to treat early-stage breast cancer. Indeed, at that time the manufacturer, Roche, had not even submitted data to the MHRA in support of a licensing application to have the drug approved to treat early-stage breast cancer in the UK. However, in May 2005, a U.S. trial of the drug with women suffering from early-stage breast cancer reported promising results. A few months later, when a woman with early-stage breast cancer in England was refused Herceptin on the NHS, she threatened litigation in the national media. After publication of the promising U.S. trial, Roche hired a public relations firm to contact some women in the UK with breast cancer to ask them if they would be willing to help to get the drug funded on the NHS before NICE, or even MHRA, approval (BBC News 24 2006b). In October 2005, the secretary of state for health, Patricia Hewitt, responded to the increasingly public controversy by stating on national television that all breast-cancer sufferers should have access to the drug, even though Roche had still not made a licensing application for full regulatory review of Herceptin for such use. After Hewitt's intervention, the NHS reversed its decision, obviating the need for a very public court case. However, when the NHS withheld Herceptin from another woman with early-stage breast cancer, its decision was overruled in a high-profile court case in April 2006 (BBC News 24 2006a). In June 2006, after Herceptin had been licensed for treatment of early-stage breast cancer by the MHRA, NICE speedily recommended it for such use on the NHS under a cloud of suspicion that it had been rushed into doing so by patient pressure (BBC News 24 2006b).

Further evidence of the significance of access-oriented collaborative consumerism may be observed regarding drugs for Alzheimer's disease. In March 2005, NICE recommended that the NHS not fund four drug treatments licensed for Alzheimer's (Aricept, Exelon, Reminyl, and Ebixa) because they were not cost-effective. However, following a high-profile campaign in the media and a formal appeal involving patient groups such as the Alzheimer's Society, NICE revised its guidance to allow NHS funding of the drugs for people in moderate stages of the disease, but still not those with early-stage Alzheimer's. The Alzheimer's Society then took NICE to the courts, which ultimately insisted that NICE should investigate ways of making the drugs available to all those with the disease (BBC News 24 2007). Notably, the manufacturers of these Alzheimer's drugs were the lead claimants in the court case and centrally involved in the formal appeal to NICE—a form of collaborative activism that also occurred with the Multiple Sclerosis Society's campaign for access to beta-interferon on the NHS (BBC News 24 2007).

The evidence suggests that the apparent power of consumer/patient activism to achieve its objectives in pharmaceutical controversies depends significantly on whether it is supporting or contravening the fundamental interests of the pharmaceutical industry. Failure is not inevitable when opposing the industry, as some adversarial consumerism in the United States has shown, but success is much more likely with industry support. More germane to the analysis here, the failures of injury-oriented adversarial consumerism and the successes of access-oriented collaborative consumerism almost certainly combine to produce pro-pharmaceuticalization consequences that outweigh the counter-vailing effects of the less pervasive successes of adversarial consumerism.

Moreover, collaborative consumerism is likely to become a permanent feature of the pharmaceutical landscape, because many patient organizations that campaign for availability of better treatments for various medical conditions not only have formed alliances with drug manufacturers when tactically advantageous but also, in the last decade, have become increasingly *funded* by pharmaceutical companies (O'Donovan 2007). For example, in the United States, the preeminent advocacy group for people with ADHD is Children and Adults with Attention Deficit/Hyperactivity Disorder (CHADD), 22 percent of whose revenue in 2004–2005 came from the pharmaceutical industry (Phillips 2006, 434). While the precise effects of pharmaceutical firms' financial support on patient groups are difficult to gauge, such close associations are clearly important to the industry as an additional pathway, beyond doctors, for creating consumer demand for their products (Herxheimer 2003). In a survey of U.S. executives from fourteen pharmaceutical companies, 75 percent of respondents cited "patient education" as the top-ranked marketing activity necessary to bring a brand to "the number one spot" (HCHC 2005b, 74–76).

The interaction between pharmaceuticalization and consumerism is even more complex if one includes debates about patient education and direct-to-consumer advertising (DTCA) of prescription drugs. In Europe and most other Western industrialized countries, pharmaceutical companies are not allowed to advertise or promote their prescription medicinal products directly to patients or the general public, but such DTCA is legal in the United States and New Zealand. In the United

States, many physicians at the FDA and even many pharmaceutical companies believed that DTCA of prescription drugs was inappropriate when it first entered FDA policy debate in the early 1980s (U.S. House Subcommittee 1984). Indeed, historically, the claim by the research-based firms that they produced solely medical drugs for the medical profession and did not flirt with the fancies of the general public was how that part of the industry defined itself as "ethical" (Abraham 1995b, 39). However, when the FDA lifted its moratorium on DTCA in 1985, the industry could not resist the lure of sales and profits, and U.S. pharmaceutical companies spent US$12 billion on (mostly print) DTCA in 1989 (Conrad and Leiter 2009, 17).[6] However, the FDA retained cumbersome "fair balance" and "brief summary" regulations for *broadcast* DTCA, which greatly limited the industry's use of that media. In 1997 the FDA markedly relaxed these regulations in line with demands from the pharmaceutical industry and the Republican-dominated antiregulation Congress, now keen to expand DTCA. The extent of patient demand for extensive broadcast DTCA is unclear, though consumer expectations were often cited by the industry, Congress, and FDA as the justification for relaxing the regulations. Broadcast DTCA in the United States grew from US$55 million in 1991 to US$4.2 billion in 2005 with a 330 percent growth in DTCA from 1996 to 2005 (Conrad and Leiter 2009).

The experience of print, and especially broadcast, DTCA in the United States since 1997 is that it has contributed to the growth in medicalization and pharmaceuticalization because it has encouraged consumers to self-diagnose and then increasingly to ask doctors for advertised pharmaceutical products, which, in turn, has led to increased prescribing of those products (Mintzes et al. 2003). To a much greater extent than before, physicians have become gatekeepers for drugs advertised directly to consumers, rather than initiators of pharmaceutical treatment. The health informational value of DTCA for patients has proved questionable, as most U.S. physicians believe that the advertisements do not provide balanced information. Moreover, there is evidence that patients prompted by DTCA to request drugs from their doctors are much more likely to receive prescriptions for those drugs than are patients who make no such requests, even though, in some cases, as many as half of those prescriptions might be for drugs without evidence to support therapeutic efficacy in treating the condition (Conrad and Leiter 2009, 21).

Meanwhile, in Europe during the last decade, the pharmaceutical industry, with support from the European Commission's director-general for enterprise, has campaigned vigorously but so far unsuccessfully for the legalization of DTCA of prescription drugs in the European Union (EU).[7] This campaign characterized patients as consumers able to decide which drugs are best for them without doctors' supervision. It utilized a discourse of "the informed patient" and the "expert patient," which was subsequently adopted uncritically by some national European governments, including the UK Department of Health (2001). Doctors' failure to adequately inform patients about prescription medicines is a significant problem (Britten 2008). However, as the U.S. experience has shown, while DTCA can sometimes raise awareness about illnesses and availability of medical treatments, it is a considerable leap of faith to embrace a policy based on the assumption that pharmaceutical companies will fill the gap left by doctors in this respect. Furthermore, that assumption lacks any analysis of the interests involved and remarkably ignores the evidence of widespread problems for public health and health-care resources posed by misleading advertisements to doctors, let alone patients.

The expert-patient discourse can be put in its proper sociological context by relating it to the interests of those planning to provide the information intended to construct patient expertise and to the ideological nature of its emergence. The UK research-based pharmaceutical industry led the way, probably because London is home to the EU's drug-regulatory agency, the European Medicines Evaluation Agency (EMEA). Quoting from a speech by the director-general of the Association of the British Pharmaceutical Industry (ABPI), Medawar and Hardon (2004, 121) report that the 1998 "Informed Patient Initiative" was the first part of the industry's "battle plan," while the second part was the ABPI's publication "The Expert Patient," which according to the director-general was "part of a softening-up assault to be mounted through those interested parties and opinion leaders by stimulating debate." Evidently, the purpose of the campaign was to promote a consumerist ideology of patient self-care and self-medication in order to create a basis for arguing that patients are sufficiently knowledgeable to evaluate advertising claims about powerful prescription drugs. As the following passage from an article published in *Pharmaceutical Marketing* suggests, the industry hoped that the creation of such consumerist ideology would be sufficient to compel European regulators and governments to legalize DTCA throughout the EU:

> The ABPI battle plan is to employ ground troops in the form of patient support groups, sympathetic medical opinion and healthcare professionals which will lead the debate on the informed patient issue. This will have the effect of weakening political, ideological and professional defences. ... Then the ABPI will follow through with high-level precision strikes on specific regulatory enclaves in both Whitehall and Brussels. (Jeffries 2000, quoted in Medawar and Hardon 2004, 121)

To date, the European Parliament has refused complete legalization of DTCA. It has concluded that it would not be in the interests of patients' health. Nevertheless, the consumerist ideology surrounding the campaign left its mark on European pharmaceutical policy frameworks. For example, after consultation with the pharmaceutical industry, and following the extensive opposition to complete legalization of DTCA, the EU Commission proposed new legislation in 2008 that would maintain the general ban on DTCA but would allow industry to provide "additional information" to the public via the media (Richards 2008). Many EU public-health organizations, medical professionals, and some national government health agencies have opposed relaxation of the ban, underlining the crucial role of health professionals in the provision of tailored information to patients, and pointing to the practical difficulties of regulating and enforcing the distinction between "information" and "advertisement" (Association Internationale de la Mutualité et al. 2008).

Specifically, DTCA might encourage doctors to prescribe obesity drugs (recommended only after patients' lifestyle modifications are unsuccessful) when a change in diet, exercise, or some other lifestyle change is more appropriate (Padwal and Majumdar 2007). In highly prevalent conditions such as obesity, this could create major problems for public health (McCarthy 2004). In the UK, between 1980 and 1996, the prevalence of obesity increased from 6 to 17 percent of the population, and between 1993 and 2002 the percentage of overweight and obese adults rose from 59 to 65 (Ferriman 1999; Kopelman 2005, 65). With the number of obese adults in England predicted to exceed twelve million by 2010, the cost to the NHS just to treat all those people clinically defined as obese with drugs is estimated at £750 million per year (BBC News 24 1999; O'Dowd 2006).

Biomedicalism, Pharmaceutical Innovation, and Deregulatory Ideology

By looking at case studies and macro-organizational factors, I suggested in the previous sections that the sociological processes of medicalization, industry promotion, deregulatory ideology, and consumerism are much more likely explanations for growing pharmaceuticalization than the biomedicalism thesis that such growth simply reflects advances in science to meet medical need. However, it is clearly possible that, while such sociological processes might be significant, the biomedicalism thesis could still be correct, because *most* of the explanation for increased pharmaceuticalization lies in technoscientific advances in drug therapy. For instance, if a new antibiotic that could kill previously resistant strains of TB were discovered, then one would not readily attribute its uptake by doctors and patients to medicalization, industry promotion, deregulatory ideology, or consumerism. This could be because TB is already a well-recognized medical condition, the drug has been shown to eliminate the relevant bacterial strain by the most rigorous regulatory standards, irrespective of industry promotion, and patients really get better by any measure of respiratory condition. Thus, to obtain a more comprehensive characterization of pharmaceuticalization, sociological analysis must also examine the extent to which pharmaceutical product innovation contributes new medical drugs that are really needed by doctors and patients (therapeutic advance).

Such an analysis is conceptually intricate and empirically imperfect because of the incomplete nature of databases. Nevertheless, one begins by noting that, in all conventional pharmaceutical-policy literature, a drug product innovation is defined as a new molecular entity (NME) that is brought to the market. An NME is defined as a patentable *technical* novelty—it has a unique molecular structure (Vos 1991). Thus, a patent is awarded to protect commercially the intellectual property embedded in the discovery of the NME, and the transformation of an NME into a drug innovation depends only on meeting the commercial criterion of advance into the marketplace. It follows that the conventional definition of pharmaceutical product innovation is based on technological and commercial criteria, but does not necessarily imply that a new drug innovation offers any therapeutic advance *unless that is a requirement for marketing approval imposed by regulatory agencies.* However, regulatory agencies in the EU, North America, Australasia, and most other industrialized countries have never imposed such a requirement.[8] Pharmaceuticals legislation requires only that manufacturers demonstrate the quality, safety, and efficacy of their products. It does not require that those new products deliver therapeutic advance over drugs already available (Abraham 2004; Abraham and Lewis 2000).

A distinction, therefore, has to be drawn between pharmaceutical innovation and therapeutic advance—the latter necessarily involving a product that provides some therapeutic advantage in relation to efficacy, safety, or ease of administration and use over existing therapies (International Society of Drug Bulletins 2001). For example, many NMEs do not represent any (significant) therapeutic advance, no matter how novel in technological terms or how extensive their entrance into the marketplace. Conversely, new indications or new dosing schedules for, and new combinations of, already marketed products may well offer a therapeutic advantage for patients, no matter how old the products (HCHC 2005b). While product innovation retains commercial significance for pharmaceutical manufacturers, irrespective of therapeutic advance, it is generally the latter that satisfies the medical needs of patients, public health, and health professionals.

Thus, a major challenge for the sociology of pharmaceuticals is to untangle the dominant policy and popular discourse on innovation, which conflates technological novelty and commercial viability with therapeutic progress, and to refocus attention on innovations that offer therapeutic advance, rather than on innovation per se. Before considering the contentious issue of trends in therapeutic advance, it is worth noting that data from the FDA and the UK-based, ABPI-funded Centre for Medicines Research show that pharmaceutical product innovation in the United States and globally has been declining over the same period in which growing pharmaceuticalization has been witnessed (Figures 6.2.1 and 6.2.2). Between 2004 and 2008, FDA data show that the number of NMEs continued to decline at an annual average of twenty per year. Of course, these data do not reveal whether the number of NMEs, which offer significant therapeutic advance, has also been falling, but it is highly suggestive that the biomedicalism thesis is unlikely to explain most of the growth in pharmaceuticalization.

Remarkably, neither the MHRA nor the EMEA even collect data on the subset of NMEs that offer significant therapeutic advance, and the MHRA testified in 2005 that they saw no need to do so (HCHC 2005a). Nor does the Japanese drug-regulatory agency provide any English-language data on the proportion of NMEs offering therapeutic advance.[9] Consequently, there is no quantitative official government data on the extent to which the pharmaceutical industry is producing new drugs that offer therapeutic advance in the second- and third-largest pharmaceutical markets in the world, namely the EU and Japan, respectively. This demonstrates the influence of the dominant technical and commercial discourses on pharmaceutical innovation within governments and policy making, even though the primary objective of new drugs, which governments represent to citizens in public discourse, is to meet health needs.

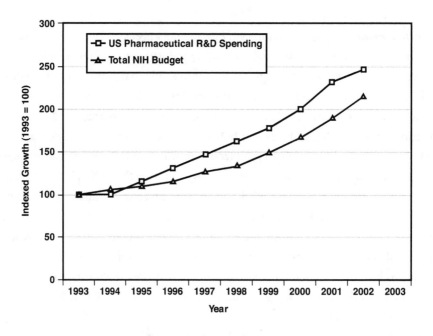

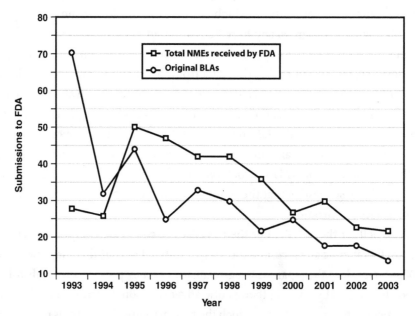

FIGURE 6.2.1 Ten-year trends in major drug and biological product submissions to FDA (fda.gov/oc/initiatives/criticalpath/nwoodcodk0602.html). NMEs are new molecular entities; BLAs are biologics license applications.

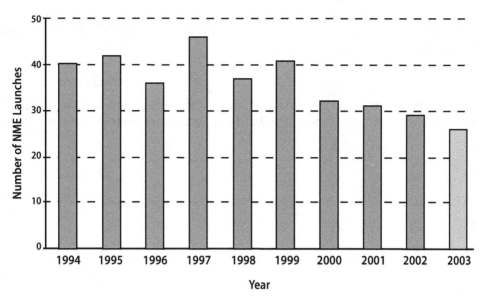

FIGURE 6.2.2 Number of new molecular entities first launched onto the world market between 1994 and 2003 (Center for Medicines Research 2005).

Nevertheless, in the United States, the world's largest pharmaceutical market, the FDA does distinguish between NMEs that offer significant therapeutic advance and those that do not as part of its drug-regulatory review process. Those that do are given "priority" review status, while the others receive "standard" review status. Table 6.2.1 shows that between 1993 and 2003, only 152 of the total 359 (42 percent) NMEs were judged to offer significant therapeutic advance. From 2004 to 2008, the figure rose slightly but remained below 50 percent (FDA 2009). Each year typically more than half the drugs, conventionally defined as innovations and submitted to the FDA, offered little or no therapeutic advantage over the drugs already on the market. More importantly to my concerns in this chapter, the number of NMEs offering significant therapeutic advance has also been declining in this period of growth in pharmaceuticalization. The situation may be worse than the FDA figures imply, because when the French organization of medical and pharmaceutical professionals, La Revue Prescrire (2005), reviewed 3,100 new drugs or new indications for existing drugs in the period 1981 to 2004 (most of which were on the French, EU, or U.S. markets), they concluded that only 10 percent offered moderate to significant therapeutic advance. From the perspective of therapeutic contribution to global health needs, the picture is stark. Of the 1,393 NMEs approved between 1975 and 1999, only 13 drugs (less than 1 percent) were specifically indicated for much-needed treatment of tropical diseases (Selgelid and Sepers 2006, 156).

Thus, there is no convincing evidence to support the biomedicalism thesis that, overall, most of the growth in pharmaceuticalization in the last fifteen years is the result of scientific discoveries

TABLE 6.2.1 FDA Review and Approval Times (in Months) for Priority and Standard New Molecular Entities, 1993–2003

Calendar Year	Priority			Standard		
	Number Approved	Median FDA Review Time	Median Total Approval Time	Number Approved	Median FDA Review Time	Median Total Approval Time
1993	13	13.9	14.9	12	27.2	27.2
1994	12	13.9	14.0	9	22.2	23.7
1995	10	7.9	7.9	19	15.9	17.8
1996	18	7.7	9.6	35	14.6	15.1
1997	9	6.4	6.7	30	14.4	15.0
1998	16	6.2	6.2	14	12.3	13.4
1999	19	6.3	6.9	16	14.0	16.3
2000	9	6.0	6.0	18	15.4	19.9
2001	7	6.0	6.0	17	15.7	19.0
2002	7	13.8	16.3	10	12.5	15.9
2003	9	6.7	6.7	12	13.8	23.1

Source: fda.gov/AboutFDA/ReportsManualsForms/Reports/UserFeeReports/PerformanceReports/PDUFA/default.htm

producing a plethora of new medicines addressing unmet health needs. On the contrary, the evidence suggests that, while pharmaceuticalization has been growing, the contribution from scientific R&D to deliver drugs that are really needed to treat illnesses has been declining. These findings also signify that a much more complex sociological analysis of pharmaceutical innovation and markets is required than the conventional wisdom among industry and governments that if the sector is less regulated, then the potential of biomedicine can be released to produce therapeutically valuable innovations. That conventional wisdom may be regarded as a policy ally of the biomedicalism thesis because, like the biomedicalism thesis, it tends to deny the enormous importance of sociological factors such as medicalization, industry promotion, deregulatory ideology, and consumerism.

In fact, by examining trends in both drug-regulatory policies and innovation in Europe and the United States, one finds that deregulatory policies during the 1980s and 1990s (e.g., of Reagan and Bush Senior administrations and the Republican Congress in the United States, and the Thatcher, Major, and Blair governments in the UK) have been followed by *declines* in innovation. As I noted earlier, from 1990 the FDA drastically cut its time to review and approve both priority *and* standard NMEs largely in response to complaints by the pharmaceutical industry and anti-regulation think tanks that overregulation was inhibiting innovation (Kaitin and DiMasi 2000; Kessler et al. 1996). The industry-funded American Enterprise Institute and the Tufts Centre had attacked the FDA for depriving U.S. doctors and patients of innovations because the agency was relatively cautious about approving new drugs compared with the UK and some other European countries (Grabowski, Vernon, and Thomas 1978; Wardell 1973). For these U.S. critics, whose views became influential during the Reagan–Bush Senior era, the UK's lighter-touch regulation was superior to the FDA's approach because, they argued, it delivered in a more timely manner more pharmaceutical innovations that patients and doctors needed.

It is true that during the 1970s and 1980s, the FDA was slower in approving NMEs overall than were regulatory authorities in the UK and many other European countries. However, Schweitzer, Schweitzer, and Sourty-Le Guellec (1996) analyzed the approval dates of thirty-four pharmaceuticals marketed in the G-7 countries plus Switzerland between 1970 and 1988 and designated especially therapeutically significant by panels of doctors and pharmacists in the United States and France. The FDA was found to have approved *more* of these drugs *before* the UK regulatory authorities had and ranked third out of the eight countries in approving these drugs onto the market. This suggests that the FDA's comparative slowness in approving NMEs as a whole, during the 1970s and 1980s, may be largely irrelevant to a discussion about the crucial subset of NMEs that are of significant therapeutic value to patients, medical professionals, and public health.

Similar trends have occurred in Europe. For example, the average net in-house review times of the UK regulatory agency for new drugs fell from 154 working days in 1989 to just 44 days by 1998. The regulatory review times of Germany, Sweden, and many other EU countries also fell dramatically in this period (Abraham and Lewis 2000, 20). It is generally acknowledged that there is a ten-year lag between a regulatory reform and its effects on pharmaceutical innovation, so the declines in innovation between 1995 and 2005 are associated with the deregulatory reforms between the early 1980s and early 1990s in the United States and Europe. Hence, it appears that deregulatory ideology (and associated policies) were drivers of growing pharmaceuticalization *not* primarily by releasing many more innovations needed by patients and medical professionals, as the biomedicalism thesis would have it, but rather mainly by allowing the industry to expand its markets for drugs that offer little or no therapeutic advance in a sea of declining innovation.

Nowhere is this more evident than in the case of antibiotics. By the late 1980s and early 1990s, it was known to biomedical scientists that bacterial resistance to existing antibiotics was becoming a significant health problem in both developed and developing countries (Blumberg, Carroll, and Wachsmuth 1991; Mastro et al. 1991; O'Neill and McIntosh 1987; Vallejo, Kaplan, and Mason 1991; van Klingeren, Dessens-Kroon, and Verheuvel 1989). This problem has grown steadily since. By

2004, the World Health Organization ranked infections caused by drug-resistant bacteria as the area of medical need where there was the largest "**pharmaceutical gap**," above even AIDS and malaria (WHO 2004). Clearly, then, between the late 1980s and 2004, there was a real health need for the development of new antibiotics to which bacteria would not be resistant. This was also a period of growing pharmaceuticalization and deregulatory-reform policies and ideology.

Yet, between 1983 and 2004, the development of antibiotics declined steadily: the FDA approved 16 between 1983 and 1987; 14 between 1988 and 1992; 10 between 1993 and 1997; 7 between 1998 and 2002; and just 3 in 2003 and 2004 (Infectious Diseases Society of America 2004, 15). Regarding antibiotics under development that might be approved after 2004, Spellberg et al. (2004) found that of 506 molecules under development in 2002 at twenty-two major pharmaceutical and biotechnology companies, only 6 were antibiotics. Despite this, Bradley and colleagues (2007, 68), from the Antimicrobial Availability Task Force of IDSA, find that "two years later, very little has changed." Talbot and colleagues (2006) identified six resistant pathogens posing serious threats to patients for which there are few or no drugs in late-stage development. To explain this, Bradley and colleagues (2007, 68) conclude: "Anti-infective drug products are less profitable than other types of medicines, particularly those for chronic conditions. ... As a result, many major pharmaceutical companies have decided to focus their research and development efforts elsewhere, leaving the pipeline in this essential field dangerously dry." Evidently, pharmaceuticalization and the production of new drugs that are needed for world health are quite different, and only loosely related, phenomena, because the political economy of the pharmaceutical industry as currently constituted, not therapeutic value, tends to determine the nature and direction of innovation.

Conclusion

Overall, pharmaceutical markets have expanded in the last few decades in many societies. While this may partly result from general economic growth, there is considerable evidence that it is largely due to increased pharmaceuticalization of our societies. The biomedicalism thesis, popular among many scientists and media discourses, that growing pharmaceuticalization simply reflects discoveries in biomedical science that correspond to health needs is not plausible. Some pharmaceuticalization may fall into this category, but there is no good reason to support the thesis that most of it can be explained in this way. Indeed, there is evidence to suggest that, while pharmaceuticalization has increased, the number of medications needed by patients and public health is actually decreasing, along with pharmaceutical innovation.

Growing pharmaceuticalization seems to be best explained by sociological factors such as the political economy of the pharmaceutical industry and associated medicalization (especially promotion and advertising activities involving physicians and clinicians), deregulatory ideology toward drug development and innovation, and access-oriented collaborative consumerism, which outweighs the countervailing effects of adversarial consumerism. The sociological analysis required to explain pharmaceuticalization is complex because those factors are not mutually independent; rather they interact with each other. Medicalization can facilitate, even stimulate, pharmaceutical development and promotion, but it can also be shaped by industry-driven technoscience and marketing strategies. Furthermore, medicalization can be encouraged as an interim stage toward pharmaceuticalization by patients' self-diagnoses and demands for medications. Yet, such demands may themselves be strongly influenced, sustained, or even created by industry promotion, advertising, and financial support. While industry promotion, medicalization, and consumerism can all encourage the growth of pharmaceuticalization, such growth is substantially, though not entirely, de pen dent on a regulatory state that is willing to grant marketing approval to drugs that offer no therapeutic advance, to lower regulatory standards of efficacy in order to accelerate more NMEs on to the market, and indeed to relax restrictions or prohibitions on DTCA of prescription medications.

The pharmaceutical industry has proved versatile. Its presence is notable in all the areas contributing to the growth of pharmaceuticalization. Drug firms work with (and undermine when necessary) members of the medical profession in order to secure the viability of products while simultaneously supporting DTCA and the discourse of "expert patient," which are generally opposed by medical and health professionals. The industry encourages consumerism when it is about patients' access to medications but vigorously contests the relevance and expertise of consumerism when it condemns the safety problems of some pharmaceutical products. Perhaps most importantly, the industry has persuaded government drug-regulatory agencies that the economic performance of the industry is so important that state intervention should become involved in fostering its commercial success, rather than give unambiguous and unrivalled priority to the protection of public health, irrespective of the private interests of industry.

One may conclude that pharmaceuticalization has expanded largely because the drug industry has used its power to have a central influence on all the key sociological factors driving the phenomenon. Consequently, pharmaceuticalization has increased mainly in accordance with the commercial interests of the pharmaceutical industry. However, contrary to what would follow from the biomedicalism thesis, a pharmaceuticalization process driven by the interests of the industry has not to a very significant extent delivered drug products in response to medical and health needs.

Notes

1. For the purposes of brevity and focus, this chapter is almost exclusively concerned with prescription pharmaceuticals in Europe and North America.

2. Off-label use occurs when a doctor prescribes a medication for a condition not sanctioned by the regulatory authorities, and hence not stipulated on the label.

3. Arguably, there is a third type, namely access-oriented adversary, which has been particularly relevant to some developing countries where patient activists have campaigned against pharmaceutical firms in order to force them to sell their drugs at affordable prices, especially antiretroviral medications for HIV/AIDS.

4. In 2005, the UK introduced a Freedom of Information Act, but it is very weak compared with its U.S. counterpart and has made only a tiny dent in the conventional secrecy of British pharmaceutical regulation.

5. This activism may not have been in the interests of HIV/AIDS patients, because subsequent research has suggested that the early drugs that were rushed on to the market, such as AZT, may have offered little or no therapeutic benefit, were highly toxic, and may even have weakened patients' immune systems (WTO 2006).

6. The FDA represented this shift as a response to inferred patient demand, but it may have been influenced by the deregulatory ideology of the Reagan administration.

7. A proposal to relax the ban on DTCA in the EU is currently under consideration by the European Parliament. If passed, then from 2010 the industry would be permitted to provide some "information" about their products directly to consumers via some media.

8. Norway had a "needs" clause (requiring new drugs to demonstrate therapeutic advance over existing products on the market) in its pharmaceutical regulation until 1994, when the national government abandoned it in expectation of joining the EU and hence of conforming to the EU's supranational rules of "fair competition."

9. I have been unable to ascertain data availability in Japanese.

References

Abraham, John. 1994a. "Bias in Science and Medical Knowledge: The Opren Controversy." *Sociology* 28:717–36.
———. 1994b. "Distributing the Benefit of the Doubt: Scientists, Regulators and Drug Safety." *Science, Technology and Human Values* 19:493–522.
———. 1995a. "The Production and Reception of Scientific Papers in the Medical-Industrial Complex: Clinical Evaluation of New Medicines." *British Journal of Sociology* 46:167–90.

———. 1995b. *Science, Politics and the Pharmaceutical Industry.* London and New York: UCL/St. Martin's Press/Routledge.

———. 2002. "Transnational Industrial Power, the Medical Profession and the Regulatory State: Adverse Drug Reactions and the Crisis over the Safety of Halcion in the Netherlands and the UK." *Social Science and Medicine* 55:1671–90.

———. 2004. "Pharmaceuticals, the State and the Global Harmonisation Process." *Australian Health Review* 28:150–61.

Abraham, John, and Graham Lewis. 2000. *Regulating Medicines in Europe: Competition, Expertise and Public Health.* London: Routledge.

———. 2002. "Citizenship, Medical Expertise and the Capitalist Regulatory State in Europe." *Sociology* 36:67–88.

Abraham, John, and Julie Sheppard. 1999. *The Therapeutic Nightmare: The Battle over the World's Most Controversial Sleeping Pill.* London: Earthscan.

Angell, Marci. 2004. *The Truth about Drug Companies.* New York: Random House.

Applbaum, K. 2006. "Pharmaceutical Marketing and the Invention of the Medical Consumer." *Public Library of Science Medicine* 3:445–47.

Association Internationale de la Mutualité (AIM), European Social Insurance Platform (ESIP), Health Action International (HAI), International Society of Drug Bulletins (ISDB), and Medicines in Europe Forum (MiEF). 2008. "Legal Proposals on 'Information' to Patients by Pharmaceutical Companies: A Threat to Public Health." Joint briefing paper. March 6. prescrire.org/docus/LegalProposalsInfoPatient_JointPaper_March2009.pdf.

Barkley, Russell. 1997. "Behavioral Inhibition, Sustained Attention, and Executive Functions: Constructing a Unifying Theory of ADHD." *Psychological Bulletin* 121:65–94.

———. 2003. "Attention-Deficit/Hyperactivity Disorder." In *Child Psychopathology*, ed. Russell Barkley and Eric Mash, 75–143. New York: Guildford Press.

BBC News 24. 1999. "Tough Guidance on Obesity Drugs." January 13. news.bbc.co.uk.

———. 2006a. "Herceptin: Was Patient Power Key?" June 9. news.bbc.co.uk.

———. 2006b. "Woman Wins Herceptin Court Fight." April 12. news.bbc.co.uk.

———. 2007. "Alzheimer's Drugs Remain Limited." August 10. news.bbc.co.uk.

Berenson, A. 2007. "Analysts See Merck Victory in Vioxx Deal." *New York Times*, November 10.

Bird, H., T. J. Yager, B. Staghezza, and M. S. Gould. 1990. "Impairment in the Epidemiological Measurement of Childhood Psychopathology in the Community." *Journal of the American Academy of Childhood and Adolescent Psychiatry* 29:796–803.

Blumberg, H. M., D. J. Carroll, and I. K. Wachsmuth. 1991. "Rapid Development of Ciprofloxacin Resistance in Methicillin-Susceptible and -Resistant Staphylococcus Aureus." *Journal of Infectious Diseases* 163:1279–85.

Bradley, J. S., R. Guidos, S. Baragona, and J. G. Bartlett. 2007. "Anti-Infective Research and Development—Problems, Challenges, and Solutions." *Lancet Infectious Diseases* 7:68–69.

Britten, Nicola. 2008. *Medicines and Society.* Basingstoke, Eng.: Palgrave.

Carpenter, Daniel P. 2004. "The Political Economy of FDA Drug Review: Processing, Politics and Lessons for Policy." *Health Affairs* 23:52–63.

Castellanos, X. 2002. "Development Trajectories of Brain Volume Abnormalities in Children and Adults with ADHD." *Journal of the American Medical Association* 288:1740–48.

Centre for Medicines Research. 2005. "Innovation on the Wane?" Latest News. www.cmr.org.

Code of Federal Regulations. 1992. "Accelerated Approval of New Drugs for Serious or Life-Threatening Illnesses." CFR Part 314, Subpart H.

Conrad, Peter, and Valerie Leiter. 2009. "From Lydia Pinkham to Queen Levitra: Direct-to-Consumer Advertising and Medicalization." In *Pharmaceuticals and Society: Critical Discourses and Debates*, ed. Simon J. Williams, Jonathon Gabe, and Peter Davis, 12–24. Chichester, Eng.: Wiley-Blackwell.

Conrad, Peter, and D. Potter. 2000. "From Hyperactive Children to ADHD Adults." *Social Problems* 47:559–82.

Conrad, Peter, and J. W. Schneider. 1992. *Deviance and Medicalization: From Badness to Sickness*. Philadelphia: Temple University Press.

Cornwall, John. 1996. *The Power to Harm: Mind, Murder and Drugs on Trial*. Harmondsworth, Eng.: Penguin.

Couvoisie, H., and S. R. Hooper. 2003. "Neurometabolic Functioning and Neuro-Psychological Correlates in Children with ADHD: Preliminary Findings." *Journal of Neuro-Psychiatry and Clinical Neuro-Sciences* 16:63–69.

Daemmrich, Arthur, and Georg Krucken. 2000. "Risk versus Risk: Decision-Making Dilemmas of Drug Regulation in the U.S. and Germany." *Science as Culture* 9:505–34.

DeGrandpre, R. 2000. *Ritalin Nation: Rapid-Fire Culture and the Transformation of Human Consciousness*. New York: W. W. Norton.

Diller, L. 1998. *Running on Ritalin: A Physician Reflects on Children, Society and Performance in a Pill*. New York: Bantam Books.

Drug Enforcement Administration. 2001. *Aggregate Production Quota History, 1992–2002*. Washington, D.C.: Department of Justice.

Edgar, H., and D. J. Rothman. 1990. "New Rules for New Drugs: The Challenge of AIDS to the Regulatory Process." *Milbank Quarterly* 68, suppl. 1:111–42.

Eli Lilly. 2000. *Eli Lilly Annual Report 2000*.

Epstein, Steven. 1996. *Impure Science: AIDS, Activism, and the Politics of Knowledge*. Berkeley: University of California Press.

FDA [Food and Drug Administration]. 1997. Modernization Act. Section 506(b)(3) of the Food, Drug and Cosmetic Act (as amended by Section 112 of FDAMA). Washington, D.C.: GPO.

————. 2004. "Review and Approval Times for Priority and Standards NMEs." www.fda.gov.

————. 2009. "CDER Approval Times for Priority and Standard NMEs, 1993–2008." www.fda.gov/cder/rdmt/default.htm.

Ferriman, A. 1999. "Fat Is a Medical Issue." *British Medical Journal* 318:144.

Fleming, T. R. 2005. "Surrogate Endpoints and FDA's Accelerated Approval Process." *Health Affairs* 24:67–78.

Gale, E. A. M. 2001. "Lessons from the Glitazones." *Lancet* 357:1871.

Glenmullen, J. 2000. *Prozac Backlash: Overcoming the Dangers of Prozac, Zoloft and Paxil and Other Antidepressants with Safe, Effective Alternatives.* New York: Simon and Schuster.

Goldman, L. S., M. Genel, and R. J. Bezman. 1998. "Diagnosis and Treatment of ADHD in Children and Adolescents." *Journal of the American Medical Association* 279:1100–1107.

Grabowski, H., J. Vernon, and L. Thomas. 1978. "Estimating the Effects of Regulation on Innovation: An International Comparative Analysis of the Pharmaceutical Industry." *Journal of Law and Economics* 21:133–63.

Harding, R. 2001. "Unlocking the Brain's Secrets." *Family Circle*, November 20, 10–11.

Healy, David. 2004. *Let Them Eat Prozac.* London: New York University Press.

———. 2006a. "The Latest Mania: Selling Bipolar Disorder." *Public Library of Science Medicine* 3:441–44.

———. 2006b. "The New Medical Oikumene." In *Global Pharmaceuticals*, ed. Adriana Petryna, Andrew Lakoff, and Arthur Kleinman, 61–84. Durham, N.C.: Duke University Press.

Herxheimer, Andrew. 2003. "Relationships between the Pharmaceutical Industry and Patients' Organizations." *British Medical Journal* 326:1208–10.

HCHC [House of Commons Health Committee]. 2005a. "Evidence" Nos. 354–56 in *Proceedings of the Health Select Committee Hearings on Inquiry into the Influence of the Pharmaceutical Industry*, January 20. London: TSO.

———. 2005b. *Inquiry into the Influence of the Pharmaceutical Industry: Health Select Committee Report.* London: TSO.

IMS Health. 2008. "Global Pharmaceutical Sales 2000–2007." imshealth.com/deployedfiles/imshealth/global/content/statcfile.pdf.

Infectious Diseases Society of America. 2004. *Bad Bugs, No Drugs: As Antibiotic Discovery Stagnates, a Public Health Crisis Brews.* Alexandria, Va.: ISDA.

International Society of Drug Bulletins. 2001. *ISDB Declaration on Therapeutic Advance in the Use of Medicines*, Paris, November 15–16.

Jeffries, M. 2000. "The Mark of Zorro." *Pharmaceutical Marketing*, May, 4–5.

Kaitin, Kenneth I., and J. DiMasi. 2000. "Measuring the Pace of New Drug Development in the User Fee Era." *Drug Information Journal* 24:673–80.

Kessler, David A., A. E. Hass, K. L. Feiden, M. Lumpkin, and R. Temple. 1996. "Approval of New Drugs in the U.S.: Comparison with the UK, Germany and Japan." *Journal of the American Medical Association* 276:1826–31.

Kopelman, P. G. 2005. "Clinical Treatment of Obesity: Are Drugs and Surgery the Answer?" *Proceedings of the Nutrition Society* 64:65–71.

Krause, K-H., S. H. Dresel, J. Krause, C. La Fougere, and M. Ackervell. 2003. "The Dopamine Transporter and Neuro-Imaging in ADHD." *Neuro-Science Bio-Behavioral Review* 27:605–13.

La Revue Prescrire. 2005. "A Review of New Drugs in 2004: Floundering Innovation and Increased Risk-Taking." *Prescrire International* 14:68–73.

Lexchin, Joel, L. A. Bero, B. Djulbegovic, and O. Clark. 2003. "Pharmaceutical Industry Sponsorship and Research Outcomes and Quality." *British Medical Journal* 326:1167–70.

Mastro, T. D., J. S. Spika, R. R. Facklam, C. Thornberry, A. Ghafoor, N. K. Nomani, Z. Ishaq, F. Anwar, and D. M. Granoff. 1991. "Antimicrobial Resistance of Pneumococci in Children with Acute Lower Respiratory Tract Infection in Pakistan." *Lancet* 337:156–59.

McCarthy, M. 2004. "The Economics of Obesity." *Lancet* 364:2169–70.

Medawar, Charles. 1992. *Power and Dependence: Social Audit on the Safety of Medicines.* London: Social Audit.

Medawar, Charles, and Anita Hardon. 2004. *Medicines out of Control? Antidepressants and the Conspiracy of Goodwill.* Amsterdam: Askant.

Mintzes, Barbara, M. L. Barer, R. L. Kravitz, K. Bassett, J. Lexchin, A. Kazanjian, R. G. Evans, R. Pan and S. A. Marion. 2003. "How Does Direct-to-Consumer Advertising (DTCA) Affect Prescribing? A Survey in Primary Care Environments with and without Legal DTCA." *Canadian Medical Association Journal* 169:405–12.

Mitka, M. 2003. "Accelerated Approval Scrutinized—Confirmatory Phase 4 Studies on New Drugs Languish." *Journal of the American Medical Association* 289:3227–29.

Moynihan, Raymond. 2006. "Obesity Task Force Linked to WHO Takes 'Millions' from Drug Firms." *British Medical Journal* 332:1412.

O'Donovan, Orla. 2007. "Corporate Colonization of Health Activism?" *International Journal of Health Services* 37:711–33.

O'Dowd, A. 2006. "More Than 12 Million Adults in England Will Be Obese by 2010." *British Medical Journal* 333:463.

O'Neill, P., and S. McIntosh. 1987. "Bacteria Resistant to Antibiotics Spread Concern." *New Scientist*, August 27, 16. Parsons, Talcott. 1951. *The Social System.* New York: Free Press.

Padwal, R. S., and S. R. Majumdar. 2007. "Drug Treatments for Obesity." *Lancet* 369:71–77.

Phillips, C. B. 2006. "Medicine Goes to School: Teachers as Sickness Brokers for ADHD." *Public Library of Science Medicine* 3:433–35.

Richards, T. 2008. "Border Crossing: Purely Medicinal?" *British Medical Journal* 336:693.

Roberts, T. G., and B. A. Chabner. 2004. "Beyond Fast Track for Drug Approvals." *New England Journal of Medicine* 351:501–3.

Schweitzer, S. O., M. E. Schweitzer and M-J. Sourty-Le Guellec. 1996. "Is There a U.S. Drug Lag? The Timing of New Pharmaceutical Approvals in the G-7 Countries and Switzerland." *Medical Care Research and Review* 53:162–78.

Scrip News. 1988. "Bush Calls for Speedier U.S. Approvals." Scripnews 1335:16.

———. 1995. "SSRIs—Unprecedented U.S. Growth." Scripnews 2020:23.

———. 1999. "Pfizer's Pharma Sales Soar 28%." Scripnews 2405:8.

Selgelid, M. J., and E. M. Sepers. 2006. "Patents, Profits, and the Price of Pills: Implications for Access and Availability." In *The Power of Pills*, ed. Jillian Clare Cohen, Patricia Illingworth, and Udo Schuklenk, 153–63. London: Pluto Press.

Sharma, V., J. M. Halpern, and J. H. Newcorn. 2000. "Diagnostic Co-morbidity, Attentional Measures, and Neuro-Chemistry in Children with ADHD." In *Ritalin: Theory and Practice*, ed. L. Greenhill and B. Osman, 15–24. Larchmont, Md.: Liebert.

Spellberg, B., J. H. Powers, E. P. Brass, L. G. Miller, and J. E. Edwards. 2004. "Trends in Antimicrobial Drug Development: Implications for the Future." *Clinical Infectious Diseases* 38:1279–86.

Talbot, G. H., J. Bradley, J. E. Edwards, D. Gilbert, M. Scheld, and J. G. Bartlett. 2006. "Bad Bugs Need Drugs: An Update on the Development Pipeline from the Anti-Microbial Availability Task Force of IDSA." *Clinical Infectious Diseases* 42:657–68.

Thambirajah, M. 1998. "Attention Deficit Hyperactivity Disorder in Children: Danger Is One of Over-Diagnosis." *British Medical Journal* 317:1250.

Timmerman, L. 2003. "Impotence Drug *Cialis* Gets OK for Sales in U.S." *Seattle Times*, November 22.

UK Department of Health. 1994. *Prescription Cost Analysis*. London: Government Statistical Service.

———. 2001. *The Expert Patient—A New Approach to Chronic Disease Management for the 21st Century*. London: HMSO.

———. 2003. *Prescription Cost Analysis*. London: Government Statistical Service.

U.S. Congress. House. Committee on Energy and Commerce. Subcommittee on Oversight and Investigations. 1984. *Prescription Advertising to Consumers*. Washington, D.C.: GPO.

Vallejo, J. G., S. L. Kaplan, and E. O. Mason. 1991. "Treatment of Meningitis and Other Infections due to Ampicillin-Resistant Haemophilus Influenzae Type B in Children." *Reviews of Infectious Diseases* 13:197–200.

Van Klingeren, B., M. Dessens-Kroon, and M. Verheuvel. 1989. "Increased Tetracycline Resistance in Gonococci in The Netherlands." *Lancet* 334:1278.

Vos, Rein. 1991. *Drugs Looking for Diseases: Innovative Drug Research and the Development of the Beta Blockers*. Dordrecht, Netherlands: Kluwer.

Wardell, William. 1973. "Introduction of New Therapeutic Drugs in the U.S. and Great Britain: An International Comparison." *Clinical Pharmacology and Therapeutics* 14:773–90.

WHO [World Health Organization]. 2004. *Priority Medicines for Europe and the World*. Geneva: WHO.

———. 2006. "TRIPs and Pharmaceutical Patents." WTO Fact Sheet, 1–8. wto.org/english/tratop_E/TRIPS_e/factsheet_pharm00_e.htm.

Yuwiler, A., G. L. Brammer, and K. C. Yuwiler. 1994. "The Basics of Serotonin Neuro-Chemistry." In *The Neuro-Transmitter Revolution: Serotonin, Social Behavior, and the Law*, ed. R. Masters and M. McGuire, 37–46. Carbondale: Southern Illinois University Press.

Zametkin, A. J., T. E. Nordhal, M. Gross, A. C. King, W. E. Semple, J. Rumsey, S. Hamburger, and R. M. Cohen. 1990. "Cerebral Glucose Metabolism in Adults with Hyperactivity of Childhood Onset." *New England Journal of Medicine* 323:1361–66.

CRITICAL THINKING QUESTIONS

1. How does medical technology impact medical practice? Provide at least one example from the reading by Casper and Morrison and one example from your own knowledge and experience.

2. How has medical technology reconfigured human bodies and our conceptions of them? Identify a medical technology from your own experience and knowledge that has done this and discuss it. Use Casper and Morrison's discussion on ultrasound as a template for your own discussion.

3. Define the biomedical thesis and then compare it to Abraham's thesis of pharmaceuticalization. Be sure to identify and define pertinent concepts and provide examples from the reading, as well as your own knowledge and experience.

4. Define *pharmaceuticalization*. What three sociological factors explain it? Identify and define pertinent concepts, give examples, and use the reading by Abraham in your discussion.

US and Global Healthcare

....

Editor's Introduction

The purpose of unit VII is to provide you with an overview of the history of the US healthcare system, introduce some of the myriad methods that could be used to improve that system, and illustrate some of the serious barriers that poor nations encounter in trying to develop and maintain their own healthcare systems.

Globally, all developed nations and many developing nations offer universal healthcare to their citizens and legal residents. The United States is the only developed nation that does not offer universal healthcare to citizens. Instead of universal care, the United States has a conglomeration of private and public institutions that often work in competition with one another. This results in a highly fragmented system that patients find difficult to navigate and to afford. For example, a patient who has cancer can often expect to receive treatment that will require multiple visits and even admissions to a hospital, where the equipment resides. For each treatment, the patient will receive a bill for every part of their treatment, including bloodwork; radiology or technical support; nursing services; and hospital services such as provision of the room, pharmaceuticals, and more. If the patient has insurance, the insurance will be billed, and the patient will be responsible for the remainder due. Patients often receive bills that are so detailed, they cannot understand them. The insurance/doctor/hospital/technician/pharmaceuticals odyssey is virtually impossible to disentangle. At the systems level, an inordinate number of labor hours are spent accounting and billing, and then enforcing payment, which takes money that might be better invested elsewhere. It is common knowledge that the United States spends the most on healthcare yet has worse health outcomes than other industrialized nations.

universal coverage: regarding healthcare, the guarantee that all citizens and legal residents will receive needed care.

portability: regarding healthcare, the guarantee that people will not lose coverage if their life or job circumstances change.

The World Health Organization (WHO)[1] proposes a variety of elements that comprise a successful healthcare system. Among these is **universal coverage**, the guarantee that all citizens and legal residents of a nation will receive needed care. Another is **portability**, the guarantee that people will not lose coverage if their life or job circumstances change. A third is the protection of people from the financial consequences of poor health. As you may imagine, balancing these and the myriad additional elements of successful healthcare systems can be tricky! However, industrialized nations across the world manage to provide some degree of all of these to their citizens, and their health outcomes show it.

In "Ironies of Success: A New History of the American Healthcare 'System,'" Donald W. Light provides us with a historical investigation of how the medical profession organized itself to become politically powerful, how the profession used the state to destroy early healthcare markets and end competition, **and, finally,** how the profession established exclusive guild markets. For example, what became known as *the Davis Strategy* was developed to knock out competition. The strategy involved establishing state licensing boards *outside* the medical profession; however, members were chosen by the profession and the boards made graduating from a certified medical school a prerequisite for licensing. These and other machinations of the medical profession enabled the profession to hold a virtual monopoly over medicine in the United States and determine whatever fees it thought were reasonable, especially in the years following World War II. *Today, the United States is left with numerous reports indicating that this system is unjust and discriminates against the vulnerable; causes avoidable deaths, injuries, and treatment-induced illnesses; wastes more than any other comparable system in administration and marketing; and has a very weak public health component.* The US healthcare market ranks below all other affluent nations while many citizens and legal residents remain un- and underinsured. Even those who do have coverage receive a quality of care that varies widely. The *irony* that Light's work uncovers is that the actions taken by these early medical professionals led to the establishment of an ideal of *good medicine*, which produced its own lapses and excesses,

---

1 "Key Components of a Well-Functioning Health System," World Health Organization, May 2010, https://www.who.int/healthsystems/publications/hss_key/en/.

and resulted in *strong buyers* who are working to transform the medical profession today.

In "The Healthcare System under French National Health Insurance: Lessons for Reform in the United States," by Victor G. Rodwin provides an assessment of achievements, problems, and reforms of the French healthcare system over time, then makes suggestions about how the United States might use the French experience to work toward universal coverage. The belief in **American exceptionalism** often prevents Americans from investigating the pros and cons of other nations' experiences with healthcare systems. This reading contributes to a very important discussion that Americans have avoided until recently. In 2000, France finally closed the gaps in coverage for its citizens by covering the remaining uninsured and by subsidizing those whose incomes are below a certain threshold and who were under-covered. The French now provide universal coverage with a combination of private and public hospitals and ambulatory care. France oversees its hospital system, to which all citizens and legal residents have access, and a variety of public and private ambulatory care services are offered, as well. There are no gatekeepers to the French system, so everyone has full access to care. While these elements end in a bit of organizational diversity or fragmentation, the French propose it is the best step toward **pluralism**, which the French value. France also manages the system without the overt costs that burden the US system. Rodwin ends the reading with four propositions the French system can offer the United States, including that the United States must not, necessarily, reach universal coverage all at once and may do so incrementally. The French experience also demonstrates that it is possible to achieve universal coverage without instituting a single-payer system; additionally, the French system demonstrates that private insurers don't necessarily need to be excluded from the development of the universal coverage system; and, finally, the French experience shows that it is possible to attain universal coverage without having to fully and immediately modernize the system.

In "Austerity in Africa: Audit Cultures and the Weakening of Public Sector Health Systems," James Pfeiffer illustrates how postcolonial measures imposed by the International Monetary Fund (IMF) and the World Bank work to undermine the development and maintenance of Mozambique's public health efforts. Pfeiffer records how the World

American exceptionalism: the idea that the U.S. is uniquely different from other countries; this is often experienced by Americans as a belief that there is nothing to learn from other nations.

pluralism: the coexistence of two or more groups, services, states, authorities, etc.

Bank and IMF came to have significant impacts on global health over the last thirty years. Due to their role as primarily financial institutions, these lenders require a great deal of data related to such things as *cost effectiveness*, *business models*, and much more. The data currently required by the lenders to undertake any public health program in Mozambique is so massive and costly to compile that these requirements make it impossible for Mozambique to compete with wealthy, American healthcare corporations to take care of their own people. Termed *audit culture* by anthropologists, medicine in poor nations is partly characterized by the presence of managers and accountants in place of health experts. Ultimately, economists came to direct Mozambique's healthcare system, the public health elements of which have been impoverished by funds being diverted to corporations who can provide the numbers. Increasingly, Mozambique's health sector is focused on the *pet* health issues of wealthy countries, such as HIV, while community health is severely minimized.

Together, these articles provide a small taste of the variety of issues investigated in the sociology of global health.

Ironies of Success

A New History of the American Health Care "System"*

By Donald W. Light

The context for contemporary research and policy is set through a theoretically informed history of the modern American health care system that draws on the concept of counter-vailing powers and Fligstein's theory of control. In this context, the papers of this special issue are then introduced.

Having watched "ruinous competition" undermine both the achievements and potential of historic scientific breakthroughs, James Peter Warbasse wrote the following words in 1912, already with a certain sense of despair just twelve years into the 20th century:

> The matter with the medical profession is that the doctor is a private tradesman engaged in a competitive business for profit ... It is difficult, nay, impossible for him to do otherwise. He is surrounded by the competitive system, and unless he conforms to the methods of warfare about him, he must go down. ... The science of medicine has made wonderful progress in the past fifty years ... The whole history of medicine ... is a glorious refutation of the sophistry that competition for profit is important to human progress. The competitive system, which surrounds and harnesses medical advancement, hindered it from the beginning and retards it still ... (Warbasse 1912:274).

A distinguished surgeon and author of a major text on the subject, a bench scientist and author of numerous scientific articles and books, Warbasse had also published three years earlier the first book entitled, *Medical Sociology* (1909). He provides an apt starting point for undertaking an institutional, political, and cultural assessment of how the medical profession reorganized into a political powerhouse and used the state to deconstruct early health care markets, stop "ruinous competition," and develop closed guild markets that produced the "golden era of medicine" after World

* This essay is based on historical work sponsored by the Century Fund, to whom I am most grateful. Librarians are the most wonderful people, masters of their collections, curious and always willing to help. Without the help of those at Countway, Princeton, and the College of Physicians, this research could not have been done. References here are kept to a minimum.

War II. However, the professional ideal of good medicine produced its own lapses and excesses that have led to strong buyers returning with a force that is transforming the medical profession. As an introduction to new research on contemporary health care, this essay will help readers understand the dilemmas and ironies that seem to have the American health care system in their grip today. This essay also contributes to the research on how specific markets form (for overviews, see Fligstein 2001; Swedberg 2003). Much (but not all) of this literature overlooks the predatory ways in which major stakeholders get legislators and governmental agencies to disadvantage or even eliminate others and to make large sums of taxpayers' money available to them. Preemptive actions commonly known to actors get little attention from researchers. One could say that the dominant actor tried to "stabilize its market," but that would reflect only the actor's point of view, rather than a critical, societal perspective.

Two great strengths that sociology brings to the policy table, or to any effort at understanding how some aspect of society works, are its analysis of how past structural or organizational forces influence life and of how people or organizations construct their own reality. Most economics and much of journalism focus on the individual and on psychological explanations. They leave out the institutional and organizational forces that shape how people perceive their reality and the options from which they make choices. For example, nearly half of all employers in the American employer-based, voluntary health insurance system do not offer health insurance, in part because they see how terribly expensive it is and want to avoid getting involved. What most do not realize is the degree to which key stakeholders—the medical and hospital associations, insurance companies, employers unions, and more recently health care corporations and a raft of secondary industries that have grown up to support the **medical-industrial complex**—have designed the American health care system to minimize any party's ability to provide integrated, cost-effective care in a system that could manage the major sources of inefficiency, fragmentation, and escalating costs. American employers cannot choose, as Dutch or Finnish or British employers can, to participate in a system that controls costs, waste, and inefficiency and puts primary and secondary prevention at the center of health care.

EDITOR'S NOTES

medical-industrial complex: the health industry in the United States, composed of doctors, hospitals, nursing homes, insurance companies, drug manufacturers, hospital supply and equipment companies, real estate and construction businesses, health systems consulting and accounting firms, banks, and more.

Besides attending to institutional and organizational forces, sociology also differs from most of economics and psychology in documenting how deeply culture and history shape present organizations, institutions, and individual behavior. The past becomes embedded in the organizations, rules, and habits of the present. Sociology thus provides the substance and analytic tools that policy makers and citizens need to understand the world around them. This collection of specially commissioned and peer reviewed essays by talented sociological analysts makes manifest what the discipline can offer.

Why is the American "health care system" in such organizational, financial, and clinical disarray?[1] Even the orthodox, elite Institute of Medicine has issued a stream of reports showing that the system is deeply unjust; discriminates against the vulnerable and disadvantaged; causes plane-loads of avoidable deaths, injuries, and treatment-induced illnesses; wastes far more than any other comparable system in administration, marketing, and other non-clinical costs; and has a weak public health foundation (Institute of Medicine 2001, 2003). Why does "the best health care system in the world" rank below health care in every other affluent country and below several others as well (World Health Organization 2000)? Even if we put aside the one-sixth of the nation that has no insurance (but why should we?), and another one-fifth that have limited health insurance that continues to be diluted (most accurately called "unsurance," not insurance), the patients with coverage get patchy care.

The quality of clinical medicine that patients receive is also patchy and overall falls far short of the self-congratulatory claim that we have "the best health care system in the world." A few years ago, the Institute of Medicine (1999) discovered the large number of preventable deaths, injuries, and illnesses that patients in American hospitals suffer each month, a pattern that has existed for decades (McCleery et al. 1971; Illich 1976). A recent systematic review found that clinicians provide the services to patients their own professional bodies recommend only 54.9 percent of the time (McGlynn et al. 2003). Consistency of quality ranged from 78.7 percent for cataracts to 10.5 percent for alcohol dependence. A carefully designed survey of sicker patients in five nations found that U.S. patients were more likely to claim a medical mistake had been made in their care than patients in the United Kingdom, Canada, New Zealand, or Australia (Davis et al. 2004). The United States ranked lowest in both efficiency and effectiveness measures, as experienced by patients. Equity was also lowest in the United States among patients with above-average incomes, and the equity gap is substantially wider among patients with below-average incomes.

Why does the simple goal to add coverage for prescription drugs for the elderly to Medicare result in a bizarre piece of legislation with quite poor coverage except for the most seriously ill and with over 90 percent of its cost going to large, additional profits for drug companies; to insurers, pharmaceutical benefit management corporations, and other intermediaries; and to rural hospitals? (Sager and Socolar 2003; Shearer 2003; Goldstein 2003 (24 November)). The week-by-week developments of the bill centered around the many corporate sectors that have grown up over the past 40 years using their profits for lobbying to be sure they would receive millions for themselves, so that the new coverage became a vehicle for taxing employers and individuals in order to increase corporate profits on a no-risk basis. Such behavior is rare in other countries because they do not have a fragmented, for-profit corporate structure (Roemer 1991; White 1995; Giarelli 2004). No wonder they are so much more efficient and cost-effective. They can cover essentially everyone for what are considered medically necessary services for about one-third less. This essay provides a historical and sociological framework for understanding how mainstream American health care acquired its contemporary problems.

Early Markets and Competition

The most formative period of the modern American health care system occurred between about 1880 and 1920. In the last quarter of the 19th century mainstream physicians faced several competitive forces:

1. Price competition among the surplus of doctors, due to scores of loosely assembled "medical schools" by physicians trying to make extra money by collecting lecture fees;

2. Competition for fees from a raft of alternative healers, often popular for their more naturalistic, gentle forms of therapy, and aided by weak licensure laws;

3. Free care at dispensaries as part of the revolutionary success of public health based on germ theory and the new science of medicine;

4. A proliferation of nostrums, cure-alls, and other medicines widely advertised in newspapers and magazines that substituted for seeing the doctor and competed with doctors' own concoctions made up in their offices; and

5. The rapid proliferation of wholesale contracts and services that threatened the autonomy and income of physicians (Starr 1982).

A Surplus of Competing Providers

The census of 1870 found 64,414 medical practitioners; by 1900 there were about 132,000, and this did not include a large number of "irregular" practitioners using alternative methods that were popular in many areas (Stem 1945). By the 1890s, a serious surplus was widely discussed, though this might have had more to do with sharp recessions in the general economy than with the growth in numbers. The period also witnessed a rapid proliferation of "medical schools," so that by 1900 there were 126 "regular" schools and perhaps 40 homeopathic, osteopathic, and eclectic schools. Altogether, these schools graduated up to 5,700 new physicians a year (Rothstein 1972).

Initially, regular or orthodox physicians had no clear technical or therapeutic advantage, and many of their therapies were as likely to do harm as good. However, advances in scientific medicine came rapidly so that by World War I, the orthodox school of what came to be called scientific medicine had distinct advantages which were largely enjoyed by the medical elite among their ranks who had attended the leading schools of scientific medicine in Europe. Thus, while the number of herbalists, bone setters, and healers proliferated, normal market dynamics were rewarding those with new, effective skills.

Public Health and Dispensaries

Originally created in the 18th century as a humanitarian gesture towards the sick poor, dispensaries took on a new meaning and posed a competitive threat to the rank and file profession at the end of the 19th century. That fact has profound implications for today. As scientific medicine rapidly advanced, dispensaries proliferated as the place where new specialty techniques were first tried out on "clinical material." Since the leading specialists worked and trained at dispensaries, the affluent came in disguise: "There was also the millionaire in poor clothes, the lawyer, the broker ... fully fifty percent of 'charity' patients are persons whose financial position puts them wholly beyond the scope of charity" (DeVeaux 1904). Dispensaries proliferated in response to the millions of new immigrants. In New York City, for example, the number of dispensaries increased from 100 in 1900 to 574 in 1910 and exceeded 700 by 1915 (Goldwater 1915). They were considered superior to ordinary doctors because they offered a skilled team of specialists at the leading edges of scientific medicine, and the famous Boston Dispensary (affiliated with Harvard Medical School) integrated social work and a home health care plan as well as a service for detecting occupational health problems.

Goldwater and other leaders of major public health departments, where the greatest gains in reducing morbidity and mortality were taking place, found it natural to extend their successes in applying scientific advances to improve the health of whole cities to the clinical diagnosis and treatment of individual patients. One could say they were achieving David Kindig's (1997) vision at the end of the 20th century of what the American health care system should look like if it wanted to raise the health status of the nation and improve productivity in a cost-effective way. Nothing could more threaten the leaders of autonomous private practice at county medical societies.

A Proliferation of Cure-Alls

As if backbiting within the ranks, aspersions between sects, and the proliferation of dispensaries were not enough, everyone had a cure for everything. Physicians made up their own cures and advertised them on their calling cards. Pharmacists made new compounds and stole the compounds of others whose prescriptions they filled. Companies sprang up with thousands of medicines. Most threatening of all was Lydia Pinkham's compound, because she in effect said, "Why go see a doctor? Write me and I will personally advise you about your health problem." Her compound cured all female ills, she claimed, and she further guaranteed that no man's eyes would see the letters of her clients (Caplan 1981; Starr 1982). Lydia Pinkham became one of the most successful businesswomen in the industry, and every letter was one less visit and one less fee for a local doctor. Patent medicines were sold at grocery, dry-goods, and hardware stores. Sales nearly doubled in five years, from $74.5 million in 1904 to $141.9 million in 1909. As one essay in the *Journal of the American Medical Association* put it,

"... as the proprietary manufacturer becomes richer, the physician becomes poorer" (AMA Council on Pharmacy and Chemistry 1905). The manufacturers produced a plethora of prepackaged, ready-made drugs to make medical practice easy. G. Frank Lydston (1900), a prominent critic and professor at the University of Illinois School of Medicine, called such manufacturers "fakirs" and wrote a scathing commentary on the effects:

> How gently flows the current of Doctor Readymade's professional life. No more incurable cases. No more midnight oil. No more worry. ... All the doctor has to do now-a-days is to read the labels on the bottles and boxes of samples the fakir brings him. Does the patient complain of stomach disturbance? He is given "Stomachine" ... Give him one of these pretty little tablets with a hieroglyph on it, which nobody knows the composition of ... (p. 1403).

Contract Medicine

Besides the relevance of Dr. Readymade to the billions spent today on commercializing prescription decisions (Wazana 2000; anonymous 2003; Goodman 2004), the other most relevant form of competition that frames our current era was wholesale contracts to provide services to groups of employees or people belonging to an association, or union, or working for a company or a branch of government. The corporate practice of medicine began during the 19th century in the railroad, mining, and lumber industries, where remote locations, high accident rates, and the growth of lawsuits by injured workers called for companies to organize medical services (Williams 1932; Starr 1982). They contracted for services on a retainer basis or on salary; some even owned hospitals and dispensaries for their workers. Some textile industries also established comprehensive medical services in mill towns. Thousands of doctors were involved in these contracts or worked on salary.

By the end of the 19th century, however, more and more businesses with none of these special needs also began to contract on a competitive basis for the health care of their employees. For example, the Michigan State Medical Society reported in 1907 that many companies of various sizes were contracting for the health care of their employees (Langford et al. 1907). The Plate Glass Factory contracted with physicians and hospitals for all medical and surgical care needed by its employees and their families for $1.00 a month apiece. The Michigan Alkali Company did the same but did not include family members. Several other companies had contracts for the treatment of accidents and injuries. Commercial insurance companies of the day also got involved, putting together packages of services for a flat amount per person per year (capitation) or for a discounted fee schedule. Their profits must have been enormous and the doctors' pay low, since several reports allude to the "usual" 10 percent of premiums that physicians received.

More widespread than early corporate health care plans were comprehensive health care medical services offered for a flat subscription price per year to members of the fraternal orders that had proliferated rapidly during the same period. The national and regional orders of the Eagles, the Foresters, the Moose, the Orioles as well as other fraternal associations, offered medical care at deeply discounted prices through their local lodges (Gist 1937). Various reports from Louisiana, Rhode Island, California, and New York attest to the prevalence of such plans and of "contract practice," as competitive health care was then called. A 1909 report on Rhode Island stated, "The English, Irish, Scotch, Germans, French-Canadians, and Jews have clubs employing the contract doctor. The Manchester Unity, Foresters, Sons of St. George, Eagles, Owls and others are in this number" (Mathews 1909).

The government also became heavily involved in organized buying at the turn of the 20th century. Most of the more comprehensive reports on contract practice describe municipal, county, and state agencies putting out for bid service contracts for the poor, for prisoners, and for government employees. At the federal level, the armed services and Coast Guard had long contracted for medical services at wholesale prices (Richardson 1945; Burrow 1977). The rates for the physician varied from $1.00 to $2.50 per member per annum. A committee of physicians in 1916 reported, "[T]he growth of contract practice has been so amazingly great during the last twenty-five years as almost to preclude belief. ... Practically all of the large cities are fairly *honeycombed* with lodges, steadily increasing in number, with a constantly growing membership" (Woodruff 1916:508).

Hospitals also designed prepaid insurance plans, a little-known fact that reframes the commonly held view that this did not happen before the origins of Blue Cross at Baylor Hospital (Richardson 1945). "Hospital service associations" were also formed and organized prepaid contract services. For example, the Hospital Service Association of Rockford, Illinois offered in 1912 hospitalization up to six weeks a year and surgery, with defined benefit ceilings, for an entrance fee of $10, an annual fee of $1 and a weekly contribution of 10 cents. A report from Chicago stated that by 1910, over 25 percent of hospitals in Chicago had some form of contract practice (in Burrow 1977:Ch 8).

Contract practice was considered the most dangerous threat to medicine as a profession. A typically scathing report claimed that "A certain institution which advertises as a hospital engages in wholesale contracts for an infinitesimal amount to care for its policy-holders ... for any illness of any nature whatsoever. This institution has a dispensary where colored solutions under alphabetical labels are dispensed by an undergraduate" (Haley 1911: 395). Through contract practice, critics claimed, employers obtained the records of each worker's physical and mental condition and used it if there was litigation: "This clearly invalidates the pre-established idea that the first duty of the physician is toward his patient" (Woodruff 1916: 509). Despite these criticisms, there seemed to be considerable evidence that a wholesale market of volume discount plans and capitated medical services with selected willing providers were being established on several fronts and growing, long before Sidney Garfield and Henry Kaiser put together the first Kaiser plan.

A Profession in Crisis

These five sources of competition were said to contribute to the historically low income of physicians—about $1,200 a year, the same as skilled craft workers (Burrow 1977:15). State medical societies reported that fierce competition had fostered backbiting, fee splitting, and open criticism between members. From their point of view, no one was in control and matters were deteriorating rapidly. However, it was a favorable situation for consumers and institutional buyers, who felt they were exercising the control they wanted to secure adequate services at reasonable prices. No one had good market information about quality, so patients and payers did not know what they were getting for their money. (Fortunately, we no longer have this problem!) In a rough and ready way, however, based on hearsay and testimonials, competition was steadily favoring the new scientific medicine, and winnowing out ineffective therapies, poorly trained doctors, and inferior medical schools. The average income of poorly trained physicians was being driven down, but specialists were earning three to ten times as much, even with only the skeleton of modern licensing and with no specialty boards (Stevens 1971; Burrow 1977; Rosen 1983). Their growing stature complemented the efforts by hospitals to attract middle and upper-class patients. The proprietary medical schools, established by physicians who used lecture fees to supplement their income from private practice, were beginning to face competition from the serious, university-based schools, whose graduates were earning the respect of the marketplace (Billings 1903; Flexner 1911). Thus, quality and value were being recognized by "the market" on several fronts. Nevertheless, the organized profession campaigned hard for regulations, arguing that the public must be protected from inferior medicine.

Suppressing Competition

The ability of organized medicine to address the sources of "ruinous competition" both within its ranks and from outside remained weak until, in 1901, new leadership revised the American Medical Association's constitution so that medical societies became a pyramid of coherent power. The new AMA was a confederation of state medical societies, which in turn became a confederation of county societies, with delegates elected at each level to make up the committees and House of Delegates at the next level. A physician could not be a member in good standing at the national or state levels without being in good standing at the county level, which was made the basis for hospital privileges, group malpractice insurance, and other benefits (Starr 1982: Ch. 3). This ingenious design transformed the AMA into a pyramid of power and control. Medical societies reorganized and membership shot up from 8,000 in 1900 to 70,000 in 1910. The whole structure formed a hierarchy of networks, coordinated by small groups of influential physicians at the center of each. These networks were used to mount campaigns against competition and contract medicine and universal health insurance (Quadagno 2004). A key tool was the *Journal of the American Medical Association,* whose circulation rose with membership as it became the authoritative voice of AMA leadership against "unscientific sects."

Leading this transformation of the AMA from a weak association to the uniting center of "organized medicine" was the legendary Joseph McCormick. This charismatic president traveled tirelessly across the country to attack the bitter fruits of competition and oversupply: rivalry, advertising, contract medicine, price competition, unethical behavior, and a surplus of badly trained doctors. He held out a uniting alternative: higher standards, good schools, fewer doctors, and fees set at reasonable levels (Burrow 1963; 1977).

Eliminating Sects and Reducing Supply

One campaign aimed to eliminate competing sects and reduce the supply of physicians by gaining control of licensure and setting high standards based on the new scientific medicine. In the early 1900s, medical societies launched a campaign to eliminate dual licensing boards and to give themselves more influence on who was selected to the boards. The boards, in turn, supervised state licensing examinations, and through these the educational leaders of the societies constantly raised the standards in terms of scientific medicine, thus forcing other sects to train their students allopathically or fail the licensing exams. This reflected **"the Davis strategy,"** formulated by N. S. Davis, a founder of the AMA and its first president. The way to control the profession but avoid charges of monopoly, Davis wrote, was to establish state licensing boards outside the profession, but whose members would be chosen by the profession, and to make graduating from a certified medical school a prerequisite for licensure (Davis 1851). Licensure had suffered a national setback in the 1830s as part of populism and suspicion of privilege, but it returned in the 1870s as part of a cultural celebration of science and professionalism of everything: undertakers, librarians, social workers, pharmacists, dentists, accountants, and others (Bledstein 1976). By 1877, the first Davis-style medical practice act was passed. "Irregular" practitioners objected that open competition based on patient choice was being replaced by one sect using state power to create a professional monopoly. They took the new laws to court, but the laws were upheld. By 1898, every state had an act and licensing board (Shyrock 1967).

A related tactic was to broaden the legal definition of medicine so that all sects would be subject to the medical practice laws and then define "unprofessional behavior" in those laws by allopathic standards. By 1904, the AMA's Committee on National Legislation had lobbying organizations in every state except Nevada and Virginia, staffed by 1,940 members. In many states this political machine succeeded in obtaining single boards or increasing power over composite boards (Burrow 1963; Burrow 1977).

EDITOR'S NOTES

Davis strategy: a strategy, developed by N. S. Davis, to suppress the "irregular" practice of medicine by requiring state licensing boards for all medical practitioners, which favored allopathic medicine and required graduation from a certified medical school.

Frank Billings, president of the American Medical Association in 1903, displayed a demographic understanding and nicely summarized the profession's campaign. There was one physician to every 600 people in the population, and there was a net surplus of 2,000 new graduates a year "thrown on the profession, overcrowding it, and steadily reducing the opportunities of those already in the profession to acquire a livelihood" (Billings 1903: 1272). Billings recommended that about three-fourths of the 156 medical schools be closed and the rest upgraded. He also sketched out the concept of special, regional hospitals, devoted to research and teaching. At the same time that Billings advocated the elimination of "unfit and irregular" doctors by training small cohorts in scientific medicine, he conceded that diagnosis amounted to little more than naming the disease and that "in the vast majority of the infectious diseases we are helpless to apply a specific cure." This is important, because today we commonly assume that mainstream medicine's therapeutic superiority justified its strong actions in the early years to eliminate competing sects and monopolize services.

In the same spirit, the profession captured or professionalized other markets. It attacked midwives, who attended one-half of all births in 1910, as the cause of high infant mortality and sought legislation outlawing them. This campaign largely succeeded, even though midwives surpassed physicians in all measures of safe birth across the country, such as puerperal fever and infant and maternal morbidity and mortality (Wertz and Wertz 1989). In Washington, D.C., infant mortality rose as the percent of physicians delivering increased. Moreover, few medical schools had a strong curriculum in obstetrics with which to prepare physicians for the responsibilities they had insisted on assuming (Burrow 1977).

This massive lobbying effort to squeeze out competing sects by mobilizing the power of the state was joined by the second prong of the campaign, to drive inferior medical schools out of business and reduce the supply of physicians. As Abraham Flexner noted, "The state boards are the instruments through which reconstruction of medical education will be largely effected" (Flexner 1911).

The *Journal of the American Medical Association (JAMA)* began collecting and publishing data on the quality of every medical school in 1901, and in 1904 the AMA created the Council of Medical Education. Composed of a distinguished group of academic physicians trained at the leading centers of medicine in Europe, the Council quickly became the voice of the profession on educational matters, and that voice advocated high admission standards, long and expensive training, training in laboratories and hospitals, and tough examinations for licensure. Working closely with *JAMA,* the Council started to publish the failure rates by school of graduates taking licensing examinations. The Council established committees on medical education in the states and territories to carry out its work, and it held national conferences on medical education where it propagated its ideas about model curricula based on the new medical sciences. These efforts constituted market information on quality, and enrollments at proprietary schools with low pass rates declined. What went beyond marketing was the incorporation of the Council's model into the requirements for state board licensing examinations.

The elite members of the Council on Medical Education developed a detailed framework for quality education and began to visit every medical school in the land. It recruited state medical societies and governments along the way, and in 1907 it launched its first attack on medical schools that could not meet its high standards: a four-year curriculum of 3,600 hours. The Council launched a second inspection by Abraham Flexner at the Carnegie Foundation that led to his famously scathing report of 1910. He charged most commercial medical schools to be little more than money machines for their faculty, and he recommended that all but 31 medical schools be shut down. The Flexner report is widely regarded as single-handedly ushering in scientific medical education. In fact, however, the report was part of a systematic campaign started some years earlier by the new elite at the AMA to reduce physician supply and raise quality. The Flexner report played another important role—that of recruiting the great fortunes of Andrew Carnegie and John D. Rockefeller to the AMA's cause (Fox 1980; Light 1983). Between 1911 and 1938, they together gave the staggering amount of $154 million to a small circle of medical schools that agreed to install the new, costly curriculum. To this amount was added $600 million in other grants and matching funds from the fortunes of other industrialists. Historical research shows that Flexner and the foundation staff systematically disguised the degree to which they insisted that medical schools receiving their millions adhere to their model of medical education. By these means, a very small group of socially and professionally elite physicians were able to recast the entire profession in their image (Fox 1980; Light 1983).

This two-pronged campaign of building the new curriculum and standards into state licensure exams and giving large sums only to schools that would implement it worked. The number of graduates plummeted, from 5,440 in 1910 to 2,529 in 1922. Medical schools, which were already closing from competitive pressures before 1910, could not keep up with the rising expense of teaching the new curriculum that was increasingly reflected in state licensing exams. By 1924 there were only 80 schools left. Six of the eight "Negro" medical schools were forced to close, and quotas on ethnic groups could be found in many places (Burrow 1977). Women's medical schools were closed, on the false expectation that women would be admitted to the new medical mainstream. This might be regarded as a byproduct of scientific medicine, but that would ignore how few effective scientific techniques the orthodox practitioners had and how central to the campaign was the leaders' goals of reducing supply and raising incomes. Between 1900 and 1928, physicians' incomes more than doubled, even after accounting for inflation (Starr 1982).

What the Council had done with the help of Flexner and the two great foundations was to redefine professional education so that all the small, marginal, and for-profit medical schools had to close, and medical schools could only survive if they towed the line and thus received philanthropy from foundations dedicated to implementing the Council's new vision of professionalism. This might be regarded as monopoly capitalism shaping modern medicine after its own image (Navarro 1976; McKinlay and Arches 1985), but the evidence supports the obverse: Leaders of professionalism mobilized monopoly capital to their goal of creating a professional monopoly. Only decades later did investors exploit the protected markets that the organized profession had constructed.

Eliminating Price Competition and Free Care

A third campaign which contributed to the doubling of incomes focused on minimizing the growth of free care at dispensaries, price competition among physicians, and external price competition by sponsors of contract medicine. To battle contract medicine, county and state medical societies took a number of actions (Burrow 1977). They conducted studies and reported on the allegedly terrible conditions under which contract physicians worked. Strangely enough, the few times that remarks were published by physicians doing contract work, they said they liked the guaranteed income rather than having to deal with the large number of unpaid bills, often from patients who could barely make a living. County medical societies were also forced to acknowledge that a sizable proportion of their own members actively bid for contracts and did contract work (Langford et al. 1907; Haley 1911; Woodruff 1916).

To those leading this campaign, however, complicity was reason to redouble their efforts and save their colleagues from their own bad judgment. Some medical societies drew up lists of physicians known to practice contract medicine in order to embarrass them. Others drew up "honor rolls" of members who promised to swear off competitive contracts. Committee members would ferret out every recalcitrant colleague and make group visits to pressure him to abandon contract practice. Some societies threatened to expel or censure members who did not cooperate in stamping out price-competitive medicine. On other fronts, state and county medical societies pressured departments of public health, legislators, and their members who worked at dispensaries to have public health stop where clinical medicine begins and to turn over patients with diseases of concern to public health to private practitioners.

They also transformed hospitals from charitable institutions, where the local poor could receive rest and nursing, to centers of surgery and the latest scientific techniques, wooing the paying middle-class patient. Trustees of charitable hospitals reluctantly began to woo physicians in private practice, needing their well-to-do patients, yet fearing that the doctors would demand too much control in return (Vogel 1980; Rosner 1982). The pursuit of paying patients changed the character of hospitals, just as trustees had feared. Historian David Rosner (1982) writes, "By 1915, doctors at many institutions had essentially wrested control from the trustees and had gained the power to make the decisions that were in their best interests, regardless of the traditional charity goals of the hospital" (121). In changing from wards to semi-private or private rooms and to specialized departments, the architecture and organization of hospitals reflected the new power relations and the new social composition of patients. Commercialism, Rosner points out, was also evident in the national movement to transform "the old rich charity hospitals into a 'scientifically' managed medical enterprise" (Rosner 1982:121). By 1912, there was enough of an organized audience for a magazine called *Hospital Management* to start, featuring techniques to attract well-heeled customers out of the comfort of their homes and into the "superior" accommodations of the hospital for serious medical problems. Towns, counties, states, governmental departments, religious sects, labor unions, and fraternal orders built hospitals at the turn of the century, and in places where no one built hospitals, doctors converted a large home to a small "hospital." By 1928, 38.9 percent of the 4,367 of the nongovernmental general hospitals were proprietary—a much higher percentage than in the 1980s when hospital chains proliferated. They had only 16 percent of the beds, however, and often lost money, so that doctors were only too happy when a growing town or voluntary association supplanted them with a larger community hospital (Light 1986).

Although organized medicine never eliminated competitive contracts entirely, it greatly reduced their numbers and shifted them from service to cash contracts. Fraternal orders did not want to cause a row with county and state medical societies, and they shifted benefits to partial payments for wages lost and reimbursement for medical bills rather than for prepaid contracted services. Reimbursement allowed doctors to set their own fees and eliminated any intermediaries setting the terms of service. Several court decisions supported the profession's opposition to the corporate practice of medicine, even though its legal basis was weak. In a number of states, societies persuaded state legislators to pass laws prohibiting the corporate practice of medicine or the practice of medicine by organizations run by nonphysicians. They got other laws passed against the organized practice of medicine for profit. Medical societies meanwhile dusted off their old fee schedules and raised their prices to a professionally respectable level (Schwartz 1965). Historian James Burrow (1977) observed, "Hardly had the United States Steel Corporation succeeded in its consolidation effects that raised prices of basic steel products in 1901 from 200 to 300 percent above the most competitive level of 1898, when the medical profession began its income uplift and price maintenance program" (p. 106).

The goal of these and other efforts to gain control over the practice of medicine has not been to eliminate competition entirely but rather to keep outsiders (i.e., consumers and buyers) from setting terms, especially price. As Max Weber (1968) understood, guilds secured a monopoly over a domain and then let members compete freely within it. By the 1920s, the medical profession had confined contract medicine to a few industries with special needs, to group purchasing of services for the poor and the military, and to a few maverick experiments on the periphery of medicine (Williams 1932).

"No Middlemen" was a call to arms by the Propaganda Department of the AMA in the 1920s and 30s; for they were the ones who had created contract medicine and commercialized medicine by pitting one doctor against another for the lowest bid. Having patients pay doctors directly was the only way to keep the profession free of commercial agents. It also directly links professional services to the pocketbook. The drive for national health insurance between 1910 and 1915 posed a threat, especially since the reformers advocated paying doctors by capitation. While initially attracted to the idea of universal coverage, the rank and file of medical societies made clear they would have none of it.

Reining in the Nostrums Industry

As part of the assault on competing sects, dispensaries, public health clinics, midwives, and other forms of treatment that reduced the demand for professional medical care, the AMA mounted an intense campaign against patent medicines. Many basic professional issues spurred this action. First doctors faced relentless competition from drug salespeople, peddling their wares directly to customers and through massive advertising. Second, this $100 million industry (in 1905) promoted self care and home remedies instead of going to the expense and trouble of seeing a doctor. Patent pharmaceutical companies not only sold drugs which they widely advertised, but they published guides for laypeople and set up advisory services such as the popular "Write Mrs. Pinkham." Third, many doctors made up their own secret remedies and promoted them as superior to others, thus tacitly undermining their colleagues. Fourth, druggists competed with the doctors by refilling prescriptions without a return visit and by stealing doctors' remedies and offering them independently. Scientifically, none of these patent medicines or doctors' remedies were tested. Starr (1982) observed, "The nostrum makers were the nemesis of the physicians. They mimicked, distorted, derided, and undercut the authority of the profession" (p. 127). One article estimated that the money spent on nostrums was enough in 1905 to more than double physicians' incomes (cited in Caplan 1981:320). Yet the medical journals were implicated, and only a few were immune from manufacturers' demands that promotions appear disguised as articles or editorials (Young 1961:207).

In 1900, the AMA published an eight-part series of unsigned articles which provided an overview of issues and policies towards relations with pharmaceutical firms (anonymous 1900). The series called for drugs to have names that reflected their composition rather than their allegedly healing qualities. It discussed the problem of substitution and warned against the widespread use of "polypharmacy," the combination of more than one drug in a pill or dose. It identified the pernicious pattern of companies donating drugs to hospitals and dispensaries where medical students learn, "with the result that the average medical student's ideas and experience concerning medicines are largely confined to the proprietary articles, which his 'professors' used in their demonstrations" (p. 1115). It described the problem of secret proprietary drugs.

In concert with its other actions to promote scientifically based medicine, the newly reorganized AMA created in 1905 the Council on Pharmacy and Chemistry to professionalize drugs by providing the public and its doctors with an AMA-approved list of drugs. It required a drug manufacturer to reveal the ingredients and formula of any drug submitted for the Council's review, and it set itself up as the arbiter of advertising copy in professional journals. The overall goal was to have a list of drugs that were known only to doctors and prescribed by them. It established professional rules of acceptability which included a prohibition against advertising to the public or stating on the label the diseases for which the drug was indicated. Doctors would decide that, as they often do today for disorders for which drugs have not been tested.

The AMA wished to professionalize the large and growing market of self-administered medicines. Without advertising or indications, the profession hoped that patent medicines would disappear. At the same time, the power to prescribe the more effective, AMA-tested medicines would add to the profession's powers to certify sick leaves from work and admit patients to hospitals. The AMA also established what it called the Propaganda Department to publish books and articles warning the public against patent medicines and self-diagnosis. These articles repeatedly told the public that medicine was now a complex scientific field that required years of training, and the articles reported deaths, injuries, and disabilities which patent medicines had purportedly caused. Of great assistance was an exposé by Samuel Hopkins Adams (1905), detailing the dangers and deceptions of patent medicine manufacturers. The Propaganda Department of the AMA also put pressure on lay publications to refuse ads for prescription drugs and even for patent drugs. All these efforts met with partial success, particularly in reducing the number of doctors who developed their own remedies and in stopping druggists from competing directly with them.

Consolidating Professional Control

By 1920, the organized profession had largely succeeded in transforming medical care from an open marketplace where providers and therapeutic schools competed on price and claims of effectiveness to a professional monopoly that claimed to end "ruinous competition," guarantee quality, and establish true patient choice. Freedom and choice were central values. But as Charles Weller (1983) has pointed out, professional "free choice" is a restraint on trade. It is *guild* free choice rather than *market* free choice, that is to say free choice within the profession's terms of training, licensure, fees, and the structure of services. Market free choice would mean competing on price as well as different kinds of services offered by competing kinds of providers. The profession had in effect created a trust during the era of trust-busting, because professions were regarded then as benevolent forms of social control as developed by E.A. Ross ([1901] 1969). His best seller, *Social Control* helped shape efforts by community leaders to clean up corrupt political machines, monopoly trusts, and companies that would sell contaminated meat or dangerous drugs to an unsuspecting public. However, Ross noted that social control could become class control when done by a closely knit elite. They would pass laws and regulations that appeared to treat all parties equally, yet most benefited their own class. Leaders of the medical profession did much to clean up the medical profession in ways that brought civilizing order to modern communities, and they were exempted from anti-trust law. They did so, however, in ways that resembled class control more than community-based social control, especially by creating professionally controlled monopoly markets.

Later, Parsons (1975; [1939] 1954) admired the professions as viable alternatives to business but did not see the degree to which the tactics of the organized profession echoed those of business monopolies (compare them with those in Jones 1921). Weber (1968) understood better the nature of guilds, which pursue quality, prestige, and profits for their members by forming an interest group and then pursuing a legal monopoly. What the profession did not anticipate was the degree to which the very success of their harnessing the nostrum manufacturers would commercialize it. Many of the practices which the AMA attacked returned, but now within the professional fold.

The prevailing sociological theory of modern medicine has been that of professional dominance (Freidson 1970b; 1970a; Starr 1982). The proletarianization of the medical profession by capitalists also has its followers (Navarro 1976; McKinlay and Arches 1985). Both theories identify part of the whole but do not provide a comparative, historical framework (Light and Levine 1988). One emphasizes the rise to dominance and the other the decline to subordination, but neither can explain both. The concept of countervailing powers offers a more fruitful framework, one which invites researchers to consider the changing dynamics over time among key stakeholders and across countries (Light 1995a; 2000b).

Larson (1977) has provided a cogent theoretical and historical account of how the medical profession turned expertise into market power, by creating a new kind of monopoly market (p. 56). The key is to define and defend a unique service, or commodity; to standardize it and the training of professionals in it; to get the backing of the state in the name of safety; and thereby to exclude all other claimants. One creates, then, a professional **caste** centered on autonomy and control. Ironically, the profession is "allowed to define the very standards by which its superior competence is judged ... professionals live within ideologies of their own creation, which they present to the outside as the most valid definitions of specific spheres of social reality" (p. xiii). This collective monopolistic project takes place within a specific economic and institutional context which shapes the structure of professional markets. This provides a framework for understanding both the ferocious campaigns to eliminate or contain other countervailing powers and the unanticipated consequences that have led to the pathologies of the health care system today.

From a comparative perspective, however, we need to realize that accounts of the rise of professionalism by Larson, Starr, and others that are focused on the American case overlook fundamental differences in professionalism orchestrated top-down by the state in a number of other countries or bilaterally between professional associations and the state in other countries. All share the rise to dominance of medicine, especially hospital-based specialty medicine, but in the other cases professional dominance is framed by societal needs and state power to determine the number and distribution of specialists, what they charge, and how

EDITOR'S NOTES

caste: a group or class of people who inherit exclusive privileges and are socially distinct.

they fit into a national system of health care (Burrage and Torstendahl 1990; Immergut 1992; Light 1994; Giarelli 2004). As this history shows, the "accidental logics" of the contemporary system and its lack of universal health coverage were hardly accidental (Touhy 1999).

This institutional history provides a quite different but complementary example to economic sociology of the rise of large corporations (Roy 1997; Perrow 2002). Roy's emphasis on power rather than on efficiency as the more accurate way to explain the rise of large corporations fits the rise of professional medicine as well. Markets, in this view, are constructed by the participants with the cooperation of government. Control over training and licensure gave the profession property rights over medical knowledge. Although in retrospect the promotion of scientific medicine seems enlightened and correct, evidence indicates it was winning converts rapidly on its own merits, and one must remember that at the time, the strong medicines and aggressive therapies did as much harm as good.

The Professionally Driven Health Care System

The health care system that evolved from the campaigns of organized medicine fulfilled the professional vision of what a good system should look like, a system that strives to provide the best clinical care for every sick patient who could pay, to develop scientific medicine to its highest degree, to preserve the autonomy of the physician, and to increase the dominance of the medical profession (for comparative visions, see Light 1997). Power centers on the profession, and the organization of work centers on physicians' choices of specialty, location, and clinical judgment. The result is a loosely linked network of autonomous offices, clinics, hospitals and related facilities. The image of the individual is of a private person who lives as he or she sees fit and comes in for help as she or he chooses. Financing in this ideal type centers on the fees that doctors choose to charge.

This vision has several flaws from a societal point of view. Organized medicine destroyed medical schools for women and "Negroes," crushed midwifery and alternative sects, used scare tactics to discredit national health insurance, and cared little about patients in low income and rural areas. Its almost exclusive focus on clinical care for sick patients who can pay began the historic separation of medicine from public health, even though public health achieved more spectacular successes using the same scientific foundation and discoveries, and a disinterest in prevention and primary care as low-status work of little interest. The organizational profession's vision of good medicine also lacked a sense of responsibility for communities or community health, because doing so would require forms of financing and governance that compromised professional autonomy. Concepts of interprofessional teams were resisted as threats to professional authority.

The organized profession, however, rarely behaves as a servant of humanity or public good. For that to happen, it needs a strong societal framework, precisely what other countries provided where the state constructed the modern profession or where the state and profession worked in harness together as equally strong partners (Roemer 1991; White 1995; Giarelli 2004). This is shown in column three of Table 7.1.1. This point is put more broadly in a reinterpretation of Parsons: one cannot expect a profession to be much different from the economic, organizational, and political framework of the society in which it operates (Light 2000a). If that society sanctions a for-profit, financial system that does not reward disease prevention and care of poorer patients, one cannot expect the medical profession alone to make up the difference. Emanuel (1991) likewise showed

TABLE 7.1.1 Contrasting Visions and Values of a Good Health Care System

Corporate Providers, Suppliers, and Middlemen	The Organized Profession	Governments or Other Larger Payer
Key Values & Goals: To maximize market share and profits. To maximize the size, range and expenditures of markets.	To provide the best possible clinical care to every sick patient (who can pay and who lives near a doctor's practice).	To have a healthy, vigorous workforce.
To increase demand and form new markets.	To develop scientific medicine to its highest level.	To minimize illness and maximize selfcare.
To minimize, neutralize or circumvent regulations by government or payers.	To protect the autonomy of physicians and services.	To minimize the cost of medical services.
	To increase the power and wealth of the profession.	Perhaps to provide good, accessible care to all.
Image of the Individual: An object of marketing to maximize expenditures.	A private person who chooses how to live and when to use the medical system.	An employee, and somewhat the responsibility of the employer.
Power: Centers on corporate headquarters. State and profession relatively weak.	Centers on the medical profession, and uses state powers to enhance its own.	Centers on key governmental officials, politicians, sometimes unions.
Key Institutions: Health care and supplier corporations. Governments and employers as sources of revenues and managers of competition.	Professional associations. Autonomous physicians and hospitals.	Departments of health, social security, and related departments.

the limitations of professional ethics and the need for a societal ethic to set the larger context. This fundamental point is illustrated by contrasting the professional ideal health care system with the societal ideal that is manifested in a strong state. The societal system seeks to promote a healthy, vigorous population and to minimize illness. Medical services are therefore universal, equitably distributed, and focused on primary care and prevention. The number and distribution of specialists, hospitals, and costly technology, as well as costs, are subject to institutional rules and regulations within which the profession works. For-profit services have been rare, and for-profit suppliers are held in check. By contrast, the American case illustrates the professional health care system unleashed and unfettered.

Creating Provider-friendly Insurance

This sociological interpretation of American medical services offers a different perspective on subsequent events than most accounts. It explains the extreme reluctance of the organized profession to allow any form of insurance and the absence of a state that would direct the skills of the profession to the needs of society, even when evidence showed that millions of poor and elderly people were being impoverished and not getting needed care. When unpaid hospital bills became so great that the American Hospital Association broke ranks with the AMA, it began the search for a non-profit, passive form of hospital insurance that would become Blue Cross. Great care was taken to avoid comprehensive prepaid plans and consumer-based plans, and to endorse only private, voluntary, no-profit insurance that covered just the hospital part of the bill (Rorem 1940; Richardson 1945; Reed 1947). The AMA's Bureau of Medical Economics remained steadfastly opposed. Insurance, its reports had maintained, depends on compensating for defined liabilities (like fires or thefts), which are impossible in medicine (Bureau of Medical Economics 1935). Service-based coverage, like Blue Cross, leads to standardized, cookie-cutter care for the wide variations among individual patients. This degrading of professional medicine was what contract medicine had brought 30 year earlier, the AMA's Bureau pointed out, and it must not be allowed again. But open rebellion among physicians during the Depression and their development of various insurance schemes led the AMA reluctantly to develop Blue Shield several years after the AHA launched Blue Cross. Great care was taken to be sure it was pass-through reimbursement of what doctors charged, largely focused on hospital-based specialists, rather than based on a fee schedule (Rayack 1967). Passive intermediaries and physician autonomy were the key goals, not any collective sense of access or managing costs. Thus the organized profession laid the institutional and cultural foundations for private, voluntary, and pass-through approaches to covering medical bills that would ironically become their nemesis.

Both of the Blues required a majority of directors to be hospital trustees, administrators, or specialists, hardly an auspicious group to restrain costs but considered the natural and obvious choices at the time. The Blues were professionally controlled insurance organizations that covered only those who could afford to pay, and laid the institutional foundation for commercial insurance companies to cover lower-risk groups (Bodenheimer, Cummings, and Harding 1974). The authoritative Louis Reed envisioned in 1947 that although most hospitals were not for profit,

> ... under a situation in which a large proportion of the population was enrolled and hospitals were paid on a cost basis, hospital administrators would wish in general to provide a more and more perfect or elaborate service, and to make this possible would ask for higher and higher rates of payment. (Reed 1947:89).

This is precisely what happened over the next 30 years. With the enemies of professionalism vanquished and the victories won before 1920 anchored in institutional reforms, the professionally driven health care system roared ahead, magnifying its successes as well as its pathologies. Professionally designed passive insurance led to ever-higher charges for evermore procedures and bed-days.

Professionally Crafted Public Funding

World War II had many effects on society and medicine, including great advances in surgery and medical science. After the war, the Public Health Service was transposed into the National Institutes of Health. Further federal support for research and academic medicine came from a realignment and expansion of the Veteran's Administration hospital system around medical schools. Hospital reconstruction received central attention through the Hill-Burton program, guided by a national commission through which the American Hospital Association outlined a huge, 40 percent expansion in beds. Hill-Burton regulations favored poorer and Southern states but required that community hospitals raise two-thirds of the funds for construction and be financially viable, thus favoring middle-class communities. In a carefully constructed argument, Starr (1982) demonstrates that these major infusions of public money were designed to reinforce professional sovereignty and local institutions. Requirements that recipient hospitals treat those unable to pay remained ignored for decades.

Federal funds also greatly influenced the growth and shape of academic medicine. The incomes of medical schools tripled during the 1940s, more than doubled in the 1950s, and nearly tripled again during the 1960s, but largely from federal funds concentrated on research. This focus enhanced the technical prowess of American medicine, but diverted attention from organizing medical schools, the recruitment of students, and the distribution of specialists to meet the health needs of the population. It led to building academic health care "empires" that exploited the poor more than serving their considerable health care needs (Ehrenreich and Ehrenreich 1976; Waitzkin 1983).

In the private sector, commercial health insurance grew rapidly. These for-profit giants had no relation to the non-profit, community-based ethos of Blue Cross and proceeded to draw away the lower-risk groups with lower premiums. Risk-rated private insurance left the Blues with an ever higher-risk profile of patients left in their community-rated pools. Eventually they had to cave in and risk-rate too (Somers and Somers 1961). Focused on quarterly returns to investors, corporate insurers eventually turned on professional autonomy itself in order to contain costs for their true clients, the employers who hired them. Through the 1950s and 1960s, however, health insurance covered just about anything doctors wanted to order. This exacerbated the super-professionalism of academic health complexes (Ludmerer 1999: Part II).

Pathologies of Professionalism

Most accounts of American health care since the 1970s describe its fragmentation, inefficiencies, run-away costs, impersonal care, uneven distribution, variable quality, and over-specialization, but without acknowledging how these emanated from a professionally driven health care system operating in its own professionally constructed markets. In time, corporations realized that protected professional markets were a capitalist's dream of a market with virtually no downside risk. After 1920, the drive to develop the best clinical medicine based on physician autonomy led quite naturally to more and more specialization. Specialists charged higher fees, and subspecialists charged even more. Since doctors were to be free to choose their specialty and where they practiced, rural and poor areas were underserved, as was primary care; so that by the 1970s a double crisis of uneven distribution became a central policy concern. Impersonal care was also an unanticipated consequence of specialization leading to highly bureaucratic care divided into compartments of expertise. This problem can be overcome, but it takes a shared vision of specialty-based care that is not common.

Specialization, when combined with professional autonomy, produces fragmented care. Around the need for coordination arose secondary industries of intermediaries—just what the profession wanted to avoid at all costs and yet an ironic consequence of its ideal system. Another pathology resulted from presuming that quality was whatever a licensed physician did. This led to great variation in actual skills, preferences, and practices without any evidence that more costly care produces better results (Wennberg and Gittelsohn 1982; Wennberg 1984). The whole system, as well as its hierarchy of values and prestige, centered on hospital care for the seriously ill. As hospitals grew and became elaborated, costs not only rose faster, but they became large institutions in their own right, and this led to a new profession to run them: professionally trained administrators. Thus, by the 1970s, the professionally ideal health care system had led to widespread complaints about impersonal, over-specialized, fragmented care; run-away costs; widely varying and uneven quality; and a neglect of public health, prevention, and primary care (Cray 1970; Kennedy 1972; Ehrenreich and Ehrenreich 1976; Illich 1976).

One pathology of professionalism was to make medical care and charity less and less affordable to the poor and elderly who did not have pass-through commercial insurance. Despite these untenable gaps, the AMA fought long and hard against all efforts to provide coverage and relief, though Medicaid and Medicare finally passed in a form that explicitly extended the profession's ideal of autonomous physicians in private practice charging what they liked. While the medical profession insisted that charges be reimbursed, community hospitals insisted that their debt service be built into the bed-day rate, including **Hill-Burton** assets funded by taxpayers. This meant that "community hospitals" would no longer have to appeal to their communities to raise funds, though they did anyway. All costs for medical equipment were rolled into the bed rate too, so even mistakes were fully paid for. Fledgling corporate chains hired lobbyists to insert phrasing that enabled them to use taxpayers' money to develop large corporate chains (Feder 1977). In short, the values, mind-set, and regulations built into major new public funding reflected the professional model on a binge. Physicians exercised their uncontrolled autonomy by raising their fees almost three-fold between 1965 and 1980. Hospital bed-day charges quadrupled (U.S. Department of Health and Human Services 1982).

Leaders and advocates of professional medicine now look back at the postwar period as "the Golden Age of Medicine" (McKinlay and Marcceau 2002); however, while there were legendary individuals, the period looks more like an Age of Gold. Physicians incorporated themselves and became increasingly commercial in their approach to patient care. As early as the mid-1950s, physicians led the movement to establish for-profit hospitals and made many times more than they could in their practices. An early detailed report noted that these doctors' hospitals did not provide any community services that did not make money and elaborately used legal strategies to create interlocking sets of corporations (O'Neil 1956 (Dec)). Leaders of the profession rarely admit that the corporatization of direct services was a natural outgrowth of the system the profession put in place. They do not admit that physicians commercialized themselves and related services before corporations commercialized them. When combined with insurance that passively reimbursed charges, the professionally driven health care system was a capitalist's dream. Soon, outside investors began to realize the low-risk, high-profit character of medical services, and the corporatization of medicine moved into full swing.

Investor-owned health care corporations grew rapidly, a logical extension, I would argue, of the monopoly markets that the organized profession set up for itself in the absence of a national health care system. When O'Neil reported in 1956 that some doctors had discovered that building a private hospital pumped out more profit than having an oil well, investors were not be far behind. By 1964, the early chains had lobbyists insert into Medicare legislation extraordinarily profitable phrases, and the floodgates opened. Reiman's (1980) famous essay about the "new medical-industrial complex" missed the point: It was a natural extension of the old medical-industrial complex centered on the medical profession which Reiman excused as not the point. Two years later, Starr (1982) concluded his much-celebrated history by discerning that "Medical care in America now appears to be in the early stages of a major transformation in its institutional structure, comparable to the rise of professional sovereignty at the opening of the twentieth century" (p. 428). He predicted a shift in ownership to for-profit corporations and a concentration of ownership into conglomerates that would integrate hospitals, clinics, and physicians both horizontally and vertically. Several articles in this volume, and the more recent studies on which they build, provide a more differentiated analysis of this prediction (Wholey et al., Casalino 2004; Rundall, Alexander, and Shortell 2004).

A famous chapter of Waitzkin's (1983) important book described how a high-tech fad (coronary care units) proliferated without any evidence that it was effective, based on campaigns of academic and corporate entrepreneurs who profited from the costly, un-evidenced fad. And when the U.S. market reached saturation, the major corporations involved turn to exporting their costly, latest product lines to countries in Latin America and Asia that have fixed, much smaller budgets, where they persuaded by various means the ministers to give their people "the latest" and "the best" from the global center of academic-medical capitalism (Jasso-Aguilar, Waitzkin, and Landwehr 2004). A modified version of Waitzkin's figure appears in Figure 7.1.1.

In sum, the financial, political, organizational and clinical pathologies of professionalism (Table 7.1.1) were built into Medicare and Medicaid and accelerated after them. It is for these reasons that I do not think the second era of American health care began with this legislation (Scott et al. 2000), but rather a few years later when all the payers began to revolt as a countervailing power and launched a series of efforts to rein in costs and rationalize medicine.

The Revolt of Countervailing Powers

Unrestrained growth in utilization, variation, and charges in this age of gold for doctors and hospitals generated an intense feeling from the right to the left that professionally driven health care had led to greed, waste, inequities, and dubious quality. In the 1960s, the thalidomide affair documented how medical hubris could wreak havoc on the lives of trusting patients and how professional arrogance led to abuses (Hilts 2003). Friedson's (1970a, 1970b) studies of the "golden age of medicine" described in detail the structural dominance of the profession in the United States and the resulting pathologies. He concluded that an organized profession could not discipline itself effectively. Dr. Robert McCleery (1971) produced a graphic report, now forgotten, that detailed the low quality of clinical work and injury to patients by ordinary physicians (in contrast to

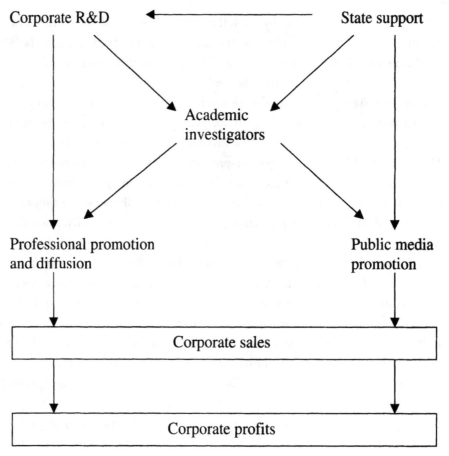

FIGURE 7.1.1 The Medical-industrial Complex of Corporations, Universities, and the State in the 1980s.

Note: Adapted from Waitzkin (1983)

those celebrated in the press at the great medial centers) and the very limited ability of medical societies and state boards to do much about it. In 1972, Senator Abraham Ribicoff, who had been Secretary of Health, Education and Welfare, published *The American Medical Machine* and described the machine's relentless ability to generate bills. In Tulsa, Oklahoma, he found, medical debts accounted for 60 percent of all personal bankruptcies (Ribicoff and Dandaceau 1972). In the same year, Senator Ted Kennedy (1972) published his critique, *In Critical Condition,* based on vivid testimony from citizens at hearings his committee held across the country.

These books were read and discussed widely and set the stage for the most radical critique of all, *Medical Nemesis: The Expropriation of Health,* by the Jesuit priest, Ivan Illich (1976). Drawing on research reports in the leading medical journals, Illich held up a mirror that both shocked and fascinated the public as well as the medical world, a world of medicine gone mad, of error and

iatrogenesis. Yet as Navarro (1976) and Waitzkin (1983) pointed out, underlying Illich's critique was a radically conservative individualism—each person should take responsibility for his or her health and treat himself or herself—when many causes of illness as well as pathologies of the medical-industrial complex that had grown up around the profession's vision of an ideal system stemmed from a sharply inequitable class structure and a capitalist economy with fewer compensatory programs than any other advanced capitalist society (Moller et al. 2003).

Weak Regulatory Reforms

The countervailing powers of payers, including Congress and state legislators as the new dominant payers, had had enough. Moreover, the state as regulator had become worried about lapses in quality; the unshakeable trust in the profession to safeguard standards of care began to crumble. During the 1970s, Congress and the states developed large-scale programs to rationalize physician referrals and hospitalization, to plan more equitable capital expenditures, to develop a comprehensive cost base for reasonable charges, to establish hospital rate-setting systems, to establish quality review, and to transform American health care into a network of self-regulatory health care systems that rewarded prevention and primary care called "HMOs." These national and state systems and proposals were all undermined in various ways by hospitals and doctors (Starr 1982: Bk. 2, Ch 4).

Meantime, Paul Ellwood realized that prepaid group health plans—those "hotbeds of socialism" so adamantly opposed by the medical profession—could be recast as private, self-regulating health care systems in which incentives were aligned with keeping people healthy and keeping costs down (Brown 1983). These "health maintenance organizations" (HMOs) were just what the newly elected President Nixon needed: a private alternative to socialized medicine. In 1970 he gave the first speech on health care to the joint houses of Congress and proposed universal health care delivered by 1,700 HMOs. The corporate lobbies of all the suppliers, providers, and insurers opposed it. Watergate discredited Nixon, and a severe recession sealed its fate (Starr 1982:Bk 2, Ch 4). What came out the other end was the HMO Act of 1973, which lobbyists tried to block and then weighed down with so many requirements that federally qualified HMOs would collapse under their weight (Starr 1982; Brown 1983). The nation's leaders concluded that "regulation does not work," despite its working reasonably well in every other advanced medical system. A signal event occurred when the U.S. Supreme Court reversed in 1975 the long-standing exemption of professions from anti-trust regulations, on the grounds that professions were, after all, businesses. These events, despite their limitations and failures, signaled a transformation in values and vision and a new balance between countervailing powers.

Strong Corporate Reforms

With the "failure" of regulation, the stage was set for the Reagan era of market-based solutions to social problems. Employers, who had increasingly self-insured to avoid a thicket of regulations that had developed over the years, turned from years of complaining to staging what I have called a Buyers' Revolt (Light 1988). Table 7.1.2 outlines the basic cultural, economic, organizational, political, and technological changes wrought by a re-balance of countervailing powers. As employers aggressively sought ways to rein in costs, insurance companies took on a new role of developing techniques to monitor, gatekeep, and select providers. Secondary industries developed to select providers into "preferred provider organizations" (PPOs), to deliver services within a fixed budget (network HMOs), to screen and monitor physicians' clinical decisions for costly procedures, and to redesign health benefit plans. These various techniques and new organizational forms came to be known collectively as "managed care," and the macro theory and policy for getting them to drive better value for less cost was called "managed competition." The rise of managed competition and managed care centered on the medical profession's refusal to take responsibility for the highly variable quality and rapidly rising costs that resulted from physician autonomy.

As originally conceived by Enthoven (1988), managed competition was aggressively promoted as the solution to the extensive problems of market failure in health care. The many commentators on managed competition fail to note that deep sources of market failure remain, only hidden behind the walls of the managed care organizations as they compete for contracts and market share (Light 1995b). Using a rhetoric of "choice," they restrict choice of provider and procedures by design. Competing managed care organizations are usually oligopolies in most markets, and oligopolies usually do not compete on price. Yet price competition is supposed to be the key goal of managed competition. Managed competition also leaves no one responsible for common issues of public health. Managed competition, ironically, is based on a distrust of doctors but a trust of managers. Investor-run network HMOs are in this way profoundly different from the original, non-profit, physician-run HMOs such as Kaiser. Based on the distrust of doctors, they require a great deal of regulation, and they commercialize clinical decision-making by relying on payments and penalties. Evidence of greater "efficiency" usually turns out to be the surreptitious result of enrolling fewer sick or disabled patients. In these ways, managed care corporations of various forms undermined the moral foundations on which successful markets depend (Etzioni 1988). The health economist, Uwe Reinhardt, is said to have asked, if managed care companies

TABLE 7.1.2. The Buyer's Revolt: Axes of Change

Dimensions	From Provider-driven	To Buyer-driven
Ideological	Sacred trust in doctors	Distrust of doctors' values, decisions, even competence
Clinical	Exclusive control of clinical decision-making	Close monitoring of clinical decisions, their cost and their efficacy
Economic	*Carte blanche* to do what seems best: power to set fees; incentives to specialize;	Fixed prepayment or contract with accountability for decisions and their efficacy
	Emphasis on state-of-the-art specialized interventions;	Emphasis on prevention, primary care, and functioning
	Lack of interest in prevention, primary care, and chronic care;	Minimize high-tech and specialized interventions
	Informal array of cross subsidizations for teaching, research, charity care, community services	Elimination of "cost shifting" pay only for services contracted
Organizational	Cottage industry	Corporate industry
Political	Extensive legal and administrative power to define and carry out professional work without competition, and to shape the organization and economics of medicine	Reduced legal and administrative power over professional work and also the organization and economics of services
Technical	Political and economic incentives to develop new technologies in protected markets	Political and economic disincentives to develop new technologies
Potential disruptions and dislocations	• Overtreatment • Iatrogenesis • High cost • Unnecessary treatment • Fragmentation • Depersonalization	• Undertreatment • Cuts in services • Obstructed access • Reduced quality • Swamped in paperwork

require another 15 percent more overhead than Medicare and Medicaid and want to make at least 10 percent return, can they really reduce costs by 25 percent without cutting into needed care? The chief result, in Medicare and in the general markets, has been cost shifting and cost avoidance through risk selection, and these remain the more common ways to "contain costs" in a system that lacks universal coverage. Patients (as well as doctors) rebelled (Mechanic 2004).

Managed care profoundly altered the balance among countervailing powers. The imbalances of professional dominance first led to a powerful alliance with the rapidly expanding medical-industrial complex. Corporate employers and public legislators developed what might be called a *managed-care-industrial complex,* replete with large new secondary industries that designed benefits, select providers, manage services, define outcomes, and establish systems of quality, performance, and value—precisely the functions that the profession promised to perform. Clinicians "... face an increasing set of organized stakeholders who question the content, quality, and cost of professional work, increasingly 'shop around' for the professional services they want, and otherwise act to control professional activity in ways that were unheard of as late as 20 years ago" (Leicht and Fennell 2001; 226). In sum, the consequences of a professionally designed health care system and the efforts to deal with its social and clinical pathologies has led to the most costly, inefficient, wasteful, and inequitable health care system in the industrialized world, and to a complex of secondary industries that thrive on these four characteristics. Inefficiency, waste, and risk selection are good business, and the multi-billion dollar beneficiaries lobby hard against efforts to reduce them.

This transformation of corporate control extends Fligstein's (1990) seminal research and theory on that subject. He posits that major corporations develop a "conception of control" that is collectively held and enables them to solve core problems in their organizational field so that they can re-establish stability and control over their economic environment. When an industry faces an historic crisis,

TABLE 7.1.3. Tragic Flaws of Managed Competition/Care

The model of having self-contained HMOs (such as Kaiser) compete for quality, service, and value seems to overcome most of the serious dangers of market failure in medicine that can harm patients and exploit buyers. Yet the model has several inherent flaws:

1. Creates oligopolies, which usually minimize price competition.
2. Competitive systems require much more regulation (not less) than non-competitive systems.
3. The major competitors become the regulators of the market.
4. Based on a distrust of doctors but a trust of managers. (Are managers a different breed?)
5. Assumes patients will maximize value, but usually they do not.
6. Assumes efficiency gains will exceed sharp rise in administrative and marketing costs that markets require when compared to non-competitive systems.
7. Reduces provider choice by design, to choosing between plans and then providers within plans.
8. Encourages discrimination against higher risk patients.
9. Undermines a public health or community-wide agenda, because based on plans competing for market share.
10. The uncertain, emergent, contingent nature of clinical work that makes medicine so ill-suited to competition remains, only hidden within the walls of each managed care organization.

the conception of control changes. Of particular note is the corporate definition of efficiency as "the conception of control that produces the relatively higher likelihood of growth and profits for [leading] firms, given the existing set of social, political and economic circumstances" (p. 295). Fligstein applies this theoretical characterization of historical changes to corporations as sellers, but it can apply, as outlined here, to corporate buyers as well.

Managed competition and the rise of managed care organizations arose because corporate and government buyers faced a crisis of excess created by the stakeholders of professionalized markets and needed a new concept of how to control rising costs. They sought to rein in the excesses, replace professional autonomy with accountable performance measures, and reorganize the center of care from hospital-based acute intervention to community-based prevention and primary care. As Fligstein notes, such concepts are loosely applied, as suits different stakeholders. A deep distrust and distaste for government and a belief in markets as the way to solve social problems has precluded the alternatives that employers in every other capitalist economy support. The result, not considered in *The Architecture of Markets* (Fligstein 2001), are socially destructive markets "designed" by legislative architects who take contributions from all the major sellers as well as the corporations that are supposed to manage the market. Managed care corporations, as agents for corporate employers, have designed markets in a society with few of the social protections deemed essential in other countries; so that "consumers" get harmed as insurers and providers de-select costly, sick patients or shift the costs of care back to the households of sick patients. Prevention and wellness get attention to the extent that one can charge for them. In short, power and interests need to be given full attention in sociological theory and research.

Contributions to Follow

The original contributions that follow were commissioned to provide long-term sociological perspectives on the American health care system as it enters a troubled new century. Quadagno (2004) provides original archival research on how "interests" stymied universal health care legislation. Caronna (2004) offers an insightful historical analysis of mis-alignments and inconsistencies between the institutional pillars that hold up the health care system. Casalino (2004) provides original explanations of how managed care evolved and health care markets formed as jurisdictional arenas. Meantime, the legitimacy of the entire enterprise suffered a massive consumer backlash, and David Mechanic (2004) assesses why it happened. Kitchener and Harrington (2004) provide a detailed history of how for-profit chains co-opted the government's power to regulate and tax to enrich themselves and disadvantage non-profit services. Two distinguished teams of sociologists, led by Tom Rundall (2004) and Doug Wholey (2004), draw together organizational and economic concepts to explain the dynamics of physician-hospital relations and the dynamics of national firms in local markets, both central aspects of the managed care revolution.

The final trio of original papers goes beyond managed corporate care as an American conception of control to more global matters. The team headed by Rebeca Jasso-Aquilar (2004) draws on their original, in-depth research to describe how managed care corporations took their profits here and then went abroad to profit from corporatizing the public health care systems of other countries. Exporting corporate managed care is still thriving, and several European countries are weakening the equity and efficiency of their universal systems by implementing "modern" ideas of management. Beyond and surrounding managed care is the commercialization of illness, and now risk, as "health" needing medical attention (Conrad and Leiter 2004). Professional knowledge itself has been changed in the process, and Stefan Timmermans and Emily Kolker (2004) show how this has changed the nature of the medical profession. A disturbing tension is created between these last two essays. If clinicians are held to "evidence-based" guidelines, how will this be reconciled with the care of "health" expanding as far as corporate marketers can stretch it without increasing forms of inequality and health disparities? As a whole, these papers vindicate the JHSB editorial board's decision more than two years ago to commission a special issue of this distinguished, highly cited journal that would feature original contributions providing sociological insights into the development and deeper nature of the American health care system over the past decades.

Note

1. As has become the custom, "health care system" refers to the organization, financing and delivery of medical services.

References

Adams, Samuel Hopkins. 1905. *The Great American Fraud*. New York: Collier & Son.

AMA Council on Pharmacy and Chemistry. 1905. "The Secret Nostrum vs the Ethical Proprietary Preparation." *Journal of the American Medical Association* 44:718–19.

Anonymous. 1900. "Relations of Pharmacy to the Medical Profession." *Journal of the American Medical Association* 34:986–68, 1049–51, 1114–47, 1178–79, 1327–29, 1405–47 and 35:27–29, 89–91.

————. 2003. "U.S. Promotional Spending on Prescription Drugs, 2002 ($21 Billion)." *Canadian Medical Association Journal* 169:699.

Billings, Frank. 1903. "Medical Education in the United States." *Journal of the American Medical Association* 40:1271–76.

Bledstein, Burton. 1976. *The Culture of Professionalism*. New York: W.W. Norton.

Bodenheimer, Thomas, Steve Cummings, and Elizabeth Harding. 1974. "Capitalizing in Illness: The Health Insurance Industry." *International Journal of Health Service* 4:583–98.

Brown, Lawrence D. 1983. *Politics and Health Care Organization: HMOs as Federal Policy*. Washington, DC: Brookings Institution.

Bureau of Medical Economics. 1935. *An Introduction to Medical Economics*. Rev. ed. American Medical Association, Chicago, IL.

Burrage, M. and R. Torstendahl. 1990. *Professions in Theory and History*. London: Sage.

Burrow, James G. 1963. *The AMA: Voice of American Medicine*. Baltimore, MD: Johns Hopkins University Press.

—————. 1977. *Organized Medicine in the Progressive Era: The Move toward Monopoly*. Baltimore, MD: Johns Hopkins University Press.

Caplan, Ronald L. 1981. "Pasteurized Patients and Profits: The Changing Notion of Self-care in American Medicine." PhD Thesis, Department of Economics, University of Massachusetts, Amherst, MA.

Caronna, Carol. 2004. "The Alignment of Institutional 'Pillars': Consequences for the U.S. Health Care Field of Normative, Cognitive and Regulative (in)Conconsistency." *Journal of Health and Social Behavior* 45(Extra Issue): 45–58.

Casalino, Larry. 2004. "Unfamiliar Tasks, Unsettled Jurisdictions: Describing the U.S. Health Care Market." *Journal of Health and Social Behavior* 45(Extra Issue):59–75.

Conrad, Peter and Valerie Leiter. 2004. "Medicalization, Markets and Consumers." *Journal of Health and Social Behavior* 45(Extra Issue): 158–76.

Cray, Ed. 1970. *In Failing Health: The Medical Crisis and the AMA*. New York: Bobbs-Merrill.

Davis, Karen, Cathy Schoen, Stephen C. Schoenbaum, Anne-Marie J. Audet, Michelle M. Doty, and Katie Tenny. 2004. *Mirror, Mirror on the Wall: Looking at the Quality of American Health Care through the Patients Lens*. New York City: The Commonwealth Fund.

Davis, N.S. 1851. *History of Medical Education and Institutions in the United States*. Chicago, IL: S.C. Grigges & Co.

DeVeaux, Edith P. 1904. "Free Dispensaries and Their Abuse." *Northwest Medicine* 2:151.

Ehrenreich, Barbara and John Ehrenreich. 1976. *The American Health Empire: Power, Profits and Politics*. New York: Vintage.

Emanuel, Ezekiel J. 1991. *The Ends of Human Life*. Cambridge, MA: Harvard University Press.

Enthoven, A.C. 1988. *Theory and Practice of Managed Competition in Health Care Finance*. Amsterdam, Netherlands: North-Holland.

Etzioni, Amitai. 1988. *The Moral Dimension*. New York: Free Press.

Feder, Judith M. 1977. *Medicare: The Politics of Federal Hospital Insurance*. Lexington, MA: Lexington Books.

Flexner, Abraham. 1911. "Medical Colleges." *The World's Work* 21:1438–42.

Fligstein, Neil. 1990. *The Transformation of Corporate Control*. Cambridge, MA: Harvard University Press.

—————. 2001. *The Architecture of Markets*. Princeton, NJ: Princeton University Press.

Fox, Daniel M. 1980. "Abraham Flexner's Unpublished Report: Foundations and Medical Education, 1909–28." *Bulletin of the History of Medicine* 54:475–96.

Freidson, Eliot. 1970a. *Profession of Medicine.* New York: Dodd, Mead.

———. 1970b. *Professional Dominance.* New York: Atherton.

Giarelli, Guido. 2004. "Convergence or Divergence? A Multi-Dimensional Approach to Health Care Reforms." *International Review of Sociology* 14:171–203.

Gist, Noel. 1937. "Secret Societies: A Cultural Study of Fratemalism in the United States." *University of Missouri Studies* 15:(entire issue).

Goldstein, Amy. 2003 (24 November). "Medicare Bill Would Enrich Companies." Pp. Al in *Washington Post.*

Goldwater, S. S. 1915. "Dispensaries: A Growing Factor in Curative and Preventive Medicine." *The Boston Medical and Surgical Journal* 17:613–17.

Goodman, Robert. 2004. "No Free Lunch." vol. 2004: Goodman, Robert.

Haley, Edward E. 1911. "The Evils of the Contract System." *New York State Journal of Medicine* 11:394–96.

Hilts, Philip J. 2003. *Protecting Americas Health.* New York: Alfred A. Knopf.

Illich, Ivan. 1976. Medical Nemesis: *The Expropriation of Health.* New York: Pantheon.

Immergut, Ellen M. 1992. *Health Politics: Interests and Institutions in Western Europe.* New York: Cambridge University Press.

Institute of Medicine. 1999. *To Err Is Human.* Washington, DC: National Academy Press.

———. 2001. *Coverage Matters: Insurance and Health Care.* Washington, DC: The National Academy Press.

———. 2003. *Hidden Costs, Value Lost: Uninsurance in America.* Washington, DC: The National Academy Press.

Jasso-Aguilar, Rebecca, Howard Waitzkin, and Angela Landwehr. 2004. "Multinational Corporations and Health Care in the United States and Latin America." *Journal of Health and Social Behavior* 45(Extra Issue): 136–57.

Jones, Eliot. 1921. *The Trust Problem in the United States.* New York: Macmillan.

Kennedy, Edward M. 1972. *In Critical Condition: The Crisis in America's Health Care.* New York: Simon & Schuster.

Kindig, David. 1997. *Purchasing Population Health.* Madison, WI: University of Wisconsin Press.

Kitchener, Martin and Charlene Harrington. 2004. "The U.S. Long-Term Care Sector: A Dialectic Analysis in Institutional Dynamics." *Journal of Health and Social Behavior* 45(Extra Issue): 87–101.

Langford, T.S., A.S. Kimball, H.B. Gamer, E.H. Flynn, and T.E. DeGurse. 1907. "Report of the Committee on Contract Practice." *Journal of the Michigan State Medical Society* 6:377–80.

Larson, Magali Sarfatti. 1977. *The Rise of Professionalism: A Sociological Analysis.* Berkeley: University of California Press.

Leicht, Kevin and Mary L. Fennell. 2001. *Professional Work: A Sociological Approach.* Malden, MA: Blackwell Publishers.

Light, Donald W. 1983. "The Development of Professional Schools in America." Pp. 345–65 in *The Transformation of Higher Learning: 1860–1930*, edited by K. Jarausch. Stuttgart, Germany: Klett-Cotta.

———. 1986. "Corporate Medicine for Profit." *Scientific American* 225(6):38–45.

———. 1988. "Towards a New Sociology of Medical Education." *Journal of Health and Social Behavior* 29:307–22.

———. 1994. "Comparative Models of 'Health Care' Systems, with Application to Germany." Pp. 455–70 in *The Sociology of Health and Illness*, edited by P. Conrad and R. Kern. New York: St. Martin's Press.

———. 1995a. "Countervailing Powers: A Framework for Professions in Transition" Pp. 25–41 in *Health Professions and the State in Europe*, edited by T. Johnson, G. Larkin, and M. Saks. London: Routledge.

———. 1995b. "*Homo Economicus*: Escaping the Traps of Managed Competition." *European Journal of Public Health* 5:145–54.

———. 1997. "The Rhetorics and Realities of Community Health Care: Limits of Countervailing Powers to Meet the Health Care Needs of the 21st Century." *Journal of Health Politics, Policy and Law* 22:105–45.

———. 2000a. "The Medical Profession and Organizational Change: From Professional Dominance to Countervailing Power." Pp. 201–216 in *Handbook of Medical Sociology*, edited by C. Bird, P. Conrad, and A. Fremont. Engelwood Cliffs, NJ: Prentice-Hall.

———. 2000b. "The Sociological Character of Markets in Health Care." Pp. 394–408 in *Handbook of Social Studies in Health and Medicine*, edited by G. L. Albrecht, R. Fitzpatrick, and S. C. Scrimshaw. London: Sage.

Light, Donald W. and Sol Levine. 1988. "The Changing Character of the Medical Profession: A Theoretical Overview." *Milbank Quarterly* 66 (Supplement 2): 10–32.

Ludmerer, Kenneth M. 1999. *Time to Heal: American Medical Education from the Turn of the Century to the Era of Managed Care.* New York: Oxford University Press.

Lydston, G. Frank. 1900. "Medicine as a Business Proposition." *Journal of the American Medical Association* 35:1403.

Mathews, George S. 1909. "Contract Practice in Rhode Island." *Bulletin of the American Academy of Medicine* 10:599–603.

McCleery, R.S., L.T. Keelty, M. Lam, R.E. Phillips, and T.M. Quinn. 1971. *One Life-One Physician: An Inquiry into the Medical Professions Performance in Self-Regulation.* Washington DC: Public Affairs Press.

McGlynn, Elizabeth A., Steven M. Asch, John Adams, and Joan Keesey. 2003. "The Quality of Health Care Delivered to Adults in the United States." *New England Journal of Medicine* 348:2635—45.

McKinlay, John and Joan Arches. 1985. "Toward the Proletarianization of Physicians." *International Journal of Health Services* 15:161–95.

McKinlay, John and L Marcceau. 2002. "The End of the Golden Age of Doctoring." *International Journal of Health Services* 32:379–416.

Mechanic, David. 2004. "The Rise and Fall of Managed Care." *Journal of Health and Social Behavior* 45(Extra Issue):76–86.

Moller, Stephanie, Evelyne Huber, John D. Stephens, David Bradley, and Francois Nielsen. 2003. "Determinants of Relative Poverty in Advanced Capitalist Democracies." *American Sociological Review* 68:22–51.

Navarro, Vicente. 1976. *Medicine under Capitalism*. New York: Prodist.

O'Neil, Will 1956 (Dec). "How to Get Rich: Own a Hospital?" *Modern Hospital*, pp. 51–55, 134, 138, 140, 142.

Parsons, Talcott. 1975. "The Sick Role and the Role of the Physician Reconsidered." Pp. 66–81 in *Action Theory and the Human Condition*, edited by Talcott Parsons. New York: The Free Press.

———. [1939] 1954. "The Professions and Social Structure." Pp. 34–49 in *Essays in Sociological Theory*, edited by Talcott Parsons. Glencoe, IL: The Free Press.

Perrow, Charles. 2002. *Organizing America: Wealth, Power and the Origin of Corporate Capitalism*. Princeton, NJ: Princeton University Press.

Quadagno, Jill. 2004. "Why the United States Has No National Health Insurance: Stakeholder Mobilization against the Welfare State, 1945–1996." *Journal of Health and Social Behavior* 45(Extra Issue):25–44.

Rayack, Elton. 1967. *Professional Power and American Medicine: The Economics of the American Medical Association*. Cleveland, OH: World Publication Co.

Reed, Louis. 1947. *Blue Cross and Medical Service Plans*. Washington D.C.: Federal Security Agency.

Reiman, Arnold S. 1980. "The New Medical-Industrial Complex." *New England Journal of Medicine* 303:963–70.

Ribicoff, A. and P. Dandaceau. 1972. *The American Medical Machine*. New York: Saturday Review Press.

Richardson, J.T. 1945. "The Origins and Development of Group Hospitalization in the United States." *University of Missouri Studies* 20:9–102.

Roemer, Milton I. 1991. *National Health Systems of the World*. New York: Oxford University Press.

Rorem, C. Rufus. 1940. *Non-Profit Hospital Service Plans*. Chicago, IL: Commission on Hospital Services.

Rosen, George. 1983. *The Structure of American Medical Practice, 1875–1941*. Philadelphia, PA: University of Pennsylvania Press.

Rosner, David. 1982. *A Once Charitable Enterprise: Hospitals and Health Care in Brooklyn and New York: 1885–1915*. New York: Cambridge University Press.

Ross, E.A. [1901] 1969. *Social Control: A Survey of the Foundations of Order*. Cleveland, OH: The Press of Case Western Reserve University.

Rothstein, William G. 1972. *American Physicians in the Nineteenth Century: From Sects to Science*. Baltimore, MD: Johns Hopkins University Press.

Roy, William G. 1997. *Socializing Capital: The Rise of the Large Industrial Corporation in America*. Princeton, NJ: Princeton University Press.

Rundall, Thomas G, Jeffrey A. Alexander, and Stephen M. Shortell. 2004. "A Theory of Physician-Hospital Integration." *Journal of Health and Social Behavior* 45(Extra Issue): 102–17.

Sager, Alan and Deborah Socolar. 2003. "61 Percent of Medicare's New Prescription Drug Subsidy Is Windfall Profit to Drug Makers." Boston, MA: Boston University School of Public Health, Health Reform Program.

Schwartz, Jerome 1.1965. "Early History of Prepaid Medical Care Plans." *Bulletin of the History of Medicine* 39:450–75.

Scott, W. Richard, Martin Ruef, Peter J. Mendel, and Carol Caronna. 2000. *Institutional Change and Healthcare Organizations: From Professional Dominance to Managed Care.* Chicago, IL: University of Chicago Press.

Shearer, Gail. 2003. *Medicare Prescription Drugs.* Washington D.C.: Consumers Union.

Shyrock, Richard H. 1967. *Medical Licensing in America: 1650–1965.* Baltimore: Johns Hopkins University Press.

Somers, Herman M. and Anne H. Somers. 1961. *Doctors, Patients, and Health Insurance.* Washington DC: The Brookings Institution.

Starr, Paul. 1982. *The Social Transformation of American Medicine.* New York: Basic.

Stem, Bernhard J. 1945. *American Medical Practice in the Perspective of a Century.* New York: The Commonwealth Fund.

Stevens, Rosemary. 1971. *American Medicine and the Public Interest.* New Haven, CT: Yale University Press.

Swedberg, Richard. 2003. *Principles of Economic Sociology.* Princeton, NJ: Princeton University Press.

Timmermans, Stefan and Emily Kolker. 2004. "Clinical Practice Guidelines and the Implications of Shifts in Knowledge for Sociological Accounts of Professional Power." *Journal of Health and Social Behavior* 45 (Extra Issue): 177–93.

Touhy, Carolyn Hughes. 1999. *Accidental Logics.* New York: Oxford University Press.

U.S. Department of Health and Human Services. 1982. "Health United States, 1982." U.S. Department of Health and Human Services, Washington DC.

Vogel, Morris. 1980. *The Invention of the Modern Hospital.* Chicago, IL: University of Chicago Press.

Waitzkin, Howard. 1983. *The Second Sickness: Contradictions of Capitalist Health Care.* New York: The Free Press.

Warbasse, James P. 1909. *Medical Sociology.* New York: D. Appleton and Company.

————. 1912. "What Is the Matter with the Medical Profession?" *Long Island Journal of Medicine* 6:271–75.

Wazana, Ashley. 2000. "Physicians and the Pharmaceutical Industry." *Journal of the American Medical Association* 283:373–80.

Weber, Max. 1968. *Economy and Society.* New York: Bedminster Press.

Weller, Charles. 1983. "'Free Choice' as a Restraint of Trade, and the Counterintuitive Contours of Competition." *Health Matrix* 3 (2):3—23.

Wennberg, J. 1984. "Dealing with Medical Practice Variations: A Proposal for Action." *Health Affairs* 3:6–32.

Wennberg, J. and A. Gittelsohn. 1982. "Variations in Medical Care among Small Areas." *Scientific American* 246:120–35.

Wertz, Richard W. and Dorothy C. Wertz. 1989. *Lying-in: A History of Childbirth in America (Expanded Ed.).* New Haven, CT: Yale University Press.

White, Joseph. 1995. *Competing Solutions: American Health Care Proposals and International Experience.* Washington DC: Brookings Institution.

Wholey, Douglas R., Jon B. Christianson, Debra A. Draper, Cara S. Lesser, and Lawton R. Bums. 2004. "The Response of Local Communities to Entry by National Healthcare Firms." *Journal of Health and Social Behavior* 45(Extra Issue): 118–35.

Williams, Pierce. 1932. *The Purchase of Medical Care through Fixed Periodic Payments.* New York: National Bureau of Economic Research.

Woodruff, John V. 1916. "Contract Practice." *New York State Journal of Medicine* 16:507–11.

World Health Organization. 2000. *The World Health Report 2000.* Geneva, Switzerland: World Health Organization.

Young, James Harvey. 1961. *The Toadstool Millionaires: A Social History of Patent Medicines in American before Federal Regulation.* Princeton, NJ: Princeton University Press.

The Health Care System Under French National Health Insurance

Lessons for Health Reform in the United States

By Victor G. Rodwin

....

T he French health system combines universal coverage with a public–private mix of hospital and ambulatory care and a higher volume of service provision than in the United States. Although the system is far from perfect, its indicators of health status and consumer satisfaction are high; its expenditures, as a share of gross domestic product, are far lower than in the United States; and patients have an extraordinary degree of choice among providers.

Lessons for the United States include the importance of government's role in providing a statutory framework for universal health insurance; recognition that piecemeal reform can broaden a partial program (like Medicare) to cover, eventually, the entire population; and understanding that universal coverage can be achieved without excluding private insurers from the supplementary insurance market. (*Am J Public Health.* 2003;93:31–37)

THE FRENCH HEALTH CARE System has achieved sudden notoriety since it was ranked No. 1 by the World Health Organization in 2000.[1] Although the methodology used by this assessment has been criticized in the Journal and elsewhere,[2–5] indicators of overall satisfaction and health status support the view that France's health care system, while not the best according to these criteria, is impressive and deserves attention by anyone interested in rekindling health care reform in the United States (Table 7.2.1). French politicians have defended their health system as an ideal synthesis of **solidarity** and **liberalism** (a term understood in much of Europe to mean market-based economic systems), lying between Britain's "nationalized" health service, where there is too much rationing, and the United States' "competitive" system, where too many people have no health insurance. This view, however, is tempered by more sober analysts who argue

EDITOR'S NOTES

solidarity: ties that bind people together in a group or society and their sense of connection with each other; unity or agreement of feeling or action, especially among people with a common interest.

EDITOR'S NOTES

liberalism: a market-based economic system.

TABLE 7.2.1 Health Status and Consumer Satisfaction Measures: France, United States, Germany, United Kingdom, Japan, and Italy

	France	US	Germany	UK	Japan	Italy
Health status						
Infant mortality (deaths/1000 live births), 1999[a]	4.3	7.2[b]	4.6	5.8	3.4	5.1
LEB (female), 1998[a]	82.2	79.4	80.5	79.7	84.0	81.6[c]
LEB (male), 1998[a]	74.6	73.9	74.5	74.8	77.2	75.3[c]
LE at 65 (female), 1997[a]	20.8	19.2	18.9	18.5	21.8	20.2
LE at 65 (male), 1997[a]	16.3	15.9	15.2	15.0	17.0	15.8
Severe disability-free life expectancy (female), 1990/1991[d]	14.8	NA	NA	13.6	14.9	NA
Severe disability-free life expectancy (male), 1990/1991[d]	18.1	NA	NA	16.9	17.3	NA
Potential years of life lost per 100000 population (female), 1993[e]	2262	3222	2713	2642	1914	2136
Potential years of life lost per 100000 population (male), 1993[e]	5832	6522	5752	4688	4003	4873
Consumer satisfaction, %						
Only minor changes needed, 1990[f]	41	10	41	27	29	12
Very satisfied, 1996[g]	10	NA	12.8	7.6	NA	0.08
Fairly satisfied, 1996[g]	55.1	NA	53.2	40.5	NA	15.5

Note. US=United States; UK=United Kingdom; LEB=life expectancy at birth; LE=life expectancy; NA=not available.
a *Source.* Organization for Economic Cooperation and Development.[6(p27)]
b 1998.
c 1997.
d Defined as life expectancy with the ability "to perform those activities essential for everyday life without significant help."[6(p27,31)]
e *Source.* Organization for Economic Cooperation and Development.[6(p30)]
f *Source.* Harvard–Louis Harris Interactive 1990 Ten-Nation Survey, cited by Blendon et al.[7]
g *Source.* Eurobarometer Survey, 1996, cited in Mossialos.[8]

that excessive centralization of decisionmaking and chronic deficits incurred by French national health insurance (NHI) require significant reform.[9,10]

Over the past 3 decades, successive governments have tinkered with health care reform; the most comprehensive plan was Prime Minister Juppé's in 1996.[11,12] Since then, whether governments were on the political left or right, they have pursued cost control policies without reforming the overall management and organization of the health system. This strategy has exacerbated tensions among the state, the NHI system, and health care professionals (principally physicians), tensions that have long characterized the political evolution of French NHI.[13-15]

Although the French ideal is now subject to more critical scrutiny by politicians, the system functions well and remains an important model for the United States. After more than a half century of struggle, in January 2000, France covered the remaining 1% of its population that was uninsured and offered supplementary coverage to 8% of its population below an income ceiling.[16] This extension of health insurance makes France an interesting case of how to ensure universal coverage through incremental reform while maintaining a sustainable system that limits perceptions of health care rationing and restrictions on patient choice. Following an overview of the system, and an assessment of its achievements, problems, and reform, this article explores lessons for the United States of the French experience with NHI.

The French Health Care System

The French health care system combines universal coverage with a public–private mix of hospital and ambulatory care, higher levels of resources (Table 7.2.2), and a higher volume of service provision (Table 7.2.3) than in the United States.[32] There is wide access to comprehensive health services for a population that is, on average, older than that of the United States, and yet France's health expenditures in 2000 were equal to 9.5% of its gross domestic product (GDP) compared with 13.0% of GDP in the United States.[17]

The health system in France is dominated by solo-based, **fee-for-service** private practice for ambulatory care and public hospitals for

EDITOR'S NOTES

fee-for-service billing: a billing method in which doctors and other health care providers are paid for each *service* performed.

TABLE 7.2.2 Health Care Resources: France and United States, 1997–2000

Resources	France	US
Active physicians per 1000 population	3.3[a] (1998)	2.8[a] (1999)
Active physicians in private, office-based practice per 1000 population	1.9[b] (2002)	1.7[c] (1999)
General/family practice, %	53.3[b] (2002)	22.5[c] (1999)
Obstetricians, pediatricians, and internists, %	7.5[b] (2002)	35.6[c] (1999)
Other specialists, %	39.2[b] (2002)	41.0[c] (1999)
Nonphysician personnel per acute hospital bed[d]	1.9 (2001)[e]	5.7 (2000/01)[f]
Total inpatient hospital beds per 1000 population[g] (1998)	8.5[a]	3.7[a]
Short-stay hospital beds per 1000 population	4.0[h] (2000)	3.0[i] (1998)
Share of public beds, %	64.2[h] (2000)	19.2[i] (1999)
Share of private beds, %	35.8[h] (2000)	80.8[i] (1999)
Proprietary beds as percentage of private beds (1999), %	56[j]	12[i]
Nonprofit beds as percentage of private beds (1999), %	44[j]	88[i]
Share of proprietary beds, %	27[k] (1998)	10.7[i] (1999)

a *Source.* Organization for Economic Cooperation and Development.[17]
b *Source.* CNAMTS.[18]
c *Source.* National Center for Health Statistics.[19] (These figures exclude federally employed physicians as well as all anesthesiologists, pathologists, and radiologists.)
d Nonphysician personnel include all hospital employees—administrative, technical, and clinical—excluding physicians. Among the category of physicians in the United States, we included chiropractors and podiatrists.
e *Source.* CREDES.[20]
f *Source.* Acute care beds: American Hospital Association[21]; nonphysician personnel: Bureau of Labor Statistics.[22]
g These differences reflect the use of long-term care beds in French hospitals—public and private nonprofit—as nursing homes.
h *Source.* DRESS.[23]
i *Source.* American Hospital Association.[21]
j *Source:* DRESS.[24]
k *Source.* DRESS.[25]

acute institutional care, among which patients are free to navigate and be reimbursed under NHI. All residents are automatically enrolled with an insurance fund based on their occupational status. In addition, 90% of the population subscribes to supplementary health insurance to cover other benefits not covered under NHI.[33] Another distinguishing feature of the French health system is its

TABLE 7.2.3 Use of Health Services: France and United States, 1997–2000

Use	France	US
Physician office visits per capita[a] (1999)	6.0[b]	2.8[c]
Specialist visits per capita (1999)	1.9[b]	1.4[c]
Hospital days per capita (1999)	2.4[d]	0.9[d]
Short-stay hospital days per capita (1999)	1.1[d]	0.7[d]
Admission rate for short-stay hospital services per 1000 population	170.1[e] (2000)	118.0[f] (1998)
Average length of stay for all inpatient hospital services (1999)	10.6[b]	7.0[g]
Average length of stay in short-stay beds (1999)	6.2[e]	5.9[f]
Per capita spending on pharmaceuticals, PPP, $ (1999)	484[h]	478[h]
MRIs per million population	2.5[i] (1997)	7.6[i] (1998)

Note. $PPP=purchasing power parity; MRI=magnetic resonance imaging unit.

a Organization for Economic Cooperation and Development (OECD) Health Data has traditionally published a figure of around 6 physician consultations per capita for the United States. According to the 2002 edition, this figure is based on the National Health Interview Survey of the National Center for Health Statistics. This source, however, includes telephone contacts with physicians, as well as contacts with physicians in hospital outpatient departments and emergency rooms (ERs).The French figure includes consultations with all physicians in private practice including health centers (5.4) and home visits by physicians (0.6). It excludes all telephone contacts and hospital outpatient and ER consultations. Thus, to obtain comparable data, the US figure is taken from the National Ambulatory Medical Care Survey (NAMCS), a survey of visits to physicians' offices, hospital outpatient departments, and ERs. According to the 1995 NAMCS, visits to physician offices account for 81% of ambulatory care use, and visits to emergency rooms and hospital outpatient departments account, respectively, for 11.2% and 7.8% of ambulatory care use. Taking these proportions into account, as well as the fact that patients are seen by physicians in only 71% of outpatient department visits, the 1999 per capita rate of physician visits would only increase to 3.04.

b *Source.* CREDES.[20]

c *Source.* National Center for Health Statistics.[19] (These figures exclude federally employed physicians as well as all anesthesiologists, pathologists, and radiologists.)

d *Source.* OECD.[27]

e *Source.* Ministry of Health and Social Affairs.[28]

f *Source.* National Center for Health Statistics.[29]

g *Source.* National Center for Health Statistics.[30]

h These figures, cited in Reinhardt et al.[31] understate differences in the per capita volume of prescription drugs sold because increases in drug prices have been significantly higher in France than in the United States since 1980. When expenditure data on prescription drugs in France and the United States are adjusted by the OECD index of pharmaceutical price inflation in both nations, the volume of prescription drug purchases in France exceeds that in the United States by a factor of 2. *Source:* OECD Health Data 1999, cited in S. Chambaretaud.[26]

i *Source.* OECD Health Data 2001.

proprietary hospital sector, the largest in Europe, which is accessible to all insured patients. Finally, there are no gatekeepers regulating access to specialists and hospitals.

French NHI evolved from a 19th-century tradition of mutual aid societies to a post–World War II system of local democratic management by "social partners"—trade unions and employer representatives—but it is increasingly controlled by the French state.[34] Although NHI consists of different plans for different occupational groups, they all operate within a common statutory framework.[35–37] Health insurance is compulsory; no one may opt out. Health insurance funds are not permitted to compete by lowering health insurance premiums or attempting to micromanage health care. For ambulatory care, all health insurance plans operate on the traditional indemnity model—reimbursement for services rendered. For inpatient hospital services, there are budgetary allocations as well as per diem reimbursements. The French indemnity model allows for direct payment by patients to physicians, coinsurance, and balance billing by roughly one third of physicians.

Like Medicare in the United States, French NHI provides a great degree of patient choice. Unlike Medicare, however, French NHI coverage increases as individual costs rise, there are no deductibles, and pharmaceutical benefits are extensive. In contrast to Medicaid, French NHI carries no stigma and provides better access. In summary, French NHI is more generous than what a "Medicare for all" system would be like in the United States, and it shares a range of characteristics with which Americans are well acquainted—fee-for-service practice, a public–private mix in the financing and organization of health care services, cost sharing, and supplementary private insurance.

National Health Insurance

NHI evolved, in stages, in response to demands for extension of coverage. Following its original passage in 1928, the NHI program covered salaried workers in industry and commerce whose wages were under a low ceiling.[38,39] In 1945, NHI was extended to all industrial and commercial workers and their families, irrespective of wage levels. The extension of coverage took the rest of the century to complete. In 1961, farmers and agricultural workers were covered; in 1966, independent professionals were brought into the system; in 1974, another law proclaimed that NHI should be universal. Not until January 2000 was comprehensive first-dollar health insurance coverage granted to the remaining uninsured population on the basis of residence in France.[40]

NHI forms an integral part of France's social security system, which is typically depicted— following an agrarian metaphor—as a set of 3 sprouting branches: (1) pensions, (2) family allowances, and (3) health insurance and workplace accident coverage.[20] The first 2 are managed by a single national fund, while the third is run by 3 main NHI funds: those for salaried workers (Caisse Nationale d'Assurance Maladie des Travailleurs Salariés, or CNAMTS), for farmers and agricultural workers (Mutualité Sociale Agricole, or MSA), and for the independent professions (Caisse Nationale d'Assurance Maladie des Professions Indépendentes, or CANAM). In addition, there are 11 smaller funds for workers in specific occupations and their dependents, all of whom defend their "rightfully earned" entitlements.[41]

The CNAMTS covers 84% of legal residents in France, which includes salaried workers, those who were recently brought into the system because they were uninsured, and the beneficiaries of 7 of the smaller funds that are administered by the CNAMTS.[33] The CANAM and MSA cover, respectively, 7% and 5% of the population, with 4% covered by the remaining 4 funds.

All NHI funds are legally private organizations responsible for the provision of a public service. In practice, they are quasi-public organizations supervised by the government ministry that oversees French social security. The main NHI funds have a network of local and regional funds that function somewhat like fiscal intermediaries in the management of Medicare. They cut reimbursement checks for health care providers, look out for fraud and abuse, and provide a range of customer services for their beneficiaries.

French NHI covers services ranging from hospital care, outpatient services, prescription drugs (including homeopathic products), thermal cures in spas, nursing home care, cash benefits, and to a lesser extent, dental and vision care. Among the different NHI funds, there remain small differences in coverage.

Smaller funds with older, higher-risk populations (e.g., farmers, agricultural workers, and miners) are subsidized by the CNAMTS, as well as by the state, on grounds of what is termed "demographic compensation." Retirees and the unemployed are automatically covered by the funds corresponding to their occupational categories. In France, the commitment to universal coverage is accepted by the principal political parties and justified on grounds of solidarity—the notion that there should be mutual aid and cooperation between the sick and the well, the active and the inactive, and that health insurance should be financed on the basis of ability to pay, not actuarial risk.[42]

Organization of Health Care

The organization of health care in France is typically presented as being rooted in principles of liberalism and pluralism.[32,42] Liberalism is correctly invoked as underpinning the medical profession's attachment to cost sharing and selected elements of *la médecine libérale* (private practice): selection of the physician by the patient, freedom for physicians to practice wherever they choose, clinical freedom for the doctor, and professional confidentiality. It is wrongly invoked, however, in the case of fee-for-service payment with reimbursement under universal NHI, for such a system is more aptly characterized as a bilateral monopoly whereby physician associations accept the monopsony power of the NHI system in return for the state's sanctioning of their monopoly power. In the hospital sector, liberalism provides the rationale for the coexistence of public and proprietary hospitals, the latter accounting for 27% of acute beds in France in contrast to 10.7% in the United States (Table 7.2.2). Also, unit service chiefs in public hospitals have the right to use a small portion of their beds for private patients.

The French tolerance for organizational diversity—whether it be complementary, competitive, or both—is typically justified on grounds of pluralism. Although ambulatory care is dominated by office-based solo practice, there are also private group practices, health centers, occupational health services in large enterprises, and a strong public sector program for maternal and child health care. Likewise, although hospital care is dominated by public hospitals, including teaching institutions with a quasi-monopoly on medical education and research, there are, nevertheless, opportunities for physicians in private practice who wish to have part-time hospital staff privileges in public hospitals.

The private hospital sector in France (both nonprofit and proprietary hospitals) has 36% of acute beds, including 64% of all surgical beds, 32% of psychiatric beds, and only 21% of medical beds.[24] The nonprofit sector, which operates only 9% of all beds, has over 44% of private long-term care beds.[24] Proprietary hospitals, typically smaller than public hospitals, have traditionally emphasized elective surgery and obstetrics, leaving more complex cases to the public sector. Over the past 15 years, however, although there has been no change in its relative share of beds, the proprietary sector has consolidated, and many proprietary hospitals have developed a strong capacity for cardiac surgery and radiation therapy.

The number of *nonphysician* personnel per bed is higher in public hospitals than in private hospitals; in the aggregate, it is 67% lower than in US hospitals (Table 7.2.2). This difference in hospital staffing may reflect a more technical and intense level of service in US hospitals. It also reflects differences between an NHI system and the US health system, which is characterized by large numbers of administrative and clerical personnel whose main tasks focus on billing many hundreds of payers, documenting all medical procedures performed, and handling risk management and quality assurance activities.

Financing and Provider Reimbursement

In 2000, roughly half of French NHI expenditures were financed by employer payroll taxes (51.1%) and a "general social contribution" (34.6%) levied by the French treasury on all earnings, including investment income.[43] (Remaining sources of financing for the CNAMTS and its affiliated health insurance funds included payroll taxes on employees [3.4%], special taxes on automobiles, tobacco and alcohol [3.3%], a specific tax on the pharmaceutical industry [0.8%], and subsidies from the state [4.9%].) The general social contribution, a supplementary income tax (5.5% of wages and all other earnings) raised specifically for NHI, was introduced in 1991 to make health care financing more progressive and to increase NHI revenues by enlarging the tax base. As a share of total personal health care expenditures, French NHI funds finance 75.5%, supplementary private insurance covers 12.4% (7.5% for the nonprofit sector *mutuelles* and 4.9% for commercial insurers), and out-of-pocket expenditures represent 11.1%.[44]

Physicians in private practice (and in proprietary hospitals) are paid directly by patients on the basis of a national fee schedule. Patients are then reimbursed by their local health insurance funds.

Proprietary hospitals are reimbursed on a negotiated per diem basis (with supplementary fees for specific services) and public hospitals (including private nonprofit hospitals working in partnership with them) are paid on the basis of annual global budgets negotiated every year between hospitals, regional agencies, and the Ministry of Health. As for prescription drugs, unit prices allowable for reimbursement under NHI are set by a commission that includes representatives from the Ministries of Health, Finance, and Industry.

In contrast to Medicare and private insurance in the United States, where severe illness usually results in increasing out-of-pocket costs, when patients become very ill in France their health insurance coverage improves. For example, although coinsurance and direct payment is symbolically an important part of French NHI, patients are exempted from both when (1) expenditures exceed approximately $100, (2) hospital stays exceed 30 days, (3) patients suffer from serious, debilitating, or chronic illness, or (4) patient income is below a minimum ceiling, thereby qualifying them for free supplementary coverage.

Charges for services provided by health professionals—whether in office-based practice, in outpatient services of public hospitals, or in private hospitals—are negotiated every year within the framework of national agreements concluded among representatives of the health professions, the 3 main health insurance funds, and the French state. Once negotiated, fees must be respected by all physicians except those who have either chosen or earned the right to engage in extra billing, typically specialists located in major cities. Indeed, in Paris, up to 80% of physicians in selected specialties engage in extra billing, in contrast to the national average of 20% among general practitioners (GPs). In consulting these physicians, patients are reimbursed only the allowable rate by NHI; supplementary insurance schemes cover the remaining expenditures, with different limits set by each plan.

Services, Perceptions, and Health Status

Existing data (Table 7.2.3)—whether they come from surveys or are byproducts of the administrative system—indicate consistently that, compared with Americans, the French consult their doctors more often, are admitted to the hospital more often, and purchase more prescription drugs. Owing to strict controls on capital expenditures in the health sector, France has fewer scanners and magnetic resonance imaging units than the United States. But France stands out as having more radiation therapy equipment than the United States, Japan, and the rest of Europe.

In contrast to Great Britain and Canada, there is no public perception in France that health services are "rationed" to patients. In terms of consumer satisfaction (Table 7.2.1), a Louis Harris poll placed France above the United Kingdom, the United States, Japan, and Sweden.[7] A more recent European study reports that two thirds of the population is "fairly satisfied" with the system.[8]

France also ranks high on most measures of health status (Table 7.2.1). A recent report by the Organization for Economic Cooperation and Development (OECD), for example, indicates that

France is well above the OECD average on a range of key indicators.[12] A more critical view would emphasize that France has high rates of premature mortality compared with the rest of Europe, but most analyses of this phenomenon suggest that it has less to do with health care services than with inadequate public health interventions to reduce alcoholism, violent deaths from suicides and road accidents, and the incidence of AIDS.[45,46]

Achievements, Problems, and Reform

The French health care system delivers a higher aggregate level of services and higher consumer satisfaction with a significantly lower level of health expenditures, as a share of GDP, than in the United States. Add to this the enormous choice of health delivery options given to consumers, the low level of micromanagement imposed on health care professionals, and the higher level of population health status achieved by the French, and some would argue that the French model is a worthy export product. Others, however, would emphasize the problems that accompany this model.

First, despite the achievement of universal coverage under NHI, there are still striking disparities in the geographic distribution of health resources and inequalities of health outcomes by social class.[45,47,48] In response to these problems, there is a consensus that these issues extend beyond health care financing and organization and require stronger public health interventions.[49]

Second, there is a newly perceived problem of uneven quality in the distribution of health services. In 1997, a reputable consumer publication issued a list of hospitals delivering low-quality, even dangerous care.[50] Even before this consumer awareness, there was a growing recognition that one aspect of quality problems, particularly with regard to chronic diseases and older persons, is the lack of coordination and case management services for patients. These problems are exacerbated by the anarchic character of the French health system—what might be called the darker side of laissez-faire.[51]

Third, although, compared with the United States, France appears to have controlled its health care expenditures, within Europe, France is still among the higher spenders. This has led the Ministry of Finance to circumscribe health spending since the early 1970s.[52] Much like the prospective payment system for Medicare in the United States, France has imposed strong price control policies on the entire health sector. Greater cost containment has been achieved through such controls in France than in the United States.[32]

Although the level of health services use is high in France (Table 7.2.3), prices per service unit are exceedingly low by US standards, and this has led to increasing tensions (physicians' strikes and demonstrations) between physician associations and their negotiating partners—the NHI funds and the state. The allowable fee for an office visit to a GP, for example, is only 20 €, and one half of all French physicians are GPs. Physician specialists also receive low fees (23 €), except for cardiologists (46 €), psychiatrists (36 €), and those who do not accept assignment. The $55000 average net annual income of French physicians—salaried hospital-based doctors as well as GPs and specialists in private practice—is barely one third that of their US counterparts ($194000)[53,54] (C. LePen and E. Piriou, written communication, August 2002). In addition to price controls, capital controls on the health system are stringent. They include limits on the number of medical students admitted to the second year of medical school, controls on hospital beds and medical technologies, imposition (since 1984) of global budgets on hospital operating expenditures, and the more recent Juppé plan that imposed annual expenditure targets for all NHI expenditures.

Prime Minister Juppé's plan and more recent reforms have addressed the problems noted above; none of them, however, have been solved. The Juppé government established a slew of national public health agencies to strengthen disease surveillance and monitor food safety, drug safety, and the environment.[55] It organized a new national agency, the Agence National d'Accréditation et d'Évaluation en Santé, to promote health care evaluation, prepare hospital accreditation procedures, and establish medical practice guidelines.[56,57] It also set up regional hospital agencies with new powers to coordinate public and private hospitals and allocate their budgets.[58]

In addition, the Juppé plan included measures to modernize the French health care system by improving the coding and collection of information on all ambulatory care consultations and prescriptions and by allowing experiments to improve the coordination of health services. This represents an emerging form of French-style managed care—a centrally directed attempt to rationalize the delivery of health services.[51] The institutional barriers to such reform are considerable, but whatever transpires in the future, the French experience with NHI may be instructive for the United States.

Lessons for the United States

Perceptions of health systems abroad can become caricatures of what we wish to promote or avoid at home. It is thus a risky venture to derive lessons from the French experience for health care reform in the United States. Nonetheless, I set forth 5 propositions to provoke further debate.

First, the French experience demonstrates that it is possible to achieve universal coverage without a "single-payer" system. To do this, however, will still require a statutory framework and an active state that regulates NHI financing and provider reimbursement. Of course, French NHI was not designed from scratch as a pluralistic, multipayer system providing universal coverage on the basis of occupational status. It is the outcome of sociopolitical struggles and clashes among trade unions, employers, physicians associations, and the state. This suggests that NHI in the United States could similarly emerge from our patchwork accumulation of federal, state, and employer-sponsored plans so long as we recognize the legitimate role of government in overseeing the rules and framework within which these actors operate.

Second, the evolution of French NHI demonstrates that it is possible to achieve universal coverage without a "big bang" reform, since this was accomplished in incremental stages beginning in 1928, with big extensions in 1945, 1961, 1966, 1978, and finally in 2000. Of course, the extension of health insurance involved political battles at every stage.[13,38] In the United States, since it is unlikely that we will pass NHI with one sweeping reform, we may first have to reject what Fuchs calls the "extreme actuarial approach" of our private health insurance system[60] and then accept piecemeal efforts that extend social insurance coverage to categorical groups beyond current beneficiaries of public programs.

Third, French experience demonstrates that universal coverage can be achieved without excluding private insurers from the supplementary insurance market. The thriving nonprofit insurance sector (*mutuelles*) as well as commercial companies (e.g., Axa) are evidence in support of this proposition. Of course, it is easier to achieve this model before the emergence of a powerful commercial health insurance industry such as exists in the United States today. Nevertheless, so long as NHI covers the insurance functions, why prevent the private insurance industry from providing useful services, on a contractual basis, under a NHI program?

Fourth, coverage of the remaining 1% of the uninsured in France suggests that national responsibility for entitlement is more equitable than delegating these decisions to local authorities. This lesson is consistent with the experience of Medicare versus Medicaid in the United States, as exemplified by the differences among states and counties in dealing with the uninsured.

Finally, and perhaps most important for the United States, the French experience suggests that it is possible to solve the problem of financing universal coverage before meeting the challenge of modernizing and reorganizing the health care system for the 21st century. The Clintons' plan attempted to do both and failed. France may be more prepared and willing to implement the Clintons' plan than the United States. The United States would do better to follow the French example in solving the tough entitlement issues before restructuring the entire health care system.

About the Author

Victor G. Rodwin is with the Wagner School, New York University, New York, NY, and the World Cities Project, New York, a joint venture of NYU Wagner and the International Longevity Center-USA.

Requests for reprints should be sent to Victor G. Rodwin, PhD, MPH, 4 Washington Sq North, New York, NY 10003 (e-mail: victor.rodwin@nyu.edu).

This article was accepted September 10, 2002.

Note

1. A bibliography in English on the French health care system is available on the author's Web site at http://www.nyu.edu/projects/rodwin/main.html.

Acknowledgments

I thank the R.W. Johnson Foundation for a Health Policy Investigator Award that enabled me to explore this topic and others.

I am grateful to Dr Robert Butler, president and CEO, ILC-USA, and to my colleagues in the New York Group on Rekindling Health Care Reform for sponsoring the seminars and lecture on which this article is based and for helpful discussion during its preparation. I thank Claude LePen, William Glaser, Michael Gusmano, and Marc Duriez for their insights; Birgit Bogler, Gabriel Montero, and Eric Piriou for precious research assistance; and 3 anonymous French reviewers for provocative and thoughtful comments.

References

1. World Health Report 2000. Available at: http://www.who.int/whr/2001/archives/2000/en/index.htm. Accessed October 18, 2002.

2. Coyne JS, Hilsenrath P. The World Health Report 2000: can health care systems be compared using a single measure of performance? *Am J Public Health.* 2002;92:30, 32–33.

3. Navarro V. The World Health Report 2000: can health care systems be compared using a single measure of performance? *Am J Public Health.* 2002; 92:31, 33–34.

4. Murray C, Frenk J. World Health Report 2000: a step towards evidence-based health policy. *Lancet.* 2001;357: 1698–1700.

5. Navarro V. World Health Report 2000: a response to Murray and Frenk. *Lancet.* 2001;357:1701–1702.

6. *A Caring World: The New Social Policy Agenda.* Paris: Organization for Economic Cooperation and Development; 1999:27.

7. Blendon R, Leitman R, Morrison I, Donelan K. Satisfaction with health systems in ten nations. *Health Aff (Millwood).* 1990;9(2):185–192.

8. Mossialos E. Citizens' views on health care systems in the 15 member states of the European Union. *Health Econ.* 1997;6:109–116.

9. de Kervasdoué J. *Pour une Révolution sans Réforme.* Paris, France: Gallimard; 1999.

10. Le Pen C. *Les Habits Neufs d'Hippocrate.* Paris, France: Calmann-Lévy; 1999.

11. Sorum P. Striking against managed care: the last gasp of la médecine libérale? *JAMA.* 1998;280:659–664.

12. Imai Y, Jacobzone S, Lenain P. *The Changing Health System in France.* Paris, France: Economics Department, Organization for Economic Cooperation and Development; November 2000. Working Paper 268.

13. Hatzfeld H. *Le Grand Tournant de la Médecine Libérale*. Paris, France: Editions Ouvriéres; 1963.

14. Wilsford D. *Doctors and the State: The Politics of Health Care in France and the United States*. Durham, NC: Duke University Press; 1991.

15. Immergut E. *Health Politics: Interests and Institutions in Western Europe*. Cambridge, England: Cambridge University Press; 1992:chap 3.

16. Grignon M. Quel filet de sécurité pour la santé? Une approache économique et organisationelle de la couverture maladie universelle. *Revue Française des Affaires Sociales*. 2002;2: 145–176.

17. *OECD Health Data, 2002*. Paris, France: Organization for Economic Cooperation and Development; 2002.

18. *Carnets Statistiques no. 108*. Paris, France: Caisse Nationale de l'Assurance Maladie des Travailleurs Salariés (CNAMTS); 2002.

19. *1999 National Ambulatory Medical Care Survey*. Washington, DC: National Center for Health Statistics, Centers for Disease Control and Prevention; 1999.

20. *Eco-Santé 2001*. Paris, France: Centre de Recherche, d'Étude et de Documentation en Economie de la Santé (CREDES); 2001.

21. *Hospital Statistics 2000*. Chicago, Ill: American Hospital Association; 2001.

22. National industry specific occupational employment and wage estimates, specific industry code 806, hospitals, US Dept of Labor, Bureau of Labor Statistics. Available at: www.bls.gov/oes/2000/oesi3_806.htm. Accessed October 29, 2002.

23. *L'activité des Établissements de Santé en 2000*. Paris, France: Direction de la Recherche, des Études, de l'Évaluation et des Statistiques (DRESS); 2002. Études et Résultats no. 177.

24. *Les Établissements de Santé en 1999*. Paris, France: Direction de la Recherche, des Études de l'Évaluation et des Statistiques (DRESS), Ministère de l'Emploi et de la Solidarité; 2001.

25. *Annuaire des Statistiques Sanitaires et Sociales 1999*. Paris, France: DRESS Collection Études et Statistiques; 2000.

26. Chambaretaud S. 2000. *La Consommation de Médicaments dans les Principaux Pays Industrialisés*. Paris, France: Direction de la Recherche, des Etudes, de l'Évaluation et des Statistiques (DRESS); 2000. Études et Résultats no. 47.

27. *OECD Health Data, 2001*. Paris, France: Organization for Economic Cooperation and Development; 2001.

28. *Programme de Médicalisation des Systèmes d'Information*. Paris, France: Ministry of Health and Social Affairs; 2000.

29. *1998 National Hospital Discharge Survey.* Washington, DC: National Center for Health Statistics, Centers for Disease Control and Prevention; 1999.

30. *Health in the United States.* Washington, DC: National Center for Health Statistics, Centers for Disease Control and Prevention; 2001.

31. Reinhardt U, Hussey P, Anderson G. Cross national comparisons of health systems using 1999 OECD data. *Health Aff (Millwood).* 2002;21(3):169–181.

32. Rodwin V, Sandier S. Health care under French national health insurance. *Health Aff (Millwood).* 1993;12(3): 113–131.

33. Sandier S, Polton D, Paris V, Thompson S. France. In: Dixon A, Mossialos E, eds. *Health Care Systems in Eight Countries: Trends and Challenges.* London, England: London School of Economics and Political Science; 2002: 30–45.

34. Catrice-Lorrey A. *Dynamique Interne de la Sécurité Sociale.* Paris, France: Economica; 1982.

35. *White J. Competing Solutions: American Health Care Proposals and International Experience.* Washington, DC: Brookings Institute; 1995:chap 4 and 5.

36. Glaser W. *Health Insurance in Practice.* San Francisco, Calif: Josey Bass; 1992.

37. Dupéyroux JJ. *Sécurité Sociale.* Paris, France: Dalloz; 1997

38. Galant H. *Histoire Politique de la Sécurité Sociale Française.* Paris, France: Armand Colin; 1955.

39. Duriez M, Lancry JP, Lequet-Slama D, Sandier S. *Le Système de Santé en France.* Paris, France: Presses Universitaires de France; 1996.

40. Boisguerin B. *La CMU au 31 Mars 2002.* Paris, France: Direction de la Recherche, des Études de l'Évaluation et des Statistiques (DRESS); July 2002. Études et Résultats no. 179.

41. *La Population Protégée par les Régimes de Sécurité Sociale: Répartition Géographique par Département et par Circonscription de Caisse au 31 Décembre 1999.* Paris, France: Caisse Nationale d'Assurance Maladie des Travailleurs Salaries (CNAMT); May 2001. Dossier Études et Statistiques no. 48.

42. Rodwin V. The marriage of national health insurance and la médecine libérale: a costly union. *Milbank Mem Fund Q Health Soc.* 1981;59:16–43.

43. *Rapport de la Commission des Comptes Nationaux de la Santé, 2000.* Paris, France: Direction de la Recherche, des Études de l'Évaluation et des Statistiques (DRESS); 2001.

44. *Commission des Comptes de la Sécurité Sociale.* Paris, France: Direction de la Recherche, des Études de l'Évaluation et des Statistiques (DRESS); 2002.

45. Haut Comité de la Santé Publique. *La Santé des Français*. Paris, France: La Découverte; 1999.

46. Rodrigue JM, Garros B. Regards sur la Santé des Français. In: de Kervasdoué J, ed. *Le Carnet de Santé de la France en 2000*. Paris, France: Mutualité Française; 2000,

47. Salem G, Stephane R, Jougla E. *Les Causes de Décès*. London, England: John Libbey Eurotext; 1999. Atlas de la Santé en France; vol 1.

48. Leclerc A, Fassin D, Grandjean H, Kaminski M, Lang T, eds. *Les Inégalités Sociales de Santé*. Paris, France: La Découverte/INSERM; 2000.

49. Got C. *Risquer Sa Peau*. Paris, France: Bayard; 2001.

50. *La Liste Noir des Hôpitaux*. Paris, France: Sciences et Avenir; October 1997.

51. Rodwin V. The rise of managed care in the United States: lessons for French health policy. In: Altenstetter C, Bjorkman JW, eds. *Health Policy Reform, National Variations, and Globalization*. New York, NY: St Martin's Press; 1997: 39–58.

52. Rodwin V. Management without objectives: the French health policy gamble. In: McLachlan G, Maynard A, eds. *The Public/Private Mix for Health*. London, England: Nuffield Provincial Hospitals Trust; 1982:289–325.

53. *Data from the Socio-Economic Monitoring System 1984–1999*. Chicago, Ill: American Medical Association. Available at: http://www.ama-assn.org/ama/ pub/category/7801.html. Accessed November 20, 2002.

54. Audric S. *Les Disparités de Revenus et de Charges des Médecins Liberaux*. Paris, France: Direction de la Recherche, des Études de l'Évaluation et des Statistiques (DRESS), Ministère de l'Emploi et de la Solidarité; 2001. Études et Résultats no. 146.

55. Jourdain A, Duriez M, eds. Les agences dans le système de santé. *Actualité et Dossier en Santé Publique*. December 2001;37:18–60.

56. Matillon Y, Loirat P, Guiraud-Chaumeil B. Les rôles de l'ANAES dans la régulation du système de santé Français. *Actualité et Dossier en Santé Publique*. December 2001;37:46–50.

57. Durieux P, Chaix-Couturier C, Durand-Zaleski I, Ravaud P. From clinical recommendations to mandatory practice: the introduction of regulatory practice guideline in the French healthcare system. *Int J Technol Assess Health Care*. 2000;16:969–975.

58. Coudreau D. Les agences régionales de l'hospitalisation dans le système de santé. *Actualité et Dossier en Santé Publique*. December 2001;37: 50–54.

59. Lancry PJ, Sandier S. Rationing health care in France. *Health Policy*. 1999;50:23–38.

60. Fuchs V. What's ahead for health insurance in the United States? *N Engl J Med*. 2002;346:1822–1824.

Austerity in Africa

Audit Cultures and the Weakening of Public Sector Health Systems

By James Pfeiffer

Abstract: Austerity across Africa has been operationalized through World Bank and IMF structural adjustment programs since the 1980s, later rebranded euphemistically as poverty reduction strategies in the late 1990s. Austerity's constraints on public spending led donors to a "civil society" focus in which NGOs would fill gaps in basic social services created by public sector contraction. One consequence was large-scale redirection of growing foreign aid flows away from public services to international NGOs. Austerity in Africa coincides with the emergence of what some anthropologists call "**audit cultures**" among donors. Extraordinary data collection infrastructures are demanded from recipient organizations in the name of transparency. However, the Mozambique experience described here reveals that these intensive audit cultures serve to obscure the destructive effects of NGO proliferation on public health systems.

> **EDITOR'S NOTES**
>
> **audit culture:** applications of the principles and techniques of accountancy and financial management to the governance of people and organizations.

The reliance on metrics and evaluation in global health is not in itself new. Public health has long been defined as primarily a quantitative discipline dominated by biostatistics and epidemiology that constitute its core disciplines. However, the past two decades in global health have witnessed an increased emphasis on massive data extraction and big data modeling of public health challenges, projects, and progress. In one major instance, the Bill & Melinda Gates Foundation financed the creation of the Institute for Health Metrics and Evaluation in Seattle with $100 million to produce data on the "global burden of disease" using the disability-adjusted life year (DALY) as its key measure (Murray et al. 2013). The increasing focus on big data collection and metrics parallels the rise of a range of concepts and terms imported from the private sector in public health such as "cost effectiveness," "return on investment," "business model," "results-based management," and "performance-based financing," among others that have been integrated into the global health lexicon.

The heightened emphasis on massive data collection began to dominate global health practice nearly three decades ago and coincides with the publication of the World Bank's *Investing in Health*

James Pfeiffer, "Austerity in Africa: Audit Cultures and the Weakening of Public Sector Health Systems," *Focaal-Journal of Global and Historical Anthropology*, vol. 2019, no. 83, pp. 51–61. Copyright © 2019 by Stichting Focaal and Berghahn Books. Reprinted with permission.

treatise in 1993 that rolled out the use of the DALY and the concept of "cost effectiveness" while making the case for privatization of health care and imposition of user fees in the developing world (WB 1993). The report signaled the emergence of the World Bank as the leading multilateral determinant of global health policy superseding the WHO. This shift is typical of what some anthropologists see as an emergent "audit culture" (Adams 2016; Shore and Wright 2015; Storeng and Béhague 2014; Strathern 2000) that is in part characterized by managers and accountants usurping the role of actual experts in evaluating and measuring performance. Audit culture became integral to the neoliberal logics of austerity, privatization, downsizing, outsourcing, and decentralization. Economists were now telling health providers how to "invest" in health. This rollout came amid the ongoing Third World debt crisis and austerity operationalized through "**structural adjustment programs**" that were imposed across Africa since the 1980s and managed by the IMF and the World Bank (Kentikelenis et al. 2015; Pfeiffer and Chapman 2010; Prince and Marsland 2013; Turshen 1999). As structural adjustment programs sharply reduced public spending on national health systems across the continent, **NGOs** were recruited by major donors (such as the United States Agency for International Development (USAID), other bilaterals, and large foundations) to fill in the service gaps in a sort of "thousand points of light" approach for Africa.

The remarkable proliferation of NGOs in the past several decades is a defining feature of the neoliberal period in most African countries as they have become dominant forces in health and development fueled by aid dollars diverted away from public sector services. The health sector became defined increasingly by NGO projects substituting for shrinking public systems. In many countries, the funds flowing to NGOs have been greater than entire health system budgets and were fully outside government planning or management. But along with the "**projectification**" and "**vertical funding**" of public health in Africa came imposition of huge data collection demands by donors to demonstrate short term and narrowly defined outcomes and "cost effectiveness" of interventions to address specific health challenges such as HIV, tuberculosis, and malaria (cf. Meinert and Whyte 2014; Prince and Marsland 2013). The resulting "audit culture" has infused global health practice, resulting in a narrow siloing of public health practice and an abandonment of support for public sector health systems that provide integrated primary health care services. While global health aid has quadrupled in the past 20 years, the great majority of this new funding cannot flow "on budget" (i.e., onto the formal state budget) to support public sector systems because of the structural adjustment program (SAP) constraints on public spending so is instead channeled to NGOs that are "off budget." This crucial distinction is rarely considered in donor-mandated indicators and metrics:

> What is new about audit culture is the extent to which these calculative practices of measurement and ranking have become institutionalised, extended and above all, financialised. This is particularly evident in the way that the language of financial accounting is increasingly used in the governance of organisations and their employees. Keywords from audit and accountancy ("assets," "income," "liability," "opportunity costs," "products," "output," "overheads," "revenue," "return on investment," "transparency," "value for money") have been combined to form new semantic clusters that have become the bedrock of a new ideology of calculating and monetarised self-governance ... The shift from government to governance is often called a move from "rowing" the post-war welfare state to "steering" service delivery from a distance. The process entailed turning large organisations into smaller, strategic central offices, downsizing public sector bureaucracies and outsourcing their operations to multiple, independent spin-off companies, or contracting out activities to private providers. (Shore and Wright 2015: 24)

Audit culture's inexorable moral logic within public health makes it an especially insidious element of the new global health architecture. As burdensome as new data demands have become, public health practitioners are reluctant to denounce or resist the push for more data and metrics, since measurement lies at the heart of the professional discipline, whether in fieldwork or in the university:

> The challenge is that these new accountabilities are at once obstructive and enabling of good practice. Through accountability the financial and the moral meet in the twinned

EDITOR'S NOTES

vertical funding: global programs for allocating assistance to countries in crisis that focus on a specific issue or theme, for example HIV/AIDS treatment and services.

precepts of economic efficiency and ethical practice. Audit practices have direct consequences, and, in the view of many, dire ones for intellectual production. Yet audit is almost impossible to critique in principle—after all, it advances values that academics generally hold dear, such as responsibility, openness of enquiry and widening of access. (Strathern 2000: 2)

The perspective advanced here therefore takes aim not so much at the principle of measurement and evaluation in the new age of global health but rather at its selective deployment and unequal application, and its use in a feigned scientific rigor to assert and frame which indicators and outcomes should be measured. The unequal distribution of resources to collect, manage, and analyze data collected from the Global South further lays bare the glaring and growing disparities in global health practice. Information is power and these inequalities assure control over data by Western donors, creditors, and agencies. Big data management requires major infrastructure investment and legions of highly trained and expensive analysts unavailable to the Global South and concentrated in cities such as Seattle, Geneva, Washington, DC, and Boston. The disguising of how power works is one of audit culture's key features:

> By taking what is essentially a political problem, removing it from the realm of political discourse, and recasting it in the neutral language of science (Dreyfus and Rabinow 1982: 196), political technologies establish institutional procedures that are presented in the ostensibly detached language of science, reason, normality and common sense. This seemingly neutral language conceals the ways institutional mechanisms operate to introduce new forms of power. (Shore and Wright 2015: 559)

EDITOR'S NOTES

indicator culture: the increasing reliance on indicators, measuring everything from violence against women to happiness, and which disseminates corporate ways of thinking and governance into broader social spheres.

Sally Engle Merry (2016) similarly argues that "**indicator culture**" and metrics systems exercise this power by incorporating ideologies of social change but rarely acknowledging them: "Indicators, particularly those that rely on ranks or numbers, convey an aura of objective truth and facilitate comparisons. However, indicators typically conceal their political and theoretical origins and underlying theories of social change and activism" (Merry and Conley 2011: 84).

The massive expansion of the data collection apparatus and data demands by donors in global health in this new audit culture have two major functions in the age of austerity. The choice of indicators to be measured elides an assessment of how aid impacts public sector health systems under the cover of supposed scientific rigor, objectivity, and transparency that the exaggerated quantification process seeks to signify. The scale of activities required to gather data, the major resources needed to analyze them, and the framing of what is important to measure further empower Western donors to set the health agenda and obscure the impact of privatization and austerity policies on health care access. The audit regimes also provide the disciplinary tool to punish NGO contractors who stray from the strategy and fail to deliver on the narrow outcomes, even if achieving those outcomes might compromise or damage local health systems:

> The creation of indicators reveals a slippage between the political and the technical. The slippage occurs in the way issues and problems are defined, in the identity and role of experts, in the relative power of the people engaged in producing and using indicators, and in the power and clout of the sponsoring organization. They represent the perspectives and frameworks of those who produce them, as well as their political and financial power. What gets counted depends on which groups and organizations can afford to count. (Merry and Conley 2011: 88)

Audit culture, in other words, provides a kind of clever obfuscation that is crucial to the neoliberal project. Its rhetoric of technical rigor and accountability in service of humanitarian goals provides cover for the work it does in support of undermining local sovereignty, retaining Western hegemony in southern Africa, and privatizing local resources.

Mozambique provides an illustrative case study of austerity in Africa to underscore the key function of audit culture in the effort to enable and enforce the broader privatization project, justify but confine NGO activity, smother innovation, and prevent public sector health system strengthening. The selective data demands imposed by key Western donors and agencies not only are onerous, expensive, and time consuming but also conceal and distract from the more crucial accounting for how aid funds are diverted away from supporting public sector system performance and sustainability in an age of structural adjustment and austerity.

The Mozambique Story

A brief history is important to track the impact of austerity on the health sector, and the emergence of NGOs and the audit cultures that control them as dominant actors in Mozambique. After independence in 1975, Mozambique's new socialist government began the design and development of a primary health care (PHC) system drawing on Alma-Ata principles to scale up basic services to its largely rural impoverished population. Most Mozambicans had no access to western biomedical care during the Portuguese colonial period, and Mozambique's first president, Samora Machel (a former nurse) and his independence party known as the Mozambique Liberation Front (FRELIMO) made creation of a national health system a top priority. The new public system drew the attention of the World Health Organization, which heralded it as a model for PHC in the developing world (Walt and Melamed 1983). The design centered on an integrated public sector system of health posts, health centers, rural hospitals, provincial hospitals, and development and training of cadres of both mid-level providers and community health workers all managed by the Ministry of Health (MISAU). However, after the successful initial rollout of the system, including construction of more than a thousand health facilities together with health workforce training, Rhodesia and later apartheid South Africa funded and trained an insurgency, the Mozambique National Resistance (known in Portuguese as Resistência Nacional de Moçambique (RENAMO)) that waged a war of "destabilization" with attacks on government infrastructure including the health system, schools, roads, and civilian communities in rural areas (Cliff and Noormahomed 1988). After a decade of conflict, Mozambique was virtually bankrupt, and its public services were frayed.

By the late 1980s, in the midst of the ongoing war, the government was heavily indebted leading it to sign onto an SAP in 1987 that imposed austerity measures on the ravaged public sector. Health workforce was cut and salaries reduced (Cliff 1993; Pfeiffer 2003). As the government gradually adopted a privatized market economy in the late 1980s, foreign aid from Western countries increasingly focused on specific health "projects" rather than support for the health system itself. USAID and European bilaterals began to channel aid through international nongovernmental organizations to implement those projects that often functioned independently of MISAU plans or finances. When apartheid ended, RENAMO agreed to a ceasefire in 1992 followed by elections in 1994 that FRELIMO won easily. Post-cease-fire, NGOs proliferated throughout the 1990s with little or no coordination with the National Health System as the nation struggled to rebuild (Cliff 1993; Pfeiffer 2003). By 2000, there were hundreds of health projects managed by NGOs across the country with only superficial linkages to the local health system itself.

Since structural adjustment was introduced in the late 1980s, Mozambique's health "sector" has been financed by a range of donors, agencies, and foundations managed in varying degrees of collaboration with the MISAU's local government funding (for extended description of these funding flows, see Pfeiffer et al. 2017). It is important to distinguish between foreign aid that flows on budget into the health "system" itself on the public/government budget, and aid that is considered off budget in the health "sector" and spent separately from the MISAU budget and planning. Most resources that flow to NGOs for specific projects are off budget. "Vertical" funding refers to resources used to address a specific disease or health problem such as HIV/AIDS, TB, or malaria and are generally not used for long-term system building. Nearly all funding that goes to NGOs is considered vertical and off budget. On the other hand, "**horizontal funding**" focuses on the strengthening of basic health system building blocks and recurrent costs. This type of funding is nearly always on budget, where it can be included in long-term planning to maintain or extend the system. The contrast between on budget and off budget lies at the heart of the austerity project. The SAP placed caps on financing on budget but allows project specific aid funding to increase substantially as long as it flows to non-state actors. Public services were downsized while NGOs were upsized.

By 2000, Mozambique was included in the Heavily Indebted Poor Countries initiative, and the Government of Mozambique finalized its first Action Plan for the Reduction of Absolute Poverty (PARPA) with the IMF and the World Bank (Martínez 2006). The PARPA was a shift away from the structural adjustment paradigm to new Poverty Reduction Strategies Papers (PRSPs) and the Poverty Reduction and Growth Facility that replaced the Enhanced Structural Adjustment Facility (IMF 2002). The new PRSP process was to differ from SAPs through greater inclusion of government and civil society actors in planning and decision-making. For some, however, the PRSP was a rebranding of structural adjustment and appeared to be "old wine in new bottles" (Pfeiffer and Chapman 2010). During the early 2000s, a consortium of European bilaterals and UN agencies agreed to pool resources in a "common fund" to support the health system and manage funds together with the MISAU. However, a handful of other donors, including USAID, decided to stay out and continue funding NGOs rather than the health system in part so that government budgets stay below IMF mandated limits.

The President's Emergency Plan for AIDS Relief (PEPFAR)

In 2004, the United States government introduced major new funding to fight the HIV/AIDS crisis in Mozambique. PEPFAR is by far the largest increase in health aid in the country's history (and in much of Africa). However, PEPFAR funding flowed off budget to NGO "implementing" partners through vertical projects (Høg 2014). Only a small amount of

EDITOR'S NOTES

horizontal funding: programs funded within countries that allocate assistance to address prevailing problems within that country, for example prevention and primary care in a healthcare system.

funding was channeled to the MISAU through the Centers for Disease Control and Prevention (CDC) for blood bank work and to cover other small gaps. The implementing partners included several with US university affiliations including the International Center for AIDS Care and Treatment Programs at Columbia University, the Vanderbilt Institute for Global Health, and Health Alliance International at the University of Washington, while others included large NGOs such as the Elizabeth Glaser Pediatric AIDS Foundation, Family Health International 360, and Abt Associates, among others. The country is divided up geographically, and provinces are allocated to the NGO partners usually without direct MISAU involvement in the actual decision-making.

Paradoxically, the NGOs must graft their HIV work onto the national health system itself, since the great majority of Mozambicans get health care there (there is still only a small private care industry in several cities). The application of PEPFAR off-budget funding to help deliver HIV care and treatments services within the public system is a fraught process. NGOs will help pay for health worker trainings (but not more health workers), HIV-specific equipment and materials, "technical assistance," and data collection, but almost no funding goes to basic system building blocks such as long-term workforce expansion, transport, and infrastructure. Health workers are therefore asked to do more and more in increasingly crowded facilities. Beginning in the early 2000s, other HIV/AIDS funding also increased to Mozambique, including the UN's Global Fund to Fight AIDS, Malaria and TB in 2002 and the World Bank in 2003 and 2004 (Mussa et al. 2013; Visser-Valfrey and Bibi Umarji 2010). By 2007, external health funding in Mozambique had reached $400 million per year (AFD 2008). In 2008, fully 60 percent of this health aid was off-budget flowing to international NGOs conducting HIV and other vertical projects rather than basic health system strengthening. The public sector health budget itself continued to be capped by the PRSP, so on-budget support was still constrained.

This surge in aid funding therefore spurred another proliferation of NGOs in the health sector across the country and further shifted the power dynamics to the aid community where NGOs became even more influential due to large influxes of PEPFAR dollars. Mozambique was not alone in this experience. A recent policy paper from the Center for Global Development states, "There were 477 PEPFAR prime partners in FY2008. 22 of the largest 25 recipients were based in the US. Only 8% of the total ($301 million) was allocated to developing-country governments as prime partners" (Fan et al. 2013: 1). To be sure, the scale of PEPFAR funding has allowed Africa to place millions on antiretroviral treatment and should be seen as a public health success. But critics point out that data are scarce, and it remains unexamined whether the funding could have had an even greater impact if it had focused on health system building (Swanson et al. 2009).

PEPFAR and Audit Culture

While PEPFAR has channeled most of its funding to US-based agencies, it has also imposed major demands on those partners to gather enormous amounts of data. While increasing data collection demands are common to nearly all donors in global health as they compete to show "transparency," productivity, and cost effectiveness, PEPFAR's data demands are experienced as especially onerous. Each PEPFAR implementing partner has been required to set up its own parallel health information system that uses separate forms, data entry, data transfer systems, and analysis (PEPFAR 2016b). Data are uploaded into a separate PEPFAR database that essentially has limited availability to the MISAU itself. Annual Program Reports (APRs) and Semi-Annual Program Reports (SAPRs) are produced each year and scrutinized by PEPFAR staff in USAID and CDC in Maputo and in Washington, DC. The number of people tested for HIV and/or placed on antiretroviral treatment are the primary outcomes, but data on hundreds of variables for each partner are required. From 2010 and 2017, while the number of key PEPFAR reporting indicators decreased from 40 to 29, new required collection targets for **disaggregated data** per indicator skyrocketed. About 30 additional data points were needed to comply with disaggregation requirements in 2010, but by 2017, up to 350 data points were required (Gimbel et al. 2017; PEPFAR 2009, 2016a).

While hard figures are nearly impossible to collect from each NGO, millions of dollars and dozens of staff at each organization are required just to collect and manage the enormous quantities of data. In principle, the APRs and SAPRs are used to hold the NGOs accountable to achieve high, short-term treatment targets. However, managers in donor offices are often career bureaucrats rather than experienced clinical providers or health systems experts, and oversee and second-guess the work of physicians and public health experts doing the challenging work on the ground. Rarely if ever are the data analyzed in detail and used for planning in a collaborative way with the MISAU itself. The data are notoriously difficult to extract and examine independently (Fan et al. 2013; Kavanagh and Baker 2014). Within the implementing partners themselves, the tyranny of the data collection processes and fear of missing treatment targets often leads project managers to prioritize their own data needs over the broader needs of the health system itself. Health system staff members are often required to allocate scarce time to providing PEPFAR data and filling out forms in a system that is parallel and redundant to their own. Perhaps most remarkably, the enormous investment in data collection by PEPFAR barely touches the

EDITOR'S NOTES

disaggregated data: data that has been broken down to smaller subpopulations, such as by sex, race/ethnicity, age, income, etc.

health system's own health information system and epidemiologic surveillance system (Gimbel et al. 2017). Despite this huge drain on resources, PEPFAR's investment in public sector health information systems in Mozambique and across recipient countries in general has been scattered and anemic.

But perhaps most telling in the PEPFAR audit culture is what is not measured or examined. Curiously, the APR and SAPR formats provide almost no meaningful metrics on health system performance—population coverage of basic services, effectiveness of service integration, supply chain effectiveness, health worker/population ratios, waiting times for services, quality measures, and metrics for effective integration of services. Long-term targets for system building are not included. Since PEPFAR activities are grafted onto the public system without providing wider systemic support, the activities can pull scarce health staff away from other routine duties (see reports of similar challenges in Uganda in Lohman et al. 2017). The vertical funding is often rushed in to hastily train clinical providers, install new lab equipment just for HIV care, or divert health workers into HIV care at the expense of other neglected services. Yet, within this audit culture, there has been no sanctioned and rigorous study or even a monitoring process to examine how PEPFAR funded activities might affect other routine services in a system in which health staff time is a zero-sum game. One recent study of PEPFAR in Uganda suggested a negative impact of PEPFAR dollars on some non-HIV services (Luboga et al. 2016). The austerity-driven audit culture keeps the HIV/AIDS industry and its private NGO contractors focused on narrow outcomes and distracted from the vital work of building a sustainable and effective public sector health system. NGO implementers are driven to achieve these narrowly construed outcomes even if their strategies might harm the local health system itself. In one especially poignant example, NGOs often recruit highly qualified doctors and nurses from the health system itself luring them out of the public sector with comparatively very high salaries and benefits (Pfeiffer et al. 2014). A 2012 study of this "internal brain drain" in Mozambique revealed that nearly half of the physicians who had left the health system in recent years had been recruited by PEPFAR-funded projects (Sherr et al. 2012). This brain drain is especially concerning in Mozambique, since it still has one of the worst health provider-to-population ratios in the world (MISAU 2015).

While certain data are collected to extraordinary levels of detail (e.g., HIV tests conducted, trainings implemented), the budgets of PEPFAR implementing partners are nearly always opaque. As one recent comment in *The Lancet Global Health* points out:

> It is striking that there is probably more data for the planning, spending, and outcomes of PEPFAR programmes than for any other aid programme in the world. PEPFAR undertakes a careful and detailed planning process every year for every country that receives aid … However, PEPFAR refuses to make data fully public in a timely manner … It is time for PEPFAR to become a leader in transparency, to share its data in the service of its mission to end the AIDS crisis, and to expand real country ownership … Knowledge of exactly what PEPFAR-funded non-governmental organisations are doing, what gaps they are filling,

and what outcomes they are expected to achieve should be central to the planning of the AIDS response in these countries.

The authors point out that a recent analysis in the Aid Transparency Index ranked PEPFAR poorly as 50th of 67 aid agencies worldwide and that PEPFAR does not disclose information on contracts consistent with the US Open Data Policy (Kavanagh and Baker 2014: 13).

Many private implementing partners are known for their high administrative costs, very high expatriate salaries, and sometimes-lavish in-country infrastructures, while the health systems they work through remain dilapidated and understaffed (Pfeiffer et al. 2017; Sherr et al. 2012). However, internal NGO budgets are not made public, and rigorous costing analyses are rare or nonexistent. Fieldworkers and MISAU staff in Mozambique have wondered aloud if the hundreds of millions in PEPFAR dollars channeled through US NGOs had been instead invested in long-term system strengthening would they have produced much greater AIDS treatment outcomes that were better integrated into stronger comprehensive services. But the data are not available to effectively make the counterfactual analysis. The lack of data and public information on PEPFAR financial flows was furthered cited by the Center for Global Development in a 2013 report: "Little is known about the [PEPFAR] financial flows within the [US] government, to its contractors, and to countries ... Further work is needed to quantitatively evaluate the extent of contractor proliferation and its effects on PEPFAR's efficiency and long-term sustainability. The US government should disclose its contracts to prime partners and sub-partners in a machine-readable and open format consistent with the USG Open Data Policy" (Fan et al. 2013: 1). The regime of accountability somehow failed to account for this fundamental aspect of aid.

The hundreds of millions of dollars in PEPFAR funding provided to Mozambique over the past decade were primarily channeled to US-based NGOs tasked with generating enormous quantities of data for the ostensible purpose of rigorous evaluation. It is instructive to note that over this same period, total Mozambique government on-budget allocation for health expenditure as a proportion of overall government expenditure declined as a result of PARPA austerity constraints from 13.4 percent in 2006 to 11.9 percent in 2009, 7.8 percent in 2014, and 9 percent in 2015, moving away from the Abuja target of 15 percent (UNICEF 2015; Visser-Valfrey and Bibi Umarji 2010; WHO 2011). In 2014, the workforce for health per population ratio was still among the five worst in the world at 71 per 10,000, while the ratio of health facilities per capita worsened since 2009 to only 1 per 16,795 inhabitants by 2014, also among the very lowest in the world (MISAU 2015). In other words, all the work to put millions more people on AIDS treatment landed on many of the same health workers and overcrowding the same facilities. In 2011, 65 percent of the population lived more than 45 minutes' walking distance from the closest health facility. Many health facilities lack basic infrastructure for quality health care; almost 50 percent of health centers do not have access to electricity and 60 percent to water (MISAU 2016). These basic systemic challenges all have a direct effect on the capacity to expand quality HIV/AIDS care and treatment, but PEPFAR and other major donors do not measure these fundamentals.

Some Conclusions

The Mozambique case is startling given the contrast between the scale of investment in AIDS treatment and the appallingly poor progress across the health system itself in the midst of the nearly fivefold increase in aid to the health sector since 2000. PEPFAR has selectively used its data to construct a triumphalist narrative about the fight against AIDS and the "AIDS free generation" just on the horizon (Green 2016). To be sure, the scale-up of HIV/AIDS care and treatment financed by PEPFAR and others has had major successes, and some have argued that the positive narrative is vital to keep the aid reauthorized by the US Congress. However, the audit culture that PEPFAR and other major global health donors have promoted has a range of additional functions in the austerity regimes that have undermined the fight against AIDS in Africa (Rowden 2009). Despite purported zealousness for rigor in evaluation, these data extraction and audit regimes have served to conceal and obfuscate the massive diversion of funding to US contractors/NGOs and away from sustainable public sector health systems.

The failure to track what has been called "phantom aid" that finds its way back into the pockets of Western agencies betrays the deeper ideological project at work (Bond 2007). Under the guise of transparency, rigor, and responsibility, the accountability regime conceals perhaps the most important dynamic in contemporary global health aid flows, that is, the lavishing of public money on private contractors at the expense of dilapidated public systems in an "atmosphere of private opulence and public squalor." The narrowly construed accountability regimes serve to distract from measuring more fundamental and comprehensive public health progress. The excessive data that PEPFAR and other donors now demand provide an illusory "rigor" in the service of privatized health care while failing to measure what counts most.

Audit culture's focus on vertical NGO projects and narrow measurement of projects and indicators rather than systems has led the global health community to ignore the most important cost-effectiveness conclusion from the experience of the last decade in global health aid expansion. If the billions of dollars of global health money spent on NGOs over the past decade were invested in the public national health system instead, it is likely that health workforce might have expanded substantially in Mozambique, population coverage increased many fold, and thousands more put on AIDS treatment and kept on treatment. An AIDS treatment crisis may be looming in Africa, as recent data show poor long-term adherence to treatment and retention in care revealing the weakness of struggling health systems and staff shortages to keep millions of new patients in chronic care.

The imposition of audit culture combined with the large-scale rechanneling of foreign aid for public health in developing countries to international NGOs and other non-state actors is a key strategy in the neoliberal project to undermine local sovereignty and public sectors in Africa, in service to the core mission of opening up the region to private investment and resource extraction. Hidden behind its rhetoric of accountability, rigor, and humanitarianism is a deeper ideological commitment not only to privatization and market fundamentalism but also to maintenance of Western hegemony in the region at great cost to the impoverished majority.

However, turn the audit tools around and they can be deployed to resist this project. To borrow from the language of privatization and the MBAs that increasingly populate the global health professional landscape, the return on investment of the NGO business model is looking measurably worse. The best value for the money is likely to be found in the public sector. Better metrics and science will show that.

References

Adams, Vincanne, ed. 2016. *Metrics: What counts in global health.* Durham, NC: Duke University Press.

AFD (Agence Francaise de Developpement). 2008. "Aid effectiveness in the health sector in Mozambique: Challenges to be met." Paris: AFD.

Bond, Patrick. 2007. "The dispossession of African wealth at the cost of Africa's health." *International Journal of Health Services* 37 (1): 171–192.

Cliff, Julie. 1993. "Donor dependence or donor control? The case of Mozambique." *Community Development Journal* 28 (3): 237–244.

Cliff, Julie, and Abdul Razak Noormahomed. 1988. "Health as a target: South Africa's destabilization of Mozambique." *Social Science and Medicine* 27 (7): 717–722.

Dreyfus, Hubert L., and Paul Rabinow. 1982. *Michel Foucault: beyond structuralism and hermeneutics.* Chicago: University of Chicago Press.

Fan, Victoria, Rachel Silverman, Denizhan Duran, and Amanda Glassman. 2013. "The financial flows of PEPFAR: A profile." Center for Global Development Policy Paper no. 27.

Gimbel, Sarah, Baltazar Chilundo, Nora Kenworthy, Celso Inguane, David Citrin, Rachel Chapman, Kenneth Sherr, and James Pfeiffer. 2017. "Donor data vacuuming: Audit culture and the use of data in global health partnerships." *Medical Anthropology Theory* 5 (2): 79–99.

Green, Andrew. 2016 "Obama Dreams of an AIDS-Free Generation." *Foreign Policy,* 18 April. http://foreignpolicy.com/2016/04/18/obama-wants-anaids-free-generation-pepfar-africa.

Høg, Erling. 2014. "HIV scale-up in Mozambique: Exceptionalism, normalisation and global health." *Global Public Health* 9 (1–2): 210–223.

IMF. 2002. "Review of the poverty reduction strategy paper (PRSP) approach: Early experience with interim PRSPs and full PRSPs." IMF Policy Paper.

Kavanagh, Matthew M., and Brook K. Baker. 2014. "Governance and transparency at PEPFAR." *The Lancet Global Health* 2 (1): 13–14.

Kentikelenis, Alexander E., Thomas H. Stubbs, and Lawrence P. King.2015. "Structural adjustment and public spending on health: Evidence from IMF programs in low-income countries." *Social Science and Medicine* 126: 169–176.

Lohman, Nathaniel, Amy Hagopian, Samuel Abimerech Luboga, Bert Stover, Travis Lim, Frederick Makumbi, Noah Kiwanuka, et al. 2017. "District health officer perceptions of PEPFAR's influence on the health system in Uganda, 2005–2011." *International Journal of Health Policy and Management* 6 (2): 83–95.

Luboga, Samuel Abimerech, Bert Stover, Travis W. Lim, Frederick Makumbi, Noah Kiwanuka, Flavia Lubega, Assay Ndizihiwe, et al. 2016. "Did PEPFAR investments result in health system strengthening? A retrospective longitudinal study measuring non-HIV health service utilization at the district level." *Health Policy and Planning* 31 (7): 897–909.

Martínez, Javier. 2006. "Implementing a sector wide approach in health: The case of Mozambique." HSLP Institute Technical Approach Paper.

Meinert, Lotte, and Susan Reynolds Whyte. 2014. "Epidemic projectification: AIDS responses in Uganda as event and process." *Cambridge Journal of Anthropology* 32 (1): 77–94.

Merry, Sally Engle 2016. *The seductions of quantification: Measuring human rights, gender violence, and sex trafficking.* Chicago: University of Chicago Press.

Merry, Sally Engle, and John M. Conley. 2011. "Measuring the world: Indicators, human rights, and global governance." *Current Anthropology* 52 (S3): 83–95.

MISAU (Ministério de Saúde). 2015. *Plano estratégico do sector da saúde* [Health sector strategic plan]. Maputo: MISAU.

MISAU (Ministério de Saúde). 2016. *Plano estratégico do sector da saúde* [Health sector financing strategy]. Ministry of Health, ed. Maputo: MISAU.

Murray, Christopher J. L., Theo Vos, Rafael Lorenzo, Mohsen Naghavi, Abraham D. Flaxman, Catherin Michaud, Majid Ezzati, et al. 2013. "Disability-adjusted life years (DALYs) for 291 diseases and injuries in 21 regions, 1990–2010: A systematic analysis for the Global Burden of Disease Study 2010." *The Lancet* 380 (9859): 2197–2223.

Mussa, Abdul H., James Pfeiffer, Stephen Gloyd, and Kenneth Sherr. 2013. "Vertical funding, non-governmental organizations, and health system strengthening: Perspectives of public sector health workers in Mozambique." *Human Resources for Health* 11 (26): 1–9.

PEPFAR (President's Emergency Plan for AIDS Relief). 2009. *PEPFAR next generation indicators reference guide.* Washington, DC: PEPFAR.

PEPFAR (President's Emergency Plan for AIDS Relief). 2016a. *PEPFAR monitoring, evaluation, and reporting (MER 2.0).* Washington, DC: PEPFAR.

PEPFAR (President's Emergency Plan for AIDS Relief). 2016b. *PEPFAR results reporting guidance: FY 2016 quarter 2 and quarter 3.* Washington, DC: PEPFAR.

Pfeiffer, James. 2003. "International NGOs and primary health care in Mozambique: The need for a new model of collaboration." *Social Science and Medicine* 56 (4):725–738.

Pfeiffer, James, and Rachel Chapman. 2010. "Anthropological perspectives on structural adjustment and public health." *Annual Review of Anthropology* 39: 149–165.

Pfeiffer, James, Sarah Gimbel, Baltazar Chilundo, Stephen Gloyd, Rachel Chapman, and Kenneth Sherr. 2017. "Austerity and the 'sector-wide approach' to health: The Mozambique experience." *Social Science and Medicine* 187: 208–216.

Pfeiffer, James, Julia Robinson, Amy Hagopian, Wendy Johnson, Meredith Fort, Kenneth Gimbel-Sherr, Rick Rowden, et al. 2014. "The end of AIDS and the NGO code of conduct." *The Lancet* 384 (9944): 639–640.

Prince, Ruth J., and Rebecca Marsland, eds. 2013. *Making and unmaking public health in Africa: Ethnographic and historical perspectives.* Athens: Ohio University Press.

Rowden, Rick. 2009. *The deadly ideas of neoliberalism: How the IMF has undermined public health and the fight against AIDS.* London: Zed Books.

Sherr, Kenneth, Antonio Mussa, Baltazar Chilundo, Sarah Gimbel, James Pfeiffer, Amy Hagopian, and Stephen Gloyd. 2012. "Brain drain and health workforce distortions in Mozambique." *PLoS One* 7 (4): 1–7.

Shore, Cris, and Susan Wright. 2015. "Governing by numbers: Audit culture, rankings and the new world order." *Social Anthropology* 23 (1): 22–28.

Storeng, Katerini T., and Dominique P. Béhague. 2014. "Playing the numbers game: Evidence-based advocacy and the technocratic narrowing of the safe motherhood initiative." *Medical Anthropology Quarterly* 28 (2): 260–279.

Strathern, Marilyn. 2000. "New accountabilities." In *Audit cultures: Anthropological studies in accountability, ethics and the academy,* ed. Marilyn Strathern, 1–18. London: Routledge.

Swanson, R. Chad, Henry Mosley, David Sanders, David Egilman, Jan De Maeseneer, Mushtaque Chowdhury, Claudio F. Lanata, et al. 2009. "Call for global health-systems impact assessments." *The Lancet* 374 (9688): 433–435.

Turshen, Meredith. 1999. *Privatizing health services in Africa.* New Brunswick, NJ: Rutgers University Press.

UNICEF. 2015. "Moçambique: Informe orçamental 2015—Saúde" [Mozambique: Budget report 2015—Health]. Maputo: UNICEF.

Visser-Valfrey, Muriel, and Mariam Bibi Umarji. 2010. "Sector budget support in practice: Health sector in Mozambique." Overseas Development Institute case study.

Walt, Gillian, and Angela Melamed. 1983. *Toward a people's health service.* London: Zed Books.

WHO (World Health Organization). 2011. "The Abuja Declaration: Ten years on." Geneva: WHO.

WB (World Bank). 1993. *World development report: Investing in health.* Washington, DC: World Bank.

CRITICAL THINKING QUESTIONS

1. According to Light, how did the medical profession "reorganize into a political power-house and use the state to deconstruct early healthcare markets?" Please be specific, identify pertinent concepts, and provide examples.

2. Define the *Davis strategy*. Explain three things that the Davis strategy did for the American medical profession.

3. Summarize the main facets of the French healthcare system. Use two examples to compare and contrast the French and American healthcare systems.

4. Define *vertical funding* and *horizontal funding*. Use Pfeiffer's discussion of the president's HIV/AIDS plan to discuss how each of these types of funding have been used in Mozambique. What are the consequences?

UNIT 8
Bioethics

· ·

Editor's Introduction

Bioethics is a very rich and voluminous topic in medical sociology. The purpose of unit VIII is to provide you with some history of bioethics, to illustrate a real-life bioethical problem, and to expose you to some recent theoretical work about the ethics of the doctor–patient relationship.

    The formal study of bioethics is predominantly rooted in the aftermath of World War II. Throughout the development of medicine, medical practitioners and researchers have behaved in some truly horrific ways. For example, James Marion Sims, the so-called *father* of modern gynecology, used slave women for experimentation and exploration, which included such things as purposely infecting women with a variety of pathogens to practice curing them and performing a variety of surgical removals and adjustments, without the benefit of anesthesia.[1] Shortly after coming into power, Nazi Germany passed a number of laws that, among other things, required the sterilization of anyone considered likely to give birth to a person doctors considered genetically defective and prohibited the marriage of persons with certain medical conditions and diseases. Not long after, the Nazis began systematically killing patients in mental hospitals and then gassing people in concentration camps. Much of this was directed by doctors and other medical personnel. Doctors played additional key roles in the Nazi **genocide** policy, including meeting trains full of people to decide which of them went to work and which went to gas chambers. Doctors also forced hundreds of people to be the subjects of medical experimentation, including surgeries. Following the

bioethics: the study of ethical issues that arise in biology and medicine, as well as the moral reasoning related to such issues.

genocide: the deliberate and systematic killing of a racial/ethnic, cultural, or political group.

---

1   Harriett A. Washington. *Medical Apartheid: The Dark History of Medical Experimentation on Black Americans from Colonial Times to the Present* (New York: Doubleday, 2006).

war the allies prosecuted 23 Nazi doctors for *crimes against humanity*, though as many as 350 doctors took part in these horrific acts.

The decisions in these trials form the basis of the *Nuremberg Code*[2], a set of principles recognized across the globe regarding human experimentation. Among other things, the Nuremberg Code outlines ten principles for human experimentation. These are listed below.

1. "The voluntary consent of the human subject is absolutely essential.

2. The experiment should be such as to yield fruitful results for the good of society, unprocurable by other methods or means of study, and not random and unnecessary in nature.

3. The experiment should be so designed and based on the results of animal experimentation and a knowledge of the natural history of the disease or other problem under study that the anticipated results will justify the performance of the experiment.

4. The experiment should be so conducted as to avoid all unnecessary physical and mental suffering and injury.

5. No experiment should be conducted where there is an a priori reason to believe that death or disabling injury will occur; except, perhaps, in those experiments where the experimental physicians also serve as subjects.

6. The degree of risk to be taken should never exceed that determined by the humanitarian importance of the problem to be solved by the experiment.

7. Proper preparations should be made and adequate facilities provided to protect the experimental subject against even remote possibilities of disease, injury, or death.

8. The experiment should be conducted only by scientifically qualified persons. The highest degree of skill and care should be required through all stages of the experiment of those who conduct or engage in the experiment.

9. During the course of the experiment the human subject should be at liberty to bring the experiment to an end if he has reached the physical or mental state where continuation of the experiment seems to him to be impossible.

10. During the course of the experiment the scientist in charge must be prepared to terminate the experiment at any stage, if he has probable cause to believe, in the exercise of good faith, superior skill and careful judgment required of him that a continuation of the experiment is likely to result in injury, disability, or death to the experimental subject."[3]

These principles should be very familiar to you, especially if you have been to a doctor or in a hospital. Informed consent is so common as to be almost ubiquitous. However, the forms that we sign, most

---

2   "Nuremberg Code," United States Holocaust Memorial Museum, https://www.ushmm.org/information/exhibitions/online-exhibitions/special-focus/doctors-trial/nuremberg-code.

3   "Nuremberg Code," United States Holocaust Memorial Museum.

times without thinking, are rooted in humanity's answers to serious questions about the values of human agency and autonomy.

In the *New England Journal of Medicine's* "Perspective Roundtable: Physicians and Execution—Highlights from a Discussion of Lethal Injection," representatives from the medical and legal community remind us that questions of medical ethics can never really be ubiquitous, because human sociocultural life is always so dynamic. The brief article covers the highlights of a discussion that surveys the protocol for execution by lethal injection, discusses the legal issues related to cruel and unusual punishment, investigates the risk of errors, and debates whether, and if so how, doctors should be involved in lethal injection executions. On the one hand, arguments are made that participation in executions goes against everything meaningful about being a doctor, such as healing and saving lives. On the other hand, execution by lethal injection is a fact of life in the United States and history tells us that unskilled and under-skilled application of the protocols can result in mistakes, culminating in the frighteningly painful deaths of those inmates to whom they are applied. Perhaps, some suggest, doctors who participate in lethal injection executions are relieving suffering that might otherwise occur in their absence.

In "Vulnerability and Trustworthiness: Polestars of Professionalism in Healthcare," David Barnard explains the differences between *patient-focused* and *patient-based* standards for healthcare professionalism, then proposes patient-based standards that emphasize the professional's commitment to *trustworthiness in response to the vulnerability of those seeking professional help*. Barnard gets to the heart of the ethical responsibility of physicians, building on Sokoloski's and Pellegrino's work, indicating that illness renders humans involuntarily needful of others' help—the epitome of vulnerability. This vulnerability, Barnard suggests, is what physicians' obligations to patients should be rooted in. As humans, we are vulnerable to illness and injury, and when these occur, we often must seek help to heal and improve. In essence, we *surrender control of the steering of our life* to those who can assist us in getting back on course. This is a profound vulnerability, which necessitates an equally profound trustworthiness in the physician. This insight is the basis of the Nuremberg Code and all bioethics that has come since.

Together, the roundtable discussion on doctors' participation in lethal injection executions and the reading by Barnard examine the deeper meanings of vulnerability and trustworthiness—and therefore consent and voluntarism—and provide a strong introductory foundation to the study of bioethics in medical sociology.

Perspective Roundtable

Physicians and Execution—Highlights from a Discussion
of Lethal Injection

By Atul Gawande, Deborah W. Denno, Robert D. Truog, and David Waisel

1. Introduction

DR. ATUL GAWANDE: Welcome to a Perspective Roundtable from the *New England Journal of Medicine.* I am Atul Gawande, a staff surgeon at the Brigham and Women's Hospital here in Boston and an associate professor at the Harvard Medical School and the Harvard School of Public Health.

In 1977, Oklahoma became the first state to adopt lethal injection as a method of carrying out the death penalty, in the belief that it would be more humane than electrocution. The design of the original protocol for the procedure was written quickly, without any prior study, by A. Jay Chapman, Oklahoma's chief medical examiner at the time. And Chapman's approach became the de facto standard, as other states followed Oklahoma in switching to the new method.

That method and the attempt it represents to medicalize execution, in order to make it more morally acceptable, have led to ongoing tensions between the legal community and the medical community over whether physicians and other health care professionals should be involved in the process of putting convicted criminals to death.

On January 7, 2008, the U.S. Supreme Court heard oral arguments in **Baze v. Rees**, the case of two Kentucky death-row inmates who argued that the current three-drug lethal-injection protocol violates the Constitution's Eighth Amendment guarantees against cruel and unusual punishment.

With me today to discuss this important case and its implications for the health care community, we have Professor Deborah Denno, Arthur A. McGivney Professor of Law at Fordham University School of Law and an expert on death-penalty law, Dr. Bob Truog, professor of medical ethics, anesthesiology, and pediatrics at Harvard Medical School and also a coauthor of a brief to the U.S. Supreme Court

EDITOR'S NOTES

Baze v. Rees: a 2008 Supreme Court case in which three Kentucky death row inmates challenged the use of lethal injection, which they illustrated could be improperly administered, arguing it violated the Eighth Amendment against "cruel and unusual punishment." The Court ruled in favor of Kentucky.

arguing that the lethal-injection protocol, as currently constituted, does violate the ban on cruel and unusual punishment. And we also have Dr. David Waisel, associate professor of anesthesiology at Harvard Medical School and also the author of a much-discussed article arguing that physicians should be involved in executions, in order to relieve suffering. Thank you, all three of you, for joining today.

2. The Lethal-Injection Protocol

DR. GAWANDE: I want to start with you, Professor Denno. Now, as I understand it, the case of *Baze v. Rees* doesn't ask if the death penalty is unconstitutional; it doesn't ask whether lethal injection is unconstitutional in general; it asks only whether the specific formula used in the state of Kentucky is unconstitutional. So the puzzle of it, to me as a doctor, and to plenty of people who are not lawyers, is what is the big deal about this case?

PROFESSOR DEBORAH DENNO: Well, the big deal about this case is immediately when the method was adopted, A. Jay Chapman conceded that there were problems with this formula. There certainly have been problems within the 30 years that the formula has been examined and used. And now the Supreme Court is confronting that. The biggest problem with the formula is the second chemical, pancuronium bromide, that is a paralytic agent. There seems to be no real reason for its use. There's evidence that it paralyzes an inmate, so that inmate is not able to—to express himself if in fact he's suffering from the effects of the other chemicals.

DR. GAWANDE: So then, let me ask a little bit about the formula, Dr. Waisel. Can you describe that three-drug protocol and how it's at least supposed to work?

DR. DAVID WAISEL: Yes. The three-drug protocol is based, at least a great deal, on what was considered a normal induction of anesthesia when it was developed. First comes thiopental, also known as sodium thiopental or pentothal, which is a barbiturate, which is designed to put you to sleep, create amnesia and anesthesia. Second comes pancuronium bromide, which is designed to paralyze the muscles. And the third drug, which is not a drug used in anesthesia, is potassium chloride, which is designed to rapidly stop the heart. The doses used are massive compared to the doses that would be used in a normal anesthetic induction.

DR. GAWANDE: You raised, Dr. Truog, whether these are the right drugs in the first place, in your brief.

DR. ROBERT TRUOG: We've taken a pretty strong stand that paralytic agents have no role in end-of-life care. The concern, at the end of life, is that they can mask the behavioral signs that we look to, as to whether or not a patient is comfortable. And we are deeply committed to making sure that patients are comfortable and as free of pain and suffering as possible during the dying process. And since we have medications that do relieve pain, that do sedate perfectly adequately, there's no need to be introducing paralytic agents into end-of-life care.

DR. GAWANDE: One thing that came up in the course of the oral arguments before the Supreme Court was: Why do they administer pancuronium as part of the protocol? Can you explain a little bit about the thought that emerged from their discussion about this, Professor Denno?

PROFESSOR DENNO: Well, according to the state, pancuronium bromide is used in order to enhance the dignity of the inmate who's dying, because evidence came out that without pancuronium there might be some jerking or involuntary movements that would disturb some of the witnesses. So this would enhance the dignity. That I find problematic, and Justice Stevens certainly did.

DR. GAWANDE: Dr. Truog, is there a medical reason behind it? And has it lasted only just because of this until-now-unstated role of making things look dignified?

DR. TRUOG: Well, from the point of view of the inmate, the argument seems bizarre, at best. You know, imagine saying to the inmate, "You have a choice. You can either be assured of a pain-free death and you may have some twitching and grimacing, or we can expose you to the risk of an excruciating death, but we'll make sure that you don't twitch or grimace." I can't imagine that an inmate would actually consider that to be a real choice.

So if we're talking about the dignity of the inmate, it's only in the eyes of those who are watching that—and, in fact, you know, if that's all you cared about, don't even bother with any of the other drugs, just paralyze the inmate. They will look just as peaceful. So I think it's completely specious and has no weight at all.

The number one alternative that's been proposed has been a very large dose of a barbiturate. And, you know, I know that there's a number of experts who have said that 2 or 3 or 5g of pentothal is absolutely going to be lethal. The fact is that, at least in this country, if there's anyone who's ever had experience with giving a huge dose of pentothal and watching an otherwise healthy person die—now, I'd be very interested in knowing the circumstances—I mean the fact is none of us have any experience with this. And my concern is that if you look at a country where they really do have some experience with it, their findings are pretty concerning.

So, if we go to Holland, where euthanasia is legal, and we look at a study from 2000 of 535 cases of **euthanasia**, I was stunned to see that in 69% of

EDITOR'S NOTES

euthanasia: the act of deliberately ending a person's life to end their suffering.

those cases, they used a paralytic agent. Now, what do they know that we haven't figured out yet? I think what they know is that it's actually very difficult to kill someone with just a big dose of a barbiturate. And in fact they report that in 6% of those cases, there was problems with completion—you know, getting the person dead. And in—what was it?—I think five of those, the person actually woke up, came back out of coma, you know, despite an intention to give a lethal dose.

3. Cruel and Unusual Punishment

DR. GAWANDE: Professor Denno, in turning to this three-drug protocol back in 1977, one of the things you've written is you said, "The law turned to medicine to rescue the death penalty." What did you mean by that?

PROFESSOR DENNO: By virtue of coming up with a method of execution that makes an inmate look serene, comfortable, and sleeping during the death process, by virtue of using a paralytic agent, the death penalty in this country was rescued. The humane application of a method of execution was a key goal. And the presence of doctors, their involvement, and the association with medicalizing the procedure enhanced its Constitutional acceptability.

DR. GAWANDE: What does it mean to be not cruel and not unusual punishment?

PROFESSOR DENNO: This is what the petitioner was asking the court to do: "Please provide us some Eighth Amendment guidance, so states can know how to judge whether lethal injection is cruel and unusual punishment." So the court is in the position, or at least we hope, of answering this question.

The Eighth Amendment has never said, nor have the petitioners ever argued, that executions are to be pain-free. The question is whether or not that pain is unnecessary, whether there are alternatives.

DR. GAWANDE: Chief Justice Roberts asked, "Do you agree that if the protocol is properly followed, that there is no risk of pain?" And the attorney for the prisoners waffled. And I think he waffled because it's a medical question. And so I want to turn to both of you, Dr. Waisel and Dr. Truog. What's your take on the answer? Is there no risk of pain with the three-drug protocol, if properly followed?

DR. WAISEL: Define "properly followed." In other words, the protocols list that this should happen and that should happen. But does that mean if everything happens correctly, there are no problems with insertion of intravenous catheters, if there's no problems with mixing up the medications, there's no problem with delivery of the medications, then yes, it would be pain-free.

DR. TRUOG: I think I agree with Dave. You know, thousands of times, every day, people are getting anesthetics around this country. Many of them involve the use of paralytic agents. The risk of awareness under anesthesia is very, very small. It does occur, and that's, you know, that's the risk of the anesthesia being too light under the cover of a paralytic agent. And that's what, you know, anesthesiologists live in fear of that happening. And fortunately, it occurs very, very rarely.

4. Risk of Errors

DR. TRUOG: I think the issue, here, is that people go to school for a long time and do years of training in order to be able to do this well. And certainly, everything that I've read is that the adequacy of the training for the people that are doing it in lethal injection is nowhere near adequate.

DR. GAWANDE: So there is a practical empirical question, which is: How likely is it that errors will occur with the current process of lethal injection? By one measure, there have been 40 clear botched executions out of a little over 900, which suggests a 4 to 5% rate of failure. But then, Dr. Waisel, you started to talk about other problems that occur along the way, starting with drug preparation, where we've seen problems appear, perhaps, at an even higher rate. What's your sense of how often problems occur, and what the problems are?

DR. WAISEL: We have no idea what the error rate is, because there is no oversight, there is no public reporting. So there's no way of knowing what's happening where. And the information you hear worries me, that the process is of less concern. So, for example, I believe the case was from Missouri, in which they pushed the three drugs, and the inmate didn't go to sleep. He was sitting there looking at them.

And he realized the strap holding the arm was functioning as a tourniquet, not permitting the drugs through. So they loosened it up, all the drugs came in at once. Now in that case, I'm highly confident that the inmate experienced a great deal of pain from the potassium chloride. And yet I believe it was the sheriff who was quoted as saying, "Eh, no big deal. It's not like we hurt the guy," or something like that. And so I think that your 4 to 5% number is dramatically underestimated.

Second, I would argue that, you know, when we talk about medical error, we also talk about the consequences of if that medical error occurs. We should approach this with the gravest manner possible. And this should be done perfectly.

DR. GAWANDE: Dr. Truog, we're talking about you put an IV in, you give some medications, that's a routine kind of procedure that occurs thousands of times a day in any typical hospital across the country.

DR. TRUOG: First of all, putting an IV in is not as easy as it may sound. And being certain that it continues to remain in the same place also requires, actually, quite a bit of experience, because these catheters can become dislodged, they can go into the tissue, and then they won't work anymore. Furthermore, we know that many of these inmates, by virtue of their past history of drug abuse or obesity or being muscular, can be very difficult to start IVs in.

Now, in a hospital setting, we have a lot of different ways of approaching the situation when we can't get an IV in or it's going to be difficult. Most commonly, we'll just put in a central venous line. But there again, that requires a great deal of training, far beyond anything that would be readily available outside of the medical profession. The mixing, the administration of the medications, routine in any operating room in this country, but far from routine if you haven't done it before.

And indeed one of the mistakes that I know has occurred happened to me, as an anesthesiologist early in my training, when I injected the paralytic agent too quickly after the pentothal, and they precipitated in the tubing. The tubing turned into a piece of concrete. Suddenly, I had no IV. And, you know, thank goodness I was surrounded by very experienced anesthesiologists who stepped in, within moments had another IV, fixed the problem, and it's never happened to me since. I learned my lesson. But I know that that has happened in executions, and it could be a disaster.

5. Physician Involvement

DR. GAWANDE: When Justice Ginsberg asked of the petitioners—she asked, "Is there a way to ensure proper use of the three-drug regimen?" the petitioners said, "Yes, with the direct involvement and control by medical professionals." And so now, then, of course we come to this fundamental question that all three of you have weighed in on in various ways. And that's whether physicians should, therefore, take charge to make death less painful in these instances.

DR. GAWANDE: Dr. Truog, what's your take on that, I think, fundamental question: If you were to have to be executed, wouldn't you rather have a capable, specialized physician doing this job?

DR. TRUOG: Sort of as a philosopher, if I think of the kind of a hypothetical where you have an inmate who is about to be executed and knows that this execution may involve excruciating suffering, that inmate requests the involvement of a physician because he knows that the physician can prevent that suffering from occurring, and if there is a physician who is willing to do that, and we know from surveys that many are, I honestly can't think of any principle of medical ethics that would say that that is an unethical thing for the physician to do.

DR. GAWANDE: Let me ask a follow-up on that, because I'd be curious to hear from a nonmedical person's perspective, but also an expert in the law on this, how you take the role that physicians should play in this. You've written a recent law review where you would like physicians to actually play more of this role, at least in constituting the protocol to minimize suffering. Is that still your take on what our role should be?

PROFESSOR DENNO: If we're going to be executing people, I would prefer to have a method of execution where a doctor did not have to be involved, where medical expertise would not have to be necessary. If in fact we're going to, however, have a method that would be cruel and constitute suffering if we didn't have doctor involvement, then it suggests to me that if there are physicians in the country who are willing to be involved, or medical personnel, then I would like to think that they would not be chastised or lose their license or punished by the medical profession for volunteering to take part in an execution, to relieve suffering.

DR. GAWANDE: Well, there is an argument that I think we have to grapple with. Steven Miles has made it, a physician and medical ethicist. When he was looking into the records of what happened at Abu Ghraib, the very exact same question happened. It was: if you're a prisoner who's about to be tortured, wouldn't you rather have a doctor available, to help you survive the torture, so that it could be titrated in ways that avoid killing you inadvertently and also provide some guidance on how it might be made more effective in various ways?

DR. TRUOG: I've thought a lot about Steve Miles' work on torture, and actually I welcome the analogy to torture, because there's been a lot written, there've been symposia about whether physicians should participate in torture. And I think it all sort of misses the point. Of course, physicians shouldn't participate in torture. But, fundamentally, it's because torture is wrong. And this is sort of returning, now, to kind of my views about physician involvement in capital punishment. While I think at one level, we can justify it, as Dave does very, very well, but I think it's to miss the bigger picture. I really believe that capital punishment is ethically wrong.

And, you know, I think that living in the bubble of the United States, as we do, it's easy to lose sight of just how much of an outlier our country is. You know, the United Nations has recently voted to ban capital punishment worldwide. Over 100 countries have. We stand among a small group of countries that still do capital punishment that I really don't think we want to be, you know, in their company.

6. Remedies

DR. GAWANDE: So then, when we come to this question of where can the remedy be found, the directions that seem to be posed are we involve physicians more and let them treat the prisoner as a patient, or we come up with alternative protocols that don't involve physicians at all. The judges in the oral arguments seemed very uncomfortable with trying to reinvent the protocol, for the reasons Dr. Truog has just mentioned. That is, it's not clear that any alternative protocol has enough experience to show that it works 100% of the time and it's pain-free. And so the natural place the discussion tends to go is towards trying to make sure there's enough professional involvement. Is that right, Professor Denno? Was there a disinclination among the justices to be reinventing the protocol on the spot?

PROFESSOR DENNO: I think there was a disinclination. I think what became clear during some of the arguments is there's probably not enough information for the justices to determine what the next direction should be. You know, my recommendation has been that there be a panel of experts who would propose what would be a viable method of execution and offer information that seemed to be sorely needed during the oral arguments.

DR. GAWANDE: I have to say, it makes me deeply concerned, though, imagining us sitting around a table at a conference, trying to figure out various ways of executing people, and then the prospect of what that becomes, that we either figure out that physicians have to be continually actively involved, and we create a specialty of the execution physician.

It may not be possible for the court to say that doctors would be allowed to really treat inmates as patients. And so then my question to you, Professor Denno is: Is it a realistic thing that a physician could treat an inmate as a patient and that the court would let them control the protocol, make judgments about how to make the suffering less or more, and leave them free to have that professional role?

PROFESSOR DENNO: I guess my best answer to you is that they've been doing that for 30 years. There have been physicians, as you know, involved in lethal injection since the very first execution in 1982 in this country, in the involvement of Dr. Ralph Gray. We don't, because of secrecy and the lack of information, we'll never know, at least up to this point, the full involvement of doctors. But we have many examples of doctors having been involved—the doctor in Missouri, Dr. Carlo Musso in Georgia, etc., who have made these kinds of discretionary judgments about drugs or chemicals and what should be done.

DR. GAWANDE: So Dr. Truog, if the court says, "We need this to go to an expert panel, with physicians, lawyers, public citizens, to determine a new protocol for execution," would you participate on that panel? And should other physicians participate on that panel?

DR. TRUOG: I would not participate on that panel, because I don't think that capital punishment is ethical. I think other physicians should be free to participate on that panel. And while I wouldn't want to prejudge how they might come out, certainly, from everything I've read, I can't imagine that they are going to be able to develop an evidence base for any other approach that is likely to be successful without the immediate presence of a physician. And then, I think we have to grapple with the ethics of that.

DR. GAWANDE: Dr. Waisel, can I ask you the same question? If they say there has to be some expert panel weighing this question, would you participate on the panel to come up with a better execution method?

DR. WAISEL: I agree that it should be wholly permissible for other physicians to participate, if they wish. I would have to think about it very carefully. A large part would be depending on the intellectual freedom involved in the panel, the ability to write a dissenting opinion from what the panel comes up with, and moving away from certain constraints that are put around this that seem not to permit what I would consider to be successful ways of nonphysician involvement.

DR. GAWANDE: Well, a decision from the Supreme Court in *Baze v. Rees* is expected this spring. And whatever the decision is, it is bound to have important implications for physicians and the entire health care community about our role in punishment. I want to thank all three of you for taking the time to sort through these issues, their complexities—Professor Deborah Denno, from Fordham University School of Law, Drs. Robert Truog and David Waisel from Harvard Medical School. For the *New England Journal of Medicine*, I am Atul Gawande.

Vulnerability and Trustworthiness

Polestars of Professionalism in Healthcare

By David Barnard

Abstract: Although recent literature on professionalism in healthcare abounds in recommended character traits, attitudes, or behaviors, with a few exceptions, the recommendations are untethered to any serious consideration of the contours and ethical demands of the healing relationship. This article offers an approach based on the professional's commitment to trustworthiness in response to the vulnerability of those seeking professional help. Because our willingness and ability to trust health professionals or healthcare institutions are affected by our personality, culture, race, age, prior experiences with illness and healthcare, and socioeconomic and political circumstances—"the **social determinants of trust**"—the attitudes and behaviors that actually do gain trust are patient and context specific. Therefore, in addition to the commitment to cultivating attitudes and behaviors that embody trustworthiness, professionalism also includes the commitment to actually gaining a patient's or family's trust by learning, through individualized dialogue, which conditions would win their justified trust, given their particular history and social situation.

> **EDITOR'S NOTES**
>
> **social determinants of trust:** the attitudes and behaviors, specific to patients and their context, that gain trust.

The dignity of the physician requires that he should look healthy, and as plump as nature intended him to be; for the common crowd consider those who are not of this excellent bodily condition to be unable to take care of others. Then he must be clean in person, well dressed, and anointed with sweet-smelling unguents that are not in any way suspicious. This is, in fact, pleasing to patients. The prudent man must also be careful of certain moral considerations—not only to be silent, but also of great regularity of life, since thereby his reputation will be greatly enhanced; he must be a gentleman in character, and being this he must be grave and kind to all.

Hippocrates, *The Physician*[1]

David Barnard, "Vulnerability and Trustworthiness: Polestars of Professionalism in Healthcare," *Cambridge Quarterly of Healthcare Ethics*, vol. 25, no. 2, pp. 288–300. Copyright © 2016 by Cambridge University Press. Reprinted with permission.

At least since the time of Hippocrates physicians and other health professionals have promulgated standards of conduct for members of their profession. Genuinely patient-based justifications for these standards are relatively recent. By "patient-based" standards I mean those that are based on or derived from serious consideration of the contours and ethical demands of the healing relationship—what we might call professionalism's ethical and humanistic core. Traditionally, these standards have been profession based, promoted as necessary to protect the economic and political interests of members of the in-group, to demonstrate their elevated social status, to maintain collegiality, and to justify prerogatives of autonomy and self-regulation. To the extent that profession-based standards have included behaviors or attitudes directed to patients that physicians have considered necessary to win patients' trust and acknowledgment of the physician's authority, these standards might more properly be termed **patient focused** rather than patient based.[2]

Although we are looking at relative emphases rather than hard-and-fast dichotomies between what I have called patient- and profession-based standards, I would argue that there is considerable continuity in a centuries-long, predominantly profession-based history of such standards. This history extends from the time of the Hippocratic physicians, through Thomas Percival's *Medical Ethics* in 1803, and to what Paul Starr has described as the efforts of late nineteenth- and early twentieth-century American physicians to stand out from the myriad other practitioners of the healing arts on the basis of exclusive standards, privileges, and dignity, in order to establish what the Hippocratic physicians also sought to establish—namely, cultural authority and market control.[3]

Seen through the lens of this history, the lately burgeoning literature on medical professionalism does not look much different from what has come before. Although this recent literature abounds in recommended character traits, attitudes, and behaviors and is by self-report more patient based than prior efforts, with a few exceptions the recommendations are untethered to any serious consideration of the contours and ethical demands of the healing relationship and therefore represent little change from the profession-based, or at most patient-focused, standards of the past. After reviewing some of this more recent literature, this article offers a **patient-based** justification for standards of professionalism in healthcare that emphasizes the professional's commitment to *trustworthiness in response to the vulnerability of those seeking professional help.*

A representative example of the more recent approaches to standards of professionalism in healthcare—what Delease Wear and Brian Castellani have aptly described as "end-of-term checklists, or virtue checkpoints throughout the curriculum"[4]—is the P-MEX, or Professionalism Mini-Evaluation Exercise, proposed by Richard Cruess and colleagues.[5] A product of a literature search and a workshop for faculty and residents at McGill University intended to identify observable behaviors indicative of a medical student's professionalism, the P-MEX includes 24 such behaviors, culled from an initial list of 142, that observers may assess on a four-point scale when watching a student either in a simulation exercise or in an actual patient encounter. The 24 items are grouped into four domains (doctor-patient relationship skills, reflective skills, time management, and inter-professional relationship skills), with one item appearing in two domains. For our purposes and in our limited space, it will suffice to reproduce a few examples from two of the domains:

Doctor-Patient Relationship Skills

- Listened actively to the patient
- Showed interest in the patient as a person
- Showed respect for the patient
- Recognized and met patient needs
- Advocated on behalf of a patient and/or family member
- Maintained appropriate boundaries with patients/colleagues

Interprofessional Relationship Skills

- Maintained appropriate boundaries with patients/colleagues
- Maintained appropriate appearance
- Addressed own gaps in knowledge and skills
- Demonstrated respect for colleagues
- Avoided derogatory language
- Maintained patient confidentiality
- Respected rules and procedures of the system[6]

A second example of the behavioral checklist approach that has gained wide currency—indeed, that may have become the current gold standard in academic medical circles—is the "behavioral and systems view of professionalism" (let us call it the BSVOP), which has been erected on the foundation of a document released jointly in 2002 by the ABIM Foundation, the ACP Foundation, and the European Federation of Internal Medicine: "Medical Professionalism in the New Millennium: A Physician Charter."[7] The charter itself consists of a brief preamble on the importance of "reaffirming the fundamental and universal principles and values of medical professionals" in the context of an "explosion of technology, changing market forces, problems in health care delivery, bioterrorism, and globalization"; a list of three "fundamental principles"—the primacy of patient welfare, patient autonomy, and social justice—and a set of ten "professional responsibilities."[8]

Arguing that "simply knowing right from wrong or having an internal compass does not suffice" but, rather, that "demonstrating professionalism is based on a set of practiced skills honed over time,"[9] the authors of the BSVOP have translated the concepts and values expressed in the charter into specific "professionalism behaviors."[10] In their volume *Understanding Medical Professionalism*, Levinson and her colleagues explain how they did this.[11] Skipping over the charter's preamble and the three fundamental principles, they organize the ten professional responsibilities into four groups representing what the authors identify (without further explanation) as "four core values": patient-centered care, integrity and accountability, pursuit of excellence, and fair and ethical stewardship of healthcare resources. Within each of these core values they then propose what they call "sample behaviors that can be demonstrated by individual physicians with patients and family members, and by colleagues and team members interacting together."[12] (A separate set of behaviors refers to organizations.) The result is a table that, in form and in large measure in content, looks similar to the P-MEX. Again, in the interests of space, here are a few of the items to be demonstrated with patients and family members:

Patient-Centered Care

- Communicate effectively, demonstrating empathy and compassion, and actively work to build rapport
- Promote the autonomy of the patient, eliciting and respecting patient preferences and including the patient in decisionmaking
- Act to benefit the patient when a conflict of interest exists

Integrity and Accountability

- Maintain patient confidentiality
- Maintain appropriate relationships with patients
- Promptly disclose medical errors; accept responsibility for and take steps to remedy mistakes

Pursuit of Excellence

- Adhere to nationally recognized, evidence-based guidelines (e.g., guidelines issued by the Agency for Healthcare Research and Quality and/or the U.S. Preventive Services Task Force), individualizing as needed for particular patients but conforming with the guidelines for the majority of patients

Fair and Ethical Stewardship of Health-Care Resources

- Do no harm; do not provide unnecessary/unwarranted care
- Commit to deliver emergent care equitably, respecting the different needs and preferences of subpopulations, but without regard to insurance status or ability to pay
- Deliver care in a culturally sensitive manner[13]

No one can reasonably object to any of the items excerpted here, or to the others in the complete tables for the P-MEX and the BSVOP. They all seem to be reasonable expectations of physicians or other health professionals, and—allowing for the greater attention to patient autonomy and cost containment in modern times—resonate thoroughly with traditional profession-based or patient-focused (but not patient-based) standards, even down to the echo in the P-MEX's item "maintained appropriate appearance" of the Hippocratic admonition that "the dignity of the physician requires that he should look healthy, and as plump as nature intended him to be."

Yet, with respect to both lists, the question remains, Why these items and not others? Tellingly, Levinson and her colleagues say that the behaviors in their tables are only "samples"—that their lists "are intended to be illustrative but certainly not exhaustive"[14]—yet nowhere do they provide any principle of selection by which readers might make additions. It is not even clear why some of the items in the BSVOP have been assigned to one core value rather than another (why is "deliver care in a culturally sensitive manner" under "fair and ethical stewardship of healthcare resources" rather than "patient-centered care," for example), or how seriously we ought to take potential conflicts between items (e.g., between the mandates to "[elicit] and [respect] patient preferences" and to "adhere to nationally recognized, evidence-based guidelines").

It is hard to avoid the conclusion that these lists, like many recently proposed standards of professional conduct for physicians, are not reasoned conclusions of a process of reflection on and analysis of the healing relationship but, rather, loose compendia of whatever virtues or positive characteristics came into their authors' minds (or into the minds of their informants) when trying to describe a good doctor or colleague.[15] Judah Goldberg, in his critique of the intellectual confusion spawned by the fashion for the White Coat Ceremony at medical schools, distinguishes these parochial, socially constructed behavioral conventions typically invoked under the heading of professionalism from a

EDITOR'S NOTES

humanism: a broad category of philosophies in which human interests, values, and dignity predominate; confidence in humankind, and in human beings' power and ability to solve their own problems, through creativity, reason, the scientific method, courage, and vision.

more rigorous, philosophically grounded foundation for professional formation in medicine that he associates with **humanism**:

> In contrast to humanism, which is logically constructed out of foundational principles and can therefore develop a sophisticated hierarchy of moral responsibilities, professionalism confronts a static field of arbitrary conventions without any analytic tool for assigning moral weights. Acting unprofessionally means little more than deviating from the conventions of medicine. By itself, professionalism cannot explain why lying to a patient, for instance, is worse that wearing a T-shirt to work, other than to grade different professional traditions as more or less central to medicine.[16]

What Goldberg discusses under the term "humanism" I have been referring to as professionalism's ethical and humanistic core. And my main point with respect to the prevailing approach to standards of physicians' professional conduct is that being more explicit about this ethical and humanistic core offers a more secure justification than is often provided for particular standards, while also providing a reference point from which to oppose forces and inducements (themselves sometimes justified with reference to "professionalism") that tend to compromise professionalism's ethical and humanistic core.[17]

My interest in navigating toward standards of professional conduct for health professionals by the twin polestars of vulnerability and trustworthiness is not entirely original. My main sources of inspiration are the work of Edmund Pellegrino, Robert Sokolowski, and Jos V. M. Welie. I want to call attention briefly to their key contributions and then explain how I intend to expand and extend them.

Pellegrino's project to "reconstruct medical morality on the basis of the fact of illness and the act of profession" rests on his description of illness as an ontological assault that leaves the person in a state of "wounded humanity": subject to the loss of most of the freedoms we think of as peculiarly human, and forced to place him- or herself under the power of another person—"an involuntary need [that] grounds the axiom of vulnerability from which follows the obligations of the physician."[18] The physician's responsive "act of profession" is the promise to that needy and vulnerable person that he or she has the skills to help and will act for the patient's interest. The physician's obligations are those that make this promise authentic (i.e., one that can be trusted): technical competence, ensuring the moral agency of the patient (primarily through the process of informed consent), and respect for the individualized nature of the transaction.

Similarly for Sokolowski, it is human beings' susceptibility to an involuntary need for others' help that grounds the fiduciary relationship that is the hallmark of a profession. What is at stake in such a relationship is not merely satisfaction of passing desires or wants but decisions and actions affecting fundamental well-being and possibly the future direction of one's life, deliberations belonging to the classical sense of the word "prudence." In a fiduciary relationship, Sokolowski writes, "I submit my own prudence to that of the professional. In a limited way I hand over the steering of my life to this person. ... I must do so, because I have wandered into an area of life in which my own knowledge does not equip me to steer by myself."[19] I trust the professional with my prudence initially not because of any prior relationship or friendship that may exist between us—indeed, in many cases (paradigmatically, entering an emergency department in a foreign city) the professional is a complete stranger to me—but precisely because he or she has been certified *as a professional*, whom I therefore trust to abide by the profession's norms.

Welie also grounds his analysis of professionalism in what he calls the "existential vulnerability [that] arises out of the combination of a significant human need that must be relieved and complete dependency on experts for that relief."[20] Writing in the context of dentistry, and explicitly contrasting the patient-based aspects of professionalism with those centered on practitioners' economic well-being, Welie insists that the hallmark of professionalism is to be *deserving* of the trust placed in the professional by the vulnerable, dependent patient. He then proposes several "professional responsibilities"—for example, competence, peer review, internal discipline, noncompetition, objectively beneficial services, standardized treatments, avoidance of conflicts of interest, nondiscrimination, and fostering access—that, although not intended to be exhaustive, would seem to justify the public's trust.[21]

My contributions begin with suggestions for enriching the account of vulnerability that unites Pellegrino's, Sokolowski's, and Welie's analyses, and by noting some ambiguities in the concept and experience of trust. After proposing my own set of standards for professional conduct that I believe grow out of these reflections, I suggest three further refinements to an analysis of vulnerability and trustworthiness in the context of professionalism: (1) the importance of individualized dialogue in determining the conditions for gaining a patient's or family's justified trust, (2) the idea of the social determinants of trust, and (3) the idea of shared vulnerability between patients and the professionals who care for them.

Although a succinct and serviceable definition of vulnerability might simply read, "being at increased risk of harm, and/or having a decreased capacity to protect oneself from harm,"[22] for our purposes, vulnerability is best understood within a cluster of concepts that also includes the ideas of need and dependency, and in dialectical relationship with notions of agency and resilience. In the introduction to their rich collection of essays on vulnerability, Catriona Mackenzie, Wendy Rogers, and Susan Dodds capture the breadth of the concept:

> Human life is conditioned by vulnerability. By virtue of our embodiment, human beings have bodily and material needs; are exposed to physical illness, injury, disability, and death; and depend on the care of others for extended periods during our lives. As social and affective beings we are emotionally and psychologically vulnerable to others in myriad ways: to loss and grief; to neglect, abuse, and lack of care; to rejection, ostracism, and humiliation. As sociopolitical beings we are vulnerable to exploitation, manipulation, oppression, political violence, and rights abuses. And we are vulnerable to the natural environment and to the impact on the environment of our own, individual and collective, actions and technologies.[23]

Mackenzie, Rogers, and Dodds distinguish among three kinds of vulnerability. The first of these, **inherent vulnerability**, is the aspect that figures in the work of Pellegrino, Sokolowski, and Welie—namely, vulnerability that is directly related to the human condition, and that entails our susceptibility to illness and death. Mackenzie and her coauthors enlarge the notion by emphasizing *socially created* forms of vulnerability resulting from unequal or discriminatory social, political, or economic arrangements, which they call **situational vulnerability**, and *the aggravation or exacerbation of vulnerability* (and its associated dependency or even shame) that can arise from paternalistic or demeaning efforts to help vulnerable people, which they call **pathogenic vulnerability**.[24]

Sara Clark Miller defines as "fundamental needs [those] ends that agents cannot forgo if they are to continue to use their agency effectively in the world to make choices, set ends for themselves, and relate to others."[25] It is an essential feature of human vulnerability, Miller

EDITOR'S NOTES

inherent vulnerability: vulnerability that is directly related to the human condition and entails our susceptibility to illness and death.

EDITOR'S NOTES

situational vulnerability: socially created human vulnerability resulting from unequal or discriminatory social, political, or economic arrangements.

EDITOR'S NOTES

pathogenic vulnerability: the aggravation or exacerbation of human vulnerability and its associated dependency and shame, which arises from paternalistic or demeaning efforts to help vulnerable people.

continues, that "in order to avoid experiencing harm or to restore agency when we do, others have to meet our needs, that is, others must help us. We are dependent on them for this help, as we are not capable of meeting all our needs on our own: sometimes they must help us by developing, maintaining, or restoring our agency."[26] Her list of fundamental needs, which she develops in dialogue with Martha Nussbaum's analysis of "central human functional capabilities,"[27] includes nutrition and water, rest, shelter, a healthy environment, bodily integrity, healing, education, attachments, social inclusion, play, and security[28]—all of considerable relevance to the health professions, especially from the standpoint of a biopsychosocial model of health and disease and the social determinants of health.

When we turn to health professionals for help in meeting our needs, especially in the setting of an illness that compromises cognitive and deliberative capacities and the emotional equilibrium necessary for the thoughtful weighing of options, we are in a state of involuntary dependence. The relationship at its inception is not one between free, equal, and rational contractors. As Annette Baier has written,

> Philosophers who remember what it was like to be a dependent child, or know what it is like to be a parent, or to have a dependent parent, an old or handicapped relative, friend or neighbor will find it implausible to treat such relations as simply cases of comembership in a kingdom of ends, in the given temporary conditions of one-sided dependence.[29]

Involuntarily needy and dependent—that is, vulnerable—we *trust* that health professionals will

- *Not exploit* our vulnerability for their own self-interested ends
- *Not increase* our vulnerability through paternalistic or degrading forms of help that perpetuate dependency or undermine self-esteem
- *Reduce* our vulnerability by

  — Alleviating sources of vulnerability related to disease
  — Aligning with others to alleviate sources of health-related vulnerability aggravated by social, political, or economic arrangements
  — Enhancing our capacity for self-determination by preventing, eliminating, or reducing limitations related to disease or its treatment.

At its ethical and humanistic core, professionalism is the commitment of health professionals to be *deserving* of this trust—in other words, to be trust*worthy*. For, although patients, or other people in "temporary conditions of one-sided dependence," may trust, this trust may be misplaced, misguided, irrational, or dangerous to one's own most important interests and ends. In Baier's words,

> Where one depends on another's good will, one is necessarily vulnerable to the limits of that good will. One leaves others an opportunity to harm one when one trusts, and also shows one's confidence that they will not take it. ... Trust, then, on this first approximation,

is accepted vulnerability to another's possible but not expected ill will (or lack of good will) toward one.[30]

Thus, whereas when ill, I am primarily vulnerable due to the illness, when I trust my physician to help me I am now also vulnerable specifically to him or her.

To these structural ambiguities in trust relationships—built in, so to speak, to their structure of one-sided dependence—Jay Katz adds the psychological distortions of unconscious, irrational factors in human relationships, notably transference and countertransference reactions of patient and professional, respectively, wherein a patient's irrational fantasies of being taken care of by an idealized carer meet the caregiver's narcissistic investment in his or her own knowledge, power, and altruism.[31] Primarily concerned with establishing the need for physicians to acknowledge uncertainty as part of the process of informed consent, Katz distinguishes trust "based on blind faith—on passive surrender to oneself or to another"—from trust that is "*earned* through conversation" in which both parties acknowledge to themselves and to the other what is known and not known about the decision to be made.[32]

If we now ask what attitudes, behaviors, and standards of conduct are the criteria and embodiments of health professionals' trustworthiness when vulnerable people seek their help—which in aggregate constitute the ethical and humanistic core of professionalism—Katz's emphasis on informed consent conversations that acknowledge uncertainty is part of the answer. A more complete answer would include the following:

- Technical competence
- Respect for individuality and promotion of self-determination
- Empathy
- Truthfulness
- Transparency as to the grounds for recommended courses of action
- Protection of privacy and confidentiality
- Avoidance of harm
- Avoidance of conflicts of interest
- Nonabandonment
- Fairness in allocation of time, attention, and healthcare resources
- Advocacy for social, political, and economic arrangements that contribute to people's opportunities to lead healthy lives
- Self-criticism and willingness to demand accountability from colleagues for adherence to these professional values

This is a familiar list, and one that resonates especially with the elements of professionalism according to Pellegrino, Sokolowski, and Welie, as well as with the ten professional responsibilities in the ABIM charter. My contributions so far have been to propose, as a principle by which to generate these elements, the professional's commitment to trustworthiness in response to the vulnerability of those seeking professional help and to ground them in a more robust understanding of vulnerability—including the ways in which caregiving itself can aggravate vulnerability, intrinsically, as Baier suggests, or as a function of a particular caregiver's demeaning or dehumanizing manner of providing help, as Mackenzie, Rogers, Dodds, and Miller suggest. I have also pointed to some of the ambiguities of trust.

Notwithstanding the plausibility of these general elements of patient-based professionalism (what might be termed prime facie professional commitments), the attitudes and behaviors that actually do gain trust are patient and context specific. Our willingness and ability to trust health professionals or healthcare institutions will be affected by our personality, culture, race, age, and prior experiences with illness and healthcare, and the relative supportiveness or insecurity of our socioeconomic and political circumstances, among other factors. Therefore, in addition to the commitment to cultivating attitudes and behaviors that embody trustworthiness, a patient-based understanding of professionalism would also include the commitment to actually gaining a patient's or family's trust by learning, through *individualized dialogue*, the conditions that would win their justified trust, given their particular history and social situation.

Among many reasons to credit the importance of individualized exploration of the conditions of a patient's or family's justified trust (and the corollary responsibility to suspend automatic allegiance to particular assumptions about "professional" behaviors with that patient or family) are the diversity of patients' and families' expectations or desires for "shared clinical decision making," cultural and ethnic diversity in approaches to care near the end of life, and the widespread societal burden of trauma from adverse childhood experiences. Alexander Kon has called attention to the **"shared decision making continuum,"**[33] on which patients' or surrogates' preferences for participation with physicians in clinical decisions range from patient- or agent-driven to purely physician-driven decisionmaking. Elizabeth Murray and her coauthors demonstrated this spectrum with a cross-sectional survey of the American public, reporting that, although a majority of respondents favored some degree of shared decisionmaking, 9 percent of their large national sample preferred a paternalistic approach in which information

EDITOR'S NOTES

shared decision-making continuum: the range of patients' or surrogates' preferences for participation in clinical decisions, from completely patient/agent driven to entirely physician driven decision-making.

transfer was mainly one way from physician to patient, and deliberation about treatment took place by the physician alone or in consultation with other physicians.[34] These findings suggest (pace Pellegrino, Katz, and the authors of the ABIM charter) that for patients whose preferences are for more physician-centered deliberation and direction of treatment, defaulting to the currently favored professional standard of shared decisionmaking, without sensitive, individualized dialogue, could more easily provoke mistrust and feelings of abandonment than gain the patient's or family's justified trust.

There is also ample evidence of cultural and ethnic diversity in preferences for communication and clinical decision making near the end of life.[35] People differ in their openness to explicit discussion of prognostic information, and in their interpretations of physician recommendations to consider changing goals of care from all-out efforts to prolong life to an emphasis on palliation, quality of life, and comfort. Clinicians may regard these behaviors as enactments of responsible clinical judgment and compassion. People with particular orientations toward communication of negative information, or with individual or communal histories of oppression, discrimination, or mistreatment in society or the healthcare system, may experience them as callousness or as being manipulated into foregoing potentially beneficial care. Similar differences and similar mistrust—often similarly influenced by a community's collective memory of past abuses—emerge among potential participants in clinical trials, especially among minority populations.[36]

Another example is the decade and a half of research confirming and extending the Adverse Childhood Experiences (ACE) Study, which found "a strong graded relationship between the breadth of exposure to abuse or household dysfunction during childhood and multiple risk factors for several of the leading causes of death in adults."[37] We know from these studies, and the overwhelming evidence on the social determinants of health, that much illness is a result of the social, psychological, and economic conditions in which people grow, live, work, and age.[38] People bring their damaged bodies to the clinic, but for many people their damaged bodies are the products and consequences of damaged lives. They need medical treatment, of course, but perhaps even more they need support in finding or regaining safety, empowerment, and some measure of control in their world. Such "**trauma-informed care**"

EDITOR'S NOTES

trauma-informed care: generally, care practices that promote a culture of safety, empowerment, and healing.

must often begin with exquisitely sensitive explorations of the conditions or even the possibility of trust before treatment can begin.[39]

These latter examples suggest that even expanding the discussion of trustworthiness to include patient- or family-specific dialogue is incomplete, in that it appears to place the entire burden of conveying genuine trustworthiness to patients on the individual practitioner, without adequate recognition of the structural conditions affecting people's willingness or ability to trust health professionals—what might be termed the *social determinants of trust.* Annette Baier alludes briefly to this in her comments on "the *network* of trust," and "such society-wide phenomena as climates of trust," commenting that to treat only two-party trust relationships is unrealistic, because "any person's attitude to another in a trust relationship is constrained by all the other trust and distrust relationships in which she is involved."[40] I alluded earlier to sources of vulnerability rooted in social arrangements and the professional obligation to align with others to address these as a part of reducing our vulnerability. In the present context we might emphasize that advocacy for more just social, political, and economic arrangements contributes both to the health professional's being deserving of trust and to actually gaining trust more broadly throughout the population.[41]

One further implication of my emphasis on the necessity of dialogue with patients, families, and even communities on the conditions of their justified trust in the professionals who care for them is a strong caution against the current vogue for assessing professionalism on the basis of externally observed behavioral indicators. Shiphra Ginsburg and colleagues have previously pointed out two significant limitations to a behavioral observation approach: inconsistent interpretations and applications of evaluation criteria by faculty observers and—more directly related to the present context—the lack of access to students' *rationales* for the choices or behaviors they exhibit in the scenarios. As Ginsburg and coauthors explain, "Behaviors alone do not give us all the information we need to make accurate judgments. Knowing how a student construes a particular professional dilemma, and what values s/he perceives as conflicting, is critical information."[42]

I would go further. If the primary components of patient-based professionalism are commitments to (1) cultivating attitudes and behaviors that embody trustworthiness and (2) actually gaining a patient's or family's trust by learning the conditions that would win their justified trust through individualized dialogue, and if the conditions for gaining justified trust are context specific, then no observed conformity to items on a prefabricated behavioral checklist (no matter how thoroughly vetted and pretested by panels of experts) will, by itself, meaningfully discern patient-based professionalism on the part of a student. What is needed instead, at a minimum, is a setting in which students reflect on their encounters with patients through narratives and dialogue with peers and preceptors, analyzing them for, among other things, what they perceived and investigated about their patients' dispositions and capacities for trust in the encounter, and how their actions with the patient responded to their appreciation of these factors. Such an approach seems to be underrepresented, however, among currently fashionable methodologies for the assessment of professionalism.

Having emphasized vulnerability as one of the twin polestars of professionalism in healthcare, it is worth observing in conclusion that professionals bring their own vulnerabilities to their encounters with patients. Although this can promote empathy and solidarity in caring relationships and is therefore to be prized rather than avoided or denied,[43] the ability to translate shared vulnerability into therapeutic relationships requires continuing self-awareness and self-care. At bottom, this involves the self-understanding that we—physicians, nurses, healers from all traditions—live in the same world that our patients inhabit and share the same vulnerabilities to what John Keats (who trained as a physician himself) described as

> The weariness, the fever, and the fret Here. Where men sit and hear each other groan;
>
> Where palsy shakes a few, sad, last gray hairs,
>
> Where youth grows pale, and spectre thin, and dies.[44]

I believe that our acknowledgment of this shared vulnerability, in this common world, is the ultimate touchstone of humanism, and genuinely patient-based professionalism, in healthcare.

Notes

1. Hippocrates, *The Physician*, I. In: Jones WHS, trans. *Hippocrates.* Vol. II. Loeb Classical Library. Cambridge, MA: Harvard University Press; 1967, at 311.

2. I am grateful to Mark Wicclair for suggesting the distinction between "patient-based" and "patient-focused" standards for professional behavior.

3. Richard Cruess and Sylvia Cruess provide an historical survey of the uses and connotations of "professionalism" as understood by physicians themselves, and in the literature of medical ethics and the social sciences, in Cruess RL, Cruess SR. Teaching medicine as a profession in the service of healing. *Academic Medicine* 1997;72(11):941–52. My interpretation of the predominantly profession-based character of this history draws primarily on the following sources: Edelstein L. The professional ethics of the Greek physician. *Bulletin of the History of Medicine* 1956;30:392–418; Starr P. *The Social Transformation of American Medicine.* New York: Basic Books; 1982; Berlant JL. *Profession and Monopoly: A Study of Medicine in the United States and Great Britain.* Berkeley: University of California Press; 1975; Larson MS. *The Rise of Professionalism: A Sociological Analysis.* Berkeley: University of California Press; 1977; Johnson TJ. *Professions and Power.* New York: Macmillan; 1972; Gallagher WT. Ideologies of professionalism and the politics of self-regulation in the California state bar. *Pepperdine Law Review* 1995;22(2):485–628; Goode WJ. Community within a community: The professions. *American Sociological Review* 1957;22:194–200; and Pellegrino ED. Professionalism, profession and the virtues of the good physician. *Mount Sinai Journal of Medicine* 2002;69(6):378–84. For a discussion of Percival and his near contemporary, the Edinburgh physician John Gregory, disputing the characterization of medical ethics

from this period as predominantly profession based, and arguing that Starr, Berlant, and others have misread Percival as having been simply concerned with "medical etiquette" rather than with "medical ethics" in a more modern sense, see McCullough L. *John Gregory and the Invention of Professional Medical Ethics and the Profession of Medicine.* New York: Springer; 1998. For a similar argument concerning Percival, see Pellegrino ED. Percival's *Medical Ethics:* The moral philosophy of an 18th-century English gentleman. *Archives of Internal Medicine* 1986;146(11):2265–9. Scholars have also pointed to strands of thought concerning physicians' moral responsibilities to patients within the ancient and classical world that articulate something more closely approximating a patient-based approach; see, for example, the tradition exemplified by the first-century author Scribonius Largus, discussed by Edelstein and by Edmund Pellegrino in Pellegrino ED. Toward a reconstruction of medical morality: The primacy of the act of profession and the fact of illness. *Journal of Medicine and Philosophy* 1979;4(1):32–56.

4. Wear D, Castellani B. The development of professionalism: Curriculum matters. *Academic Medicine* 2000;75(6):602–11, at 603.

5. Cruess R, McIlroy JH, Cruess S, Ginsburg S, Steinert Y. The professionalism mini-evaluation exercise: A preliminary investigation. *Academic Medicine* 2006;81(10 Suppl): S74–S78.

6. See note 5, Cruess et al. 2006, at S76.

7. Medical Professionalism Project of the American Board of Internal Medicine. Medical professionalism in the new millennium: A physician charter. *Annals of Internal Medicine* 2002;136(3):243–6.

8. See note 7, Medical Professionalism Project of the American Board of Internal Medicine 2002, at 244.

9. Levinson W, Ginsburg S, Hafferty FW, Lucey C. *Understanding Medical Professionalism.* New York: McGraw Hill; 2014, at 3.

10. Lesser CS, Lucey CR, Egener B, Braddock CH III, Linas SL, Levinson W. A behavioral and systems view of professionalism. *JAMA* 2010;304(24):2732–7.

11. See note 9, Levinson et al. 2014, at 3–11.

12. See note 9, Levinson et al. 2014, at 7.

13. See note 10, Lesser et al. 2010, at 2734.

14. See note 9, Levinson et al. 2014, at 7.

15. Additional lists such as these, which seem to have been derived in a similar manner, can be found in Van de Kamp K, Vernouij-Dessen MJFJ, Grol RPTM, Bottema JAM. How to conceptualize professionalism: A qualitative study. Medical Teacher 2004;26(8):696–702; Green M, Zick A, Makoul G. Defining professionalism from the perspective of patients, physicians, and nurses. *Academic Medicine* 2009;84(5):566–73; Accreditation Council for Graduate Medical Education. *Advancing Education in Medical Professionalism: An Educational Resource from the ACGME Outcome Project;* 2004; available

at http://www.usahealthsystem.com/workfiles/com_docs/gme/2011%20Links/Professionalism%20-%20Faculty%20Dev..pdf (last accessed 29 Apr 2015); and Reynolds PP, Martindale J. Development of the Medical Professionalism Behavior Assessment Tool. Abstract presented at the Annual Conference of the Association for Medical Education in Europe, Milan, Italy, 2014 Aug 30–Sept 3.

16. Goldberg J. Humanism or professionalism? The white coat ceremony in medical education. *Academic Medicine* 2008; 83: 715–22, at 717.

17. Examples of self-serving compromises that can be masked by appeals to "professionalism" might include lucrative participation in pharmaceutical company speakers bureaus ("colleague education"), refusals to speak publicly about substandard practice on the part of a colleague ("maintaining public confidence"), or resistance to a broadened scope of practice for, e.g., nurse practitioners or physician assistants ("patient safety").

18. See note 3, Pellegrino 1979, at 44–5.

19. Sokolowski R. The fiduciary relationship and the nature of professions. In: Pellegrino ED, Veatch RM, Langan JP, eds. *Ethics, Trust, and the Professions*. Washington, DC: Georgetown University Press; 1991: 23–43, at 27.

20. Welie JVM. Is dentistry a profession? Part 1. Professionalism defined. *Journal of the Canadian Dental Association* 2004;70(8):529–32, at 531.

21. Welie JVM. Is dentistry a profession? Part 2. The hallmarks of professionalism. *Journal of the Canadian Dental Association* 2004;70(9):599–602. An article by Herbert M. Swick that is frequently cited in recent professionalism literature—unlike the writings of Pellegrino, Sokolowski, or Welie, oddly enough—makes similar points, but with much less analysis. See Swick HM. Toward a normative definition of medical professionalism. *Academic Medicine* 2000;75(6):612–16. See also Doukas DJ. Where is the virtue in professionalism? *Cambridge Quarterly of Healthcare Ethics* 2003;12:147–54; note 3, Pellegrino 2002; and, for a deep analysis of professionalism that ranges far beyond medicine, Sullivan WM. *Work and Integrity: The Crisis and Promise of Professionalism in America*. 2nd ed. San Francisco: Jossey-Bass; 2005.

22. Rogers W, Mackenzie C, Dodds S. Why bioethics needs a concept of vulnerability. *International Journal of Feminist Approaches to Bioethics* 2012;5(2):11–38, at 12.

23. Mackenize C, Rogers W, Dodds S, eds. *Vulnerability: New Essays in Ethics and Feminist Philosophy*. New York: Oxford University Press; 2014, at 1.

24. See note 22, Rogers et al. 2012. See also Spiers J. New perspectives on vulnerability using emic and etic approaches. *Journal of Advanced Nursing* 2000;31(3):715–21; Sellman D. Towards an understanding of nursing as a response to human vulnerability. *Nursing Philosophy* 2005;6:2–10; and Hoffmaster B. What does vulnerability mean? *Hastings Center Report* 2006;36(2):38–45.

25. Miller SC. *The Ethics of Need*. New York: Routledge; 2012, at 37.

26. See note 25, Miller 2012, at 37.

27. Nussbaum M. *Women and Human Development: The Capabilities Approach.* New York: Cambridge University Press; 2000.

28. See note 25, Miller 2012, at 41–2.

29. Baier A. Trust and antitrust. *Ethics* 1986;96:231–60, at 248.

30. See note 29, Baier 1986, at 235.

31. Katz J. *The Silent World of Doctor and Patient.* New York: The Free Press; 1984, especially at 142–50.

32. See note 31, Katz 1984, at xiv–xv; emphasis added.

33. Kon A. The shared decision-making continuum. *JAMA* 2010;304(8):903–4.

34. Murray E, Pollack L, White M, Lo B. Clinical decision-making: Patients' preferences and experiences. *Patient Education and Counseling* 2007;65:189–96.

35. Carrese JA, Rhodes LA. Bridging cultural differences in medical practice: The case of discussing negative information with Navajo patients. *Journal of General Internal Medicine* 2000;15:92–6; Crawley LM, Marshall PA, Lo B, Koenig BA. Strategies for culturally effective end-of-life care. *Archives of Internal Medicine* 2002;136(9):673–9; Wallace MP, Weiner JS, Pekmezaris R, Almendrai A, Cosiquien R, Auerbach C, et al. Physician cultural sensitivity in African American advance care planning: A pilot study. *Journal of Palliative Medicine* 2007;10(3):721–7.

36. Corbie-Smith G, Thomas SB, St. George DM. Distrust, race, and research. *Archives of Internal Medicine* 2002;162(21):2458–63; Braunstein JB, Sherber NS, Schulman SP, Ding EL, Powe NR. Race, medical researcher distrust, perceived harm, and willingness to participate in cardiovascular prevention trials. *Medicine* 2008;87(1):1–9.

37. Felitti V, Anda RF, Nordenberg D, Williamson DF, Spitz AM, Edwards V, et al. Relationship of childhood abuse and household dysfunction to many of the leading causes of death in adults: The adverse childhood experiences (ACE) study. *American Journal of Preventive Medicine* 1998;14(4):245–58, at 245. See also Corso P, Edwards V, Fang X, Mercy J. Health-related quality of life among adults who experienced maltreatment during childhood. *American Journal of Public Health* 2008;98(6):1094–100.

38. World Health Organization Commission on the Social Determinants of Health. *Closing the Gap in a Generation: Health Equity through Action on the Social Determinants of Health.* Geneva: World Health Organization; 2008.

39. Rosenberg L. Addressing trauma in mental health and substance use treatment. *Journal of Behavioral Health Services Research* 2011;38(4):428–31.

40. See note 29, Baier 1986, at 258.

41. The structural conditions affecting patients' or communities' trust are not the only factors largely outside the individual practitioner's immediate control. The institutional environment within which the practitioner works—its policies, procedures, and general atmosphere, which can be more or less welcoming or intimidating, agency-enhancing or agency-sapping, for patients and families—is also likely to affect trust. Additional constraints on professional behavior with patients and families with likely influence on the practitioner's ability to gain their trust come from institutional approaches to practice management, e.g., expectations regarding practitioner workload and patient volume, management surveillance, and pay-for-performance measures. Some of these issues have been discussed under the heading of "organizational professionalism"; see, e.g., Egener B, McDonald W, Rosof B, Gullen D. Organizational professionalism: Relevant competencies and behaviors. *Academic Medicine* 2012;87(5):668–74.

42. Ginsburg S, Regehr G, Lingard L. Basing the evaluation of professionalism on observable behaviors: A cautionary tale. *Academic Medicine* 2004;79(10 Suppl): S1–S4, at S4. It is interesting to note that Ginsburg, despite these substantial misgivings, appears two years after the publication of this critique as one of the coauthors of the report on the exclusively behavioral P-MEX discussed previously, as well as the volume elaborating on the BSVOP; see note 5, Cruess et al. 2006, and note 9, Levinson et al. 2014. For another thoughtful critique of the behavioral approach to the evaluation of trainees' professionalism, see Misch DA. Evaluating physicians' professionalism and humanism: The case for humanism "connoisseurs." *Academic Medicine* 2002;77(6):489–95. I thank Joseph Carrese for calling this article to my attention.

43. See note 22, Rogers et al. 2012, at 23; note 25, Miller 2012, at 94; note 24, Spiers 2000, at 719.

44. Keats J. Ode to a nightingale. In: Stillinger J, ed. *John Keats: Complete Poems.* Cambridge, MA: Harvard University Press; 1978: 279–81, at 280.

CRITICAL THINKING QUESTIONS

1. Should doctors participate in executions by lethal injection? Argue the positions for and against participation. Use the Perspective Roundtable discussion and information about the Nuremberg Code to support your arguments.

2. Define *patient-based* and *patient-focused* standards of healthcare professionalism. Provide an example of each.

3. Define *vulnerability* and *trustworthiness*. Discuss the significance of both in the doctor–patient relationship. Why are these concepts important to the study of bioethics?

4. What, in your opinion, should form the basis of the doctor–patient relationship? Why? Please be specific, define pertinent concepts, and provide examples when possible.